CLASSICAL OPTIMIZATION: FOUNDATIONS AND EXTENSIONS

STUDIES IN MATHEMATICAL AND MANAGERIAL ECONOMICS

Editor

HENRI THEIL

VOLUME 16

NORTH-HOLLAND PUBLISHING COMPANY – AMSTERDAM · OXFORD
AMERICAN ELSEVIER PUBLISHING COMPANY, INC. – NEW YORK

CLASSICAL OPTIMIZATION: FOUNDATIONS AND EXTENSIONS

MICHAEL J. PANIK
Associate Professor of Economics, Austin Dunham Barney School of Business and Public Administration University of Hartford

1976

NORTH-HOLLAND PUBLISHING COMPANY–AMSTERDAM · OXFORD
AMERICAN ELSEVIER PUBLISHING COMPANY, INC.–NEW YORK

Library of Congress Catalog Card Number 73–79103

ISBN North-Holland for this series 0 7204 3300 2

ISBN North-Holland for this volume 0 7204 3315 0

ISBN American Elsevier for this volume 0 444 10568 9

PUBLISHERS:

NORTH-HOLLAND PUBLISHING COMPANY – AMSTERDAM

NORTH-HOLLAND PUBLISHING COMPANY, LTD. – OXFORD

SOLE DISTRIBUTORS FOR THE U.S.A. AND CANADA:

AMERICAN ELSEVIER PUBLISHING COMPANY, INC.

52 VANDERBILT AVENUE

NEW YORK, N.Y. 10017

Printed in Singapore

INTRODUCTION TO THE SERIES

This is a series of books concerned with the quantitative approach to problems in the social and administrative sciences. The studies are in particular in the overlapping areas of mathematical economics, econometrics, operational research, and management science. Also, the mathematical and statistical techniques which belong to the apparatus of modern social and administrative sciences have their place in this series. A well-balanced mixture of pure theory and practical applications is envisaged, which ought to be useful for universities and for research workers in business and government.

The Editor hopes that the volumes of this series, all of which relate to such a young and vigorous field of research activity, will contribute to the exchange of scientific information at a truly international level.

THE EDITOR

To my Mother and the
memory of my Father

PREFACE

In many areas of the social and administrative sciences as well as in operations research and engineering, one is oftentimes faced with the problem of determining the best course of action which leads to the most efficient operation of an economic or physical system. To this end rational decision-making dictates adherence to some form of idealized decision-making process. Such a process may be formulated in essentially three stages. First, a reasonably accurate picture of the behavior of the system is required so that the decision-maker can construct a model (a complete set of structural equations which mirror the behavior of the decision unit, be it a household, a firm, or a government agency) which indicates how the system variables interact to facilitate the operation of the system. Next, an objective function (e.g. it may be a profit or cost function) which serves as a measure of effectiveness of the system is formulated in terms of the system variables. Finally, the decision-maker optimizes (maximizes or minimizes) the objective function with respect to the independent system variables so as to determine those values of the said variables yielding optimum effectiveness.

This book aims at enabling the decision-maker to carry out step three of the above decision process. In particular, it focuses on that portion of modern optimization theory commonly referred to as classical optimization and variations thereof. A typical problem in this area involves the application of the calculus in its solution. In this regard, for the strict classical case, the function to be optimized and any constraint function equalities are assumed differentiable. This same assumption is made when we extend the classical approach to cover the case where the system variables are restricted to be non-negative and/or inequalities are admitted to the functional constraint system. In either instance the objective function and the functional constraints are unrestricted in form. As will become apparent later, both the classical and extended-classical results yield only properties of optimal solutions rather than the specification of the optimal values of the system variables themselves. To circumvent this shortcoming, a battery of solution techniques involving both iterative and sequential algorithms has been included so as to enable the reader to approximate the optimal values of the system variables. Hence a marriage between theory and some of the more recent and successful numerical methods has been incorporated into the text.

My intent has been to develop an intermediate to advanced level text for students of business, economics, and operations research who need a rigorous yet readable presentation of: (1) the mathematical foundations of modern optimization theory; and (2) classical optimization theory and its extensions proper. Most students entering into graduate study in economics or related disciplines have not had a course in the advanced calculus. Yet the more recent developments in microeconomics and operations analysis are highly technical and require for their understanding the mathematical expertise of one schooled in the advanced calculus. Indeed, the vast majority of texts in mathematical programming, in particular non-linear programming, require some understanding of the topics usually included in such a course. Pursuant to this need I have taken many of the important theorems and concepts of advanced analysis and, through the use of formal proofs, geometry, and intuition, demonstrated their connection with and importance to mathematical programming. The only prerequisite is one semester of elementary calculus. The text is designed for use in a two-semester upper-division undergraduate or first-year graduate course.

Chapters 1, 2, and 5 serve to provide a compact review of the requisite mathematical tools needed to comprehend the material presented herein. Chapters 3, 4, 6, 7, and 8 pertain to the development of unconstrained classical optimization theory. Such theory involving equality functional constraints is the topic of chapters 9 and 10. Finally, chapters 11, 12, and 13 deal with the extensions of classical optimization to cover the case where non-negativity conditions along with equality and/or inequality functional constraints are present.

I wish to express my gratitude to Professor Theil for his sound advice and comments and to Mrs. Gladys Swan for her steadfast and accurate typing of the major portion of the manuscript. A note of appreciation is also in order for the professionalism exhibited by everyone at North-Holland associated with the production of this volume. Finally, a fond thank you goes to my wife Paula for her help in the preparation of the index and for her constant encouragement.

Windsor, Connecticut
November 1974

M.J.P.

CONTENTS

Chapter 1

MATHEMATICAL FOUNDATIONS I

This chapter aims at a brief review of the requisite matrix methods needed to handle the specialized computational processes that frequently arise throughout the text. Hence, the presentation herein is not meant to be an exhaustive one—our discussion will be limited to those concepts which are, for the most part, used in subsequent chapters.

1.1. A comment on necessary and/or sufficient conditions

The notions of a necessary condition and a sufficient condition will be encountered quite frequently throughout the text. To gain some insight into the nature of these concepts, let us consider the following discussion. Assume that the 'realm of all logical possibilities' $\mathscr{L}$ constitutes a set whose elements correspond to (declarative) 'statements' or 'propositions'. If we have under discussion statements p and q relative to $\mathscr{L}$, then sets $\mathscr{P}$ and $\mathscr{Q}$ may be taken to represent the subsets of $\mathscr{L}$ for which these statements are respectively true. That is, $\mathscr{P}$ and $\mathscr{Q}$ constitute the respective 'truth sets'[1] for statements p and q. Let $\mathscr{P} \subset \mathscr{Q}$ (fig. 1.1a). Now if $p \in \mathscr{P}$ is true, then $q \in \mathscr{Q}$ is also true; i.e. p implies q. Hence, the conditional statements: 'if p, then q', and 'q if p' depict the truth set inclusion $\mathscr{P} \subset \mathscr{Q}$. In this instance we shall say that p *is a sufficient condition for* q since q is true whenever p is. However, q may also be true even though p is not true, since $\mathscr{P}$ is a proper subset of $\mathscr{Q}$. Hence, p is not a necessary condition (i.e. a requirement) for q. Under what circumstances will p be a necessary condition for q?

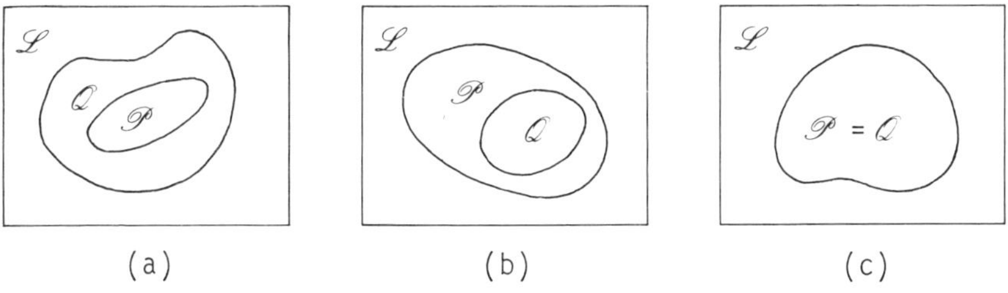

Fig. 1.1.

[1] An excellent survey of truth sets and their properties is provided by Kemeny *et al.* (1959), pp. 56–65, and Whitesitt (1961), pp. 56–58.

To answer this let us consider the converse of this sufficient condition. This corresponds to the assertion that q implies p. In this case q is true only if p is since now $\mathscr{Q} \subset \mathscr{P}$ (fig. 1. 1b). Hence the conditional statements 'if q, then p' and 'q only if p' both describe this converse implication. With $\mathscr{Q}$ a proper subset of $\mathscr{P}$, p *is a necessary condition for* q, i.e. a prerequisite, since q must be true whenever p is. In sum, the assertion of a necessary condition is the converse of the assertion of a sufficient condition (and vice versa).

Let us now take the case there $\mathscr{P} \subset \mathscr{Q}$ and, at the same time, $\mathscr{Q} \subset \mathscr{P}$, i.e. $\mathscr{P} = \mathscr{Q}$ (fig. 1.1c). Here a conditional statement and its converse are asserted simultaneously. That is, p implies q (q if p) and q implies p (q only if p) or, more succinctly, 'q if and only if p'. In this instance, we shall say that p *is a necessary and sufficient condition for* q.

1.2. Matrices and determinants

We state first

DEFINITION 1.1. *A matrix is an ordered set of elements arranged in a rectangular array of rows and columns.*

For instance, the matrix $\boldsymbol{A}$ may appear as

$$\boldsymbol{A} = \begin{bmatrix} a_{11} & a_{12} & \cdots & a_{1n} \\ a_{21} & a_{22} & \cdots & a_{2n} \\ \vdots & \vdots & & \vdots \\ a_{m1} & a_{m2} & \cdots & a_{mn} \end{bmatrix},$$

where a_{ij} represents the element in the ith row and jth column of $\boldsymbol{A}$. Since there are m rows and n columns in $\boldsymbol{A}$, the matrix is said to be of order $(m \times n)$ (read 'm by n'). When $i, j = 1, \ldots, n$, the matrix is square (it has the same number or rows and columns) and will be referred to as being of order n. A matrix may be written in shorthand fashion as

$$\boldsymbol{A} = [a_{ij}], \quad i = 1, \ldots, m; \quad j = 1, \ldots, n.$$

In this regard we have

DEFINITION 1.2. *The sum of two* $(m \times n)$ *matrices* $\boldsymbol{A} = [a_{ij}]$, $\boldsymbol{B} = [b_{ij}]$ *is itself an* $(m \times n)$ *matrix* $\boldsymbol{C} = [c_{ij}]$, *where* $c_{ij} = a_{ij} + b_{ij}$, i.e.

$$\boldsymbol{A} + \boldsymbol{B} = \boldsymbol{C} \quad or \quad [a_{ij}] + [b_{ij}] = [a_{ij} + b_{ij}], \quad i = 1, \ldots, m; \quad j = 1, \ldots, n.$$

DEFINITION 1.3. *The product of a (real) scalar* λ *and an* $(m \times n)$ *matrix*

$A = [a_{ij}]$ is the $(m \times n)$ matrix $\lambda A = [\lambda a_{ij}]$, $i = 1, \ldots, m$; $j = 1, \ldots, n$, obtained by multiplying each element of A by λ.

The properties of scalar multiplication and matrix addition may be summarized as:

(a) $A+B = B+A$ (commutative law);

(b) $(A+B)+C = A+(B+C)$ (associative law);

(c) $\lambda A = A\lambda$;

(d) $\lambda(A+B) = \lambda A+\lambda B$ (distributive laws);

(e) $(\lambda_1+\lambda_2)A = \lambda_1 A+\lambda_2 A$ (distributive laws);

(f) $A+0 = A$ (here 0 represents the *zero (null) matrix* and is taken to be the additive identity),

where it is to be understood that the λs are (real) scalars and the indicated matrices are conformable for addition, i.e. they all have the same order.

DEFINITION 1.4. *The transpose of an $(m \times n)$ matrix A, A', is the $(n \times m)$ matrix formed from A by interchanging its rows and columns, i.e. row i of A becomes column i of the transposed matrix A'.*

The following are the essential properties of matrix transposition:

(a) $(A')' = A$;

(b) $(\lambda_1 A+\lambda_2 B)' = \lambda_1 A'+\lambda_2 B'$;

(c) $(AB)' = B'A'$, where the product of A and B, AB, is assumed to exist.

In addition, we have

DEFINITION 1.5. *A matrix A of order n is symmetric if it equals its transpose, i.e. if $A = A'$ or $a_{ij} = a_{ji}$.*

Let us now concentrate on specific sets of elements within square or nth-order matrices.

DEFINITION 1.6. *The principal diagonal of an $(n \times n)$ matrix*

$$A = \begin{bmatrix} a_{11} & a_{12} & \cdots & a_{1n} \\ a_{21} & a_{22} & \cdots & a_{2n} \\ \vdots & \vdots & & \vdots \\ a_{n1} & a_{n2} & \cdots & a_{nn} \end{bmatrix}$$

is the set of elements extending from the upper left to lower right corner of A, namely $a_{11}, a_{22}, \ldots, a_{nn}$. Hence it consists of the elements a_{ii}, $i = 1, \ldots, n$.

In this case a few special types of square matrices can now be defined:

DEFINITION 1.7. *A diagonal matrix of order n is one for which all elements off the principal diagonal are zero,* i.e. *$A = [a_{ij}]$ is a diagonal matrix if $a_{ij} = 0, i \neq j$.*

DEFINITION 1.8. *The identity matrix of order n, $\boldsymbol{I}_n$, is a diagonal matrix having ones along its principal diagonal and zeros elsewhere:*

$$\boldsymbol{I}_n = \begin{bmatrix} 1 & 0 & \dots & 0 \\ 0 & 1 & \dots & 0 \\ \vdots & \vdots & & \vdots \\ 0 & 0 & \dots & 1 \end{bmatrix} = [\delta_{ij}], \quad \textit{where } \delta_{ij} = \begin{cases} 1, & i = j, \\ 0, & i \neq j. \end{cases}$$

Here δ_{ij} is termed the *Kronecker delta.*

DEFINITION 1.9. *A triangular matrix of order n is one for which all elements on one side of the principal diagonal are zero, i.e. $\boldsymbol{A} = [a_{ij}]$ is upper triangular if $a_{ij} = 0$ when $i>j$; it is lower triangular if $a_{ij} = 0$ for $i<j$.*

We shall frequently need to determine the product of two matrices. Hence, our next definition describes the process of matrix multiplication.

DEFINITION 1.10. *Given an $(m \times n)$ matrix $\boldsymbol{A}$ and an $(n \times p)$ matrix $\boldsymbol{B}$, the product $\boldsymbol{AB}$ is the $(m \times p)$ matrix $\boldsymbol{C}$ whose elements are computed from the elements of $\boldsymbol{A}$, $\boldsymbol{B}$ according to the rule*

$$c_{ij} = \sum_{k=1}^{n} a_{ik} b_{kj}, \quad i = 1, \dots, m; \quad j = 1, \dots, p.$$

The product $\boldsymbol{AB}$ exists if and only if the matrices $\boldsymbol{A}$, $\boldsymbol{B}$ are conformable for multiplication, i.e. if and only if the number of columns in $\boldsymbol{A}$ is the same as the number of rows in $\boldsymbol{B}$. Here $\boldsymbol{A}$ is referred to as the *premultiplier*, while $\boldsymbol{B}$ is termed the *postmultiplier*. It is important to note that, in general, matrix multiplication is not commutative. That is $\boldsymbol{AB} \neq \boldsymbol{BA}$. In fact, $\boldsymbol{BA}$ may not even exist. Matrix multiplication possesses the following properties:

(a) $(\boldsymbol{AB})\boldsymbol{C} = \boldsymbol{A}(\boldsymbol{BC})$ (the associative law);
(b) $\boldsymbol{A}(\boldsymbol{B}+\boldsymbol{C}) = \boldsymbol{AB}+\boldsymbol{AC}$
(c) $(\boldsymbol{A}+\boldsymbol{B})\boldsymbol{C} = \boldsymbol{AC}+\boldsymbol{BC}$ } (distributive laws);
(d) $\lambda(\boldsymbol{AB}) = \boldsymbol{A}(\lambda\boldsymbol{B}) = (\lambda\boldsymbol{A})\boldsymbol{B}$;
(e) $\boldsymbol{I}_m\boldsymbol{A} = \boldsymbol{A}\boldsymbol{I}_m = \boldsymbol{A}$ ($\boldsymbol{I}_m$ is the multiplicative identity);
(f) $\boldsymbol{0A} = \boldsymbol{A0} = \boldsymbol{0}$,

where λ is a (real) scalar and the indicated products exist.

In what follows we shall quite frequently need to compute the determinant of a (square) matrix. Specifically,

DEFINITION 1.11. *A determinant is a scalar-valued function D defined on the set of all square matrices $\mathscr{M}$.*

Hence, D maps elements in $\mathscr{M}$ into unique scalar quantities called determinants. That is, associated with each $(n \times n)$ matrix $\boldsymbol{A} \in \mathscr{M}$ is the scalar $D(\boldsymbol{A}) = |\boldsymbol{A}|$. How is $|\boldsymbol{A}|$ found? Before developing a procedure which may be used to 'expand' a determinant, let us pause briefly to develop some additional terminology.

DEFINITION 1.12. *A submatrix is the* $(k \times s)$ *matrix* $\boldsymbol{B}$ *obtained by deleting all but k rows and s columns of an* $(m \times n)$ *matrix* $\boldsymbol{A}$.

Also,

DEFINITION 1.13. *A minor is the determinant of a (square) submatrix; and a cofactor is a signed minor.*

In this regard, the minor of (i.e. associated with) the element a_{ij}, M_{ij}, is the determinant of the submatrix formed by deleting row i and column j of an nth-order matrix $\boldsymbol{A}$ while the cofactor of a_{ij}, C_{ij}, is calculated as $(-1)^{i+j}M_{ij}$. In the light of these definitions we have, for an nth-order matrix $\boldsymbol{A}$,

$$|\boldsymbol{A}| = \sum_{j=1}^{n} a_{ij}C_{ij} \quad \text{(expansion by row } i\text{)} \tag{1.1}$$

$$= \sum_{j=1}^{n} a_{ij}(-1)^{i+j}M_{ij} \quad \text{for any } i$$

or

$$|\boldsymbol{A}| = \sum_{i=1}^{n} a_{ij}C_{ij} \quad \text{(expansion by column } j\text{)} \tag{1.2}$$

$$= \sum_{i=1}^{n} a_{ij}(-1)^{i+j}M_{ij} \quad \text{for any } j.$$

Here eqs. (1.1) and (1.2) denote, respectively, the *cofactor expansion* of a determinant by a row (i.e. i is fixed and we sum over columns) or by a column (j is fixed and we sum over rows).

Some important properties of determinants are:

(a) interchanging any two rows or columns of a matrix $\boldsymbol{A}$ changes the sign of $|\boldsymbol{A}|$;

(b) if the matrix $\boldsymbol{A}$ has two rows or columns which are identical, $|\boldsymbol{A}| = 0$;

(c) if a row or column of a matrix $\boldsymbol{A}$ has all zero elements, $|\boldsymbol{A}| = 0$;

(d) if every element of a row or column of a matrix $\boldsymbol{A}$ is multiplied by a non-zero scalar λ to give a new matrix $\boldsymbol{B}$, $|\boldsymbol{B}| = \lambda|\boldsymbol{A}|$;

(e) if every element of an nth-order matrix $\boldsymbol{A}$ is multiplied by a non-zero scalar λ to give a new matrix

$$\boldsymbol{B} = \lambda\boldsymbol{A} = \begin{bmatrix} \lambda a_{11} & \ldots & \lambda a_{1n} \\ \vdots & & \\ \lambda a_{n1} & \ldots & \lambda a_{nn} \end{bmatrix},$$

$|\boldsymbol{B}| = |\lambda\boldsymbol{A}| = \lambda^n|\boldsymbol{A}|$ (here property (d) is applied n times in succession);

(f) if a row or column of a matrix $\boldsymbol{A}$ is a multiple of any other row or column, $|\boldsymbol{A}| = 0$;

(g) for an mth-order matrix $\boldsymbol{A}$, $|\boldsymbol{A}| = |\boldsymbol{A}'|$;

(h) if $\boldsymbol{A}$ is a diagonal or triangular matrix, $|\boldsymbol{A}| = a_{11}a_{22}\ldots a_{nn}$;
(i) $|\boldsymbol{I}_n| = 1, |\boldsymbol{0}| = 0$;
(j) if $\boldsymbol{A}$, $\boldsymbol{B}$ are of order n so that the product $\boldsymbol{AB}$ exists, $|\boldsymbol{AB}| = |\boldsymbol{A}|\cdot|\boldsymbol{B}|$;
(k) if $\boldsymbol{A}$ is $(m\times n)$ and $\boldsymbol{B}$ is $(n\times m)$, $|\boldsymbol{AB}| = 0$ if $m>n$;
(l) if $\boldsymbol{A}$, $\boldsymbol{B}$ are conformable for addition, then generally
$|\boldsymbol{A}+\boldsymbol{B}| \neq |\boldsymbol{A}|+|\boldsymbol{B}|$;
(m) if $\boldsymbol{A}$, $\boldsymbol{B}$ are of order n, $|\boldsymbol{AB}| = |\boldsymbol{A}'\boldsymbol{B}| = |\boldsymbol{AB}'| = |\boldsymbol{A}'\boldsymbol{B}'|$.

Often (particularly when we look to a sufficient condition for an extremum of a function of more than one independent variable) we will be faced with the expansion of a determinant of reasonably high order, perhaps one for which the order is four or five or even larger. While the cofactor expansion technique is directly applicable, it is not computationally efficient. In what follows we shall examine an alternative and more expedient method for finding the determinant of a matrix, namely the 'sweep-out' process. We first state

DEFINITION 1.14. *An elementary row (column) operation may be performed on a matrix* $\boldsymbol{A} = [a_{ij}]$ *by:*

(*a*) *interchanging any two rows (columns) of* $\boldsymbol{A}$; (*type I*)
(*b*) *multiplying a row (column) of* $\boldsymbol{A}$ *by a (real) scalar* $\lambda \neq 0$; (*type II*)
(*c*) *adding to the ith row (jth column) of* $\boldsymbol{A}$ λ *times any other row (column).* (*type III*)

Given an nth-order matrix $\boldsymbol{A}$, how do these elementary row (column) operations affect $|\boldsymbol{A}|$? Our answer may be indicated as:

(a) type I operation—see property (a) above;
(b) type II operation—see property (d) above;
(c) type III operation—if in $\boldsymbol{A}$ we add any non-zero multiple of one row (column) to a different row (column) to get a new matrix $\boldsymbol{B}$, $|\boldsymbol{B}| = |\boldsymbol{A}|$.

Hence only type III elementary row or column operations leave $|\boldsymbol{A}|$ invariant.

In this light we now state, in terms of elementary row operations, the

SWEEP-OUT PROCESS. *If* $|\boldsymbol{A}|$ *can be transformed, by elementary row operations, into the product of a constant k and the determinant of an upper-triangular matrix* $\boldsymbol{B}$,

$$|\boldsymbol{A}| = k|\boldsymbol{B}| = k\begin{vmatrix} b_{11} & b_{12} & \ldots & b_{1n} \\ 0 & b_{22} & \ldots & b_{2n} \\ 0 & 0 & \ldots & b_{3n} \\ \vdots & \vdots & & \vdots \\ 0 & 0 & \ldots & b_{nn} \end{vmatrix},$$

then $|\boldsymbol{A}| = kb_{11}b_{22}\ldots b_{nn}$ *(see property* (*h*) *above), where k is chosen to* *compensate for the cumulative effects on $|\boldsymbol{A}|$ of successive type I, II elementary row operations.*

Example 1.1. Find $|\boldsymbol{A}|$ when

$$\boldsymbol{A} = \begin{bmatrix} 2 & 1 & 0 & 1 \\ 3 & 1 & 4 & 2 \\ 0 & 0 & 1 & 2 \\ 1 & 4 & 1 & 0 \end{bmatrix}.$$

$$|\boldsymbol{A}| = 2\begin{vmatrix} 1 & \frac{1}{2} & 0 & \frac{1}{2} \\ 0 & -\frac{1}{2} & 4 & \frac{1}{2} \\ 0 & 0 & 1 & 2 \\ 0 & \frac{7}{2} & 1 & -\frac{1}{2} \end{vmatrix} = -\begin{vmatrix} 1 & \frac{1}{2} & 0 & \frac{1}{2} \\ 0 & 1 & -8 & -1 \\ 0 & 0 & 1 & 2 \\ 0 & 0 & 29 & 3 \end{vmatrix} = -\begin{vmatrix} 1 & \frac{1}{2} & 0 & \frac{1}{2} \\ 0 & 1 & -8 & -1 \\ 0 & 0 & 1 & 2 \\ 0 & 0 & 0 & -55 \end{vmatrix}$$

$$= k|\boldsymbol{B}| = 55.$$

Let us now consider a special type of minor associated with the principal diagonal of an nth-order matrix.

DEFINITION 1.15. *The kth naturally ordered principal minor of an nth-order matrix $\boldsymbol{A}$,*

$$M_k = \begin{vmatrix} a_{11} & \dots & a_{1k} \\ \vdots & & \vdots \\ a_{k1} & \dots & a_{kk} \end{vmatrix}, \quad k = 1, \dots, n,$$

is the determinant of the $(k \times k)$ submatrix obtained from $\boldsymbol{A}$ by retaining only its first k rows and columns, i.e. for

$$\boldsymbol{A} = \begin{bmatrix} a_{11} & \dots & a_{1n} \\ \vdots & & \vdots \\ a_{n1} & \dots & a_{nn} \end{bmatrix},$$

$$M_1 = a_{11}, \qquad M_2 = \begin{vmatrix} a_{11} & a_{12} \\ a_{21} & a_{22} \end{vmatrix}; \qquad M_3 = \begin{vmatrix} a_{11} & a_{12} & a_{13} \\ a_{21} & a_{22} & a_{23} \\ a_{31} & a_{32} & a_{33} \end{vmatrix}, \dots,$$

$$M_n = |\boldsymbol{A}|.$$

1.3. Vector algebra and vector spaces

In this section emphasis is placed upon the development of the notion of a vector and a vector space, and some important vector-algebraic operations.

In specifying points in n-dimensional coordinate space, reference is usually made to the concept of a vector, i.e.

DEFINITION 1.16. *A vector is an ordered n-tuple of (real) numbers expressed as a column* $(n \times 1)$ *or row* $(1 \times n)$ *matrix*

$$\boldsymbol{x} = \begin{bmatrix} x_1 \\ x_2 \\ \vdots \\ x_n \end{bmatrix}, \qquad \boldsymbol{x}' = (x_1, x_2, \ldots, x_n)$$

respectively. The n elements of a vector are called its components.

Hence the notion of a point in n-dimensional space and the concept of an n-component vector (emanating from the origin or *null vector* **0**) are one and the same (see fig. 1.1 for an example of a vector in three dimensions).

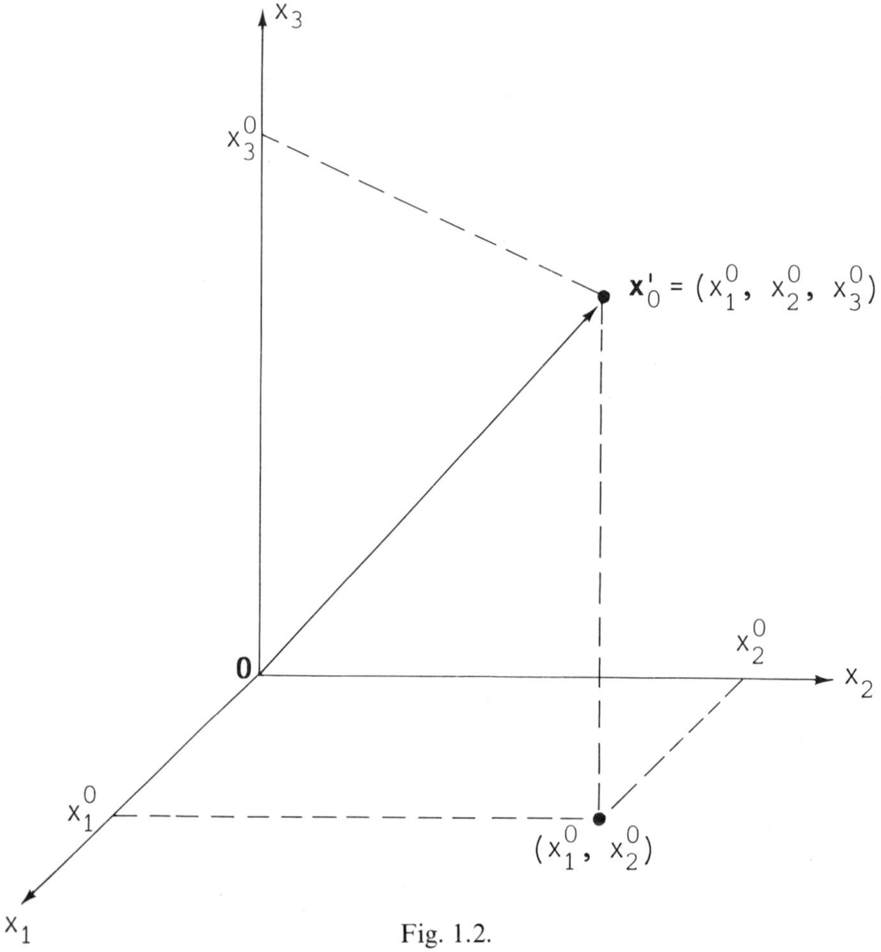

Fig. 1.2.

In this light we may now introduce the concept of an n-dimensional vector space as follows:

DEFINITION 1.17. *A vector (linear) space* $\mathscr{V}_n$ *over a field*[2] *of (real) scalars* $\mathscr{F}$ *is a collection of n-component vectors which is closed under the operations of addition and scalar multiplication. That is, if* $\mathbf{x}, \mathbf{y} \in \mathscr{V}_n$, *then* $\mathbf{x}+\mathbf{y} \in \mathscr{V}_n$ *and*

(*a*) $\mathbf{x}+\mathbf{y} = \mathbf{y}+\mathbf{x}$ *(commutative law)*;
(*b*) $\mathbf{x}+(\mathbf{y}+\mathbf{z}) = (\mathbf{x}+\mathbf{y})+\mathbf{z}$ *(associative law)*;
(*c*) *there is a unique element* $\mathbf{0} \in \mathscr{V}_n$ *such that* $\mathbf{x}+\mathbf{0} = \mathbf{x}$ *for each* $\mathbf{x} \in \mathscr{V}_n$;
(*d*) *for each* $\mathbf{x} \in \mathscr{V}_n$ *there is a unique element* $-\mathbf{x} \in \mathscr{V}_n$ *such that* $\mathbf{x}+(-\mathbf{x}) = \mathbf{0}$; *while for* $c \in \mathscr{F}$, $\mathbf{x} \in \mathscr{V}_n$, *it follows that* $c\mathbf{x} \in \mathscr{V}_n$ *and*

$$\left.\begin{aligned} &(a')\ c(\mathbf{x}+\mathbf{y}) = c\mathbf{x}+c\mathbf{y} \\ &(b')\ (c_1+c_2)\mathbf{x} = c_1\mathbf{x}+c_2\mathbf{x} \end{aligned}\right\}\text{(distributive laws)};$$

(*c'*) $(c_1 c_2)\mathbf{x} = c_1(c_2\mathbf{x})$ *(associative law)*;
(*d'*) $1\mathbf{x} = \mathbf{x}$ *for every* $\mathbf{x} \in \mathscr{V}_n$.

Exactly how does one go about adding two vectors or multiplying a vector by a scalar?

DEFINITION 1.18. *Let* $\mathbf{x}, \mathbf{y} \in \mathscr{V}_n$. *The sum of* $\mathbf{x}$ *and* $\mathbf{y}$ *is the n-component vector.*

$$\mathbf{x}+\mathbf{y} = \begin{bmatrix} x_1+y_1 \\ x_2+y_2 \\ \vdots \\ x_n+y_n \end{bmatrix} \in \mathscr{V}_n,$$

where x_i, y_i, $i = 1, \ldots, n$, *denote, respectively, the ith component of* $\mathbf{x}, \mathbf{y}$.

DEFINITION 1.19. *Let* $\mathbf{x} \in \mathscr{V}_n$. *The product of a scalar* $c \in \mathscr{F}$ *and* $\mathbf{x}$ *is the n-component vector*

$$c\mathbf{x} = \begin{bmatrix} cx_1 \\ cx_2 \\ \vdots \\ cx_n \end{bmatrix} \in \mathscr{V}_n.$$

At this point we shall now introduce the concepts of the scalar (inner) product of two vectors and the length of a vector. If we couple these two notions (which will be presented shortly) with definitions 1.17–1.19, indeed, if we define on $\mathscr{V}_n$ a norm,[3] we form what is commonly referred to as

[2] A set $\mathscr{F}$ of elements together with the operations of addition and multiplication on $\mathscr{F}$ constitutes a *field* if: both addition and multiplication are associative and commutative; additive and multiplicative inverses and identity elements exist; and multiplication distributes over addition. For an elaboration on this concept see Hoffman and Kunze (1961), pp. 1–3, and Halmos (1958), pp. 1–6.

[3] A *norm* is a generalization of the distance from $\mathbf{x} \in \mathscr{V}_n$ to the origin $\mathbf{0}$. Specifically, it is a function which assigns to each $\mathbf{x} \in \mathscr{V}_n$ some number $\|\mathbf{x}\|$ such that: (a) $\|\mathbf{x}\| \geqslant 0$ and $\|\mathbf{x}\| = 0$ if and only if $\mathbf{x} = \mathbf{0}$; (b) $\|\mathbf{x}+\mathbf{y}\| \leqslant \|\mathbf{x}\| + \|\mathbf{y}\|$ (the triangle inequality); (c) $\|c\mathbf{x}\| = |c|\,\|\mathbf{x}\|$ (homogeneity), $c \in \mathscr{F}$; and (d) $|\mathbf{x}\cdot\mathbf{y}| \leqslant \|\mathbf{x}\|\,\|\mathbf{y}\|$ (the Cauchy–Schwarz inequality).

n-dimensional *Euclidean space* (denoted $\mathscr{E}^n$). In what follows then, our discussions will pertain to operations in $\mathscr{E}^n$. To this end we state

DEFINITION 1.20. *Let* $\mathbf{x}$, $\mathbf{y} \in \mathscr{E}^n$. *The scalar product of* $\mathbf{x}$, $\mathbf{y}$ *(denoted* $\mathbf{x} \cdot \mathbf{y}$*) is the scalar*

$$\mathbf{x} \cdot \mathbf{y} = \mathbf{x}' \mathbf{y} = \sum_{i=1}^{n} x_i y_i,$$

where:

(*a*) $\mathbf{x} \cdot \mathbf{x} \geqslant 0$ *and* $\mathbf{x} \cdot \mathbf{x} = 0$ *if and only if* $\mathbf{x} = \mathbf{0}$;
(*b*) $\mathbf{x} \cdot \mathbf{y} = \mathbf{y} \cdot \mathbf{x}$ *(commutative law)*;
(*c*) $(\mathbf{x}+\mathbf{y}) \cdot \mathbf{z} = \mathbf{x} \cdot \mathbf{z} + \mathbf{y} \cdot \mathbf{z}$ *(distributive law)*; *and*
(*d*) $(c\mathbf{x}) \cdot \mathbf{y} = c(\mathbf{x} \cdot \mathbf{y})$, $c \in \mathscr{F}$.

In this light we have

DEFINITION 1.21. *Let* $\mathbf{x}$, $\mathbf{y} \in \mathscr{E}^n$. *The distance between* $\mathbf{x}$, $\mathbf{y}$ *is*

$$\|\mathbf{x}-\mathbf{y}\| = [(\mathbf{x}-\mathbf{y}) \cdot (\mathbf{x}-\mathbf{y})]^{\frac{1}{2}} = [(\mathbf{x}-\mathbf{y})'(\mathbf{x}-\mathbf{y})]^{\frac{1}{2}}$$
$$= \left[\sum_{i=1}^{n} |x_i - y_i|^2 \right]^{\frac{1}{2}}.$$

In $\mathscr{E}^2$ this distance may be calculated by employing the Pythagorean theorem (fig. 1.3).

An important special case of the previous definition appears as

DEFINITION 1.22. *Let* $\mathbf{x} \in \mathscr{E}^n$. *The length (magnitude) of* $\mathbf{x}$ *(i.e. the distance*

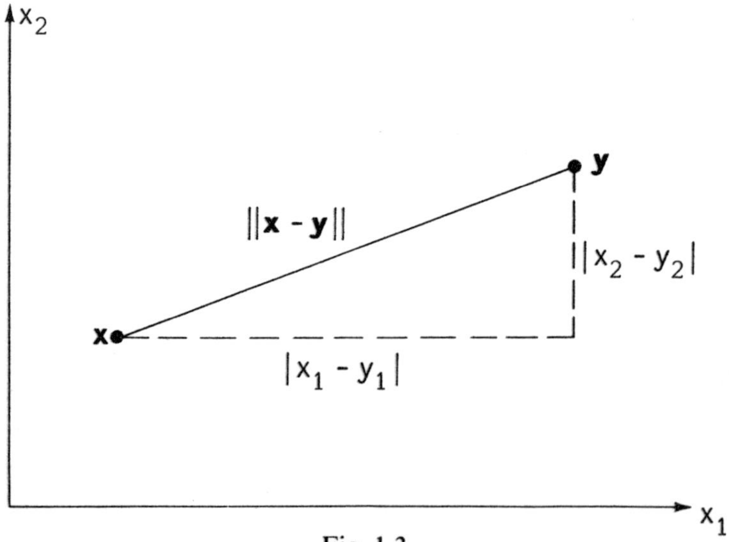

Fig. 1.3.

from $\boldsymbol{x}$ *to the origin* $\mathbf{0}$*) or Euclidean norm of* $\boldsymbol{x}$ *is*

$$\|\boldsymbol{x}\| = (\boldsymbol{x}\cdot\boldsymbol{x})^{\frac{1}{2}} = (\boldsymbol{x}'\boldsymbol{x})^{\frac{1}{2}}$$
$$= \left[\sum_{i=1}^{n} |x_i|^2\right]^{\frac{1}{2}}$$

while the direction of $\boldsymbol{x} \neq \mathbf{0}$ *is the unit vector* $\boldsymbol{x}/\|\boldsymbol{x}\|$ *whose length is one.*

We next look to the specification of the angle between two non-zero vectors.

DEFINITION 1.23. *Let* $\boldsymbol{x}, \boldsymbol{y} \in \mathscr{E}^n$ *with* $\boldsymbol{x}, \boldsymbol{y} \neq \mathbf{0}$. *The cosine of the angle* θ *between* $\boldsymbol{x}, \boldsymbol{y}$ *is*

$$\cos\theta = (\boldsymbol{x}\cdot\boldsymbol{y}/\|\boldsymbol{x}\|\ \|\boldsymbol{y}\|), \quad 0 \leqslant \theta \leqslant \pi.$$

To verify this result we may employ the *law of cosines* (in any triangle the square of any side is equal to the sum of the squares of the other sides minus twice the product of these sides and the cosine of the angle between them) and the result that $(\boldsymbol{x} \pm \boldsymbol{y})' = \boldsymbol{x}' \pm \boldsymbol{y}'$ to obtain (see fig. 1.4 for $\boldsymbol{x}, \boldsymbol{y} \in \mathscr{E}^2$)

$$\|\boldsymbol{x}-\boldsymbol{y}\|^2 = \|\boldsymbol{x}\|^2 + \|\boldsymbol{y}\|^2 - 2\|\boldsymbol{x}\|\ \|\boldsymbol{y}\| \cos\theta$$

or

$$(\boldsymbol{x}-\boldsymbol{y})'(\boldsymbol{x}-\boldsymbol{y}) = \boldsymbol{x}'\boldsymbol{x} + \boldsymbol{y}'\boldsymbol{y} - 2\|\boldsymbol{x}\|\ \|\boldsymbol{y}\| \cos\theta,$$
$$-2\boldsymbol{x}'\boldsymbol{y} = -2\|\boldsymbol{x}\|\ \|\boldsymbol{y}\| \cos\theta,$$

and thus $\cos\theta = \boldsymbol{x}\cdot\boldsymbol{y}/\|\boldsymbol{x}\|\ \|\boldsymbol{y}\|$. Note that the Cauchy–Schwarz inequality implies that $-1 \leqslant \cos\theta \leqslant 1$.

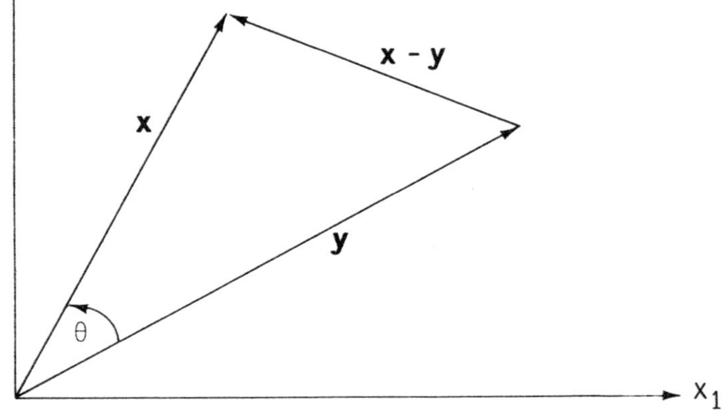

Fig. 1.4.

Example 1.2. Find (a) the distance and (b) the cosine of the angle between the vectors $\boldsymbol{x}' = (1, 2, 1)$, $\boldsymbol{y}' = (0, 2, 5)$.

(a) $\|\boldsymbol{x}-\boldsymbol{y}\| = (1^2+0^2+4^2)^{\frac{1}{2}} = \sqrt{17}$;

(b) since $\boldsymbol{x}\cdot\boldsymbol{y} = 0+4+5 = 9$, $\|\boldsymbol{x}\| = (1^2+2^2+1^2)^{\frac{1}{2}} = \sqrt{6}$, and $\|\boldsymbol{y}\| = (0^2+2^2+5^2)^{\frac{1}{2}} = \sqrt{29}$, $\cos\theta = 9/13.2$.

It is important to note that the angle between $\boldsymbol{x}$, $\boldsymbol{y}$ is acute ($<\pi/2$), right ($=\pi/2$), or obtuse ($>\pi/2$) according to whether the scalar product $\boldsymbol{x}\cdot\boldsymbol{y}$ is positive, zero, or negative.

By virtue of the converse of this argument we have

DEFINITION 1.24. *The vectors* $\boldsymbol{x}$, $\boldsymbol{y}\in\mathscr{E}^n$, $\boldsymbol{x}, \boldsymbol{y} \neq \boldsymbol{0}$, *are said to be orthogonal (i.e. mutually perpendicular) if* $\boldsymbol{x}\cdot\boldsymbol{y} = 0$.

Since $\boldsymbol{x}\cdot\boldsymbol{y} = \|\boldsymbol{x}\|\,\|\boldsymbol{y}\|\cos\theta$, $\boldsymbol{x}\cdot\boldsymbol{y} = 0$ if and only if $\theta = \pi/2$, and thus $\cos\theta = 0$.

We next look to the specification of the component of one vector in the direction of another. To enhance our understanding of this concept we first state

DEFINITION 1.25. *The vector projection of* $\boldsymbol{y}$ *onto* $\boldsymbol{x}$ *(written* $\text{proj}_{\boldsymbol{x}}\,\boldsymbol{y}$*) is a vector in the direction of* $\boldsymbol{x}$ *obtained by projecting* $\boldsymbol{y}$ *perpendicularly onto* $\boldsymbol{x}$ *(fig. 1.5 considers the case for* $\boldsymbol{x}, \boldsymbol{y}\in\mathscr{E}^2$*) and is equal to*

$$((\boldsymbol{x}\cdot\boldsymbol{y})/(\boldsymbol{x}\cdot\boldsymbol{x}))\boldsymbol{x}.$$

Accordingly, we now state

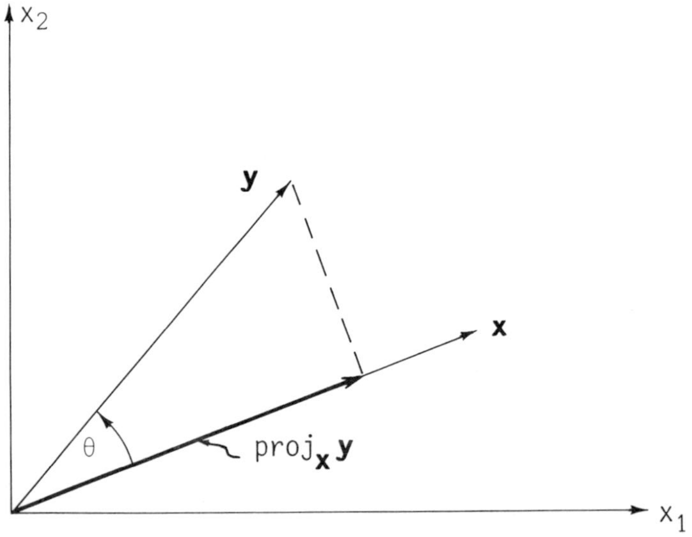

Fig. 1.5.

DEFINITION 1.26. *The component of* $\boldsymbol{y}$ *along* $\boldsymbol{x}$ *(written* $\text{comp}_{\boldsymbol{x}}\, \boldsymbol{y}$*) is the scalar projection* $\boldsymbol{y}$ *along* $\boldsymbol{x}$ *or in the* $\boldsymbol{x}$*-direction, i.e. it is the magnitude of the vector projection of* $\boldsymbol{y}$ *onto* $\boldsymbol{x}$ *or* $\text{comp}_{\boldsymbol{x}}\, \boldsymbol{y} = \pm \|\text{proj}_{\boldsymbol{x}}\, \boldsymbol{y}\| = \|\boldsymbol{y}\| \cos\theta$, *where plus or minus holds according to whether* $\boldsymbol{x}, \boldsymbol{y}$ *form an acute or obtuse angle.*

To establish the connection between the scalar product and the scalar projection of two vectors $\boldsymbol{x}, \boldsymbol{y}$ we note that

$$\boldsymbol{x}\cdot\boldsymbol{y} = \|\boldsymbol{x}\|\ \text{comp}_{\boldsymbol{x}}\, \boldsymbol{y}\ (\text{or } \|\boldsymbol{y}\|\ \text{comp}_{\boldsymbol{y}}\, \boldsymbol{x}).$$

Moreover, if $\boldsymbol{x}$ is a unit vector, then in this instance these two notions are equivalent since

$$\boldsymbol{x}\cdot\boldsymbol{y} = \text{comp}_{\boldsymbol{x}}\, \boldsymbol{y}. \tag{1.3}$$

In this regard, the $\boldsymbol{y}$ component in the $\boldsymbol{x}$-direction ($\boldsymbol{x} \neq \boldsymbol{0}$) may generally be written

$$\text{comp}_{\boldsymbol{x}}\, \boldsymbol{y} = \left(\frac{\boldsymbol{x}}{\|\boldsymbol{x}\|}\right)\cdot\boldsymbol{y}.$$

1.4. Matrix inversion

Quite often the inverse or reciprocal of a matrix will play an important role in our calculations. In fact, it will be employed in the next section when we develop a method for solving a system of simultaneous linear equations. To this end we state

DEFINITION 1.27. *Given an nth-order matrix* $\boldsymbol{A}$, *if there exists an nth-order matrix* $\boldsymbol{A}^{-1}$ *which satisfies the relation* $\boldsymbol{A}\boldsymbol{A}^{-1} = \boldsymbol{A}^{-1}\boldsymbol{A} = \boldsymbol{I}_n$, *then* $\boldsymbol{A}^{-1}$ *is termed the 'inverse' of* $\boldsymbol{A}$.

Before looking to the calculation of $\boldsymbol{A}^{-1}$ two additional definitions are in order. First,

DEFINITION 1.28. *The adjoint of an nth-order matrix* $\boldsymbol{A}$, $\boldsymbol{A}^{+}$, *is the nth-order matrix obtained from* $\boldsymbol{A} = [a_{ij}]$ *by replacing each element* a_{ij} *by its cofactor* C_{ij} *and transposing.*

In addition,

DEFINITION 1.29. *An nth-order matrix* $\boldsymbol{A}$ *is said to be singular if* $|\boldsymbol{A}| = 0$ *and non-singular if* $|\boldsymbol{A}| \neq 0$.

Thus the inverse of our nth-order matrix $\boldsymbol{A}$ is calculated as

$$\boldsymbol{A}^{-1} = \boldsymbol{A}^{+}/|\boldsymbol{A}|. \tag{1.4}$$

Under what circumstance will the indicated inverse exist? Since the determinant of $\boldsymbol{A}$ appears in the denominator of (1.4), clearly $\boldsymbol{A}^{-1}$ exists if and only if A is non-singular, i.e. if and only if $|A| \neq 0$. Hence, only non-singular matrices have inverses; moreover, every non-singular matrix has an inverse. Additionally, if A^{-1} exists, it is unique. That is, given A_1^{-1}, A_2^{-1}, if $A_1^{-1}A = A_2^{-1}A = I_n$, then $A_1^{-1} = A_2^{-1}$.

Example 1.3. Find A^{-1} when

$$A = \begin{bmatrix} 1 & 2 & -1 \\ 0 & 3 & 1 \\ 4 & 1 & 2 \end{bmatrix}.$$

The first step in finding the inverse of A is to determine whether or not it exists. Since $|A| = 25$, A is non-singular and thus possesses an inverse. Next determine A^+. Since

$$\begin{bmatrix} C_{11} & C_{12} & C_{13} \\ C_{21} & C_{22} & C_{23} \\ C_{31} & C_{32} & C_{33} \end{bmatrix} = \begin{bmatrix} 5 & 4 & -12 \\ -5 & 6 & 7 \\ 5 & -1 & 3 \end{bmatrix},$$

$$A^+ = \begin{bmatrix} 5 & -5 & 5 \\ 4 & 6 & -1 \\ -12 & 7 & 3 \end{bmatrix}.$$

Then from (1.4),

$$A^{-1} = \frac{A^+}{|A|} = \begin{bmatrix} \frac{1}{5} & -\frac{1}{5} & \frac{1}{5} \\ \frac{4}{25} & \frac{6}{25} & -\frac{1}{25} \\ -\frac{12}{25} & \frac{7}{25} & \frac{3}{25} \end{bmatrix}.$$

The reader may easily verify that $AA^{-1} = I_3$. In fact, this latter equality provides us with a check that A^{-1} has been calculated without error.

The essential properties of matrix inversion are:

(a) $(A^{-1})^{-1} = A$;

(b) $|A^{-1}| = 1/|A|$;

(c) $(A')^{-1} = (A^{-1})'$; and

(d) given that A, B are non-singular and conformable for multiplication, $(AB)^{-1} = B^{-1}A^{-1}$.

From a computational viewpoint, the adjoint method of inverting a non-singular matrix A may become quite tedious when the order of A is large. An alternative and more effective procedure utilizes elementary row operations. As a first step let us form the $(n \times n+n)$ matrix:

$$[A \vdots I_n] = \left[\begin{array}{cccc:cccc} a_{11} & a_{12} & \dots & a_{1n} & 1 & 0 & \dots & 0 \\ a_{21} & a_{22} & \dots & a_{2n} & 0 & 1 & \dots & 0 \\ \vdots & \vdots & & \vdots & \vdots & \vdots & & \vdots \\ a_{n1} & a_{n2} & \dots & a_{nn} & 0 & 0 & \dots & 1 \end{array}\right].$$

If a sequence of elementary row operations applied to $[A \vdots I_n]$ reduces A to I_n, that same sequence of operations transforms I_n to A^{-1}, i.e.

$$[A \vdots I_n] \rightarrow [I_n \vdots A^{-1}].$$

Example 1.4. Find A^{-1} given A from the preceding example. Our calculations start with

$$[A \vdots I_3] = \left[\begin{array}{ccc:ccc} 1 & 2 & -1 & 1 & 0 & 0 \\ 0 & 3 & 1 & 0 & 1 & 0 \\ 4 & 1 & 2 & 0 & 0 & 1 \end{array}\right].$$

Then

$$\left[\begin{array}{ccc:ccc} 1 & 2 & -1 & 1 & 0 & 0 \\ 0 & 3 & 1 & 0 & 1 & 0 \\ 4 & 1 & 2 & 0 & 0 & 1 \end{array}\right] \rightarrow \left[\begin{array}{ccc:ccc} 1 & 2 & -1 & 1 & 0 & 0 \\ 0 & 3 & 1 & 0 & 1 & 0 \\ 0 & -7 & 6 & -4 & 0 & 1 \end{array}\right]$$

$$\rightarrow \left[\begin{array}{ccc:ccc} 1 & 0 & -\frac{5}{3} & 1 & -\frac{2}{3} & 0 \\ 0 & 1 & \frac{1}{3} & 0 & \frac{1}{3} & 0 \\ 0 & 0 & \frac{25}{3} & -4 & \frac{7}{3} & 1 \end{array}\right] \rightarrow \left[\begin{array}{ccc:ccc} 1 & 0 & 0 & \frac{1}{5} & -\frac{1}{5} & \frac{1}{5} \\ 0 & 1 & 0 & \frac{4}{25} & \frac{6}{25} & -\frac{1}{25} \\ 0 & 0 & 1 & -\frac{12}{25} & \frac{7}{25} & \frac{3}{25} \end{array}\right] = [I_3 \vdots A^{-1}].$$

1.5. Solution of a system of simultaneous linear equations

The system of n linear equations in n unknowns

$$\begin{aligned} a_{11}x_1 + a_{12}x_2 + \ldots + a_{1n}x_n &= c_1 \\ a_{21}x_1 + a_{22}x_2 + \ldots + a_{2n}x_n &= c_2 \\ \ldots\ldots\ldots\ldots\ldots\ldots\ldots\ldots\ldots \\ a_{n1}x_1 + a_{n2}x_2 + \ldots + a_{nn}x_n &= c_n \end{aligned}$$

may be written in matrix form as

$$\begin{bmatrix} a_{11} & a_{12} & \ldots & a_{1n} \\ a_{21} & a_{22} & \ldots & a_{2n} \\ \vdots & \vdots & & \vdots \\ a_{n1} & a_{n2} & \ldots & a_{nn} \end{bmatrix} \begin{bmatrix} x_1 \\ x_2 \\ \vdots \\ x_n \end{bmatrix} = \begin{bmatrix} c_1 \\ c_2 \\ \vdots \\ c_n \end{bmatrix}$$

or

$$AX = C, \tag{1.5}$$

where A is an $(n \times n)$ matrix of (constant) coefficients a_{ij}, X is an $(n \times 1)$ matrix of (unknown) variables x_i, and C is an $(n \times 1)$ matrix of constants c_i, $i, j = 1, \ldots, n$.

How can we obtain the values of the unknowns x_i which satisfy system (1.5)? That is, how shall we obtain X? In what follows we shall employ a solution technique known as

CRAMER'S RULE *If* $|A| \neq 0$, *then the solution of the system of n equations in n unknowns* $AX = C$ *is given by*

$$x_i = \frac{\Delta_i}{\Delta}, \quad i = 1, \ldots, n,$$

where $\Delta = |A|$, $\Delta_i = |A^{(i)}|$, *and* $A^{(i)}$ *is the matrix obtained by replacing the ith column of* A *by* C.

Proof. Let us multiply both sides of eq. (1.5) by A^{-1} in order to obtain

$$A^{-1}AX = I_n X = X = A^{-1}C$$

or

$$X = \frac{A^{+}C}{|A|} \tag{1.6}$$

$$= \begin{bmatrix} C_{11} & C_{21} & \cdots & C_{n1} \\ C_{12} & C_{22} & \cdots & C_{n2} \\ \vdots & \vdots & & \vdots \\ C_{1n} & C_{2n} & \cdots & C_{nn} \end{bmatrix} \begin{bmatrix} c_1 \\ c_2 \\ \vdots \\ c_n \end{bmatrix} / |A|$$

$$= \begin{bmatrix} c_1C_{11} + c_2C_{21} + \ldots + c_nC_{n1} \\ c_1C_{12} + c_2C_{22} + \ldots + c_nC_{n2} \\ \cdots\cdots\cdots\cdots\cdots\cdots \\ c_1C_{1n} + c_2C_{2n} + \ldots + c_nC_{nn} \end{bmatrix} / |A|$$

$$= \begin{bmatrix} \sum_{i=1}^{n} c_iC_{i1}/|A| \\ \sum_{i=1}^{n} c_iC_{i2}/|A| \\ \vdots \\ \sum_{i=1}^{n} c_iC_{in}/|A| \end{bmatrix} \qquad \text{Q.E.D.}$$

How may we interpret this result? The cofactor expansion of $|A|$ by its ith column is $\Sigma_{i=1}^{n} a_{ij}C_{ij}$ (eq. (1.2)). If we replace the ith column in $|A|$ by C and keep all other columns intact, $\Sigma_{i=1}^{n} a_{ij}C_{ij} = \Sigma_{i=1}^{n} c_iC_{ij}$. Dividing the latter sum by $|A|$ yields

$$x_i = \sum_{i=1}^{n} c_iC_{ij}/|A| \qquad \text{(Cramer's rule)},$$

the ith element in X. In general, Cramer's rule states that to obtain x_i, divide by $|A|$ the determinant of the matrix formed from A by replacing its *i*th column by $\boldsymbol{C}$. That is

$$x_1 = \begin{vmatrix} c_1 & a_{12} & \dots & a_{1n} \\ c_2 & a_{22} & \dots & a_{2n} \\ \vdots & \vdots & & \vdots \\ c_n & a_{n2} & \dots & a_{nn} \end{vmatrix} / |\boldsymbol{A}|, \qquad x_2 = \begin{vmatrix} a_{11} & c_1 & \dots & a_{1n} \\ a_{21} & c_2 & \dots & a_{2n} \\ \vdots & \vdots & & \vdots \\ a_{n1} & c_n & \dots & a_{nn} \end{vmatrix} / |\boldsymbol{A}|, \dots,$$

$$x_n = \begin{vmatrix} a_{11} & a_{12} & \dots & c_1 \\ a_{21} & a_{22} & \dots & c_2 \\ \vdots & \vdots & & \vdots \\ a_{n1} & a_{n2} & \dots & c_n \end{vmatrix} / |\boldsymbol{A}|.$$

Since each element of $\boldsymbol{A}^+\boldsymbol{C}$ in eq. (1.6) is divided by $|\boldsymbol{A}|$, it is evident that system (1.5) has a solution if and only if $\boldsymbol{A}$ is non-singular, i.e. a unique solution exists if and only if $|\boldsymbol{A}| \neq 0$.

Example 1.5. Find values of x_1, x_2, and x_3 which simultaneously satisfy the system

$$\begin{aligned} x_1+2x_2+x_3 &= 4, \\ 3x_1+x_2 &= 6, \\ x_1+4x_2+x_3 &= 3. \end{aligned}$$

Our first step in obtaining the x_i values is to determine whether or not the coefficient matrix $\boldsymbol{A}$ is non-singular. Since

$$|\boldsymbol{A}| = \begin{vmatrix} 1 & 2 & 1 \\ 3 & 1 & 0 \\ 1 & 4 & 1 \end{vmatrix} = 6,$$

a unique solution exists. Then via Cramer's rule,

$$x_1 = \begin{vmatrix} 4 & 2 & 1 \\ 6 & 1 & 0 \\ 3 & 4 & 1 \end{vmatrix} /6 = \frac{13}{6}, \qquad x_2 = \begin{vmatrix} 1 & 4 & 1 \\ 3 & 6 & 0 \\ 1 & 3 & 1 \end{vmatrix} /6 = -\frac{1}{2},$$

$$x_3 = \begin{vmatrix} 1 & 2 & 4 \\ 3 & 1 & 6 \\ 1 & 4 & 3 \end{vmatrix} /6 = \frac{17}{6}.$$

It is evident that if the coefficient matrix $\boldsymbol{A}$ is of considerably high order, the implementation of Cramer's rule becomes quite an arduous process. In instances such as this, an alternative computational scheme such as Gauss elimination or its variant, matrix reduction (to be presented shortly), should be used.

At this point we may tighten our analysis regarding the existence and uniqueness of a solution to the system $\boldsymbol{AX} = \boldsymbol{C}$, where $\boldsymbol{A}$ is $(n \times n)$, by considering the concept of the rank of a matrix. But first we have

DEFINITION 1.30. *A system of equations is consistent if it has at least one solution; it is inconsistent if it does not possess a solution.*

DEFINITION 1.31. *The rank of an $(n \times n)$ matrix $\boldsymbol{A}$, $\rho(\boldsymbol{A})$, is the order of the largest non-singular submatrix of $\boldsymbol{A}$, i.e. it is the order of the largest non-vanishing determinant in $\boldsymbol{A}$; moreover, if $\rho(\boldsymbol{A}) = k$, all submatrices of order $k+1$ are singular.*

And also,

DEFINITION 1.32. *An nth-order matrix $\boldsymbol{A}$ is said to be of full rank if $\rho(\boldsymbol{A}) = n$, i.e. if $|\boldsymbol{A}| \neq 0$.*

The important properties of the rank of a matrix are:

(a) given that $\boldsymbol{A}$ is of order $(m \times n)$, $\rho(\boldsymbol{A}) \leqslant \min\{m, n\}$;
(b) $\rho(\boldsymbol{I}_n) = n$;
(c) $\rho(\boldsymbol{0}) = 0$;
(d) $\rho(\boldsymbol{A}') = \rho(\boldsymbol{A})$;
(e) if $\boldsymbol{A}$ is a diagonal matrix, $\rho(\boldsymbol{A})$ = number of non-zero elements on the principal diagonal of $\boldsymbol{A}$;
(f) if $\boldsymbol{A}$, $\boldsymbol{B}$ are both of order $(m \times n)$, $\rho(\boldsymbol{A}+\boldsymbol{B}) \leqslant \rho(\boldsymbol{A}) + \rho(\boldsymbol{B})$;
(g) if $\boldsymbol{A}$, $\boldsymbol{B}$ are conformable for multiplication, $\rho(\boldsymbol{AB}) \leqslant \min\{\rho(\boldsymbol{A}), \rho(\boldsymbol{B})\}$;
(h) if $\boldsymbol{A}$ is of order n, $\rho(\boldsymbol{A}) = n$ if and only if $\boldsymbol{A}$ is non-singular; $\rho(\boldsymbol{A}) < n$ if and only if $\boldsymbol{A}$ is singular;
(i) if a sequence of elementary row (column) operations transforms a matrix $\boldsymbol{A}$ into a new matrix $\boldsymbol{B}$, $\rho(\boldsymbol{A}) = \rho(\boldsymbol{B})$.

Example 1.6. It is easily verified that if:

(a) $\boldsymbol{A} = \begin{bmatrix} 1 & 2 \\ 2 & 4 \end{bmatrix}, \qquad \rho(\boldsymbol{A}) = 1;$

(b) $\boldsymbol{A} = \begin{bmatrix} 1 & 2 & 1 \\ 0 & 4 & 1 \\ 0 & 3 & 2 \end{bmatrix}, \qquad \rho(\boldsymbol{A}) = 3;$

(c) $\boldsymbol{A} = \begin{bmatrix} 1 & 2 & 1 \\ 4 & 8 & 0 \\ 1 & 2 & 1 \end{bmatrix}, \qquad \rho(\boldsymbol{A}) = 2.$

We may now state

THEOREM 1.1.[4] *Given the system* $AX = C$, *where* A *is of order* $(m \times n)$, *if*

(1) $\rho[A \vdots C] > \rho(A)$, *the system is inconsistent;*

(2) $\rho[A \vdots C] = \rho(A) =$ *number of unknowns* n, *the system is consistent and possesses a unique solution; and*

(3) $\rho[A \vdots C] = \rho(A) = k <$ *number of unknowns* n, *the system is consistent and possesses an infinity of solutions, where arbitrary values may be assigned to* $n-k$ *of the variables.*

It is obvious that if A is $(n \times n)$ and the second case holds, i.e. if A is non-singular, then Cramer's rule may be employed to generate a unique solution.

At this point in our analysis we again look to considerations of computational efficiency. If A is of sufficiently high order, the determination of the rank of A by the application of def. 1.32 involves a substantial amount of work. Let us consider an alternative technique. By way of an introduction to this method we state

DEFINITION 1.33. *An* $(m \times n)$ *matrix* E *(obtained from a matrix of the same order by a series of elementary row operations) is in row-reduced echelon normal form (or simply called an echelon matrix for short) if:*

(a) the first k *rows* $(k \geqslant 0)$ *are non-zero while the last* $m-k$ *rows contain only zero elements;*

(b) the first non-zero element in the ith row $(i = 1, \ldots, k, k \geqslant 1)$ *equals one;*

(c) if c_i *denotes the column in which the unity element appears, we require that* $c_1 < c_2 < \cdots < c_k$*; and lastly, (a), (b), and (c) imply that*

(d) the lower triangle of elements e_{ij}, *where* $j < i$ *are all zero.*

For example, an echelon matrix may typically appear as

$$E = \begin{bmatrix} 0 & 1 & e_{13} & e_{14} & e_{15} \\ 0 & 0 & 1 & e_{24} & e_{25} \\ 0 & 0 & 0 & 1 & e_{35} \\ 0 & 0 & 0 & 0 & 0 \end{bmatrix}.$$

In this regard, we formulate an alternative and equivalent definition of the rank of a matrix, namely

DEFINITION 1.34. *The rank of an* $(m \times n)$ *matrix* A, $\rho(A)$, *is the number of non-zero rows in the row-reduced echelon normal form of* A.

[4] For a proof see Noble (1969), p. 91.

Example 1.7. Determine the rank of

$$A = \begin{bmatrix} 2 & 1 & 4 & 1 \\ 3 & 0 & 1 & 5 \\ 1 & 1 & 2 & 3 \\ 4 & 1 & 0 & 1 \end{bmatrix}.$$

Interchanging rows 1 and 3 yields

$$\begin{bmatrix} 1 & 1 & 2 & 3 \\ 3 & 0 & 1 & 5 \\ 2 & 1 & 4 & 1 \\ 4 & 1 & 0 & 1 \end{bmatrix} \to \begin{bmatrix} 1 & 1 & 2 & 3 \\ 0 & -3 & -5 & -4 \\ 0 & -1 & 0 & -5 \\ 0 & -3 & -8 & -11 \end{bmatrix} \to \begin{bmatrix} 1 & 1 & 2 & 3 \\ 0 & 1 & 5/3 & 4/3 \\ 0 & 0 & 5/3 & -11/3 \\ 0 & 0 & -3 & -7 \end{bmatrix}$$

$$\to \begin{bmatrix} 1 & 1 & 2 & 3 \\ 0 & 1 & 5/3 & 4/3 \\ 0 & 0 & 1 & -11/5 \\ 0 & 0 & 0 & -68/5 \end{bmatrix} \to \begin{bmatrix} 1 & 1 & 2 & 3 \\ 0 & 1 & 5/3 & 4/3 \\ 0 & 0 & 1 & -11/5 \\ 0 & 0 & 0 & 1 \end{bmatrix} = E.$$

Here $\rho(A) = 4$, the number of non-zero rows in this echelon matrix.

Example 1.8. Is the system

$$\begin{aligned} 2x_1 + x_2 &= 7, \\ 4x_1 + 2x_2 &= 5 \end{aligned}$$

consistent? Since $\rho(A) = 1$, $\rho[A \vdots C] = 2$, the system is inconsistent and does not possess a solution.

In addition to its usefulness in determining the rank of a matrix, the echelon matrix plays another important role—it may be used to generate a solution to a system of simultaneous linear equations $AX = C$, where A is $(m \times n)$. The particular method of solution to which we shall turn shortly is called the successive (Gaussian) elimination technique. But first we have

DEFINITION 1.35. *Two systems of linear equations are equivalent if every particular solution of either one is also a solution of the other.*

Hence the process of solving a system such as $AX = C$, A being of order $(m \times n)$, amounts to deducing from it an equivalent system of a prescribed form—the row-reduced echelon normal form. To this end we state the

GAUSS ELIMINATION TECHNIQUE. *If the augmented matrix* $[A \vdots C]$ *can be transformed, by a series of elementary row operations, into an echelon matrix* E, *the system of equations corresponding to* E *is (row) equivalent to that represented by* $[A \vdots C]$. *Hence any solution of the system associated with*

***E** is a solution of the system associated with* $[\boldsymbol{A} \vdots \boldsymbol{C}]$ *and conversely.*

Thus the solution of the system

$$\begin{bmatrix} a_{11} & a_{12} & a_{13} & \cdots & a_{1n} & c_1 \\ a_{21} & a_{22} & a_{23} & \cdots & a_{2n} & c_2 \\ \cdots & \cdots & \cdots & \cdots & \cdots & \cdots \\ a_{m1} & a_{m2} & a_{m3} & \cdots & a_{mn} & c_m \end{bmatrix} \tag{1.7}$$

proceeds as follows. Suppose that a_{11} is different from zero. (If a_{11} is zero, we can interchange the first equation with a later one so as to obtain a first equation with a non-zero coefficient on x_1.) Then we may use the first row of eq. (1.7) to eliminate x_1 from the remaining $m-1$ rows to obtain

$$\begin{bmatrix} 1 & \alpha_{12} & \alpha_{13} & \cdots & \alpha_{1n} & \alpha_1 \\ 0 & a'_{22} & a'_{23} & \cdots & a'_{2n} & c'_2 \\ \cdots & \cdots & \cdots & \cdots & \cdots & \cdots \\ 0 & a'_{m2} & a'_{m3} & \cdots & a'_{mn} & c'_m \end{bmatrix}, \tag{1.8}$$

where

$$\alpha_{1j} = a_{1j}/a_{11}, \qquad \alpha_1 = c_1/a_{11}, \qquad a'_{ij} = a_{ij} - a_{i1}\alpha_{1j},$$
$$c'_i = c_i - a_{i1}\alpha_1.$$

If a'_{22} is non-zero (a parenthetical expression similar to the one given above holds here also), we may use the second row of eq. (1.8) to eliminate x_2 from the remaining $m-2$ rows. An appropriate sequence of operations yields

$$\begin{bmatrix} 1 & \alpha_{12} & \alpha_{13} & \cdots & \alpha_{1n} & \alpha_1 \\ 0 & 1 & \alpha_{23} & \cdots & \alpha_{2n} & \alpha_2 \\ 0 & 0 & a''_{33} & \cdots & a''_{3n} & c''_3 \\ \cdots & \cdots & \cdots & \cdots & \cdots & \cdots \\ 0 & 0 & a''_{m3} & \cdots & a''_{mn} & c''_m \end{bmatrix}. \tag{1.9}$$

Upon repeating this procedure we ultimately obtain x_n and the termination of the successive elimination process. The remaining unknowns are then found by a process of back substitution.

Example 1.9. Solve the system of equations appearing in example 1.5 using the Gauss elimination technique. From

$$[\boldsymbol{A} \vdots \boldsymbol{C}] = \begin{bmatrix} 1 & 2 & 1 & 4 \\ 3 & 1 & 0 & 6 \\ 1 & 4 & 1 & 3 \end{bmatrix}$$

we obtain

$$E = \begin{bmatrix} 1 & 2 & 1 & 4 \\ 0 & 1 & 3/5 & 6/5 \\ 0 & 0 & 1 & 17/6 \end{bmatrix}.$$

Values of x_1, x_2, and x_3 may now be obtained from $\boldsymbol{E}$ by back substitution, i.e. from the third row,

$$x_3 = 17/6;$$

from the second row,

$$x_2 + \tfrac{3}{5}x_3 = \tfrac{6}{5}, \qquad x_2 = -\tfrac{1}{2};$$

and from the first row,

$$x_1 + 2x_2 + x_3 = 4, \qquad x_1 = 13/6.$$

The principal advantage of the Gauss elimination technique is that it may be employed to handle situations where case three of theorem 1.1 holds. In instances such as these, Cramer's rule cannot be utilized.

Example 1.10. Is the system

$$\begin{aligned} 4x_1 + 5x_2 &= 7.5, \\ 3.2x_1 + 4x_2 &= 6 \end{aligned}$$

consistent? Since $\rho(\boldsymbol{A}) = \rho[\boldsymbol{A} \vdots \boldsymbol{C}] = 1$, the answer is 'yes'. Moreover, by way of the Gauss elimination technique

$$[\boldsymbol{A} \vdots \boldsymbol{C}] = \begin{bmatrix} 4 & 5 & 7.5 \\ 3.2 & 4 & 6 \end{bmatrix} \to \begin{bmatrix} 1 & 5/4 & 7.5/4 \\ 0 & 0 & 0 \end{bmatrix} = \boldsymbol{E}$$

and thus an infinity of particular solutions corresponding to various values of x_2 is given by

$$x_1 = \tfrac{7.5}{4} - \tfrac{5}{4}x_2.$$

Let us examine a modification of Gauss's method called the *matrix-reduction* technique. A multiplication of the last $m-1$ rows of (1.8) by a_{11} yields

$$\begin{bmatrix} 1 & \alpha_{12} & \alpha_{13} & \cdots & \alpha_{1n} & \alpha_1 \\ 0 & \bar{a}_{22} & \bar{a}_{23} & \cdots & \bar{a}_{2n} & \bar{c}_2 \\ \cdots & \cdots & \cdots & \cdots & \cdots & \cdots \\ 0 & \bar{a}_{m2} & \bar{a}_{m3} & \cdots & \bar{a}_{mn} & \bar{c}_m \end{bmatrix}, \tag{1.10}$$

where

$$\alpha_{1j} = \frac{a_{1j}}{a_{11}}, \qquad \alpha_1 = \frac{c_1}{a_{11}}, \qquad \bar{a}_{ij} = a_{11}a_{ij} - a_{i1}a_{1j},$$

$$\bar{c}_j = a_{11}c_i - a_{i1}c_1.$$

Here the $\bar{a}_{ij}$'s and $\bar{c}_i$'s simply form an array of (2×2) determinants. Hence x_1 may alternatively be eliminated from eq. (1.7) according to the algorithm

$$[A \vdots C] \rightarrow \begin{bmatrix} \bar{a}_{22} & \bar{a}_{23} & \ldots & \bar{a}_{2n} & \bar{c}_2 \\ \cdots & \cdots & \cdots & \cdots & \cdots \\ \bar{a}_{m2} & \bar{a}_{m3} & \ldots & \bar{a}_{mn} & \bar{c}_m \end{bmatrix}, \tag{1.11}$$

where the resulting matrix is of order $(m-1 \times n-1)$. (Note that the first row and column of (1.10) have been eliminated in (1.11) since to further eliminate x_2 these entries are not utilized.) The procedure may be repeated until we ultimately determine whether $\boldsymbol{AX} = \boldsymbol{C}$ is consistent or not. Given that the system is consistent, back substitution through the succession of matrices yields the desired unknowns.

Example 1.11. Obtain the solution of

$$\begin{aligned} x_1 - x_2 + 5x_3 + x_4 &= 0, \\ 2x_1 + x_2 + x_3 + x_4 &= 0, \\ x_2 - x_3 + 2x_4 &= 4, \\ x_1 + x_3 + x_4 &= 1 \end{aligned}$$

via matrix reduction. Proceeding as above we generate the sequence

$$\begin{matrix} (x_1) & (x_2) & (x_3) & (x_4) & (c) \end{matrix} \quad \begin{matrix} (x_2) & (x_3) & (x_4) & (c) \end{matrix} \quad \begin{matrix} (x_3) & (x_4) & (c) \end{matrix}$$

$$\begin{bmatrix} 1 & -1 & 5 & 1 & 0 \\ 2 & 1 & 1 & 1 & 0 \\ 0 & 1 & -1 & 2 & 4 \\ 1 & 0 & 1 & 1 & 1 \end{bmatrix} \rightarrow \begin{bmatrix} 3 & -9 & -1 & 0 \\ 1 & -1 & 2 & 4 \\ 1 & -4 & 0 & 1 \end{bmatrix} \rightarrow \begin{bmatrix} 6 & 7 & 12 \\ -3 & 1 & 3 \end{bmatrix}$$

$$\begin{matrix} (x_4) & (c) \end{matrix}$$

$$\rightarrow [\,27 \quad 54\,].$$

Hence $x_4 = 2$, $x_3 = -1/3$, $x_2 = -1/3$, and $x_1 = -2/3$.

Since for n equations in n unknowns we ultimately generate a matrix of the form $[d_{11}, d_{12}]$, it is readily seen that: (1) if $d_{11}, d_{12} \neq 0$, $\boldsymbol{AX} = \boldsymbol{C}$ has a unique solution; (2) if $d_{11} = 0$, $d_{12} \neq 0$, $\boldsymbol{AX} = \boldsymbol{C}$ is inconsistent; and (3) if $d_{11} = d_{12} = 0$, $\boldsymbol{AX} = \boldsymbol{C}$ has an infinity of solutions.

At times we shall be faced with the problem of solving a system of equations of the form $\boldsymbol{AX} = \boldsymbol{0}$. Such a system is said to be *homogeneous*. By inspection it can be seen that this system can never be inconsistent, i.e. $\boldsymbol{AX} = \mathbf{0}$ always has a solution since $\rho(\boldsymbol{A}) = \rho[\boldsymbol{A} \vdots \mathbf{0}]$. Moreover, $\boldsymbol{X} = \mathbf{0}$ is always a (trivial) solution. What about the existence of non-trivial solutions? Our answer is provided by a special case of theorem 1.1, namely

THEOREM 1.2.[5] *Given the system* $\boldsymbol{AX} = \mathbf{0}$, *where* $\boldsymbol{A}$ *is of order* $(m \times n)$, *if:*

(1) $\rho(\boldsymbol{A})$ = *number of unknowns* = n, *the system has a unique (trivial) solution* $\boldsymbol{X} = \mathbf{0}$;

(2) $\rho(\boldsymbol{A}) = k <$ *number of unknowns* = n, *the system has an infinity of non-trivial solutions, where arbitrary values may be assigned to* $n-k$ *of the variables.*

In particular, if $\boldsymbol{A}$ *is* $(m \times n)$ *and* $m<n$, $\boldsymbol{AX} = \mathbf{0}$ *always possesses an infinity of non-trivial solutions.*

1.6. Linear dependence and rank

In what follows our discussion will be restricted to the class of n-component vectors which may be taken to be elements of $\mathscr{E}^n$. We state first

DEFINITION 1.36. *The vector* $\boldsymbol{x} \in \mathscr{E}^n$ *is a linear combination of the vectors* $\boldsymbol{x}_j \in \mathscr{E}^n$, $j = 1, \ldots, m$, *if there exist scalars* λ_j, $j = 1, \ldots, m$, *such that*

$$\boldsymbol{x} = \sum_{j=1}^{m} \lambda_j \boldsymbol{x}_j = \lambda_1 \boldsymbol{x}_1 + \ldots + \lambda_m \boldsymbol{x}_m. \tag{1.12}$$

In this light, we have

DEFINITION 1.37. *A set of vectors* $\{\boldsymbol{x}_j \in \mathscr{E}^n, j = 1, \cdots, m\}$ *is linearly dependent if there exist scalars* λ_j, $j = 1, \ldots, m$, *not all zero such that*

$$\sum_{j=1}^{m} \lambda_j \boldsymbol{x}_j = \lambda_1 \boldsymbol{x}_1 + \ldots + \lambda_m \boldsymbol{x}_m = \mathbf{0}, \tag{1.13}$$

i.e. the null vector is a linear combination of the vectors $\boldsymbol{x}_j$. *If the only set of scalars* λ_j *for which eq.* (1.13) *holds is* $\lambda_j = 0$, $j = 1, \ldots, m$, *the vectors* $\boldsymbol{x}_j$ *are linearly independent, i.e. the trivial combination* $0\boldsymbol{x}_1 + \ldots + 0\boldsymbol{x}_m$ *is the only linear combination of the* $\boldsymbol{x}_j$ *which equals the null vector.*

Geometrically, if two vectors $\boldsymbol{x}_1$, $\boldsymbol{x}_2$ are linearly dependent, they are collinear (point in the same direction) and one is just a scalar multiple of the other, e.g. if

$$\lambda_1 \boldsymbol{x}_1 + \lambda_2 \boldsymbol{x}_2 = \mathbf{0}, \qquad \lambda_1, \lambda_2 \neq 0,$$

[5] This theorem is also proven by Noble (1969), p. 91.

then

$$x_1 = -\frac{\lambda_2}{\lambda_1}x_2 \quad \text{or} \quad x_2 = -\frac{\lambda_1}{\lambda_2}x_1.$$

Hence the notion of linear dependence contains an element of redundancy since the vectors $\boldsymbol{x}_1$, $\boldsymbol{x}_2$ are essentially the same except for a scale factor.

The essential features of a set of linearly dependent (independent) vectors $\{\boldsymbol{x}_j \in \mathscr{E}^n, j = 1, \ldots, m\}$ are:

(a) if the set $\{\boldsymbol{x}_j \in \mathscr{E}^n, j = 1, \ldots, m\}$ is linearly dependent, one of the vectors $\boldsymbol{x}_j$ is a linear combination of the others; if no vector in the set can be written as a linear combination of the others, the set is linearly independent;

(b) the set $\{\boldsymbol{x}_j \in \mathscr{E}^n, j = 1, \ldots, m\}$ is linearly dependent if at least one of the vectors $\boldsymbol{x}_j$ is the null vector. Conversely, if $\{\boldsymbol{x}_j \in \mathscr{E}^n, j = 1, \ldots, m\}$ is a linearly independent set, it cannot contain the null vector;

(c) the set $\{\boldsymbol{x} \in \mathscr{E}^n\}$ containing a single vector $\boldsymbol{x}$ is linearly independent if and only if $\boldsymbol{x} \neq \boldsymbol{0}$;

(d) if the set $\{\boldsymbol{x}_j \in \mathscr{E}^n, j = 1, \ldots, m\}$ is linearly independent, then any non-empty subset of this set is linearly independent;

(e) if the set of m vectors $\{\boldsymbol{x}_j \in \mathscr{E}^n, j = 1, \ldots, m\}$ is linearly dependent, then the set containing $m+1$ vectors $\{\boldsymbol{x}, \boldsymbol{x}_j \in \mathscr{E}^n, j = 1, \ldots, m\}$ is also linearly dependent and conversely;

(f) if $k < m$ is the maximum number of linearly independent vectors in the set $\{\boldsymbol{x}_j \in \mathscr{E}^n, j = 1, \ldots, m\}$, every other vector in the set is linearly dependent upon (i.e. can be expressed as a linear combination of) the k linearly independent vectors.

Example 1.12. Find scalars λ_1, λ_2 such that the vector $\boldsymbol{x}' = (1, 2)$ is a linear combination of $\boldsymbol{x}_1' = (3, 5)$, $\boldsymbol{x}_2' = (1, 4)$. From eq. (1.12) we have

$$\begin{aligned} \lambda_1 \boldsymbol{x}_1 + \lambda_2 \boldsymbol{x}_2 &= (\boldsymbol{x}_1, \boldsymbol{x}_2) \begin{bmatrix} \lambda_1 \\ \lambda_2 \end{bmatrix} \\ &= \boldsymbol{A}\boldsymbol{\lambda} = \boldsymbol{x} \end{aligned}$$

or

$$\begin{aligned} 3\lambda_1 + \lambda_2 &= 1, \\ 5\lambda_1 + 4\lambda_2 &= 2. \end{aligned}$$

Since $\rho(\boldsymbol{A}) = \rho[\boldsymbol{A} \vdots \boldsymbol{x}] = 2$, this system possesses the unique solution $\lambda_1 = 2/7$, $\lambda_2 = 1/7$ (see theorem 1.1, part 2). With $\lambda_1, \lambda_2 \neq 0$, the set $\{\boldsymbol{x}, \boldsymbol{x}_1, \boldsymbol{x}_2\}$ is linearly dependent.

Example 1.13. Are the vectors $\boldsymbol{x}_1' = (2, 2)$, $\boldsymbol{x}_2' = (-4, 3)$ linearly independent?

From eq. (1.13) we obtain the homogeneous system

$$\begin{aligned}\lambda_1\boldsymbol{x}_1+\lambda_2\boldsymbol{x}_2 &= (\boldsymbol{x}_1, \boldsymbol{x}_2)\begin{bmatrix}\lambda_1\\ \lambda_2\end{bmatrix}\\ &= \boldsymbol{A\lambda} = \boldsymbol{0}\end{aligned}$$

or

$$\begin{aligned}2\lambda_1-4\lambda_2 &= 0,\\ 2\lambda_1+3\lambda_2 &= 0.\end{aligned}$$

Since $\rho(\boldsymbol{A}) = 2$, the only solution is the trivial solution $\boldsymbol{\lambda} = \boldsymbol{0}$ (by part 1 of theorem 1.2). Hence $\lambda_1 = \lambda_2 = 0$ and the set $\{\boldsymbol{x}_1, \boldsymbol{x}_2\}$ is linearly independent.

Example 1.14. Are the vectors $\boldsymbol{x}_1' = (2, 4, 8)$, $\boldsymbol{x}_2' = (2, 0, 8)$, and $\boldsymbol{x}_3' = (1, 1, 4)$ linearly independent? Upon constructing the homogeneous system

$$\begin{aligned}\lambda_1\boldsymbol{x}_1+\lambda_2\boldsymbol{x}_2+\lambda_3\boldsymbol{x}_3 &= (\boldsymbol{x}_1, \boldsymbol{x}_2, \boldsymbol{x}_3)\begin{bmatrix}\lambda_1\\ \lambda_2\\ \lambda_3\end{bmatrix}\\ &= \boldsymbol{A\lambda} = \boldsymbol{0}\end{aligned}$$

or

$$\begin{aligned}2\lambda_1+2\lambda_2+\lambda_3 &= 0,\\ 4\lambda_1\qquad\;\;+\lambda_3 &= 0,\\ 8\lambda_1+8\lambda_2+4\lambda_3 &= 0,\end{aligned}$$

we find that the echelon representation of this system is

$$\boldsymbol{E} = \begin{bmatrix}1 & 1 & \frac{1}{2} & 0\\ 0 & 1 & \frac{1}{4} & 0\\ 0 & 0 & 0 & 0\end{bmatrix}.$$

Since $\rho(\boldsymbol{A}) = 2 <$ number of unknowns $= 3$, the system has an infinity of non-trivial solutions (theorem 1.2, part 2) with $\lambda_1 = \lambda_2 = -\frac{1}{4}\lambda_3$. For example, if $\lambda_3 = 2$,

$$-\tfrac{1}{2}\boldsymbol{x}_1-\tfrac{1}{2}\boldsymbol{x}_2+2\boldsymbol{x}_3 = 0.$$

Hence the set $\{\boldsymbol{x}_1, \boldsymbol{x}_2, \boldsymbol{x}_3\}$ is linearly dependent.

Let us now generalize our test for the linear dependence of a set of vectors. This time the set in question is of the form $\{\boldsymbol{x}_j \in \mathscr{E}^m, j = 1, \ldots, n\}$. If we consider the vector $\boldsymbol{x}_j$ as the jth column of an $(m\times n)$ matrix $\boldsymbol{A}$, i.e. $\boldsymbol{A} = [\boldsymbol{x}_1, \ldots, \boldsymbol{x}_n]$, then:

(1) if $m \geqslant n$ and $\rho(\boldsymbol{A}) = n$, the set of vectors $\{\boldsymbol{x}_j \in \mathscr{E}^m, j = 1, \ldots, n\}$ is linearly independent (by part 1 of theorem 1.2); but

(2) if $m \geqslant n$ and $\rho(\boldsymbol{A}) < n$, or if $m < n$, the set of vectors $\{\boldsymbol{x}_j \in \mathscr{E}^m, j = 1, \ldots, n\}$

is linearly dependent (by part 2 of theorem 1.2).

Next, we have

DEFINITION 1.38. *A set of vectors* $\{x_j \in \mathscr{E}^n, j = 1, \ldots, m\}$ *is a spanning set for* $\mathscr{E}^n$ *if every vector* $x \in \mathscr{E}^n$ *can be written as a linear combination of the vectors* x_j, *i.e. if* $x \in \mathscr{E}^n$,

$$x = \sum_{j=1}^{m} \lambda_j x_j.$$

Here the set $\{x_j \in \mathscr{E}^n, j = 1, \ldots, m\}$ is said to *span* or *generate* $\mathscr{E}^n$ since every vector in $\mathscr{E}^n$ is (uniquely) linearly dependent on the spanning set. It is important to note that:

(a) the vectors which span $\mathscr{E}^n$ need not be linearly independent; but

(b) any set of vectors spanning $\mathscr{E}^n$ which contains the smallest possible number of vectors is linearly independent.

DEFINITION 1.39. *A basis for* $\mathscr{E}^n$ *is a linearly independent subset of vectors from* $\mathscr{E}^n$ *which spans* $\mathscr{E}^n$.

A basis for $\mathscr{E}^n$ possesses the following properties:

(a) a basis for $\mathscr{E}^n$ is not unique; but the vectors in the basis are;

(b) every basis for $\mathscr{E}^n$ contains the same number of basis vectors; and there are precisely n vectors in every basis for $\mathscr{E}^n$;

(c) any set of n linearly independent vectors from $\mathscr{E}^n$ forms a basis for $\mathscr{E}^n$; and

(d) any set of $n+1$ vectors from $\mathscr{E}^n$ is linearly dependent.

Our discussion here leads us to an alternative definition of the rank of a matrix, namely

DEFINITION 1.40. *The rank of an* $(m \times n)$ *matrix* A, $\rho(A)$, *is the maximum number of linearly independent vectors* $x_j \in \mathscr{E}^m$, $j = 1, \ldots, n$, *which span the columns of* A; *i.e. it is the number of vectors in a basis for* $\mathscr{E}^m$.

Example 1.15. The *unit column vectors* $e_j = [\delta_{ij}] \in \mathscr{E}^n$, $j = 1, \ldots, n$, form a *natural basis* for $\mathscr{E}^n$ since they are linearly independent and span $\mathscr{E}^n$. That is to say, any vector $x \in \mathscr{E}^n$ can be uniquely expressed as a linear combination of the e_j. For instance, given $x' = (1, 4, -2, 2) \in \mathscr{E}^4$,

$$x = e_1 + 4e_2 - 2e_3 + 2e_4 = \begin{bmatrix} 1 \\ 0 \\ 0 \\ 0 \end{bmatrix} + 4\begin{bmatrix} 0 \\ 1 \\ 0 \\ 0 \end{bmatrix} - 2\begin{bmatrix} 0 \\ 0 \\ 1 \\ 0 \end{bmatrix} + 2\begin{bmatrix} 0 \\ 0 \\ 0 \\ 1 \end{bmatrix}.$$

It was previously mentioned that $\mathscr{E}^n$ is an n-dimensional space. In what context shall we interpret the notion of the dimension of $\mathscr{E}^n$? Generally speaking, we have

DEFINITION 1.41. *The dimension of a vector space* $\mathscr{V}_n$, $\dim(\mathscr{V}_n)$, *is the maximum number of linearly independent vectors that span the space, i.e. it is the number of vectors in a basis for* $\mathscr{V}_n$.

Hence $\dim(\mathscr{E}^n) = n$, where n is to be interpreted as the number of vectors in a basis for $\mathscr{E}^n$ (rather than the number of components in the vectors spanning the space).

1.7. Hyperplanes and half-planes[6]

The generalization in $\mathscr{E}^n$ of the concept of a line in $\mathscr{E}^2$ or of a plane in $\mathscr{E}^3$ will be stated as

DEFINITION 1.42. *A linear form or hyperplane in* $\mathscr{E}^n$ *is the set* $\mathscr{H}$ *of all points* $\boldsymbol{x}$ *such that* $c_1x_1 + \ldots + c_nx_n = \boldsymbol{C}'\boldsymbol{x} = \alpha$, *where* $\boldsymbol{C}\in\mathscr{E}^n$ *is a non-null vector and* α *is a scalar, i.e.* $\mathscr{H} = \{\boldsymbol{x}|\boldsymbol{C}'\boldsymbol{x} = \alpha, \boldsymbol{C}(\neq\boldsymbol{0}), \boldsymbol{x}\in\mathscr{E}^n\}$.

It is obvious that any hyperplane divides $\mathscr{E}^n$ into the two *closed half-planes (spaces)*

$$[\mathscr{H}^+] = \{\boldsymbol{x}|\boldsymbol{C}'\boldsymbol{x}\geqslant\alpha, \boldsymbol{C}(\neq\boldsymbol{0}), \boldsymbol{x}\in\mathscr{E}^n\},$$
$$[\mathscr{H}^-] = \{\boldsymbol{x}|\boldsymbol{C}'\boldsymbol{x}\leqslant\alpha, \boldsymbol{C}(\neq\boldsymbol{0}), \boldsymbol{x}\in\mathscr{E}^n\}.$$

With $\boldsymbol{C}'\boldsymbol{x}>\alpha(<\alpha)$, we have the two *open half-planes (spaces)*

$$(\mathscr{H}^+) = \{\boldsymbol{x}|\boldsymbol{C}'\boldsymbol{x}>\alpha, \boldsymbol{C}(\neq\boldsymbol{0}), \boldsymbol{x}\in\mathscr{E}^n\},$$
$$(\mathscr{H}^-) = \{\boldsymbol{x}|\boldsymbol{C}'\boldsymbol{x}<\alpha, \boldsymbol{C}(\neq\boldsymbol{0}), \boldsymbol{x}\in\mathscr{E}^n\}.$$

Note that $[\mathscr{H}^+]$, $[\mathscr{H}^-]$ are closed sets, while the sets specified by $(\mathscr{H}^+)$, $(\mathscr{H}^-)$ are open.

If $\alpha \neq 0$ and $\boldsymbol{x}_1$, $\boldsymbol{x}_2$ are any two distinct points satisfying $\boldsymbol{C}'\boldsymbol{x} = \alpha$, then

$$\boldsymbol{C}'\boldsymbol{x}_1 - \boldsymbol{C}'\boldsymbol{x}_2 = \boldsymbol{C}'(\boldsymbol{x}_1 - \boldsymbol{x}_2) = 0.$$

Hence $\boldsymbol{C}$ is orthogonal to the hyperplane and will be termed the *normal* to the hyperplane. With this observation in mind we may now derive the equations of the hyperplane tangent and the line normal to a surface $y = \mathrm{f}(\boldsymbol{x})$, $\boldsymbol{x}\in\mathscr{E}^n$, at the point $(\boldsymbol{x}_0, \mathrm{f}^0)\in\mathscr{E}^{n+1}$. Since the gradient of f at $\boldsymbol{x}_0$, $\nabla\mathrm{f}(\boldsymbol{x}_0)$, is normal to the level surface f = constant at $\boldsymbol{x}_0$, the vector

$$\boldsymbol{N} = \begin{bmatrix}\nabla\mathrm{f}(\boldsymbol{x}_0)\\ -1\end{bmatrix}$$

[6] Those readers not familiar with point-set theory or the notion of the gradient of a real-valued function should turn to chapter 2, pp. 50–57.

is normal to f (and thus to the hyperplane tangent to f) at $(\boldsymbol{x}_0, \mathrm{f}^0)$. Hence the equation of the *tangent hyperplane* at $(\boldsymbol{x}_0, \mathrm{f})$ (or the *linearization of* f at $\boldsymbol{x}_0$) may be written as

$$\boldsymbol{N}' \begin{bmatrix} \boldsymbol{x}-\boldsymbol{x}_0 \\ \mathrm{f}-\mathrm{f}^0 \end{bmatrix} = 0$$

or

$$\begin{aligned} \mathrm{f} &= \mathrm{f}^0 + \nabla \mathrm{f}(\boldsymbol{x}_0)'(\boldsymbol{x}-\boldsymbol{x}_0) \\ &= \mathrm{f}_0 + \mathrm{f}_1^0(x_1 - x_1^0) + \ldots + \mathrm{f}_n^0(x_n - x_n^0). \end{aligned}$$

The *normal line* at $(\boldsymbol{x}_0, \mathrm{f}^0)$ appears as

$$\begin{bmatrix} \boldsymbol{x} \\ \mathrm{f} \end{bmatrix} = \begin{bmatrix} \boldsymbol{x}_0 \\ \mathrm{f}^0 \end{bmatrix} + t\boldsymbol{N}, \quad -\infty < t < +\infty,$$

or upon eliminating t,

$$\frac{x_1 - x_1^0}{\mathrm{f}_1^0} = \ldots = \frac{x_n - x_n^0}{\mathrm{f}_n^0} = \frac{\mathrm{f}-\mathrm{f}^0}{-1}.$$

Example 1.16. Find the equation of the plane tangent and line normal to the surface $y = \mathrm{f}(\boldsymbol{x}) = x_1^2 + 2x_2^2 + x_3^2$ at $(\boldsymbol{x}_0, \mathrm{f}^0)' = (1, 2, 2, 13)$. Since

$$\boldsymbol{N} = \begin{bmatrix} \nabla \mathrm{f}(\boldsymbol{x}_0) \\ -1 \end{bmatrix} = \begin{bmatrix} 2 \\ 8 \\ 4 \\ -1 \end{bmatrix}$$

is normal to f at $(\boldsymbol{x}_0, \mathrm{f}^0)$, the tangent plane and normal line appear respectively as

$$\begin{aligned} \boldsymbol{N}' \begin{bmatrix} \boldsymbol{x}-\boldsymbol{x}_0 \\ \mathrm{f}-\mathrm{f}^0 \end{bmatrix} &= (2, 8, 4, -1) \begin{bmatrix} x_1 - 1 \\ x_2 - 2 \\ x_3 - 2 \\ \mathrm{f} - 13 \end{bmatrix} \\ &= 2(x_1 - 1) + 8(x_2 - 2) + 4(x_3 - 2) - (\mathrm{f} - 13) \end{aligned}$$

or

$$2x_1 + 8x_2 + 4x_3 - \mathrm{f} - 13 = 0;$$

$$\begin{bmatrix} \boldsymbol{x} \\ \mathrm{f} \end{bmatrix} = \begin{bmatrix} \boldsymbol{x}_0 \\ \mathrm{f}^0 \end{bmatrix} + t\boldsymbol{N} = \begin{bmatrix} x_1 \\ x_2 \\ x_3 \\ \mathrm{f} \end{bmatrix} = \begin{bmatrix} 1+2t \\ 2+8t \\ 2+4t \\ 13-t \end{bmatrix}$$

or

$$\frac{x_1 - 1}{2} = \frac{x_2 - 2}{8} = \frac{x_3 - 2}{4} = \frac{\mathrm{f} - 13}{-1}.$$

For f = constant = f*, we obtain a level surface in $\mathscr{E}^n$. The hyperplane tangent to this level surface at $\boldsymbol{x}_0 \in \mathscr{E}^n$, where $f(\boldsymbol{x}_0) = f^*$, may be written as

$$f^* - f^* = \nabla f(\boldsymbol{x}_0)'(\boldsymbol{x} - \boldsymbol{x}_0) = 0$$

or

$$\nabla f(\boldsymbol{x}_0)'\boldsymbol{x} = \nabla f(\boldsymbol{x}_0)'\boldsymbol{x}_0.$$

Here $\nabla f(\boldsymbol{x}_0)$, the normal to the hyperplane, is normal to the level surface at $\boldsymbol{x}_0$.

We next state

DEFINITION 1.43. *The region* $\mathscr{K} \subseteq \mathscr{E}^n$ *is termed convex if for points* $\boldsymbol{x}_j \in \mathscr{K}$, $j = 1, \ldots, m$, *the convex combination of the* $\boldsymbol{x}_j$,

$$\boldsymbol{x}_c = \sum_{j=1}^{m} \theta_j \boldsymbol{x}_j, \quad \theta_j \geqslant 0, \quad \sum_{j=1}^{m} \theta_j = 1,$$

is also a member of $\mathscr{K}$.

It is easily demonstrated that the sets $\mathscr{H}$, $(\mathscr{H}^+)$, $(\mathscr{H}^-)$, $[\mathscr{H}^+]$, and $[\mathscr{H}^-]$ are all convex. For instance, if $\boldsymbol{x}_1, \boldsymbol{x}_2$ satisfy $\boldsymbol{C}'\boldsymbol{x} = \alpha$ (i.e. $\boldsymbol{C}'\boldsymbol{x}_1 = \boldsymbol{C}'\boldsymbol{x}_2 = \alpha$), then, for $\theta_1 = \theta$, $\theta_2 = 1-\theta$, and $0 \leqslant \theta \leqslant 1$,

$$\boldsymbol{C}'\boldsymbol{x}_c = \boldsymbol{C}'(\theta \boldsymbol{x}_2 + (1-\theta)\boldsymbol{x}_1) = \theta \boldsymbol{C}'\boldsymbol{x}_2 + (1-\theta)\boldsymbol{C}'\boldsymbol{x}_1 = \theta\alpha + (1-\theta)\alpha = \alpha$$

and thus $\mathscr{H}$ is a convex set. A similar argument holds for verifying that an open or closed half-space is a convex set.

In light of def. 1.42 we now turn to the specification of two specialized types of hyperplanes. First,

DEFINITION 1.44. *The hyperplane* $\mathscr{H} = \{\boldsymbol{x} \mid \boldsymbol{C}'\boldsymbol{x} = \alpha,\ \boldsymbol{C}(\neq \boldsymbol{0}),\ \boldsymbol{x} \in \mathscr{E}^n\}$ *is a separating hyperplane for the non-empty sets* $\mathscr{A}, \mathscr{B} \subseteq \mathscr{E}^n$ *if, for* $\boldsymbol{x} \in \mathscr{A}$, $\boldsymbol{C}'\boldsymbol{x} \geqslant \alpha$, *while for* $\boldsymbol{x} \in \mathscr{B}$, $\boldsymbol{C}'\boldsymbol{x} \leqslant \alpha$.

If $\mathscr{H}$ exists $\mathscr{A}, \mathscr{B}$ are said to be *separable* with $\sup_{x \in \mathscr{B}} \boldsymbol{C}'\boldsymbol{x} \leqslant \alpha \leqslant \inf_{x \in \mathscr{A}} \boldsymbol{C}'\boldsymbol{x}$. Additionally, if $\mathscr{H}$ exists and $\boldsymbol{C}'\boldsymbol{x} > \alpha$ for $\boldsymbol{x} \in \mathscr{A}$ and $\boldsymbol{C}'\boldsymbol{x} < \alpha$ for $\boldsymbol{x} \in \mathscr{B}$, then $\mathscr{A}$ and $\mathscr{B}$ are said to be *strictly separable*, i.e. $\sup_{x \in \mathscr{B}} \boldsymbol{C}'\boldsymbol{x} < \alpha < \inf_{x \in \mathscr{A}} \boldsymbol{C}'\boldsymbol{x}$. In general, separability does not imply that $\mathscr{A} \cap \mathscr{B} = \emptyset$ since $\mathscr{A}, \mathscr{B}$ may have boundary points in common. This definition simply states that all points in $\mathscr{A}$ lie in one of the closed half-planes determined by $\mathscr{H}$ and all points in $\mathscr{B}$ lie in the other (see fig. 1.6a, b).

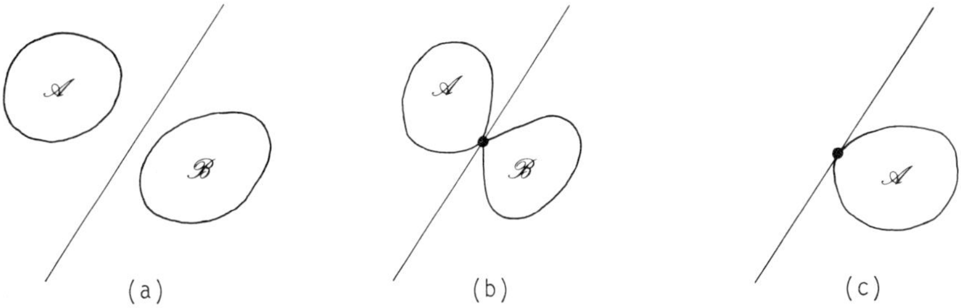

Fig. 1.6.

Secondly,

Definition 1.45. *The hyperplane* $\mathscr{H} = \{\boldsymbol{x} \mid \boldsymbol{C}'\boldsymbol{x} = \alpha,\ \boldsymbol{C}(\neq \boldsymbol{0}),\ \boldsymbol{x} \in \mathscr{E}^n\}$ *is a supporting hyperplane for a non-empty set* $\mathscr{A} \in \mathscr{E}^n$ if $\mathscr{H}$ contains at least one boundary point of $\mathscr{A}$ and $\boldsymbol{C}'\boldsymbol{x} \leqslant \alpha (\geqslant \alpha)$ for all $\boldsymbol{x} \in \mathscr{A}$.

If $\mathscr{H}$ exists all points in $\mathscr{A}$ lie in one of the closed half-planes determined by $\mathscr{H}$ (fig. 1.6c).

What are the prerequisite conditions for the existence of a separating or supporting hyperplane? The answer is provided by a battery of existence theorems for such hyperplanes. As we shall now see, the theorems to follow impose upon the sets in question conditions which are slightly more restrictive than those in the above definitions. We first look to the

Weak separation theorem.[7] *If* $\mathscr{A}, \mathscr{B} \subseteq \mathscr{E}^n$ *are two non-empty disjoint convex sets, then there exists a hyperplane*

$$\mathscr{H} = \{\boldsymbol{x} \mid \boldsymbol{C}'\boldsymbol{x} = \alpha,\ \boldsymbol{C}(\neq \boldsymbol{0}),\ \boldsymbol{x} \in \mathscr{E}^n\}$$

which separates them, i.e. there exists a non-zero vector $\boldsymbol{C}$ *and a scalar* α *such that for* $\boldsymbol{x} \in \mathscr{A}$, $\boldsymbol{C}'\boldsymbol{x} \geqslant \alpha$, *and for* $\boldsymbol{x} \in \mathscr{B}$, $\boldsymbol{C}'\boldsymbol{x} \leqslant \alpha$.

Next we state the

Strong separation theorem.[8] *If* $\mathscr{A}$, $\mathscr{B} \subseteq \mathscr{E}^n$ *are two non-empty disjoint closed convex sets and at least one of them is bounded, then there exists a hyperplane* $\mathscr{H} = \{\boldsymbol{x} \mid \boldsymbol{C}'\boldsymbol{x} = \alpha,\ \boldsymbol{C}(\neq \boldsymbol{0}),\ \boldsymbol{x} \in \mathscr{E}^n\}$ *which strictly separates them, i.e. there exists a non-zero vector* $\boldsymbol{C}$ *and a scalar* α *such that for* $\boldsymbol{x} \in \mathscr{A}$, $\boldsymbol{C}'\boldsymbol{x} > \alpha$, *and for* $\boldsymbol{x} \in \mathscr{B}$, $\boldsymbol{C}'\boldsymbol{x} < \alpha$.

Finally, we present the

---

[7] For a proof see any of the following: Karlin (1959), pp. 398–399; Berge (1963), p. 163; and Mangasarian (1969), p. 49.

[8] A proof is provided by Karlin (1959), p. 399; Berge (1963), pp. 163–164; and Mangasarian (1969), pp. 50–51.

PLANE OF SUPPORT THEOREM.[9] *If $\mathscr{A} \subseteq \mathscr{E}^n$ is a non-empty convex set with a boundary point $\boldsymbol{y} \in \mathscr{E}^n$, then there exists a supporting hyperplane $\boldsymbol{C}'\boldsymbol{y} = \alpha$, $\boldsymbol{C}(\neq \boldsymbol{0}) \in \mathscr{E}^n$, at $\boldsymbol{y}$, i.e. there exists a non-zero vector $\boldsymbol{C}$ such that $\boldsymbol{C}'\boldsymbol{y} = \alpha = \inf_{\boldsymbol{x} \in \mathscr{A}} \boldsymbol{C}'\boldsymbol{x}$.*

1.8. Finite cones

We now turn to the study of the concept of a cone, a notion which will be of utmost importance when we later turn to the specification of what are called 'theorems of the alternative'.

DEFINITION 1.46. *A cone $\mathscr{C} \subset \mathscr{E}^n$ is a set of points such that if $\boldsymbol{x} \in \mathscr{C}$, then so is every non-negative scalar multiple of $\boldsymbol{x}$, i.e. if $\boldsymbol{x} \in \mathscr{C}$, $\lambda \boldsymbol{x} \in \mathscr{C}$, $\lambda \geqslant 0$, $\boldsymbol{x} \in \mathscr{E}^n$* (see fig. 1.7a, b for cones in $\mathscr{E}^2$, $\mathscr{E}^3$ respectively).

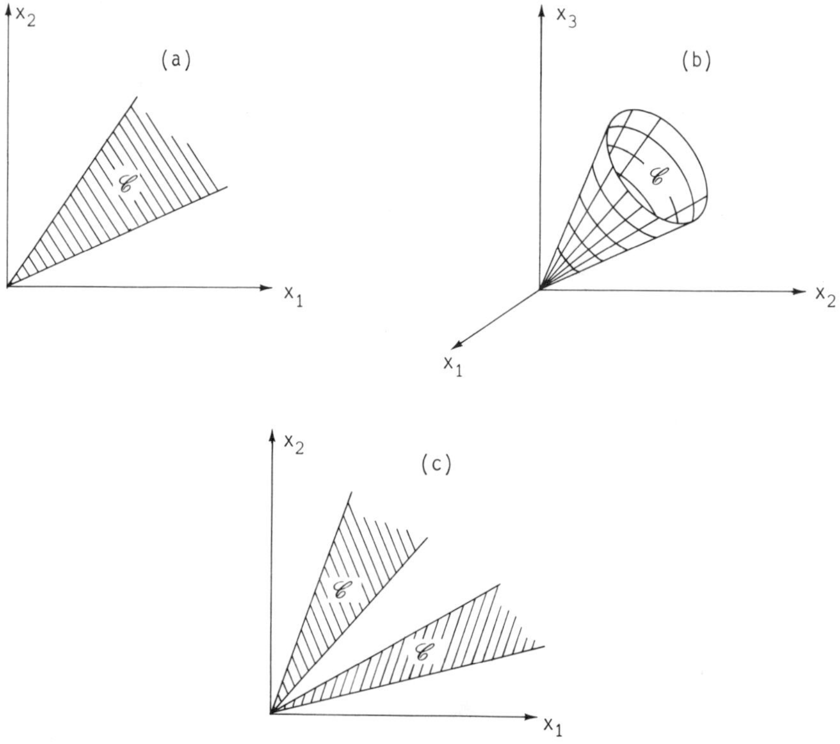

Fig. 1.7.

[9] Karlin (1959), p. 398.

Next, we have

DEFINITION 1.47. *The point* $\mathbf{0} \in \mathscr{E}^n$ *(the null vector) is termed the vertex of a cone and is an element of every cone.*

In what follows we shall consider cones which are convex. Generally speaking, a convex cone is a cone which is a convex set. More specifically,

DEFINITION 1.48. *A cone* $\mathscr{C} \subset \mathscr{E}^n$ *is termed a convex cone if and only if it is closed under the operations of addition and multiplication by a non-negative scalar, i.e.* $\mathscr{C}$ *is a convex cone if and only if: (a) for* $\mathbf{x}, \mathbf{y} \in \mathscr{C}$, $\mathbf{x}+\mathbf{y} \in \mathscr{C}$; *and (b) for* $\mathbf{x} \in \mathscr{C}$, $\lambda \mathbf{x} \in \mathscr{C}$, $\lambda \geqslant 0$, *where* $\mathbf{x}, \mathbf{y} \in \mathscr{E}^n$.

It is important to note that not every cone is convex (for instance, see fig. 1.7c). Additionally, a hyperplane $\mathscr{H}$ passing through the origin is a convex cone as are the closed half-planes $[\mathscr{H}^+]$, $[\mathscr{H}^-]$ determined by $\mathscr{H}$.

In light of def. 1.48 we state

DEFINITION 1.49. *A convex cone* $\mathscr{C} \subset \mathscr{E}^n$ *is termed a finite cone if it consists of the set of all non-negative linear combinations of a finite set of vectors, i.e. for points* $\mathbf{x}_j \in \mathscr{E}^n$, $j = 1, \ldots, m$,

$$\mathscr{C} = \left\{ \mathbf{x} \mid \mathbf{x} = \sum_{j=1}^{m} \lambda_j \mathbf{x}_j, \lambda_j \geqslant 0 \right\}.$$

Here $\mathscr{C}$ is said to be *generated* or *spanned* by the points $\mathbf{x}_j$. Hence any vector which can be expressed as a non-negative linear combination of a finite set of vectors $\mathbf{x}_j$, $j = 1, \ldots, m$, lies in the finite convex cone spanned by those vectors. Another way of looking at the concept of a finite cone encompassed in the preceding definition is as follows:

DEFINITION 1.49.1. *A convex cone* $\mathscr{C} \subset \mathscr{E}^m$ *is termed a finite cone if for some* $(m \times n)$ *matrix* $\mathbf{A} = [\mathbf{a}_1, \ldots, \mathbf{a}_n]$, *every* $\mathbf{x} \in \mathscr{C}$ *is a non-negative linear combination of the* $(m \times 1)$ *column vectors* $\mathbf{a}_j$, $j = 1, \ldots, n$, *of* $\mathbf{A}$, *i.e.*

$$\mathscr{C} = \left\{ \mathbf{x} \mid \mathbf{x} = \mathbf{A}\boldsymbol{\lambda} = \sum_{j=1}^{n} \lambda_j \mathbf{a}_j, \boldsymbol{\lambda} \geqslant \mathbf{0}, \mathbf{x} \in \mathscr{E}^m \right\}.$$

As a matter of terminology, a finite convex cone is sometimes referred to as a *convex polyhedral cone*, i.e. a convex cone is polyhedral if it is generated by a matrix $\mathbf{A}$.

Example 1.17. Is the vector $\mathbf{x}' = (1, 1, 1)$ an element of the cone spanned by the vectors $\mathbf{x}_1' = (2, 0, \frac{1}{2})$, $\mathbf{x}_2' = (1, 1, 4)$, and $\mathbf{x}_3' = (\frac{1}{2}, 1, \frac{1}{2})$? Solving the system

$$\mathbf{x} = \mathbf{A}\boldsymbol{\lambda} = [\mathbf{x}_1, \mathbf{x}_2, \mathbf{x}_3]\boldsymbol{\lambda}$$

or

$$\begin{bmatrix} 2 & 1 & \frac{1}{2} \\ 0 & 1 & 1 \\ \frac{1}{2} & 4 & \frac{1}{2} \end{bmatrix} \begin{bmatrix} \lambda_1 \\ \lambda_2 \\ \lambda_3 \end{bmatrix} = \begin{bmatrix} 1 \\ 1 \\ 1 \end{bmatrix}$$

simultaneously yields $\boldsymbol{\lambda}' = (\frac{6}{27}, \frac{3}{27}, \frac{24}{27})$. Obviously $\boldsymbol{x} = \frac{6}{27}\boldsymbol{x}_1 + \frac{3}{27}\boldsymbol{x}_2 + \frac{24}{27}\boldsymbol{x}_3$, a non-negative linear combination of $\boldsymbol{x}_1$, $\boldsymbol{x}_2$, and $\boldsymbol{x}_3$, lies in the finite convex cone spanned by these vectors.

A special case of defs. 1.49 and 1.49.1 occurs when there is but a single generator, namely

DEFINITION 1.50. *A convex cone* $\mathscr{C} \subset \mathscr{E}^n$ *generated by a single vector* $\boldsymbol{x}$ *is termed a ray or half-line (denoted as* $\mathscr{L}$*), i.e. for* $\boldsymbol{x} \in \mathscr{E}^n$, $\mathscr{L} = \{\boldsymbol{y} | \boldsymbol{y} = \lambda \boldsymbol{x}, \lambda \geqslant 0, \boldsymbol{y} \in \mathscr{E}^n\}$ (fig. 1.8a).

The essential properties of cones (convex or finite) are:

(a) if $\mathscr{C}_1, \mathscr{C}_2 \subset \mathscr{E}^n$ are convex cones (finite cones), their sum $\mathscr{C}_1 + \mathscr{C}_2 = \{\boldsymbol{x} | \boldsymbol{x} = \boldsymbol{x}_1 + \boldsymbol{x}_2, \boldsymbol{x}_1 \in \mathscr{C}_1, \boldsymbol{x}_2 \in \mathscr{C}_2\}$ is a convex cone (finite cone) (fig. 1.8b);

(b) if $\mathscr{C}_1, \mathscr{C}_2 \subset \mathscr{E}^n$ are convex cones (finite cones), their intersection $\mathscr{C}_1 \cap \mathscr{C}_2$ is a convex cone (finite cone) (fig. 1.8c).

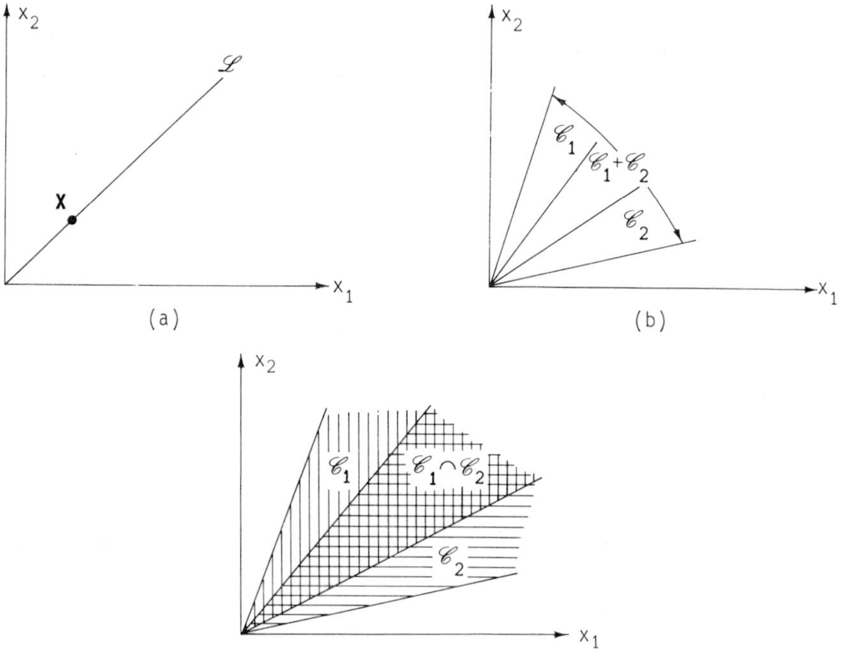

Fig. 1.8.

If we admit to our discussion of cones a finite number of half-lines, then we may arrive at an alternative specification of a finite cone, namely

DEFINITION 1.49.2. *A convex cone $\mathscr{C} \subset \mathscr{E}^m$ is termed a finite cone if there exists a finite number of half-lines $\mathscr{L}_j \subset \mathscr{E}^m$, $j = 1, \ldots, n$, such that $\mathscr{C} = \Sigma_{j=1}^n \mathscr{L}_j$.*

Here $\mathscr{C}$ is to be interpreted as the sum of the n cones $\mathscr{L}_j$ and may be represented as

$$\mathscr{C} = \left\{ y \middle| y = \sum_{j=1}^{n} y_j,\ y_j \in \mathscr{L}_j,\ y \in \mathscr{E}^m \right\}$$

by property (a) above. But since

$$y = \sum_{j=1}^{n} y_j = \sum_{j=1}^{n} \lambda_j \boldsymbol{x}_j = \boldsymbol{A\lambda}, \quad \boldsymbol{\lambda} \geqslant \boldsymbol{0},$$

$$\mathscr{C} = \{ y \mid y = \boldsymbol{A\lambda}, \quad \boldsymbol{\lambda} \geqslant \boldsymbol{0},\ y \in \mathscr{E}^m \},$$

thus establishing the equivalence of defs. 1.49, 1.49.1, and 1.49.2.

In defining a finite cone no mention was made of the linear dependence or independence of the spanning set $\boldsymbol{x}_j$, $j = 1, \ldots, n$. Indeed, the vectors $\boldsymbol{x}_j$ need not be linearly independent. The significance of the number of vectors in any linearly independent subset of the $\boldsymbol{x}_j$ is summarized by

DEFINITION 1.51. *The dimension of the finite cone $\mathscr{C}$, written* $\dim(\mathscr{C})$, *is the maximum number of linearly independent vectors in $\mathscr{C}$.*

So if $\mathscr{C} = \{\boldsymbol{x} \mid \boldsymbol{x} = \boldsymbol{A\lambda},\ \boldsymbol{\lambda} \geqslant \boldsymbol{0},\ \boldsymbol{x} \in \mathscr{E}^m\}$, $\dim(\mathscr{C}) = \rho(\boldsymbol{A})$.

It was mentioned above that any hyperplane $\mathscr{H}$ through the origin is a convex cone as are $[\mathscr{H}^+]$, $[\mathscr{H}^-]$. In addition, $\mathscr{H}$, $[\mathscr{H}^+]$, and $[\mathscr{H}^-]$ are finite. In this light we note briefly that:

(a) if $\boldsymbol{A}$ is $(m \times n)$, the solution set $\mathscr{S}$ of the system of homogeneous inequalities $\boldsymbol{Ax} \leqslant \boldsymbol{0}$ is a finite cone. ($\boldsymbol{Ax} \leqslant \boldsymbol{0}$ consists of the m inequalities $\boldsymbol{a}_i \boldsymbol{x} \leqslant 0$, each specifying a closed half-plane of the form $[\mathscr{H}_i^-] = \{\boldsymbol{x} \mid \boldsymbol{a}_i \boldsymbol{x} \leqslant 0,\ \boldsymbol{x} \in \mathscr{E}^n\}$. Since each $[\mathscr{H}_i^-]$ is a finite cone,

$$\mathscr{S} = \bigcap_{i=1}^{m} [\mathscr{H}_i^-]$$

is a finite cone by property (b) above.)

(b) If $\boldsymbol{A}$ is $(m \times n)$, the set of non-negative solutions of the homogeneous system $\boldsymbol{Ax} = \boldsymbol{0}$ forms a finite cone. (Since each of the m hyperplanes $\mathscr{H}_i = \{\boldsymbol{x} \mid \boldsymbol{a}_i \boldsymbol{x} = 0,\ \boldsymbol{x} \in \mathscr{E}^n\}$ constituting $\boldsymbol{Ax} = \boldsymbol{0}$ is a finite cone, as is the non-negative orthant $\mathscr{X} = \{\boldsymbol{x} | \boldsymbol{x} \geqslant \boldsymbol{0}, \boldsymbol{x} \in \mathscr{E}^n\}$, it follows that

$$\mathscr{X} \cap \left(\bigcap_{i=1}^{m} \mathscr{H}_i \right)$$

is a finite cone by property (b) above.)

Finally,

DEFINITION 1.52. *If $\mathscr{C} \subset \mathscr{E}^m$ is a finite cone, the dual cone $\mathscr{C}^*$ is the finite cone consisting of all vectors making a non-acute angle ($\geqslant \pi/2$) with the vectors of $\mathscr{C}$, i.e. if $\boldsymbol{A}$ is $(m \times n)$ and $\mathscr{C} = \{\boldsymbol{x} | \boldsymbol{x} = \boldsymbol{A\lambda}, \boldsymbol{\lambda} \geqslant \boldsymbol{0}, \boldsymbol{x} \in \mathscr{E}^m\}$, then $\mathscr{C}^* = \{\boldsymbol{y} | \boldsymbol{A}'\boldsymbol{y} \leqslant \boldsymbol{0}, \boldsymbol{y} \in \mathscr{E}^m\}$* (fig. 1.9a).

And,

DEFINITION 1.53. *If $\mathscr{C} \subset \mathscr{E}^m$ is a finite cone, the polar cone $\mathscr{C}^+$ is the finite cone consisting of all vectors making a non-obtuse angle ($\leqslant \pi/2$) with the vectors of $\mathscr{C}$, i.e. if $\boldsymbol{A}$ is $(m \times n)$ and $\mathscr{C} = \{\boldsymbol{x} | \boldsymbol{x} = \boldsymbol{A\lambda}, \boldsymbol{\lambda} \geqslant \boldsymbol{0}, \boldsymbol{x} \in \mathscr{E}^m\}$, then $\mathscr{C}^+ = \{\boldsymbol{y} | \boldsymbol{A}'\boldsymbol{y} \geqslant \boldsymbol{0}, \boldsymbol{y} \in \mathscr{E}^m\}$* (fig. 1.9b).

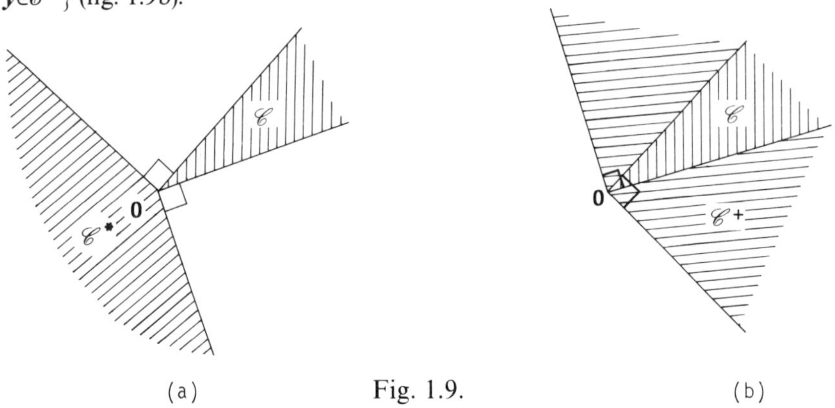

Fig. 1.9.

The essential duality properties of finite cones are:

(a) $(\mathscr{C}^*)^* = \mathscr{C}$;

(b) if $\mathscr{C}_1 \subset \mathscr{C}_2$, $\mathscr{C}_2^* \subset \mathscr{C}_1^*$;

(c) $(\mathscr{C}_1 + \mathscr{C}_2)^* = \mathscr{C}_1^* \cap \mathscr{C}_2^*$;

(d) $(\mathscr{C}_1 \cap \mathscr{C}_2)^* = \mathscr{C}_1^* + \mathscr{C}_2^*$;

(e) the dual cone of a half-line is a closed half-space and vice versa.

The important properties of polar cones are:

(a) $(\mathscr{C}^+)^+ = \mathscr{C}$;

(b) if $\mathscr{C}_1 \subset \mathscr{C}_2$, $\mathscr{C}_2^+ \subset \mathscr{C}_1^+$;

(c) $(\mathscr{C}_1 + \mathscr{C}_2)^+ = \mathscr{C}_1^+ \cap \mathscr{C}_2^+$;

(d) $(\mathscr{C}_1 \cap \mathscr{C}_2)^+ = \mathscr{C}_1^+ + \mathscr{C}_2^+$;

(e) the polar cone of a half-line is a closed half-space and vice versa.

1.9. Theorems of the alternative

We now turn to the specification of two important *theorems of the alternative.* Such theorems consist of two mutually exclusive systems of linear inequalities and/or equalities and assert that either one system has a solution or the other system does, but never both. In this regard we have the

THEOREM OF THE SEPARATING HYPERPLANE.[10] *For any* $(m \times n)$ *matrix* $\boldsymbol{A}$ *and any m-component vector* $\boldsymbol{b}$, *either* (*I*) *there exists an n-component vector* $\boldsymbol{\lambda} \geqslant \boldsymbol{0}$ *such that* $\boldsymbol{A\lambda} = \boldsymbol{b}$ *or* (*II*) *there exists an m-component vector* $\boldsymbol{y}$ *such that* $\boldsymbol{A}'\boldsymbol{y} \leqslant \boldsymbol{0}$, $\boldsymbol{b}'\boldsymbol{y} > 0$, *but never both.*

That is to say, either (I) has a non-negative solution $\boldsymbol{\lambda} \in \mathscr{E}^n$ or (II) has a solution $\boldsymbol{\lambda} \in \mathscr{E}^m$, but not both. How may we interpret this theorem? Let $\mathscr{H}$ be a hyperplane passing through the origin and orthogonal to the vector $\boldsymbol{b}$, i.e. $\mathscr{H} = \{\boldsymbol{y} | \boldsymbol{b}'\boldsymbol{y} = 0, \boldsymbol{b}(\neq \boldsymbol{0}), \boldsymbol{y} \in \mathscr{E}^m\}$. If (I) possesses a solution, then $\boldsymbol{b}$ lies within the finite cone $\mathscr{C} \subset \mathscr{E}^m$ spanned by the columns of $\boldsymbol{A}$, $\boldsymbol{a}_j$, $j = 1, \ldots, n$, i.e. $\boldsymbol{b} \in \mathscr{C} = \{\boldsymbol{x} | \boldsymbol{x} = \boldsymbol{A\lambda}, \boldsymbol{\lambda} \geqslant \boldsymbol{0}, \boldsymbol{x} \in \mathscr{E}^m\}$. In this instance $\mathscr{H}$ is a separating hyperplane for the finite cones $\mathscr{C}$ and $\mathscr{C}^* = \{\boldsymbol{y} | \boldsymbol{A}'\boldsymbol{y} \leqslant \boldsymbol{0}, \boldsymbol{y} \in \mathscr{E}^m\}$ so that $\mathscr{C}^* \cap (\mathscr{H}^+) = \{\boldsymbol{y} | \boldsymbol{A}'\boldsymbol{y} \leqslant \boldsymbol{0}, \boldsymbol{y} \in \mathscr{E}^m\} \cap \{\boldsymbol{y} | \boldsymbol{b}'\boldsymbol{y} > 0, \boldsymbol{y} \in \mathscr{E}^m\} = \emptyset$ and thus (II) has no solution (fig. 1.10a). If (II) has a solution, then $\mathscr{C}^* \cap (\mathscr{H}^+) \neq \emptyset$, implying that $\boldsymbol{b} \notin \mathscr{C}$ so that (I) has no solution (fig. 1.10b). (Alternatively, let $\mathscr{H}$ be a hyperplane through the origin and orthogonal to $\boldsymbol{y}$. If (I) does not possess a solution ($\boldsymbol{b} \notin \mathscr{C}$), (II) implies that $\boldsymbol{y}$ makes non-acute angles ($\geqslant \pi/2$) with the columns of $\boldsymbol{A}(\boldsymbol{A}'\boldsymbol{y} \leqslant \boldsymbol{0})$ and a strictly acute angle ($< \pi/2$) with $\boldsymbol{b}(\boldsymbol{b}'\boldsymbol{y} > 0)$. Hence $\mathscr{H}$ has the finite cone spanned by the columns of $\boldsymbol{A}$ on one side and the vector $\boldsymbol{b}$ on the other. In this instance $\mathscr{H}$ is a separating hyperplane for $\mathscr{C}$ and $\{\boldsymbol{b}\}$ (fig. 1.10c).)

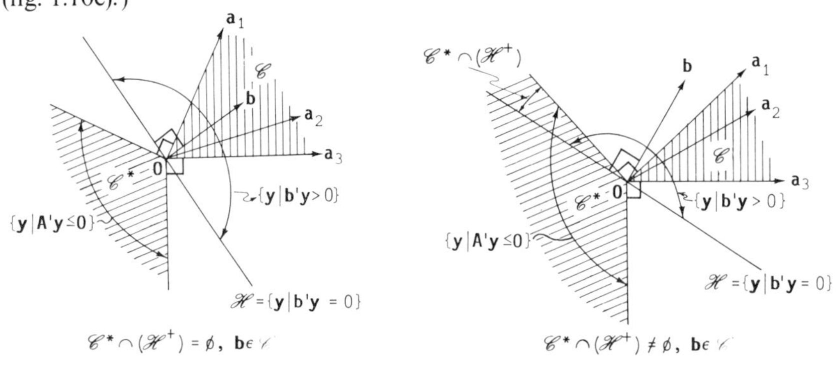

(a) (b)

Fig. 1.10.

[10] For a proof involving: (a) induction on the rows of $\boldsymbol{A}$ see Gale (1960), pp. 44–46; (b) the application of auxiliary theorems of the alternative see Mangasarian (1969), pp. 31–32.

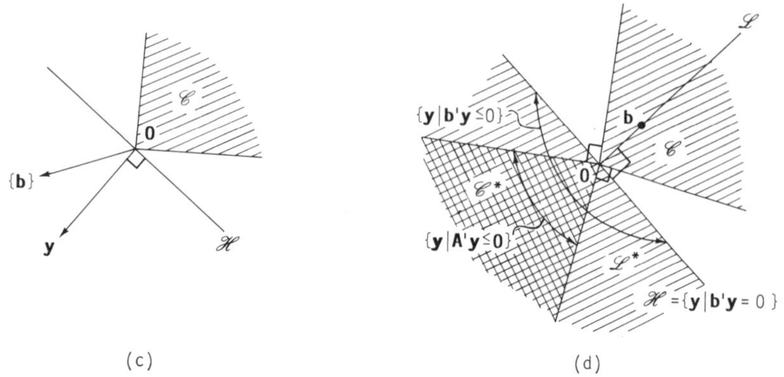

Fig. 1.10.

Our next theorem of the alternative, which is equivalent to the theorem of the separating hyperplane, is the

MINKOWSKI–FARKAS THEOREM. *If (II) above does not possess a solution, then a necessary and sufficient condition for the m-component vector* $\boldsymbol{b}$ *to lie within the finite cone spanned by the columns of the* $(m\times n)$ *matrix* $\boldsymbol{A}$ *is that* $\boldsymbol{b}'\boldsymbol{y}\leqslant 0$ *for all* $\boldsymbol{y}$ *satisfying* $\boldsymbol{A}'\boldsymbol{y}\leqslant\boldsymbol{0}$, *i.e. there exists an n-component vector* $\boldsymbol{\lambda}\geqslant\boldsymbol{0}$ *such that* $\boldsymbol{A\lambda}=\boldsymbol{b}$ *if and only if* $\boldsymbol{b}'\boldsymbol{y}\leqslant 0$ *for all* $\boldsymbol{y}$ *satisfying* $\boldsymbol{A}'\boldsymbol{y}\leqslant\boldsymbol{0}$.

Proof (sufficiency). If $\boldsymbol{A\lambda}=\boldsymbol{b}$, $\boldsymbol{\lambda}\geqslant\boldsymbol{0}$, then $\boldsymbol{\lambda}'\boldsymbol{A}'=\boldsymbol{b}'$ and $\boldsymbol{\lambda}'\boldsymbol{A}'\boldsymbol{y}=\boldsymbol{b}'\boldsymbol{y}\leqslant 0$ for all $\boldsymbol{y}$ for which $\boldsymbol{A}'\boldsymbol{y}\leqslant\boldsymbol{0}$. (Necessity.) Let $\mathscr{H}=\{\boldsymbol{y}|\boldsymbol{b}'\boldsymbol{y}=0,\ \boldsymbol{y}\in\mathscr{E}^m\}$ be a hyperplane through the origin and orthogonal to the half-line $\mathscr{L}=\{\boldsymbol{y}|\boldsymbol{y}=\lambda\boldsymbol{b},\ \lambda\geqslant 0,\ \boldsymbol{y}\in\mathscr{E}^m\}$. Then $\mathscr{L}^*=\{\boldsymbol{y}|\boldsymbol{b}'\boldsymbol{y}\leqslant 0,\ \boldsymbol{y}\in\mathscr{E}^m\}$. Since $\mathscr{C}=\{\boldsymbol{x}|\boldsymbol{x}=\boldsymbol{A\lambda},\ \boldsymbol{\lambda}\geqslant\boldsymbol{0},\ \boldsymbol{x}\in\mathscr{E}^m\}$, $\mathscr{C}^*=\{\boldsymbol{y}|\boldsymbol{A}'\boldsymbol{y}\leqslant\boldsymbol{0},\ \boldsymbol{y}\in\mathscr{E}^m\}$. For each $\boldsymbol{y}\in\mathscr{C}^*$, let it also be true that $\boldsymbol{y}\in\mathscr{L}^*$. So with $\mathscr{C}^*\subset\mathscr{L}^*$, $\mathscr{L}\subset\mathscr{C}$ or $\boldsymbol{b}\in\mathscr{C}$ (fig. 1.10d). (Note that this part of the proof has employed duality properties (b) and (e) above.) Q.E.D.

1.10. Quadratic forms

DEFINITION 1.54. *Let* Q *be a real-valued function of the n variables* $x_1, \ldots, x_n$. *Then* Q *is called a quadratic form in* $x_1, \ldots, x_n$ *if*

$$Q(x_1, \ldots, x_n) = \sum_{i=1}^{n}\sum_{j=1}^{n} a_{ij}x_ix_j,$$

where at least one of the constant coefficients $a_{ij}\neq 0$.

To determine the general properties of Q let us express the above finite double sum explicitly as

$$\begin{aligned}\sum_{i=1}^{n}\sum_{j=1}^{n} a_{ij}x_i x_j &= \sum_{j=1}^{n} a_{1j}x_1x_j + \sum_{j=1}^{n} a_{2j}x_2x_j + \cdots + \sum_{j=1}^{n} a_{nj}x_nx_j \\ &= a_{11}x_1^2 + a_{12}x_1x_2 + \ldots + a_{1n}x_1x_n \\ &\quad + a_{21}x_2x_1 + a_{22}x_2^2 + \ldots + a_{2n}x_2x_n + \ldots \\ &\quad + a_{n1}x_nx_1 + a_{n2}x_nx_2 + \ldots + a_{nn}x_n^2. \end{aligned} \tag{1.14}$$

Written in this fashion it is readily seen that Q is a homogeneous[11] polynomial of the second degree (since each term involves either the square of a variable or the product of two different variables) containing n^2 distinct terms. In addition Q is continuous for all values of the variables x_i, $i = 1, \ldots, n$, and equals zero when all of the $x_i = 0$, $i = 1, \ldots, n$.

Let us now consider an alternative mode of representing a quadratic form. Expressed in matrix form, Q equals, for all vectors $\boldsymbol{x} \in \mathscr{E}^n$, the scalar quantity

$$Q(x_1, \ldots, x_n) = Q(\boldsymbol{x}) = \boldsymbol{x}'A\boldsymbol{x}, \tag{1.15}$$

where

$$\boldsymbol{x} = \begin{bmatrix} x_1 \\ x_2 \\ \vdots \\ x_n \end{bmatrix}, \qquad \boldsymbol{A} = \begin{bmatrix} a_{11} a_{12} & \ldots & a_{1n} \\ a_{21} a_{22} & \ldots & a_{2n} \\ \vdots \quad \vdots & & \vdots \\ a_{n1} a_{n2} & \ldots & a_{nn} \end{bmatrix}.$$

To see this we first find

$$\boldsymbol{Ax} = \begin{bmatrix} a_{11}\ x_1 + a_{12}\ x_2 + \ldots + a_{1n}\ x_n \\ a_{21}\ x_1 + a_{22}\ x_2 + \ldots + a_{2n}\ x_n \\ \cdots\cdots\cdots\cdots\cdots\cdots \\ a_{n1}\ x_1 + a_{n2}\ x_2 + \ldots + a_{nn}\ x_n \end{bmatrix} = \begin{bmatrix} \sum_{j=1}^{n} a_{1j}\, x_j \\ \sum_{j=1}^{n} a_{2j}\, x_j \\ \vdots \\ \sum_{j=1}^{n} a_{nj}\, x_j \end{bmatrix}.$$

[11] A form is *homogeneous of degree t* in the variables $x_1, \ldots, x_n$ if, when each variable in the form is multiplied by a scalar λ, the whole form is multiplied by λ^t, i.e. $Q(\lambda x_1, \ldots, \lambda x_n) = \lambda^t Q(x_1, \ldots, x_n)$.

Then

$$x'Ax = (x_1, \ldots, x_n)\begin{bmatrix} \sum_{j=1}^{n} a_{1j}x_j \\ \sum_{j=1}^{n} a_{2j}x_j \\ \vdots \\ \sum_{j=1}^{n} a_{nj}x_j \end{bmatrix}$$

$$= x_1 \sum_{j=1}^{n} a_{1j}x_j + x_2 \sum_{j=1}^{n} a_{2j}x_j + \ldots + x_n \sum_{j=1}^{n} a_{nj}x_j$$

$$= \sum_{j=1}^{n} a_{1j}x_1x_j + \sum_{j=1}^{n} a_{2j}x_2x_j + \ldots + \sum_{j=1}^{n} a_{nj}x_nx_j.$$

$$= \sum_{i=1}^{n}\sum_{j=1}^{n} a_{ij}x_ix_j.$$

From eq. (1.14) it can be seen that $a_{ij}+a_{ji}$ is the coefficient of x_ix_j since a_{ij}, a_{ji} are both coefficients of $x_ix_j = x_jx_i$, $i \neq j$.

Example 1.18. Find the quadratic form $Q(x_1, x_2, x_3)$ associated with the matrix

$$A = \begin{bmatrix} 1 & 2 & 1 \\ 3 & 5 & 2 \\ 1 & 1 & 2 \end{bmatrix}.$$

From eq. (1.15) we have

$$x'Ax = x'\begin{bmatrix} 1 & 2 & 1 \\ 3 & 5 & 2 \\ 1 & 1 & 2 \end{bmatrix}\begin{bmatrix} x_1 \\ x_2 \\ x_3 \end{bmatrix} = (x_1, x_2, x_3)\begin{bmatrix} x_1+2x_2+x_3 \\ 3x_1+5x_2+2x_3 \\ x_1+x_2+2x_3 \end{bmatrix}$$

$$= x_1(x_1+2x_2+x_3)+x_2(3x_1+5x_2+2x_3)+x_3(x_1+x_2+2x_3)$$
$$= x_1^2+5x_1x_2+2x_1x_3+5x_2^2+3x_2x_3+2x_3^2.$$

Example 1.19. Find $x'Ax$ when

$$A = \begin{bmatrix} 1 & 0 & 1 \\ 3 & 0 & 0 \\ 1 & 1 & 2 \end{bmatrix}.$$

Since three elements in A are zero, Q will have $n^2-3 = 6$ individual terms.

Upon performing the indicated matrix multiplication we obtain

$$\begin{aligned} \boldsymbol{x}'\boldsymbol{A}\boldsymbol{x} &= x_1^2+0x_1x_2+x_1x_3+3x_2x_1+0x_2^2+0x_2x_3+x_3x_1 \\ &\quad +x_3x_2+2x_3^2 \\ &= x_1^2+3x_1x_2+2x_1x_3+x_2x_3+2x_3^2. \end{aligned}$$

1.11. Symmetric quadratic forms

If the matrix $\boldsymbol{A}$ is symmetric so that $\boldsymbol{A} = \boldsymbol{A}'$, then $a_{ij} = a_{ji}$, $i \neq j$. Thus we have

DEFINITION 1.55. *A quadratic form* $\boldsymbol{x}'\boldsymbol{A}\boldsymbol{x}$ *is symmetric if the matrix* $\boldsymbol{A}$ *is symmetric, i.e. if* $a_{ij} = a_{ji}$, $i \neq j$.

Hence $a_{ij}+a_{ji} = 2a_{ij}$ is the coefficient of x_ix_j since $a_{ij} = a_{ji}$ and a_{ij}, a_{ji} are both coefficients of $x_ix_j = x_jx_i$, $i \neq j$.

If $\boldsymbol{A}$ is not a symmetric matrix so that $a_{ij} \neq a_{ji}$, we can transform it into a symmetric matrix $\boldsymbol{B}$ by defining new coefficients:

$$b_{ij} = b_{ji} = \frac{a_{ij}+a_{ji}}{2} \quad \text{for all } i, j. \tag{1.16}$$

Then $b_{ij}+b_{ji} = 2b_{ij}$ is the coefficient of x_ix_j, $i \neq j$, in

$$\boldsymbol{x}'\boldsymbol{B}\boldsymbol{x} = \sum_{i=1}^{n}\sum_{j=1}^{n} \frac{a_{ij}+a_{ji}}{2} x_ix_j.$$

But, by definition, $b_{ij}+b_{ji} = a_{ij}+a_{ji}$. Hence the redefinition of coefficients leaves the value of Q unchanged. That is, if eq. (1.16) holds, then $\boldsymbol{x}'\boldsymbol{A}\boldsymbol{x} = \boldsymbol{x}'\boldsymbol{B}\boldsymbol{x}$ for any $\boldsymbol{x} \in \mathscr{E}^n$. In sum, given any quadratic form $\boldsymbol{x}'\boldsymbol{A}\boldsymbol{x}$, the matrix $\boldsymbol{A}$ may be assumed to be symmetric; if it is not, it can always be transformed into a symmetric matrix.

Example 1.20. Given that

$$\boldsymbol{A} = \begin{bmatrix} 1 & 3 & 2 \\ 1 & -1 & 6 \\ 3 & 5 & 4 \end{bmatrix}$$

transforms $\boldsymbol{A}$ into a symmetric matrix $\boldsymbol{B}$. From eq. (1.16) we set

$$\begin{aligned} b_{11} &= a_{11} = 1, \\ b_{12} &= b_{21} = \frac{a_{12}+a_{21}}{2} = \frac{3+1}{2} = 2, \\ b_{13} &= b_{31} = \frac{a_{13}+a_{31}}{2} = \frac{2+3}{2} = \frac{5}{2}, \end{aligned}$$

$$b_{22} = a_{22} = -1,$$
$$b_{23} = b_{32} = \frac{a_{23}+a_{32}}{2} = \frac{6+5}{2} = \frac{11}{2},$$
$$b_{33} = a_{33} = 4.$$

Hence

$$\boldsymbol{B} = \begin{bmatrix} 1 & 2 & \frac{5}{2} \\ 2 & -1 & \frac{11}{2} \\ \frac{5}{2} & \frac{11}{2} & 4 \end{bmatrix}.$$

Example 1.21. Find the matrix $\boldsymbol{A}$ associated with the quadratic form

$$\boldsymbol{x}'\boldsymbol{A}\boldsymbol{x} = 2x_1^2-3x_1x_2+\tfrac{7}{2}x_1x_3+x_1x_4+x_2^2+6x_2x_3-8x_3x_4+2x_4^2.$$

Since $\boldsymbol{A}$ may be assumed to be symmetric we have

$$\boldsymbol{A} = \begin{bmatrix} 2 & -\frac{3}{2} & \frac{7}{4} & \frac{1}{2} \\ -\frac{3}{2} & 1 & 3 & 0 \\ \frac{7}{4} & 3 & 0 & -4 \\ \frac{1}{2} & 0 & -4 & 2 \end{bmatrix}.$$

1.12. Classification of quadratic forms

In all there are five mutually exclusive and collectively exhaustive categories of quadratic forms. First,

DEFINITION 1.56. *A quadratic form is said to be positive definite (negative definite) if it is positive (negative) at every point $\boldsymbol{x}\in\mathscr{E}^n$ except $\boldsymbol{x} = \boldsymbol{0}$, i.e.*

(*a*) *$\boldsymbol{x}'\boldsymbol{A}\boldsymbol{x}$ is positive definite if $\boldsymbol{x}'\boldsymbol{A}\boldsymbol{x}>0$ for every $\boldsymbol{x} \neq \boldsymbol{0}$;*

(*b*) *$\boldsymbol{x}'\boldsymbol{A}\boldsymbol{x}$ is negative definite if $\boldsymbol{x}'\boldsymbol{A}\boldsymbol{x}<0$ for every $\boldsymbol{x} \neq \boldsymbol{0}$.*

It is evident that a form which is either positive or negative definite cannot assume both positive and negative values. To see this let us assume that a definite form is positive at a point $\boldsymbol{x}_1(\boldsymbol{x}_1'\boldsymbol{A}\boldsymbol{x}_1>0)$ and negative at $\boldsymbol{x}_2(\boldsymbol{x}_2'\boldsymbol{A}\boldsymbol{x}_2<0)$. Then, because of the continuity of the form, there must exist some point $\boldsymbol{x}_3 \neq \boldsymbol{0}$ between $\boldsymbol{x}_1$, $\boldsymbol{x}_2$ such that $\boldsymbol{x}_3'\boldsymbol{A}\boldsymbol{x}_3 = 0$ (see theorem 6.3, p. 99). However, this contradicts the definition of definiteness given above. Hence definite forms must be either positive or negative. We now state

DEFINITION 1.57. *A quadratic form is said to be positive semi-definite (negative semi-definite) if it is non-negative (non-positive) at every point $\boldsymbol{x}\in\mathscr{E}^n$, and there exist points $\boldsymbol{x} \neq \boldsymbol{0}$ for which it equals zero, i.e.*

(*a*) *$\boldsymbol{x}'\boldsymbol{A}\boldsymbol{x}$ is positive semi-definite if $\boldsymbol{x}'\boldsymbol{A}\boldsymbol{x}\geqslant 0$ for every $\boldsymbol{x}$ and $\boldsymbol{x}'\boldsymbol{A}\boldsymbol{x} = 0$ for some points $\boldsymbol{x} \neq \boldsymbol{0}$;*

(*b*) $x'Ax$ *is negative semi-definite if* $x'Ax \leqslant 0$ *for every* x *and* $x'Ax = 0$ *for some points* $x \neq 0$.

It is obvious that if the quadratic form $x'Ax$ is positive definite (semi-definite), then $x'(-A)x$ is negative definite (semi-definite) and conversely. In addition, we have

DEFINITION 1.58. *A quadratic form* $x'Ax$ *is said to be indefinite if it is positive for some points* $x \in \mathscr{E}^n$ *and negative for others.*

Example 1.22. From def. 1.56 it is clear that the quadratic form $x'Ax = x_1^2+x_2^2$ is positive definite while $x'(-A)x = -x_1^2-x_2^2$ is negative definite since both vanish only at the point $x = 0$.

Example 1.23. It is evident, from def. 1.57, that $x'Ax = x_1^2-2x_1x_2+x_2^2 = (x_1-x_2)^2$ is positive semi-definite and $x'(-A)x = -x_1^2+2x_1x_2-x_2^2 = -(x_1-x_2)^2$ is negative semi-definite since the former is never negative while the latter is never positive, yet both equal zero for $x_1 = x_2 \neq 0$.

Example 1.24. That the quadratic form $x'Ax = x_1x_2+x_2^2$ is indefinite can be verified from def. 1.58 by noting that, on the one hand, $x'Ax<0$ for $x_1 = -2$, $x_2 = 1$ and, on the other, $x'Ax>0$ for $x_1 = 2$, $x_2 = 1$.

We shall often find it convenient to classify matrices in terms of the sign 'definiteness' or 'semi-definiteness' of their associated quadratic forms. Specifically, we have

DEFINITION 1.59. *An nth-order symmetric matrix* A *is positive definite (negative definite) if and only if* $x'Ax > 0(<0)$ *for all* $x(\neq 0) \in \mathscr{E}^n$

DEFINITION 1.60. *An nth-order symmetric matrix* A *is positive semi-definite (negative semi-definite) if and only if* $x'Ax \geqslant 0(\leqslant 0)$ *for all* $x \in \mathscr{E}^n$.

Some of the essential features of definite matrices are:

(a) if A is an nth-order positive (negative) definite matrix, then $|A|>0(<0)$ and thus $\rho(A) = n$;

(b) if A is an nth-order positive (negative) definite matrix, then so is A^{-1}.

1.13. Necessary conditions for the definiteness and semi-definiteness of quadratic forms

In this section and the next our aim will be to provide a set of theorems with which to identify the various types of quadratic forms. We state first

THEOREM 1.3.[12] *If a quadratic form* $\mathbf{x}'\mathbf{A}\mathbf{x}$, $\mathbf{x}\in\mathscr{E}^n$, *is positive (negative) definite, all the terms involving second powers of the variables must have positive (negative) coefficients.*

Note that the theorem does not provide a sufficient condition for the definiteness of a quadratic form because its converse does not hold, i.e. a quadratic form may have positive (negative) coefficients on all its terms involving second powers yet not be definite. A case in point is provided by example 1.23 above. Similarly,

THEOREM 1.4. *If a quadratic form* $\mathbf{x}'\mathbf{A}\mathbf{x}$, $\mathbf{x}\in\mathscr{E}^n$, *is positive (negative) semi-definite, all of the terms involving second powers of the variables must have non-negative (non-positive) coefficients.*

In this case, too, the converse of the theorem does not hold, since the quadratic form $x_1^2 - x_1 x_2$ has non-negative coefficients associated with its second-degree terms, yet happens to be indefinite.

In the next section we shall find it useful to express conditions which are simultaneously necessary and sufficient for the definiteness or semi-definiteness of a quadratic form in terms of determinants. As a prelude to this type of reasoning we cite

THEOREM 1.5.[13] *If the quadratic form* $\mathbf{x}'\mathbf{A}\mathbf{x}$, $\mathbf{x}\in\mathscr{E}^n$, *is definite, the naturally ordered principal minors of* $\mathbf{A}$ *are all different from zero. In this case*

$$M_k = \begin{vmatrix} a_{11} & \dots & a_{1k} \\ \vdots & & \vdots \\ a_{k1} & \dots & a_{kk} \end{vmatrix} \neq 0, \quad k = 1, \dots, n$$

or

$$M_{11} = a_{11} \neq 0, \qquad M_2 = \begin{vmatrix} a_{11} & a_{12} \\ a_{21} & a_{22} \end{vmatrix} \neq 0,$$

$$M_3 = \begin{vmatrix} a_{11} & a_{12} & a_{13} \\ a_{21} & a_{22} & a_{23} \\ a_{31} & a_{32} & a_{33} \end{vmatrix} \neq 0, \dots, \qquad M_n = |\mathbf{A}| \neq 0.$$

So if any $M_k = 0$, $k = 1, \dots, n$, the form is not definite; it may be semi-definite or indefinite. That this theorem does not provide a sufficient condition for definiteness is illustrated by the quadratic form $\mathbf{x}'\mathbf{A}\mathbf{x} = x_1^2 - x_2^2$.

[12] This theorem represents a special case of a more general theorem provided by Bushaw and Clower (1957), p. 264.
[13] Bushaw and Clower (1957), pp. 279–280.

Here

$$A = \begin{bmatrix} 1 & 0 \\ 0 & -1 \end{bmatrix}.$$

Although $M_1 = 1 \neq 0$, $M_2 = -1 \neq 0$, $x'Ax$ is not definite but indefinite since it is positive for some values of x and negative for others.

Example 1.25. Use theorem 1.5 to verify that the quadratic forms

$$x'Ax = x_1^2 - 2x_1x_2 + x_2^2, \qquad x'Ax = x_1x_2 + x_2^2$$

are non-definite. First, for $x'Ax = x_1^2 - 2x_1x_2 + x_2^2$,

$$A = \begin{bmatrix} 1 & -1 \\ -1 & 1 \end{bmatrix}.$$

Now $M_1 = 1 \neq 0$ while $M_2 = 0$. Hence the form is not definite. It is, in fact, semi-definite, as indicated in example 1.23. Next, for $x'Ax = x_1x_2 + x_2^2$,

$$A = \begin{bmatrix} 0 & \frac{1}{2} \\ \frac{1}{2} & 1 \end{bmatrix}.$$

Here $M_1 = 0$ and we need not proceed further. In this case $x'Ax$ happens to be indefinite, as seen in example 1.24.

1.14. Necessary and sufficient conditions for the definiteness and semi-definiteness of quadratic forms

Let us modify theorem 1.5 to get

THEOREM 1.6.[14] *The quadratic form $x'Ax$, $x \in \mathscr{E}^n$, is positive definite if and only if the naturally ordered principal minors of A are all positive, i.e.*

$$M_k = \begin{vmatrix} a_{11} & \dots & a_{1k} \\ \vdots & & \vdots \\ a_{k1} & \dots & a_{kk} \end{vmatrix} > 0, \quad k = 1, \dots, n,$$

or

$$M_1 = a_{11} > 0, \qquad M_2 = \begin{vmatrix} a_{11} & a_{12} \\ a_{21} & a_{22} \end{vmatrix} > 0,$$

$$M_3 = \begin{vmatrix} a_{11} & a_{12} & a_{13} \\ a_{21} & a_{22} & a_{23} \\ a_{31} & a_{32} & a_{33} \end{vmatrix} > 0, \dots, \qquad M_n = |A| > 0.$$

[14] A proof of this theorem is provided by Hadley (1964), pp. 260–261.

We noted above that if the quadratic form $\boldsymbol{x}'\boldsymbol{A}\boldsymbol{x}$ is negative definite, then $\boldsymbol{x}'(-\boldsymbol{A})\boldsymbol{x}$ is positive definite. But if $\boldsymbol{x}'(-\boldsymbol{A})\boldsymbol{x}$ is positive definite, it follows from the preceding theorem that the naturally ordered principal minors of

$$-\boldsymbol{A} = \begin{bmatrix} -a_{11} & -a_{12} & \dots & -a_{1n} \\ -a_{21} & -a_{22} & \dots & -a_{2n} \\ \vdots & \vdots & & \vdots \\ -a_{n1} & -a_{n2} & \dots & -a_{nn} \end{bmatrix}$$

are all positive or

$$M_1 = -a_{11} > 0,$$

$$M_2 = \begin{vmatrix} -a_{11} & -a_{12} \\ -a_{21} & -a_{22} \end{vmatrix} = (-1)^2 \begin{vmatrix} a_{11} & a_{12} \\ a_{21} & a_{22} \end{vmatrix} > 0,$$

$$M_3 = \begin{vmatrix} -a_{11} & -a_{12} & -a_{13} \\ -a_{21} & -a_{22} & -a_{23} \\ -a_{31} & -a_{32} & -a_{33} \end{vmatrix} = (-1)^3 \begin{vmatrix} a_{11} & a_{12} & a_{13} \\ a_{21} & a_{22} & a_{23} \\ a_{31} & a_{32} & a_{33} \end{vmatrix} > 0,$$

$$\cdots\cdots\cdots\cdots\cdots\cdots\cdots\cdots\cdots\cdots\cdots\cdots$$

$$M_n = |-\boldsymbol{A}| = (-1)^n |\boldsymbol{A}| > 0.$$

For all these principal minors M_k, $k = 1, \dots, n$, to be positive, it must be true that

$$a_{11} < 0, \qquad \begin{vmatrix} a_{11} & a_{12} \\ a_{21} & a_{22} \end{vmatrix} > 0, \qquad \begin{vmatrix} a_{11} & a_{12} & a_{13} \\ a_{21} & a_{22} & a_{23} \\ a_{31} & a_{32} & a_{33} \end{vmatrix} < 0, \dots, \qquad (-1)^n |\boldsymbol{A}| > 0.$$

But this last sequence of determinants represents the naturally ordered principal minors of $\boldsymbol{A}$. Hence

THEOREM 1.7. *The quadratic form $\boldsymbol{x}'\boldsymbol{A}\boldsymbol{x}$, $\boldsymbol{x} \in \mathscr{E}^n$, is negative definite if and only if the naturally ordered principal minors of $\boldsymbol{A}$ alternate in sign, the first being negative, i.e.*

$$(-1)^k M_k = (-1)^k \begin{vmatrix} a_{11} & \dots & a_{1k} \\ \vdots & & \vdots \\ a_{k1} & \dots & a_{kk} \end{vmatrix} > 0, \quad k = 1, \dots, n$$

or

$$M_1 = a_{11} < 0, \qquad M_2 = \begin{vmatrix} a_{11} & a_{12} \\ a_{21} & a_{22} \end{vmatrix} > 0,$$

$$M_3 = \begin{vmatrix} a_{11} & a_{12} & a_{13} \\ a_{21} & a_{22} & a_{23} \\ a_{31} & a_{32} & a_{33} \end{vmatrix} < 0, \dots, \qquad M_n = (-1)^n |\boldsymbol{A}| > 0.$$

A similar set of theorems holds for semi-definite forms. In this regard,

THEOREM 1.8. *The quadratic form $x'Ax$, $x \in \mathscr{E}^n$, is positive semi-definite if and only if the naturally ordered principal minors of A are all non-negative.*

Now if $x'(-A)x$ is positive semi-definite, then $x'Ax$ is negative semi-definite and thus we have

THEOREM 1.9. *The quadratic form $x'Ax$, $x \in \mathscr{E}^n$, is negative semi-definite if and only if the naturally ordered principal minors of A alternate in sign, the first being non-positive.*

Example 1.26. Is the quadratic form $x'Ax = 2x_1^2+2x_1x_2+6x_2^2+4x_2x_3+x_3^2$ positive definite? To answer this question we first find

$$A = \begin{bmatrix} 2 & 1 & 0 \\ 1 & 6 & 2 \\ 0 & 2 & 1 \end{bmatrix}.$$

Employing theorem 1.6 we have $M_1 = 2$, $M_2 = 11$, and $M_3 = 3$. Hence $x'Ax$ is positive definite since all the naturally ordered principal minors of A are positive.

Example 1.27. Prove that $x'Ax = -x_1^2+x_1x_2-x_2^2-x_3^2$ is negative definite. Since

$$A = \begin{bmatrix} -1 & \frac{1}{2} & 0 \\ \frac{1}{2} & -1 & 0 \\ 0 & 0 & -1 \end{bmatrix},$$

it follows that $M_1 = -1$, $M_2 = 3/4$, and $M_3 = -1/2$. Thus the requirements of theorem 1.7 hold and $x'Ax$ is negative definite.

1.15. Quadratic functions

We shall now demonstrate that a general second-degree polynomial in the variables $x_1, \ldots, x_n$ can be written as the sum of a constant, a linear form, and a quadratic form. Specifically, let the real-valued function $y = \mathrm{f}(x)$, $x \in \mathscr{E}^n$, appear as

$$\begin{aligned} \mathrm{f}(x) = a+b_1x_1+\ldots+b_nx_n&+a_{12}x_1x_2+\ldots+a_{1n}x_1x_n \\ &+a_{23}x_2x_3+\ldots+a_{2n}x_2x_n \\ &+a_{34}x_3x_4+\ldots+a_{3n}x_3x_n \\ &+\ldots+a_{n-1,n}x_{n-1}x_n \\ &+a_1x_1^2+\ldots+a_nx_n^2. \end{aligned}$$

If

$$q_{ii} = a_i \quad \text{and} \quad q_{ij} = q_{ji} = \tfrac{1}{2}a_{ij}, \quad i \neq j, \quad i, j = 1, \ldots, n,$$

then the above expression may be rewritten as

$$\begin{aligned} \mathrm{f}(\boldsymbol{x}) &= a + \sum_{i=1}^{n} b_i x_i + \sum_{i=1}^{n} \sum_{j=1}^{n} q_{ij} x_i x_j \\ &= a + \boldsymbol{b}'\boldsymbol{x} + \boldsymbol{x}'\boldsymbol{Q}\boldsymbol{x}, \end{aligned}$$

where $\boldsymbol{b}$ is of order $(n \times 1)$ and $\boldsymbol{Q}$ is an nth-order symmetric matrix.

Chapter 2

MATHEMATICAL FOUNDATIONS II

2.1. The real number system[1]

On a given straight line of infinite length let us choose an arbitrary point as the origin 0, the direction to the right of 0 as positive, and a unit of distance l with which to mark off segments of unit length on either side of 0 (fig. 2.1). The points on this *Euclidean line* represent the set $\mathscr{E}$ of positive and negative real numbers which lie to the right and left of 0 respectively. That is, there exists a one-to-one correspondence between the set of all real numbers and the set of all points on our directed line. In this regard, since the set of real numbers and the set of points on the Euclidean line $\mathscr{E}$ are equivalent, we shall adopt the convention of using the terms 'point' and 'real number' interchangeably.

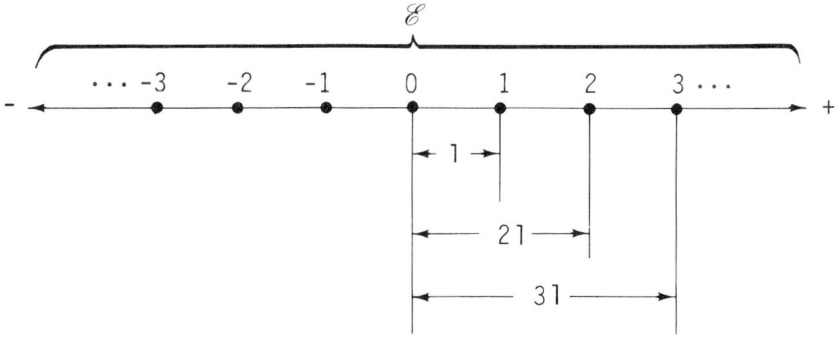

Fig. 2.1.

[1] The discussion on the real-number system (consisting of integers, rational fractions, and irrational numbers) to which we now turn, will be based largely upon geometric notions rather than analytical considerations. Indeed, a more elegant approach to the subject consists of defining (constructing) real numbers as Dedekind cuts of rational numbers, with the rational numbers, in turn, being defined in terms of the positive integers. For a presentation along these lines see Birkhoff and MacLane (1960), pp. 97–99. Alternatively, one may choose to take the real numbers as given and proceed to characterize their properties by an axiom system consisting of field axioms, order axioms, and the least upper bound or completeness axiom. For our purposes we need only consider the completeness axiom, a point to which we shall turn shortly. For a discussion on the field and order axioms see Royden (1963), pp. 21–23.

While the real line extends from minus to plus infinity, the elements $-\infty$ and $+\infty$ are not themselves members of $\mathscr{E}$, i.e. for any real number $r \in \mathscr{E}$, $-\infty < r < +\infty$. If we choose to admit infinite values to our discussion, we must modify our analysis somewhat and form what is commonly referred to as the set of *extended real numbers* $\mathscr{E}_E \equiv \{-\infty\} \cup \mathscr{E} \cup \{+\infty\}$.

The generalization of the Euclidean line $\mathscr{E}$ to higher dimensions can be undertaken by an application of

DEFINITION 2.1. *The Cartesian product of the sets* $\mathscr{X}_i \subset \mathscr{E}$, $i = 1, \ldots, n$, *written* $\overset{n}{\underset{i=1}{\times}} \mathscr{X}_i = \mathscr{X}_1 \times \cdots \times \mathscr{X}_n$, *is the set of all ordered n-tuples* $(x_1, \ldots, x_n)$, *where* $x_1 \in \mathscr{X}_1, \ldots, x_n \in \mathscr{X}_n$.

For instance, fig. 2.2 indicates the Cartesian product of sets $\mathscr{X}_1, \mathscr{X}_2 \subset \mathscr{E}$.

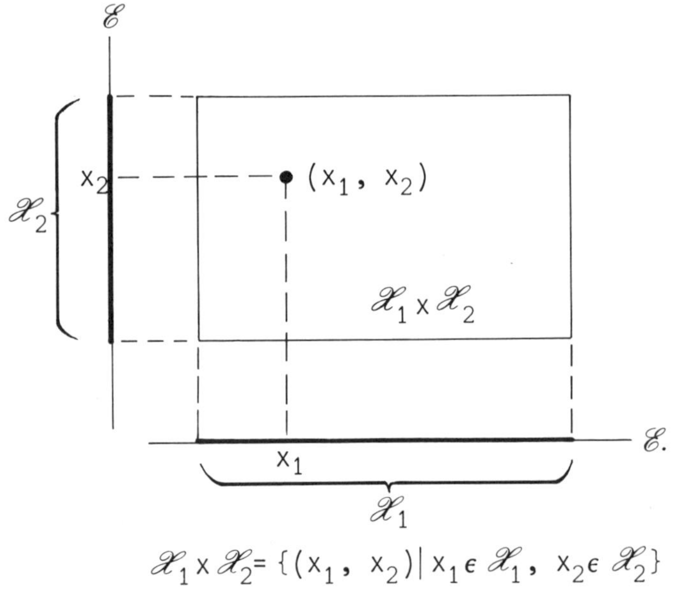

Fig. 2.2.

In this regard, if $\mathscr{X}_i = \mathscr{E}$, $i = 1, \ldots, n$, then n-dimensional (real) *Euclidean space* appears as $\overset{n}{\underset{i=1}{\times}} \mathscr{E} = \mathscr{E}^n$. As indicated in chapter 1, $\mathscr{E}^n$ may be thought of as the set of all n-component vectors $\boldsymbol{x}' = (x_1, \ldots, x_n)$.

2.2. Point-set theory

In what follows, our discussion will be restricted to sets of points within $\mathscr{E}^n$. First we state

DEFINITION 2.2. *A spherical δ-neighborhood about the point* $\boldsymbol{x}_0 \in \mathscr{E}^n$ *or hypersphere with center at* $\boldsymbol{x}_0$ *and radius* $\delta > 0$ *is the set of points* $\delta(\boldsymbol{x}_0) = \{\boldsymbol{x} \mid \|\boldsymbol{x} - \boldsymbol{x}_0\| < \delta\}$.

Here the distance between $\boldsymbol{x}_0$ and any other point $\boldsymbol{x}$ within the hypersphere is strictly less than δ, i.e. $[(\boldsymbol{x}-\boldsymbol{x}_0)'(\boldsymbol{x}-\boldsymbol{x}_0)]^{\frac{1}{2}} < \delta$.

For $\boldsymbol{x}_0 \in \mathscr{E}$, $\delta(\boldsymbol{x}_0)$ will simply be termed a *δ-neighborhood* of x_0 and written $\delta(x_0) = \{x \mid |x - x_0| < \delta\}$. In this instance the set of all x such that $|x - x_0| < \delta$ is the symmetric open interval $x_0 - \delta < x < x_0 + \delta$ of length 2δ (fig. 2.3a). At times we shall find it necessary to delete the point x_0 from $\delta(x_0)$. In this case we form what is called a *deleted δ-neighborhood* of x_0,

$$\delta_d(x_0) = \delta(x_0) - \{x_0\}.$$

Additionally, for $\boldsymbol{x}_0 \in \mathscr{E}^2$, we obtain a *circular δ-neighborhood* of $\boldsymbol{x}_0$,

$$\delta(\boldsymbol{x}_0) = \{\boldsymbol{x} \mid [(x_1 - x_1^0)^2 + (x_2 - x_2^0)^2]^{\frac{1}{2}} < \delta\}.$$

Here $\delta(\boldsymbol{x}_0)$ consists of the set of all points inside a circle with center $\boldsymbol{x}_0$ and radius δ (fig. 2.3b).

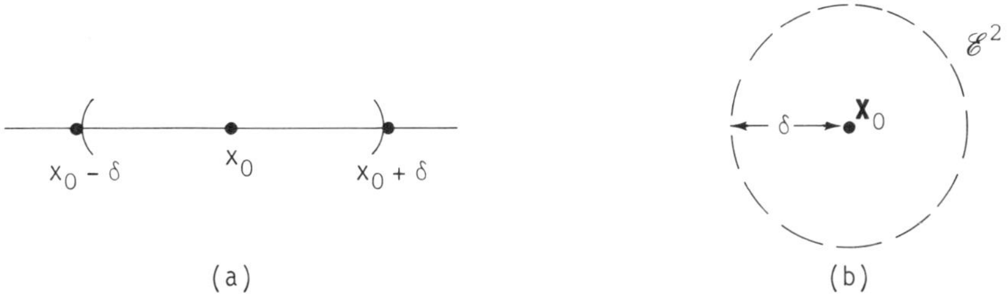

Fig. 2.3.

Our discussion now turns to the characterization of specific points within a non-empty set $\mathscr{S} \subseteq \mathscr{E}^n$. In this regard we have

DEFINITION 2.3. *A point* $\boldsymbol{x}_0 \in \mathscr{E}^n$ *is an interior point of a set* $\mathscr{S} \subseteq \mathscr{E}^n$ *if there exists a spherical δ-neighborhood about* $\boldsymbol{x}_0$, $\delta(\boldsymbol{x}_0)$, *which contains only points of* $\mathscr{S}$ (for $\boldsymbol{x}_0 \in \mathscr{E}^2$, see fig. 2.4).

Next

DEFINITION 2.4. *A point* $\bar{\boldsymbol{x}} \in \mathscr{E}^n$ *is a boundary point of a set* $\mathscr{S} \subseteq \mathscr{E}^n$ *if every spherical δ-neighborhood about* $\bar{\boldsymbol{x}}$, $\delta(\bar{\boldsymbol{x}})$, *encompasses points in* $\mathscr{S}$ *and in the complement of* $\mathscr{S}$, $\bar{\mathscr{S}}$ (fig. 2.4 depicts $\bar{\boldsymbol{x}} \in \mathscr{E}^2$).

It is important to remember that a boundary point of a set $\mathscr{S}$ need not be a member of that set. In the light of defs. 2.3 and 2.4 we have

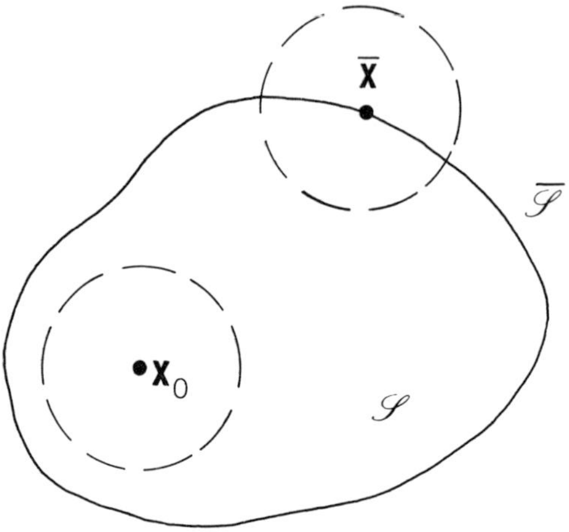

Fig. 2.4.

DEFINITION 2.5. *The interior of a set* $\mathscr{S} \subseteq \mathscr{E}^n$ *is the collection of all its interior points.*

DEFINITION 2.6. *The boundary of a set* $\mathscr{S} \subset \mathscr{E}^n$ *is the collection of all its boundary points.*

We now turn to the classification of special types of sets within $\mathscr{E}^n$, namely, those which may be regarded as open or closed.

DEFINITION 2.7. *A set* $\mathscr{S} \subseteq \mathscr{E}^n$ *is termed open if it contains only interior points.*

DEFINITION 2.8. *A set* $\mathscr{S} \subset \mathscr{E}^n$ *is closed if it contains all its boundary points.* We note briefly that if a set $\mathscr{S}$ is open, then its complement $\bar{\mathscr{S}}$ is closed and conversely.[2]

It is obvious that the boundary of a set $\mathscr{S}$ is itself a closed set while the interior of $\mathscr{S}$ is an open set. It is also evident that a spherical δ-neighborhood is an open set since strict inequality holds in def. 2.2, e.g. as fig. 2.3b indicates, $\delta(\boldsymbol{x}_0)$ includes only interior points; it does not contain any boundary points.

Next, we state

DEFINITION 2.9. *An open set* $\mathscr{S} \subseteq \mathscr{E}^n$ *is connected if any two points within the set* (such as $\boldsymbol{x}_1, \boldsymbol{x}_2 \in \mathscr{E}^2$ in fig. 2.5) *may be joined by a polygonal path (i.e. a broken line segment) lying entirely in* $\mathscr{S}$.

Hence, $\mathscr{S}$ is not connected if some of its elements are separated from others by $\bar{\mathscr{S}}$.

[2] For a proof of this statement see Simmons (1953), pp. 65–66.

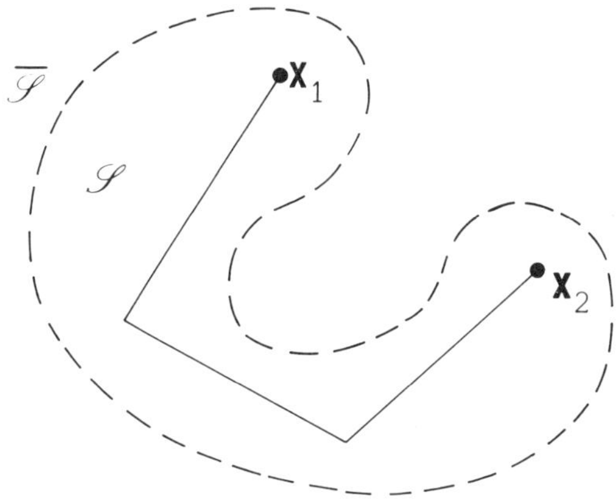

Fig. 2.5.

At times we shall find it convenient to employ

DEFINITION 2.10. *A region is either a connected set* $\mathscr{S} \subseteq \mathscr{E}^n$ *or such a set together with some or all of its boundary points.*

Frequently the sets or regions under consideration will be termed *bounded*. Thus we have

DEFINITION 2.11. *A set* $\mathscr{S} \subseteq \mathscr{E}^n$ *is bounded if and only if there exists a real number N such that for all points* $\boldsymbol{x} \in \mathscr{S}$, $\|\boldsymbol{x}\| \leqslant N$.

For $\boldsymbol{x} \in \mathscr{E}^2$, this definition implies that $\mathscr{S}$ is bounded if and only if one can find a rectangle, no matter how large, containing $\mathscr{S}$. That is to say, there exist real numbers a, b, c, and d such that, for all $\boldsymbol{x} \in \mathscr{S}$, $a \leqslant x_1 \leqslant b$, $c \leqslant x_2 \leqslant d$ or $\mathscr{S} \subset [a, b] \times [c, d]$ (fig. 2.6).

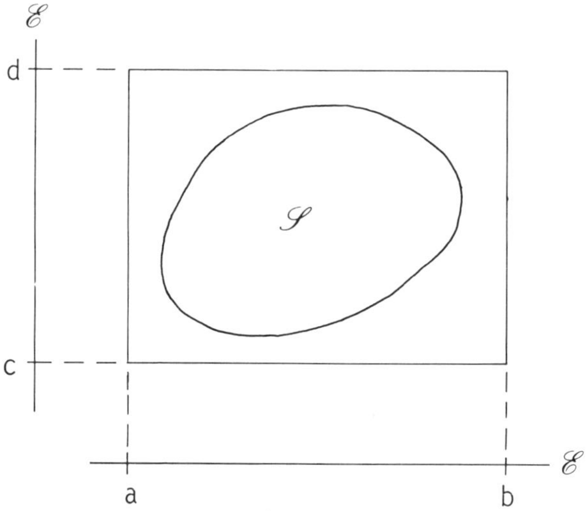

Fig. 2.6.

Since the notion of a bounded point set will, in part, be of considerable importance in our discussion of the existence of what will be termed *global extrema of real-valued functions*, a detailed analysis of the properties of such a set will now be advanced for $\boldsymbol{x} \in \mathscr{E}$. Thus we have

DEFINITION 2.12. *A set $\mathscr{S}$ of real numbers is said to be bounded from above if and only if there exists a number M such that, for every $x \in \mathscr{S}$, $x \leqslant M$. Here M is called an upper bound for $\mathscr{S}$.*

Similarly, we state

DEFINITION 2.13. *A set $\mathscr{S}$ of real numbers is said to be bounded from below if and only if there exists a number m such that, for every $x \in \mathscr{S}$, $m \leqslant x$. In this case m is said to be a lower bound for $\mathscr{S}$.*

Next, we state

DEFINITION 2.14. *A set $\mathscr{S}$ which is bounded both from above and below is bounded.*

Hence, a set is termed *unbounded* either because it fails to possess an upper or a lower bound or because it possesses neither an upper nor a lower bound.

Upper and lower bounds are not unique. That is, if M is an upper bound for $\mathscr{S}$ and $M' > M$, then M' is also an upper bound for $\mathscr{S}$; and if m is a lower bound for $\mathscr{S}$ and $m' < m$, then m' is also a lower bound for $\mathscr{S}$. In addition, an upper or lower bound for a set $\mathscr{S}$ may or may not be a member of $\mathscr{S}$. For example, if $\mathscr{S} = \{x | a \leqslant x \leqslant b\}$, then a and b are respectively lower and upper bounds for $\mathscr{S}$. Here, both $a, b \in \mathscr{S}$. Furthermore, if $\mathscr{S} = \{x | a < x < b\}$, then a and b are again respectively lower and upper bounds for $\mathscr{S}$, but now $a, b \notin \mathscr{S}$. Note that in both of these examples any number less than a is also deemed a lower bound for $\mathscr{S}$, while any number greater than b is likewise considered to be an upper bound for $\mathscr{S}$. Additionally, while the sets:

$$\mathscr{S}_1 = \{x | -\infty < x \leqslant b\}; \qquad \mathscr{S}_2 = \{x | a \leqslant x < +\infty\};$$

and

$$\mathscr{S}_3 = \{x | -\infty < x < +\infty\}$$

are all unbounded, $\mathscr{S}_1$ is bounded above, while $\mathscr{S}_2$ is bounded below.

At this point we may now ask the following question. Is there any straightforward criterion which may be directly applied to the elements of a set $\mathscr{S}$ to determine whether or not it is bounded? Our answer is provided by

THEOREM 2.1 *A set $\mathscr{S}$ of real numbers is bounded if and only if there exists a real number $N>0$ such that, for every $x \in \mathscr{S}$, $|x| \leqslant N$.*

Proof (necessity). If $\mathscr{S}$ is bounded, then it is bounded both from above and below. Define N', N'' to be lower and upper bounds for $\mathscr{S}$ respectively, i.e. $N' \leqslant x \leqslant N''$ for all $x \in \mathscr{S}$. Now, if $N = \max\{|N'|, |N''|\}$, i.e. the larger the value of $|N'|, |N''|$, then clearly $-N \leqslant N' \leqslant x \leqslant N'' \leqslant N$ or $|x| \leqslant N$ for all $x \in \mathscr{S}$. (Sufficiency.) If $|x| \leqslant N$ for all $x \in \mathscr{S}$, then $-N \leqslant x \leqslant N$. Since $-N$ is a lower bound and N is an upper bound for $\mathscr{S}$, then clearly $\mathscr{S}$ is bounded.

Let us now address ourselves to the following questions. Of all the upper bounds for a set $\mathscr{S}$, can we find one which is smaller than any other upper bound for $\mathscr{S}$? Similarly, of all the lower bounds for a set $\mathscr{S}$, is there one which is larger than any other lower bound for $\mathscr{S}$? That is, we seek to determine the *least upper bound* (supremum) and *greatest lower bound* (infimum) of $\mathscr{S}$.[3] Before answering these questions, let us specify the qualifications that sup $\mathscr{S}$ and inf $\mathscr{S}$ must possess.

DEFINITION 2.15. *L is a supremum for a set $\mathscr{S}$ if and only if:*

(a) L is an upper bound for $\mathscr{S}$;

(b) no number less than L is an upper bound for $\mathscr{S}$.

Also,

DEFINITION 2.16. *l is an infimum for $\mathscr{S}$ if and only if:*

(a) l is a lower bound for $\mathscr{S}$;

(b) no number greater than l is a lower bound for $\mathscr{S}$.

In this regard, the answer to the above questions concerning the existence of a supremum and infimum of $\mathscr{S}$ is provided by the

COMPLETENESS AXIOM. *If $\mathscr{S}$ is a bounded non-empty set of real numbers, then there exist real numbers l, L such that*

$$l = \inf \mathscr{S} \leqslant L = \sup \mathscr{S}.$$

That is to say, every non-empty set of real numbers which has an upper bound has a supremum; and every non-empty set of real numbers which has a lower bound has an infimum.

For any bounded set $\mathscr{S}$, there is at most one supremum and one infimum, i.e. sup $\mathscr{S}$ and inf $\mathscr{S}$ are unique. For instance, if both L, L' are defined as suprema for $\mathscr{S}$, then clearly these elements are also upper bounds for $\mathscr{S}$. Hence, part (*a*) of the definition of sup $\mathscr{S}$ is satisfied. From part (*b*), no number less than L, and thus less than L', is an upper bound for $\mathscr{S}$, i.e. this condition implies that $L \leqslant L'$ and $L' \leqslant L$. But if these inequalities are

[3] Henceforth, the supremum and infimum of $\mathscr{S}$ will appear respectively as sup $\mathscr{S}$ and inf $\mathscr{S}$.

to hold simultaneously, then it must be the case that $L = L'$. A similar argument holds for the uniqueness of the infimum of $\mathscr{S}$. Furthermore, the supremum and infimum of a bounded set $\mathscr{S}$ may or may not be members of that set. For instance, if $\mathscr{S} = \{x | a \leqslant x \leqslant b\}$, then a and b are respectively the infimum and supremum of $\mathscr{S}$. In addition, both a and b are contained in $\mathscr{S}$. Also, if $\mathscr{S} = \{x | a < x < b\}$, then a and b are still respectively the infimum and supremum of $\mathscr{S}$ even though they are not members of $\mathscr{S}$. Additionally, for sets $\mathscr{S}_1$, $\mathscr{S}_2$, and $\mathscr{S}_3$ defined above, $\mathscr{S}_1$ contains b as a supremum; $\mathscr{S}_2$ contains a as an infimum; while $\mathscr{S}_3$ possesses neither an infimum nor a supremum.

We shall now consider the circumstances under which a set may possess extreme elements. Let $\mathscr{S}$ be a bounded non-empty set of real numbers. Hence, $L = \sup \mathscr{S}$ and $l = \inf \mathscr{S}$ both exist. If $L \in \mathscr{S}$, then $\mathscr{S}$ is said to have a *greatest element*, namely, L; while if $l \in \mathscr{S}$, $\mathscr{S}$ possesses l as its *least element*. A δ-neighborhood of the point x_0, $x_0 - \delta < x < x_0 + \delta$, is a bounded set of points with a supremum $(x_0 + \delta)$ and an infimum $(x_0 - \delta)$. However, it possesses neither a least nor a greatest element. Moreover, any open interval (not necessarily a δ-neighborhood) is a bounded set of points $\{x | a < x < b\}$ which does not have a least or greatest element, yet possesses a supremum (b) and an infimum (a). Finally, a closed interval $\{x | a \leqslant x \leqslant b\}$ is a bounded set of points such that its supremum (b) is its greatest element while its infimum (a) is its least element. Such an interval is said to be *compact*. This notion is generalized by

DEFINITION 2.17. *A set $\mathscr{S} \subset \mathscr{E}^n$ is compact if it is closed and bounded.*

Such sets possess the property that for any point $\mathbf{x} \in \mathscr{S}$, every spherical δ-neighborhood about $\mathbf{x}$ contains other points of $\mathscr{S}$. Hence there are no gaps or holes in the set.

2.3. Real-valued functions

DEFINITION 2.18. *Let* f *be a rule or law of correspondence that associates with each vector or point $\mathbf{x} \in \mathscr{X} \subseteq \mathscr{E}^n$ a unique element $y \in \mathscr{Y} \subseteq \mathscr{E}$. That is,* f *is a mapping from $\mathscr{X}$ to $\mathscr{Y}$ (indicated as $\mathscr{X} \xrightarrow{f} \mathscr{Y}$), where y is the image of $\mathbf{x}$ under the rule* f. *To illustrate the dependence of the real number y on the point $\mathbf{x}$ we shall say that y is a real-valued function of $\mathbf{x}$ and write $y = \mathrm{f}(\mathbf{x})$ as a representation of this correspondence. Here $\mathbf{x}$ is a vector of independent variables x_i, $i = 1, \ldots, n$, and y is the dependent variable.*

Generally speaking, $\mathscr{E}^n$, $\mathscr{E}$ will be respectively termed the *domain space* and *range space* of f. Additionally, the set of elements $\mathscr{X}$ will be called the *domain* (of definition) of f, $\mathscr{D}_\mathrm{f}$, while the set of values in $\mathscr{Y}$ that the function assumes will be termed its *range* $\mathscr{R}_f(=\bigcup_i f(\boldsymbol{x}_i))$. In general, $\mathscr{R}_f \subseteq \mathscr{Y}$. If $\mathscr{R}_f \subset \mathscr{Y}$, then f is said to be a mapping of $\mathscr{X}$ *into* $\mathscr{Y}$. If any two different elements of $\mathscr{X}$ have different images under f (or alternatively, if $f(\boldsymbol{x}_1) = f(\boldsymbol{x}_2)$ implies $\boldsymbol{x}_1 = \boldsymbol{x}_2$, $\boldsymbol{x}_1, \boldsymbol{x}_2 \in \mathscr{X}$), then f is said to be a *one-to-one* mapping of $\mathscr{X}$ into $\mathscr{Y}$. If $\mathscr{R}_f = \mathscr{Y}$, f is a mapping of $\mathscr{X}$ *onto* $\mathscr{Y}$. It is evident that an onto mapping may also be classified as one-to-one if $f(\boldsymbol{x}_1) = f(\boldsymbol{x}_2)$ implies $\boldsymbol{x}_1 = \boldsymbol{x}_2$, $\boldsymbol{x}_1, \boldsymbol{x}_2 \in \mathscr{X}$.

Let us now look to the notion of the graph of a real-valued function $y = f(\boldsymbol{x})$. In this regard, we have

DEFINITION 2.19. *If $\mathscr{X} \xrightarrow{f} \mathscr{Y}$ is a mapping with domain $\mathscr{D}_f = \mathscr{X} \subseteq \mathscr{E}^n$ and range $\mathscr{R}_f \subseteq \mathscr{Y} \subseteq \mathscr{E}$, then its graph is that subset $\mathscr{G}$ of $\mathscr{E}^{n+1}$ which consists of all ordered pairs $(\boldsymbol{x}, f(\boldsymbol{x}))$.*

For $\boldsymbol{x} \in \mathscr{E}$, $\mathscr{G}$ may be depicted as a curve in $\mathscr{E}^2$ extending from g to g' (fig. 2.7).

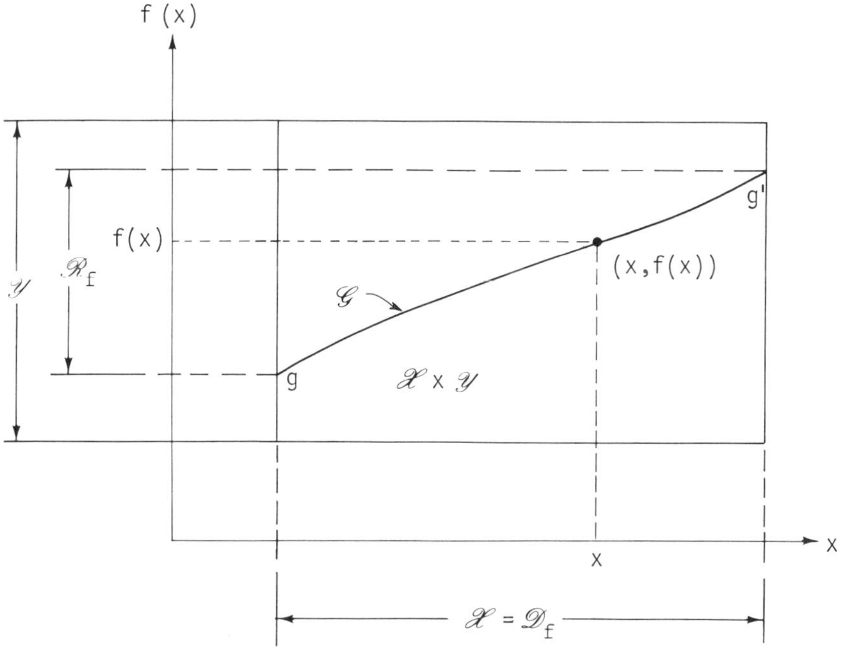

Fig. 2.7.

2.4. Continuous real-valued functions

Let the real-valued function $y = f(\boldsymbol{x})$, $\boldsymbol{x} \in \mathscr{E}^n$, have as its domain a region $\mathscr{K} \subset \mathscr{E}^n$. Additionally, let $\boldsymbol{x}_0$ be a point interior to $\mathscr{K}$ or on its boundary.

We shall assume that when $\boldsymbol{x}$ approaches a fixed point $\boldsymbol{x}_0 \in \mathscr{K}$, along any path whatever (if $\boldsymbol{x}_0$ is a boundary point of $\mathscr{K}$, $\boldsymbol{x}$ must remain in $\mathscr{K}$), f correspondingly tends towards some real number $\mathscr{A} \in \mathscr{R}_{\mathrm{f}}$, i.e.

$$\lim_{\boldsymbol{x} \to \boldsymbol{x}_0} \mathrm{f}(\boldsymbol{x}) = A.$$

Now if A equals $\mathrm{f}(\boldsymbol{x}_0)$, f is said to be continuous at $\boldsymbol{x}_0$. In this case we now state

DEFINITION 2.20. *The real-valued function* $y = \mathrm{f}(\boldsymbol{x})$, $\boldsymbol{x} \in \mathscr{E}^n$, *is continuous at* $\boldsymbol{x}_0$ *if*[4]

$$\lim_{\boldsymbol{x} \to \boldsymbol{x}_0} \mathrm{f}(\boldsymbol{x}) = \mathrm{f}(\boldsymbol{x}_0). \tag{2.1}$$

As an important special case of eq. (2.1), let us consider the instance where $\boldsymbol{x} \in \mathscr{E}$. Specifically, if $\mathscr{D}_{\mathrm{f}} = [a, b]$, then f is continuous at $x_0 \in (a, b)$ if

$$\lim_{x \to x_0 -} \mathrm{f}(x) = \lim_{x \to x_0 +} \mathrm{f}(x) = \lim_{x \to x_0} \mathrm{f}(x) = \mathrm{f}(x_0).$$

Here both the left- and right-hand limits of f exist and their common value is $\mathrm{f}(x_0)$. It now remains to define the continuity of f at the endpoints of its domain. Since $[a, b]$ is a closed set, neither

$$\lim_{x \to a -} \mathrm{f}(x) \quad \text{nor} \quad \lim_{x \to a +} \mathrm{f}(x)$$

exists. Hence, continuity at a and b is indicated, respectively, by the one-sided limits

$$\lim_{x \to a +} \mathrm{f}(x) = \mathrm{f}(a), \qquad \lim_{x \to b -} \mathrm{f}(x) = \mathrm{f}(b).$$

Example 2.1. Let the real-valued function $y = \mathrm{f}(x) = x^2 + 1$ be defined everywhere on the interval (0, 4). Is f continuous at $x = 2$? Now f(2) = 5 (point A of fig. 2.9). Applying eq. (2.1) we have

$$\lim_{x \to 2} (x^2 + 1) = 5 = \mathrm{f}(2)$$

Hence, f is continuous at $x = 2$.

From the above discussion it is evident that the notion of continuity is a 'local' property of a function. To see this we need only consider the interpretation of eq. (2.1). Quite generally, f is continuous at $\boldsymbol{x}_0 \in \mathscr{E}^n$ if when

[4] For $\lim_{\boldsymbol{x} \to \boldsymbol{x}_0} \mathrm{f}(\boldsymbol{x}) = A$ to exist, f need not be defined at $\boldsymbol{x}_0$. All that is required is that when $\boldsymbol{x}$ is near $\boldsymbol{x}_0$, $\mathrm{f}(\boldsymbol{x})$ is near A. But if f is continuous at $\boldsymbol{x}_0$, so that $A = \mathrm{f}(\boldsymbol{x}_0)$, then obviously f must be defined there also.

$\boldsymbol{x}$ is 'near' $\boldsymbol{x}_0$, $f(\boldsymbol{x})$ is 'near' $f(\boldsymbol{x}_0)$. For example, when $\boldsymbol{x}$ is contained within a spherical δ-neighborhood about $\boldsymbol{x}_0$, $f(\boldsymbol{x})$ belongs to an ε-neighborhood about $f(\boldsymbol{x}_0)$. More specifically,

DEFINITION 2.21. *The real-valued function* $y = f(\boldsymbol{x})$, $\boldsymbol{x} \in \mathscr{E}^n$, *is continuous at* $\boldsymbol{x}_0$ *if and only if to each* $\varepsilon > 0$ *there corresponds a* $\delta > 0$ *such that*

$$|f(\boldsymbol{x}) - f(\boldsymbol{x}_0)| < \varepsilon \quad \textit{whenever} \quad \|\boldsymbol{x} - \boldsymbol{x}_0\| < \delta. \tag{2.2}$$

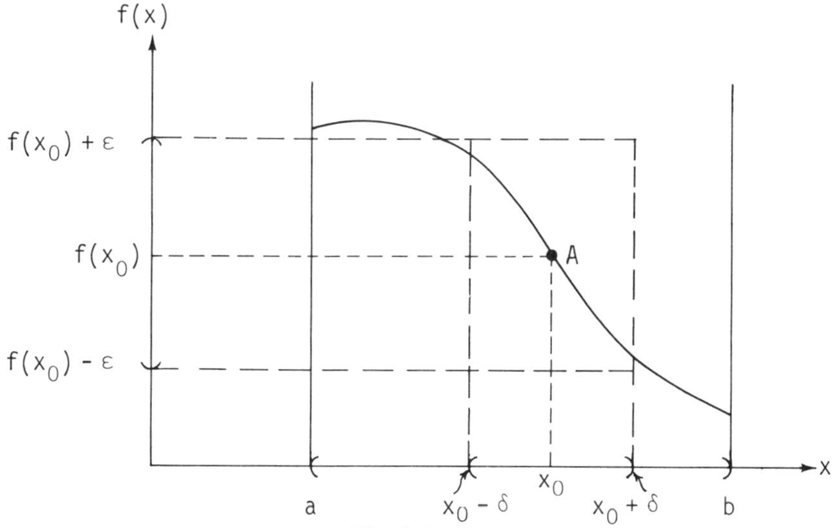

Fig. 2.8.

For $\boldsymbol{x} \in \mathscr{E}$ (fig. 2.8), f is continuous at x_0 if and only if to each $\varepsilon > 0$ there corresponds a $\delta > 0$ such that

$$f(x_0) - \varepsilon < f(x) < f(x_0) + \varepsilon \quad \text{when} \quad x_0 - \delta < x < x_0 + \delta. \tag{2.2.1}$$

That is, corresponding to any preassigned value of ε there exists an open interval (of length 2δ) about x_0, $\delta(x_0)$, such that, for $x \in (x_0 - \delta,\ x_0 + \delta)$, $f(x)$ is restricted to lie within the open interval $(f(x_0) - \varepsilon,\ f(x_0) + \varepsilon)$). And as ε is made smaller and smaller, δ must also be made smaller so that as $x \to x_0$, $f(x) \to f(x_0)$ as a limit.

We note briefly that a function is continuous over a region $\mathscr{K} \subseteq \mathscr{E}^n$ if it is continuous at every point of $\mathscr{K}$.

Example 2.2. Show that $\lim_{x \to 2} (x^2 + 1) = 5$ using an ε-, δ-argument. That is, from eq. (2.2.1), given an $\varepsilon > 0$, we seek to determine a $\delta > 0$ such that

$$|f(x) - 5| < \varepsilon \quad \text{when} \quad |x - 2| < \delta.$$

Let us restrict our discussion to those values of x for which $|x-2|<1$ or $1<x<3$ (fig. 2.9). Now $f(x)-5 = x^2-4 = (x+2)(x-2)$. In addition, $3<x+2<5$ (since $1<x<3$) so that $|f(x)-5| = |(x+2)(x-2)|<5|x-2|$. Hence, $|f(x)-5|<\varepsilon$ provided $5|x-2|<\varepsilon$ or $|x-2|<\varepsilon/5$. Thus, our required δ is simultaneously $\leqslant 1$ (from our above restriction) and $\leqslant \varepsilon/5$.

For instance, if we take $\varepsilon = 3$, $\delta = \frac{3}{5}$ and thus $f(2)-\varepsilon = 2<f(x)<8 = f(2)+\varepsilon$ when $2-\delta = \frac{7}{5}<x<\frac{13}{5} = 2+\delta$ (fig. 2.9). And as ε becomes smaller and smaller, $\delta = \varepsilon/5$ correspondingly decreases so that as

$$x\to 2(x\in(2-\delta,\ 2+\delta)), \qquad f(x)\to 5(f(x)\in(5-\varepsilon,\ 5+\varepsilon)).$$

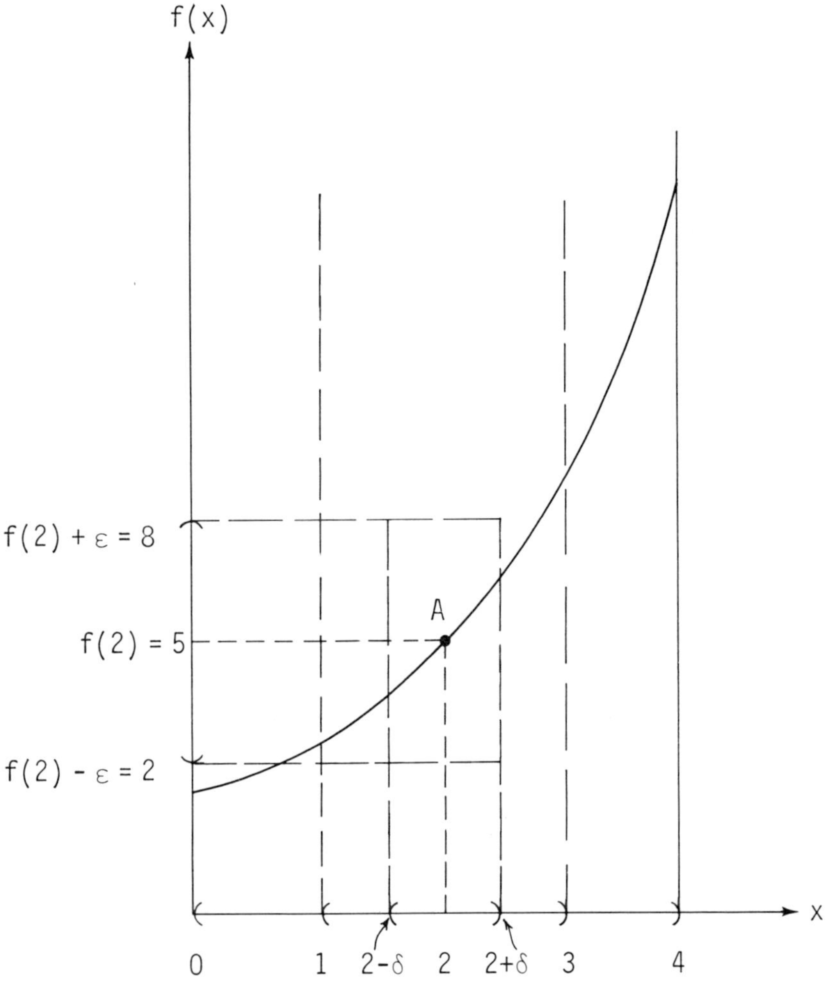

Fig. 2.9.

Example 2.3. Let the real-valued function $y = \mathrm{f}(\boldsymbol{x}) = 2x_1 + x_2$ be defined throughout the entirety of $\mathscr{E}^2$. Demonstrate that f is continuous at the point $\boldsymbol{x}_0' = (0, 0)$ using the ε-, δ-argument of def. 2.21. In this case, from eq. (2.2), given an $\varepsilon > 0$ we must determine a $\delta > 0$ such that $|\mathrm{f}(\boldsymbol{x}) - \mathrm{f}(\boldsymbol{x}_0)| < \varepsilon$ when $[(x_1 - 0)^2 + (x_2 - 0)^2]^{\frac{1}{2}} = (x_1^2 + x_2^2)^{\frac{1}{2}} < \delta$. Now

$$\begin{aligned}|(2x_1 + x_2) - 0| &\leqslant 2|x_1| + |x_2| \leqslant 2(x_1^2 + x_2^2)^{\frac{1}{2}} + (x_1^2 + x_2^2)^{\frac{1}{2}} \\ &= 3(x_1^2 + x_2^2)^{\frac{1}{2}}.\end{aligned}$$[5]

Then

$$|2x_1 + x_2| < \varepsilon \quad \text{if} \quad 3(x_1^2 + x_2^2)^{\frac{1}{2}} < \varepsilon \quad \text{or} \quad (x_1^2 + x_2^2)^{\frac{1}{2}} < \varepsilon/3.$$

Hence, the required δ is $\leqslant \varepsilon/3$.

Under what conditions may a real-valued function $y = \mathrm{f}(\boldsymbol{x})$, $\boldsymbol{x} \in \mathscr{E}^n$, fail to be continuous at a point interior to its domain? Obviously f will be discontinuous at $\boldsymbol{x}_0$ if it is not defined there. If $\mathrm{f}(\boldsymbol{x}_0)$ is defined, then f will be discontinuous at $\boldsymbol{x}_0$ if $\lim_{\boldsymbol{x} \to \boldsymbol{x}_0} \mathrm{f}(\boldsymbol{x})$ does not exist or, if it does exist, if $\lim_{\boldsymbol{x} \to \boldsymbol{x}_0} \mathrm{f}(\boldsymbol{x}) \neq \mathrm{f}(\boldsymbol{x}_0)$. As far as the types of discontinuities are concerned, we shall recognize those that are either *removable, essential, infinite*, or *ordinary*.

If f is defined at $\boldsymbol{x}_0$ and $\lim_{\boldsymbol{x} \to \boldsymbol{x}_0} \mathrm{f}(\boldsymbol{x})$ exists but $\lim_{\boldsymbol{x} \to \boldsymbol{x}_0} \mathrm{f}(\boldsymbol{x}) \neq \mathrm{f}(\boldsymbol{x}_0)$, then the point of discontinuity $\boldsymbol{x}_0$ may be 'removed' by redefining f at $\boldsymbol{x}_0$, i.e. if we can find a point $\bar{\boldsymbol{x}}$ such that $\lim_{\boldsymbol{x} \to \boldsymbol{x}_0} \mathrm{f}(\boldsymbol{x}) = \bar{\boldsymbol{x}}$, then f has a removable discontinuity at $\boldsymbol{x}_0$. Moreover, if $\mathrm{f}(\boldsymbol{x}_0)$ is undefined but $\lim_{\boldsymbol{x} \to \boldsymbol{x}_0} \mathrm{f}(\boldsymbol{x})$ exists, then we may redefine f at $\boldsymbol{x}_0$ as $\lim_{\boldsymbol{x} \to \boldsymbol{x}_0} \mathrm{f}(\boldsymbol{x})$ so that now $\boldsymbol{x}_0 \in \mathscr{D}_{\mathrm{f}}$. In this case, too, the point of discontinuity is removable. When $\lim_{\boldsymbol{x} \to \boldsymbol{x}_0} \mathrm{f}(\boldsymbol{x})$ is non-existent, no redefinition of f at $\boldsymbol{x}_0$ can make it continuous there. In this instance $\boldsymbol{x}_0$ is said to be an essential point of discontinuity of f. Additionally, if f is discontinuous at $\boldsymbol{x}_0$, then f is said to possess an infinite discontinuity at $\boldsymbol{x}_0$ if, for $\boldsymbol{x} \in \delta(\boldsymbol{x}_0)$, $|\mathrm{f}(\boldsymbol{x})| \to \infty$ as $\boldsymbol{x} \to \boldsymbol{x}_0$, i.e. when $\boldsymbol{x}$ is near $\boldsymbol{x}_0$, f assumes an arbitrarily large value. Finally, f has an ordinary (finite) discontinuity at $\boldsymbol{x}_0$ if it is discontinuous there, and for $\boldsymbol{x} \in \delta(\boldsymbol{x}_0)$, $|\mathrm{f}(\boldsymbol{x})| \leqslant N$, i.e. f is bounded (see def. 4.1) in the immediate vicinity of $\boldsymbol{x}_0$.[6]

2.5. Vector differential calculus

We now look to the definition of a special type of n-component vector, namely, the gradient of a real-valued function. As will be explained shortly,

---

[5] For a discussion on this and other inequalities used in handling problems of this sort see Taylor (1955), pp. 139–140.

[6] An elaboration on these classifications for $x \in \mathscr{E}$ is provided by Apostol (1964), pp. 76–77.

the gradient is a special type of vector-valued function. To see this we state first

DEFINITION 2.22. *A vector-valued function* $\mathbf{F}(\boldsymbol{x})$, $\boldsymbol{x} \in \mathscr{E}^n$, *whose elements are the real-valued functions* $\mathrm{f}^1(\boldsymbol{x})$, $\mathrm{f}^2(\boldsymbol{x})$, ..., $\mathrm{f}^m(\boldsymbol{x})$ *is the m-component vector*

$$\mathbf{F}(\boldsymbol{x}) = \begin{bmatrix} \mathrm{f}^1(\boldsymbol{x}) \\ \mathrm{f}^2(\boldsymbol{x}) \\ \vdots \\ \mathrm{f}^m(\boldsymbol{x}) \end{bmatrix}.$$

In this light, we state

DEFINITION 2.23. *Let* $y = \mathrm{f}(\boldsymbol{x})$, $\boldsymbol{x} \in \mathscr{E}^n$, *be a real-valued function whose first partial derivatives exist over an open region* $\mathscr{K} \subseteq \mathscr{E}^n$. *The gradient of* f, $\nabla \mathrm{f}$ *(read 'del* f*'), is a vector-valued function whose elements are the first partial derivatives of* f, *i.e. the gradient of* f *is the n-component vector*

$$\nabla \mathrm{f} = \frac{\partial \mathrm{f}}{\partial \boldsymbol{x}} = \begin{bmatrix} \mathrm{f}_1(\boldsymbol{x}) \\ \mathrm{f}_2(\boldsymbol{x}) \\ \vdots \\ \mathrm{f}_n(\boldsymbol{x}) \end{bmatrix}. \tag{2.3}$$

Example 2.4. Find the gradient of the real-valued function

$$y = \mathrm{f}(\boldsymbol{x}) = 3x_1^2 + x_1 x_2 + x_2^2 \quad \text{at} \quad \boldsymbol{x}_0' = (1, 2).$$

From eq. (2.3) we have

$$\nabla \mathrm{f} = \begin{bmatrix} 6x_1 + x_2 \\ x_1 + 2x_2 \end{bmatrix}.$$

Then

$$\nabla \mathrm{f}^0 = \begin{bmatrix} 8 \\ 5 \end{bmatrix}.$$

In what context does the gradient vector arise? To answer this question let us consider the concept of the directional derivative of f in a given direction. That is, let us determine

$$\frac{\mathrm{df}}{\mathrm{d}s} = \lim_{\Delta s \to 0} \frac{\Delta \mathrm{f}}{\Delta s},$$

where Δs depicts the distance traveled in a specified direction. To set the stage for our discussion we must first determine how we are to interpret the phrase 'a given direction'.

Let $\boldsymbol{x}_0$ be a fixed point within $\mathscr{E}^n$. In general, any vector $\boldsymbol{x}_1$ may serve as a direction, i.e. for $0 < t < +\infty$, $\boldsymbol{x} = \boldsymbol{x}_0 + t\boldsymbol{x}_1$ describes a ray emanating from $\boldsymbol{x}_0$ in the $\boldsymbol{x}_1$ direction. So as we vary the parameter t, we move along a line through $\boldsymbol{x}_0$.

Additionally, let $y = \mathrm{f}(\boldsymbol{x})$, $\boldsymbol{x} \in \mathscr{E}^n$, be differentiable throughout an open region $\mathscr{K} \subset \mathscr{E}^n$ and, given $\boldsymbol{x}_0 \in \mathscr{E}^n$, let $\mathrm{f}^0 = \mathrm{f}(\boldsymbol{x}_0)$. A displacement from $\boldsymbol{x}_0$ in the $\boldsymbol{x}_1$-direction, $t\boldsymbol{x}_1$, produces: (1) increments Δx_i which are proportional to the components of $\boldsymbol{x}_1$, i.e. $\Delta x_i = t x_i^1$; and (2) a corresponding change in f from f^0, namely $\Delta \mathrm{f} = \mathrm{f}(\boldsymbol{x}_0 + t\boldsymbol{x}_1) - \mathrm{f}(\boldsymbol{x}_0)$, where the distance traversed in the $\boldsymbol{x}_1$-direction is $\|t\boldsymbol{x}_1\| = t\|\boldsymbol{x}_1\| = \Delta s$. Now $\Delta \mathrm{f}$ may be thought of as the linear approximation to f at $\boldsymbol{x}_1$, and may be written as

$$\begin{aligned}\Delta \mathrm{f} &= \mathrm{f}(\boldsymbol{x}_0 + t\boldsymbol{x}_1) - \mathrm{f}(\boldsymbol{x}_0)\\ &= \mathrm{df} + \text{error}\\ &= \mathrm{f}_1 \Delta x_1 + \mathrm{f}_2 \Delta x_2 + \ldots + \mathrm{f}_n \Delta x_n + \text{error}\\ &= \mathrm{f}_1 t x_1^1 + \mathrm{f}_2 t x_2^1 + \ldots + \mathrm{f}_n t x_n^1 + o(t\|\boldsymbol{x}_1\|),\end{aligned}$$

where the error component $o(t\|\boldsymbol{x}_1\|)$ consists of terms of degree higher than one and

$$\lim_{t \to 0} \left| \frac{o(t\|\boldsymbol{x}_1\|)}{t\|\boldsymbol{x}_1\|} \right| = 0.$$

Then

$$\begin{aligned}\frac{\Delta \mathrm{f}}{\Delta s} &= \frac{\mathrm{f}(\boldsymbol{x}_0 + t\boldsymbol{x}_1) - \mathrm{f}(\boldsymbol{x}_0)}{t\|\boldsymbol{x}_1\|}\\ &= \mathrm{f}_1 \frac{x_1^1}{\|\boldsymbol{x}_1\|} + \mathrm{f}_2 \frac{x_2^1}{\|\boldsymbol{x}_1\|} + \cdots + \mathrm{f}_n \frac{x_n^1}{\|\boldsymbol{x}_1\|} + \frac{o(t\|\boldsymbol{x}_1\|)}{t\|\boldsymbol{x}_1\|},\end{aligned}$$

$$\lim_{\Delta s \to 0} \frac{\Delta \mathrm{f}}{\Delta s} = \lim_{t \to 0} \frac{\mathrm{f}(\boldsymbol{x}_0 + t\boldsymbol{x}_1) - \mathrm{f}(\boldsymbol{x}_0)}{t\|\boldsymbol{x}_1\|} = (\nabla \mathrm{f}^0) \cdot \boldsymbol{u},$$

where $\boldsymbol{u}$ is a unit vector in the direction of $\boldsymbol{x}_1$ whose ith component is $x_i^1/\|\boldsymbol{x}_1\|$. Hence the directional derivative df/ds, the instantaneous rate of change of f at $\boldsymbol{x}_0$ measured in units of change of f per unit distance in the $\boldsymbol{x}_1$-direction, may be written as the scalar product of the gradient of f at $\boldsymbol{x}_0$ and a unit vector specifying direction.

In what follows we shall denote the directional derivative of f at $\boldsymbol{x}_0$ in the $\boldsymbol{x}_1$-direction as $D_{\boldsymbol{x}_1}\mathrm{f}^0 = (\nabla \mathrm{f}^0)'\boldsymbol{u}$. $\boldsymbol{x}_1$ is usually taken to be a unit vector. In the light of this convention we may formalize the above discussion as

Definition 2.24. *Let the real-valued function* $y = \mathrm{f}(\boldsymbol{x})$, $\boldsymbol{x} \in \mathscr{E}^n$, *be differentiable throughout an open region* $\mathscr{K} \subseteq \mathscr{E}^n$. *The directional derivative of* f *at* $\boldsymbol{x}_0$ *in the direction* $\boldsymbol{x}_1 \neq \mathbf{0}$, $\|\boldsymbol{x}_1\| = 1$, *is*

$$D_{\boldsymbol{x}_1}\mathrm{f}^0 = \lim_{t \to 0} \frac{\mathrm{f}(\boldsymbol{x}_0 + t\boldsymbol{x}_1) - \mathrm{f}(\boldsymbol{x}_0)}{t} = (\nabla \mathrm{f}^0)'\boldsymbol{x}_1.$$ [7]

Let us now consider some important properties of the gradient vector. From eq. (1.3),

$$D_{\boldsymbol{x}_1}f = (\nabla f)'\boldsymbol{x}_1 = \|\nabla f\|\,\|\boldsymbol{x}_1\|\cos\theta = \|\nabla f\|\cos\theta = \text{comp}_{\boldsymbol{x}_1}\nabla f,$$

i.e. the directional derivative is the scalar projection of ∇f onto $\boldsymbol{x}_1$ (see fig. 2.10 for $\boldsymbol{x}_0 \in \mathscr{E}^3$).

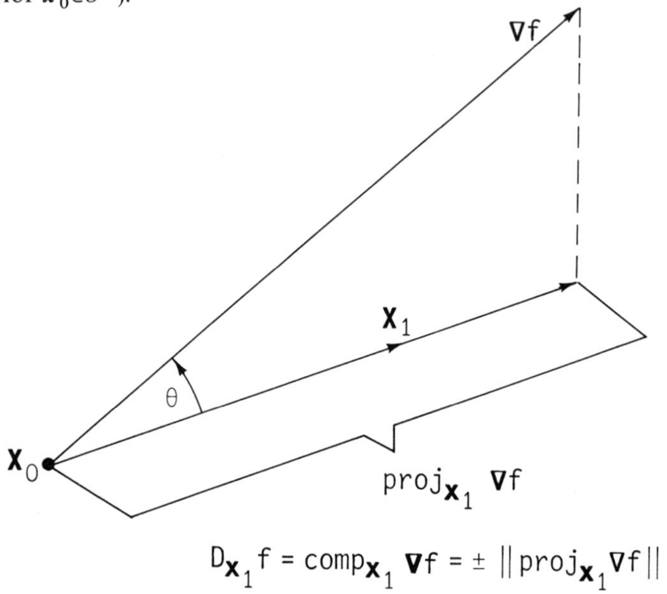

Fig. 2.10.

If $\cos\theta = 1(\theta = 0^0)$ so that

$$\boldsymbol{x}_1 = \frac{\nabla f}{\|\nabla f\|}, \qquad D_{\boldsymbol{x}_1}f = \|\nabla f\|$$

and the directional derivative attains its maximum in the direction of the gradient (by virtue of the Cauchy–Schwarz inequality, that is, $|D_{\boldsymbol{x}_1}f| \leqslant \|\nabla f\|\,\|\boldsymbol{x}_1\| = \|\nabla f\|$). Hence the gradient $\nabla f \neq \mathbf{0}$ is a vector: (1) which points locally in the direction of maximum increase of f ($-\nabla f$ points locally in the direction of maximum decrease of f); (2) whose magnitude $\|\nabla f\|$ is the maximum rate of increase of f in the ∇f-direction, i.e. the maximum value of $D_{x_1}f$; and (3) which is normal to the *contour surface* $f(\boldsymbol{x}_0) = \text{constant} = f^0$, $\boldsymbol{x}_0 \in \mathscr{E}^n$. That is to say, if $\boldsymbol{x}_1$ is tangential

[7] What is the connection between the directional derivative of f, $D_{\boldsymbol{x}_1}f$, and the ordinary partial derivative of f, f_i, $i = 1, \ldots, n$? When $\boldsymbol{x}_1 = \boldsymbol{e}_i(\|\boldsymbol{x}_1\| = \|\boldsymbol{e}_i\| = 1)$, $D_{\boldsymbol{e}_i}f = (\nabla f)'\boldsymbol{e}_i = f_i$, $i = 1, \ldots, n$. Here $\boldsymbol{e}_i$ is an $(n \times 1)$ *unit column vector*, i.e. a vector with one as its ith component and zeros elsewhere.

to $f(\boldsymbol{x}_0) = f^0$ at $\boldsymbol{x}_0$, the directional derivative of f at $\boldsymbol{x}_0$ in the direction $\boldsymbol{x}_1$ is

$$D_{\boldsymbol{x}_1} f^0 = \lim_{t \to 0} \frac{f(\boldsymbol{x}_0 + t\boldsymbol{x}_1) - f(\boldsymbol{x}_0)}{t} = \lim_{t \to 0} \frac{0}{t} = 0.$$

Now if $\nabla f^0 \neq \mathbf{0}$, $D_{\boldsymbol{x}_1} f^0 = \|\nabla f^0\| \cos\theta = 0$ only if $\cos\theta = 0$ $(\theta = \pi/2)$ or ∇f^0 and $\boldsymbol{x}_1$ are orthogonal (see fig. 2.11a and b respectively for $\boldsymbol{x}_0 \in \mathscr{E}^2, \mathscr{E}^3$).

We now turn to the notion of the partial gradient of a function. To this end we state

DEFINITION 2.25. *Let $y = f(\boldsymbol{u}, \boldsymbol{v})$, $\boldsymbol{u}' = (u_1, \ldots, u_n) \in \mathscr{E}^n$, $\boldsymbol{v}' = (v_1, \ldots, v_m) \in \mathscr{E}^m$, be a real-valued function whose first partial derivatives exist over an open region $\mathscr{K} \subseteq \mathscr{E}^{n+m}$. The partial gradient of* f *is a vector-valued function whose elements are the first partial derivatives of* f *with respect to some subset of variables, i.e. the partial gradients of* f *with respect to $\boldsymbol{u}$, $\boldsymbol{v}$ are respectively the $(n \times 1)$ and $(m \times 1)$ vectors*

$$\nabla_{\boldsymbol{u}} f = \frac{\partial f}{\partial \boldsymbol{u}} = \begin{bmatrix} f_{u_1}(\boldsymbol{u}, \boldsymbol{v}) \\ f_{u_2}(\boldsymbol{u}, \boldsymbol{v}) \\ \vdots \\ f_{u_n}(\boldsymbol{u}, \boldsymbol{v}) \end{bmatrix}, \qquad \nabla_{\boldsymbol{v}} f = \frac{\partial f}{\partial \boldsymbol{v}} = \begin{bmatrix} f_{v_1}(\boldsymbol{u}, \boldsymbol{v}) \\ f_{v_2}(\boldsymbol{u}, \boldsymbol{v}) \\ \vdots \\ f_{v_m}(\boldsymbol{u}, \boldsymbol{v}) \end{bmatrix}.$$

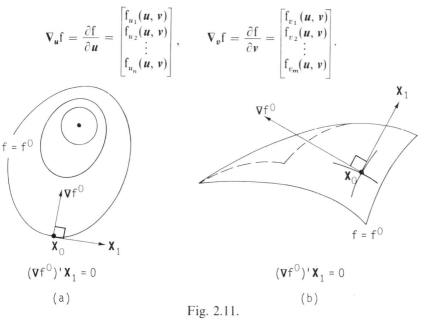

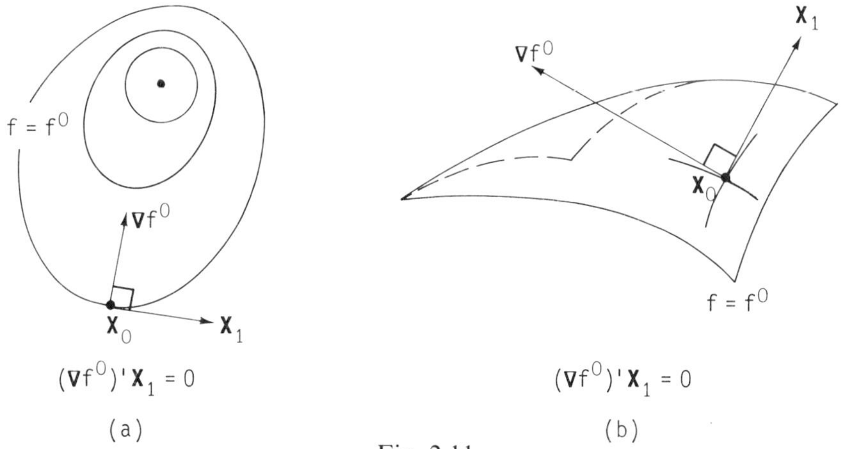

Fig. 2.11.

Example 2.5. Given the real-valued function $y = f(\boldsymbol{x}) = 6 + x_1^{-2} + x_2^{-2}$: (a) find the instantaneous rate of change of f at $\boldsymbol{x}_0' = (1, 1)$ in the $\boldsymbol{x}_1' = (3, 4)$ direction; and (b) starting at (1, 1) in what direction does f increase most rapidly and what is the maximum rate of increase of f in this direction?

(a) We want to find $D_{\boldsymbol{x}_1} f^0 = (\nabla f^0)' \boldsymbol{u}$, where $\boldsymbol{u} = \boldsymbol{x}_1 / \|\boldsymbol{x}_1\|$. Since

$$\boldsymbol{u}' = (\tfrac{3}{5}, \tfrac{4}{5}) \quad \text{and} \quad \nabla f' = (-2x_1^{-3}, \; -2x_2^{-3}),$$

we have, at (1, 1)

$$D_{x_1}f^0 = (-2, -2)\begin{bmatrix}\frac{3}{5}\\ \frac{4}{5}\end{bmatrix} = -\frac{14}{5}.$$

(b) f increases most rapidly in the direction of ∇f. In this instance $D_u f^0 = (\nabla f^0)'u$, where

$$u = \frac{\nabla f^0}{\|\nabla f^0\|} = \begin{bmatrix}-\frac{2}{\sqrt{8}}\\ \\ -\frac{2}{\sqrt{8}}\end{bmatrix}.$$

The maximum value of $D_u f$ in the u-direction is then $\|\nabla f^0\| = \sqrt{8}$.

Next,

DEFINITION 2.26. *Let the real-valued functions $f^j(x)$, $x \in \mathscr{E}^n$, $j = 1, \ldots, m$, be defined throughout an open region $\mathscr{K} \subseteq \mathscr{E}^n$. The Jacobian matrix of the m-component vector-valued function $\mathbf{F}' = [f^1, \ldots, f^m]$ is represented, at those points x where the partial derivatives of f^j exist, as the $(m \times n)$ matrix*

$$J_F(x) = \frac{\partial(f^1, \ldots, f^m)}{\partial(x_1, \ldots, x_n)} = \begin{vmatrix} f_1^1 & f_2^1 & \ldots & f_n^1 \\ f_1^2 & f_2^2 & \ldots & f_n^2 \\ \vdots & \vdots & & \vdots \\ f_1^m & f_2^m & \ldots & f_n^m \end{vmatrix}. \tag{2.4}$$

If $m = n$, then we may form the nth-order *Jacobian* (*or functional*) *determinant*

$$|J_F(x)| = \begin{bmatrix} f_1^1 & f_2^1 & \ldots & f_n^1 \\ f_1^2 & f_2^2 & \ldots & f_n^2 \\ \vdots & \vdots & & \vdots \\ f_1^n & f_2^n & \ldots & f_n^n \end{bmatrix}.$$

Equation (2.4) may be expressed in an alternative fashion as the transpose of the $(n \times m)$ matrix $\nabla \mathbf{F} = \partial \mathbf{F}/\partial x$. That is, since

$$\frac{\partial \mathbf{F}}{\partial x} = [\nabla f^1, \ldots, \nabla f^m] = \left[\frac{\partial f^1}{\partial x}, \ldots, \frac{\partial f^m}{\partial x}\right] = \begin{bmatrix} f_1^1 & f_1^2 & \ldots & f_1^m \\ f_2^1 & f_2^2 & \ldots & f_2^m \\ \vdots & \vdots & & \vdots \\ f_n^1 & f_n^2 & \ldots & f_n^m \end{bmatrix}, \tag{2.5}$$

it follows that $J_F(x) = \left[\frac{\partial \mathbf{F}}{\partial x}\right]'$. Finally, we have

DEFINITION 2.27. *Let the real-valued function $y = f(x)$, $x \in \mathscr{E}^n$, be defined over an open region $\mathscr{K} \subseteq \mathscr{E}^n$. The nth-order Hessian matrix of f is represented, at those points x where f is twice differentiable, as the nth-order Jacobian matrix* *of the first partial derivatives of* f, *or*

$$\boldsymbol{H}_{\mathrm{f}}(\boldsymbol{x}) = \frac{\partial(\mathrm{f}_1, \ldots, \mathrm{f}_n)}{\partial(x_1, \ldots, x_n)} = \begin{bmatrix} \mathrm{f}_{11} & \mathrm{f}_{12} & \ldots & \mathrm{f}_{1n} \\ \mathrm{f}_{21} & \mathrm{f}_{22} & \ldots & \mathrm{f}_{2n} \\ \vdots & \vdots & & \vdots \\ \mathrm{f}_{n1} & \mathrm{f}_{n2} & \ldots & \mathrm{f}_{nn} \end{bmatrix}. \tag{2.6}$$

Since $\mathrm{f}_{ij} = \mathrm{f}_{ji}$, $i \neq j$, the Hessian matrix is symmetric, i.e. $\boldsymbol{H}_{\mathrm{f}}(\boldsymbol{x}) = \boldsymbol{H}_{\mathrm{f}}(\boldsymbol{x})'$. In addition, the *Hessian determinant* of f is formed as

$$|\boldsymbol{H}_{\mathrm{f}}(\boldsymbol{x})| = \begin{vmatrix} \mathrm{f}_{11} & \mathrm{f}_{12} & \ldots & \mathrm{f}_{1n} \\ \mathrm{f}_{21} & \mathrm{f}_{22} & \ldots & \mathrm{f}_{2n} \\ \vdots & \vdots & & \vdots \\ \mathrm{f}_{n1} & \mathrm{f}_{n2} & \ldots & \mathrm{f}_{nn} \end{vmatrix}.$$

In terms of the calculus, since $\nabla \mathrm{f} = \partial \mathrm{f}/\partial \boldsymbol{x}$, the Hessian of f may be written as the $(n \times n)$ matrix

$$\nabla^2 \mathrm{f} = \frac{\partial \nabla \mathrm{f}}{\partial \boldsymbol{x}} = [\nabla \mathrm{f}_1, \ldots, \nabla \mathrm{f}_n] = \left[\frac{\partial \mathrm{f}_1}{\partial \boldsymbol{x}}, \ldots, \frac{\partial \mathrm{f}_n}{\partial \boldsymbol{x}}\right]$$

$$= \begin{bmatrix} \mathrm{f}_{11} & \mathrm{f}_{21} & \ldots & \mathrm{f}_{n1} \\ \mathrm{f}_{12} & \mathrm{f}_{22} & \ldots & \mathrm{f}_{n2} \\ \vdots & \vdots & & \vdots \\ \mathrm{f}_{1n} & \mathrm{f}_{2n} & \ldots & \mathrm{f}_{nn} \end{bmatrix} = \boldsymbol{H}_{\mathrm{f}}(\boldsymbol{x}) \tag{2.7}$$

by symmetry.

Example 2.6. Find the Jacobian matrix of $\mathbf{F}' = (\mathrm{f}^1, \mathrm{f}^2, \mathrm{f}^3)$ when

$$\mathrm{f}^1(x_1, x_2) = x_1^2 + x_2^2,$$
$$\mathrm{f}^2(x_1, x_2) = 2x_1 + x_1 x_2 + 4x_2,$$
$$\mathrm{f}^3(x_1, x_2) = x_1 + 3x_2^2.$$

From eq. (2.4) we obtain

$$\boldsymbol{J}_{\mathrm{F}}(\boldsymbol{x}) = \frac{\partial(\mathrm{f}^1, \mathrm{f}^2, \mathrm{f}^3)}{\partial(x_1, x_2)} = \begin{bmatrix} \mathrm{f}_1^1 & \mathrm{f}_2^1 \\ \mathrm{f}_1^2 & \mathrm{f}_2^2 \\ \mathrm{f}_1^3 & \mathrm{f}_2^3 \end{bmatrix} = \begin{bmatrix} 2x_1 & 2x_2 \\ 2+x_2 & x_1+4 \\ 1 & 6x_2 \end{bmatrix}.$$

Example 2.7. Find $|\boldsymbol{H}_{\mathrm{f}}(x_1, x_2, x_3)|$ given the real-valued function $y = \mathrm{f}(\boldsymbol{x}) = 3x_1^2 + x_2^3 + 2x_3^2$. Upon determining $\mathrm{f}_1 = 6x_1$, $\mathrm{f}_2 = 3x_2^2$, $\mathrm{f}_3 = 4x_3$ we form the Jacobian matrix of these first partial derivatives of f to obtain the Hessian matrix (eq. (2.6)). That is

$$\boldsymbol{H}_{\mathrm{f}}(x_1, x_2, x_3) = \frac{\partial(\mathrm{f}_1, \mathrm{f}_2, \mathrm{f}_3)}{\partial(x_1, x_2, x_3)} = \begin{bmatrix} \mathrm{f}_{11} & \mathrm{f}_{12} & \mathrm{f}_{13} \\ \mathrm{f}_{21} & \mathrm{f}_{22} & \mathrm{f}_{23} \\ \mathrm{f}_{31} & \mathrm{f}_{32} & \mathrm{f}_{33} \end{bmatrix} = \begin{bmatrix} 6 & 0 & 0 \\ 0 & 6x_2 & 0 \\ 0 & 0 & 4 \end{bmatrix}.$$

Then $|\boldsymbol{H}_{\mathrm{f}}(x_1, x_2, x_3)| = 144x_2$.

2.6. Derivatives of quadratic functions

We noted in chapter 1 that a general quadratic function in $\boldsymbol{x}$ may be expressed as

$$\mathrm{f}(\boldsymbol{x}) = a + \sum_{i=1}^{n} b_i x_i + \sum_{i=1}^{n} \sum_{j=1}^{n} q_{ij} x_i x_j = a + \boldsymbol{b}'\boldsymbol{x} + \boldsymbol{x}'\boldsymbol{Q}\boldsymbol{x},$$

where $\boldsymbol{b}$ is of order $(n \times 1)$ and $\boldsymbol{Q}$ is an nth-order symmetric matrix. How do we determine the first and second derivatives of f with respect to $\boldsymbol{x}$? Working first with the term $\boldsymbol{b}'\boldsymbol{x}$ it is easily seen that since

$$\frac{\partial(\boldsymbol{b}'\boldsymbol{x})}{\partial x_k} = b_k$$

is the kth component of $\boldsymbol{b}$,

$$\nabla(\boldsymbol{b}'\boldsymbol{x}) = \frac{\partial(\boldsymbol{b}'\boldsymbol{x})}{\partial \boldsymbol{x}} = \boldsymbol{b}.$$

If we next consider the term $\boldsymbol{x}'\boldsymbol{Q}\boldsymbol{x}$,

$$\begin{aligned}\frac{\partial(\boldsymbol{x}'\boldsymbol{Q}\boldsymbol{x})}{\partial x_k} &= 2q_{kk}x_k + \sum_{j \neq k} q_{kj}x_j + \sum_{i \neq k} q_{ik}x_i \\ &= \sum_{j=1}^{n} q_{kj}x_j + \sum_{i=1}^{n} q_{ik}x_i \\ &= \boldsymbol{q}_k\boldsymbol{x} + \boldsymbol{q}_k'\boldsymbol{x},\end{aligned}$$

where $\boldsymbol{q}_k$ is the kth row of $\boldsymbol{Q}$. Since $\partial(\boldsymbol{x}'\boldsymbol{Q}\boldsymbol{x})/\partial \boldsymbol{x}_k$ is the kth component of $\boldsymbol{Q}\boldsymbol{x}+\boldsymbol{Q}'\boldsymbol{x}$, it follows that, with $\boldsymbol{Q}$ symmetric,

$$\nabla(\boldsymbol{x}'\boldsymbol{Q}\boldsymbol{x}) = \frac{\partial(\boldsymbol{x}'\boldsymbol{Q}\boldsymbol{x})}{\partial \boldsymbol{x}} = \boldsymbol{Q}\boldsymbol{x} + \boldsymbol{Q}'\boldsymbol{x} = 2\boldsymbol{Q}\boldsymbol{x}.$$

In the light of these results, the first and second derivatives of f with respect to $\boldsymbol{x}$ appear respectively as

$$\nabla \mathrm{f}(\boldsymbol{x}) = \frac{\partial \mathrm{f}(\boldsymbol{x})}{\partial \boldsymbol{x}} = \boldsymbol{b} + 2\boldsymbol{Q}\boldsymbol{x},$$

$$\nabla^2 \mathrm{f}(\boldsymbol{x}) = \frac{\partial \nabla \mathrm{f}(\boldsymbol{x})}{\partial \boldsymbol{x}} = 2\boldsymbol{Q}.$$

Chapter 3

GLOBAL AND LOCAL EXTREMA OF REAL-VALUED FUNCTIONS

3.1. Classification of extrema

Our analysis in this chapter centers around a description of the extreme values which a real-valued function $y = \mathrm{f}(\boldsymbol{x})$, $\boldsymbol{x} \in \mathscr{E}^n$, may attain over some domain of definition $\mathscr{D}_\mathrm{f}$, where $\mathscr{D}_\mathrm{f}$ corresponds to a region $\mathscr{K} \subseteq \mathscr{E}^n$. Such values of f will be referred to quite generally as 'extrema'. This term shall be taken to represent either a maximum or a minimum value of f over its domain.

Extreme values of f will be defined relative to the region $\mathscr{K}$ or to some sub-region $\mathscr{G} \subseteq \mathscr{K}$. Here $\mathscr{G}$ will be interpreted as a spherical δ-neighborhood about the point $\boldsymbol{x} \in \mathscr{K}$. Accordingly, f may possess an extremum in either a global or local sense. That is, a global extremum shall be defined relative to a specific region $\mathscr{K}$ given in advance, whereas a local extremum will be defined relative to some sub-region $\mathscr{G} \subseteq \mathscr{K}$. Specifically, we have

DEFINITION 3.1. f *has a global extremum at a point* $\boldsymbol{x}$ *if* $\boldsymbol{x}$ *yields an extremum relative to all other points contained within the limits of a predetermined domain.*

And,

DEFINITION 3.2. f *has a local extremum at a point* $\boldsymbol{x}$ *if one can choose a spherical* δ*-neighborhood about* $\boldsymbol{x}$, $\delta(\boldsymbol{x})$, *such that* $\boldsymbol{x}$ *yields an extremum relative to all other points within* $\delta(\boldsymbol{x}) \subseteq \mathscr{D}_\mathrm{f}$.

We shall follow the convention of defining a global extremum over a closed region $\mathscr{K}$. But when we define a local extremum, $\mathscr{K}$ will be interpreted as an open region within $\mathscr{E}^n$ since we must be able to choose our δ-neighborhood about 'any' point within the domain of f (e.g. establishing a spherical δ-neighborhood about a boundary point of $\mathscr{K}$ encompasses points which are not members of $\mathscr{K}$).

3.2. Global extrema

Let $y = \mathrm{f}(\boldsymbol{x})$, $\boldsymbol{x} \in \mathscr{E}^n$, be a real-valued function defined on the closed region $\mathscr{K} \subseteq \mathscr{E}^n$ and let the points $\boldsymbol{x}_0, \boldsymbol{x}_1 \in \mathscr{K}$. Then

DEFINITION 3.3. f *has a global maximum at* $\boldsymbol{x}_0 \in \mathscr{K}$ *if* $f(\boldsymbol{x}_0) \geqslant f(\boldsymbol{x})$ *for all points* $\boldsymbol{x}(\neq \boldsymbol{x}_0) \in \mathscr{K}$.

Here $f(\boldsymbol{x}_0) \geqslant f(\boldsymbol{x})$ means that $f(\boldsymbol{x}_0)$ is at least as large as $f(\boldsymbol{x})$ (it may be larger) for all points $\boldsymbol{x} \neq \boldsymbol{x}_0$ within the domain of f. Also,

DEFINITION 3.4. f *has a global minimum at* $\boldsymbol{x}_1 \in \mathscr{K}$ *if* $f(\boldsymbol{x}_1) \leqslant f(\boldsymbol{x})$ *for all* $\boldsymbol{x}(\neq \boldsymbol{x}_1) \in \mathscr{K}$.

In this case $f(\boldsymbol{x})$ is at least as large as $f(\boldsymbol{x}_1)$ (it may be larger) for all values of $\boldsymbol{x}(\neq \boldsymbol{x}_1) \in \mathscr{D}_f$.

In the preceding definition of a global maximum it was implied that at no point within $\mathscr{K}$ is $f(\boldsymbol{x}) > f(\boldsymbol{x}_0)$. However, it may be true that for some point(s) $\boldsymbol{x}(\neq \boldsymbol{x}_0) \in \mathscr{K}$, $f(\boldsymbol{x}) = f(\boldsymbol{x}_0)$. When equality holds between $f(\boldsymbol{x}_0)$ and $f(\boldsymbol{x})$ for at least one point $\boldsymbol{x}(\neq \boldsymbol{x}_0) \in \mathscr{K}$, we shall say that f attains a *weak global maximum* at $\boldsymbol{x}_0$. Similarly, f is said to possess a *weak global minimum* at $\boldsymbol{x}_1$ if nowhere within $\mathscr{K}$ is $f(\boldsymbol{x}_1) > f(\boldsymbol{x})$ while $f(\boldsymbol{x}_1) = f(\boldsymbol{x})$ for at least one point $\boldsymbol{x}(\neq \boldsymbol{x}_1) \in \mathscr{K}$.

Let us now look to the definition of strong global extrema. Employing def. 3.3 we posit that f attains a *strong global maximum* at $\boldsymbol{x}_0$ if the value of f at $\boldsymbol{x}_0$ is absolutely greater than the value of f at any other point of $\mathscr{K}$, i.e. $f(\boldsymbol{x}_0) > f(\boldsymbol{x})$ for all $\boldsymbol{x}(\neq \boldsymbol{x}_0) \in \mathscr{K}$. Analogously, from def. 3.4, f has a *strong global minimum* at $\boldsymbol{x}_1$ if $f(\boldsymbol{x}_1) < f(\boldsymbol{x})$ for all points $\boldsymbol{x}(\neq \boldsymbol{x}_1) \in \mathscr{K}$.

For instance, given that $\boldsymbol{x} \in \mathscr{E}$, point A in fig. 3.1 indicates that f has a weak global maximum at x_0 since $f(x_0) \geqslant f(x)$ for all $x(\neq x_0) \in \mathscr{D}_f = [a, b]$ and

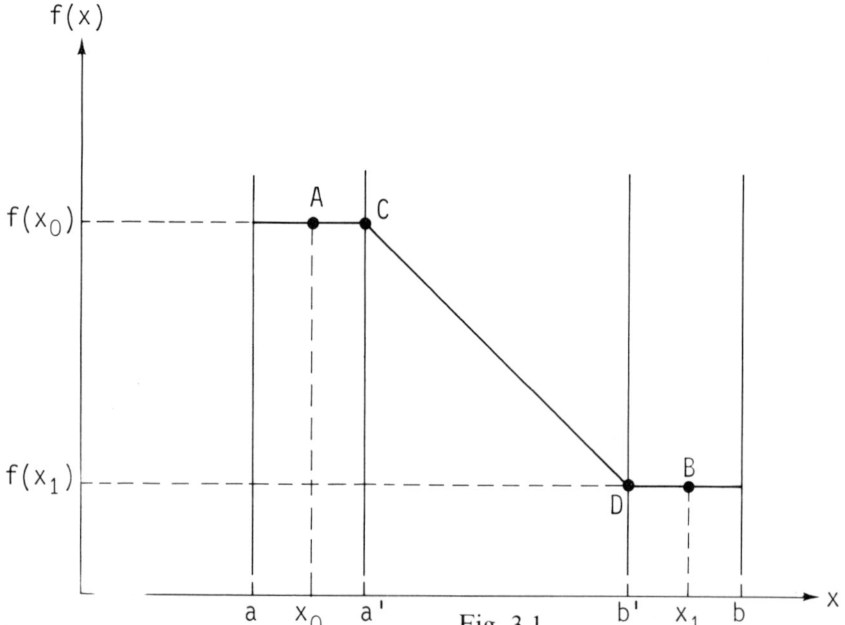

Fig. 3.1.

$f(x_0) = f(x)$ for all $x(\neq x_0) \in [a, a'] \subset [a, b]$. Analogously, f possesses a weak global minimum at x_1 (point B of fig. 3.1) since at no point within $\mathscr{D}_f$ is $f(x_1) > f(x)$ while $f(x) = f(x_1)$ for all $x(\neq x_1) \in [b', b] \subset [a, b]$.

If we redefine $\mathscr{D}_f$ in fig. 3.1 as the closed interval $[a', b']$, it is evident that $f(a') > f(x) > f(b')$ for all $x(\neq a', b') \in [a', b']$. In this instance (since strict inequality holds) f is said to possess a strong global maximum at a' (point C) and a strong global minimum at b' (point D) since $f(a')$ is the absolute maximum and $f(b')$ the absolute minimum value of f on $[a', b']$.

As a matter of notation we shall write a global maximum of f (whether strong or weak) at a point $\boldsymbol{x}_0 \in \mathscr{K}$ as

$$f(\boldsymbol{x}_0) = \underset{\boldsymbol{x} \in \mathscr{E}^n}{\text{g max}}\, f(\boldsymbol{x}).$$

If f happens to possess a global minimum (strong or weak) at $\boldsymbol{x}_1 \in \mathscr{K}$, we shall denote this extremum as

$$f(\boldsymbol{x}_1) = \underset{\boldsymbol{x} \in \mathscr{E}^n}{\text{g min}}\, f(\boldsymbol{x}).$$

Example 3.1. Let $y = f(x) = 1/x$ be defined for all real values of $x \in [2, 8]$. Then f is said to possess a strong global maximum at $x = 2$ since $f(2) = \frac{1}{2} > f(x)$ for all $x \in [2, 8]$ (fig. 3.2). Again from fig. 3.2 it is evident that, since $f(8) = \frac{1}{8} < f(x)$, $x \in [2, 8]$, f has a strong global minimum at $x = 8$. Thus

$$f(2) = \underset{x}{\text{g max}}\, f(x); \qquad f(8) = \underset{x}{\text{g min}}\, f(x).$$

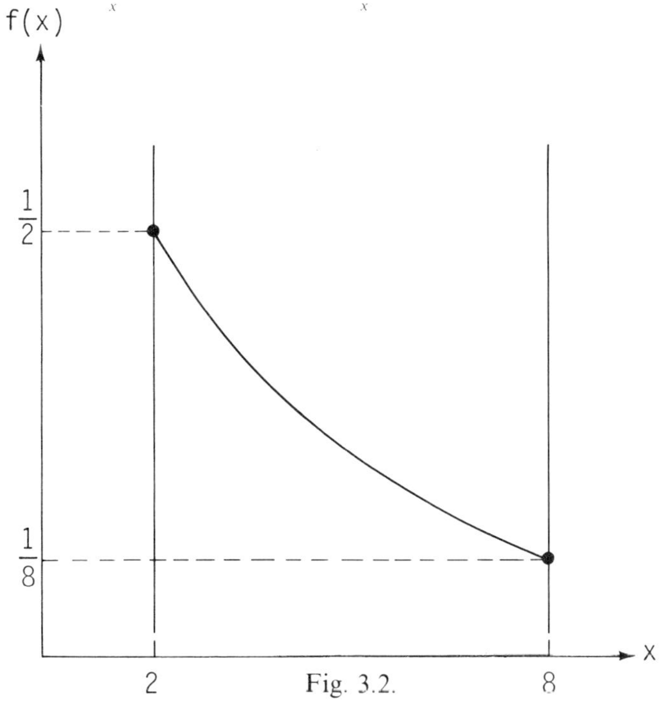

Fig. 3.2.

Example 3.2. If $y = 1/(b-a) =$ constant over $[a, b]$, $0<a<b$ (fig. 3.3), then, at each $x \in [a, b]$, the function attains a weak global maximum. However, it is also the case that this function simultaneously possesses a weak global minimum for all values of x throughout $[a, b]$. Does f attain a strong global maximum or minimum anywhere over its domain? Obviously it does not.

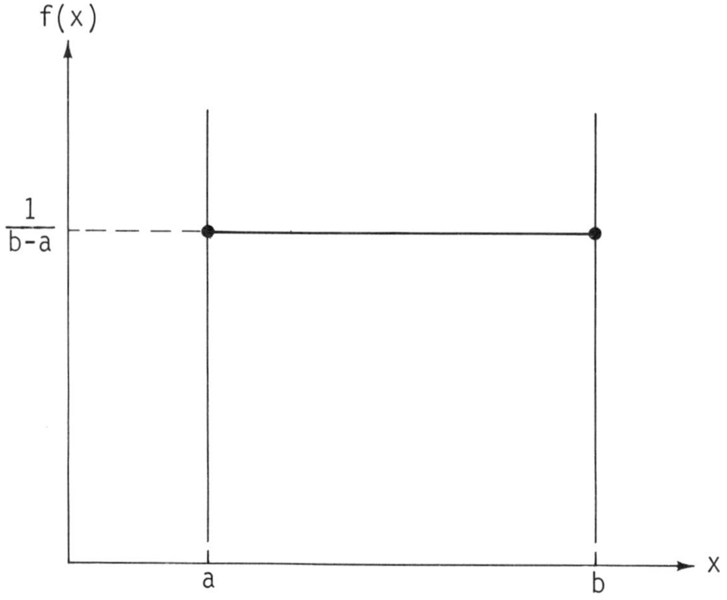

Fig. 3.3.

3.3. Local extrema

Let the real-valued function $y = \mathrm{f}(\boldsymbol{x})$, $\boldsymbol{x} \in \mathscr{E}^n$, be defined on the open region $\mathscr{K} \subseteq \mathscr{E}^n$ and let the points $\boldsymbol{x}_0, \boldsymbol{x}_1 \in \mathscr{K}$. Then we have

DEFINITION 3.5 f *has a local maximum at* $\boldsymbol{x}_0$ *if there is some spherical* δ-*neighborhood* $\delta(\boldsymbol{x}_0) \subseteq \mathscr{K}$ *about* $\boldsymbol{x}_0$, $\|\boldsymbol{x}-\boldsymbol{x}_0\| < \delta$, *such that* $\mathrm{f}(\boldsymbol{x}) \leqslant \mathrm{f}(\boldsymbol{x}_0)$ *for all* $\boldsymbol{x} \in \delta(\boldsymbol{x}_0)$.

Hence $\mathrm{f}(\boldsymbol{x}) \leqslant \mathrm{f}(\boldsymbol{x}_0)$ means that $\mathrm{f}(\boldsymbol{x}_0)$ is at least as large as $\mathrm{f}(\boldsymbol{x})$ (it may be larger) for all points $\boldsymbol{x} \neq \boldsymbol{x}_0$ for some distance δ in any direction from $\boldsymbol{x}_0$. Let us write the condition $\mathrm{f}(\boldsymbol{x}) \leqslant \mathrm{f}(\boldsymbol{x}_0)$ for all $\boldsymbol{x}(\neq \boldsymbol{x}_0) \in \delta(\boldsymbol{x}_0)$ in an alternative and computationally efficient manner. If we set $x_i = x_i^0 + h_i$, $i = 1, \ldots, n$, then f will have a local maximum at $\boldsymbol{x}_0$ if, for $\|\boldsymbol{h}\| < \delta$ sufficiently small,

$$\mathrm{f}(\boldsymbol{x}_0 + \boldsymbol{h}) - \mathrm{f}(\boldsymbol{x}_0) \leqslant 0, \tag{3.1}$$

where $\boldsymbol{x}_0+\boldsymbol{h}$ is the $(n\times 1)$ vector

$$\boldsymbol{x}_0+\boldsymbol{h} = \begin{bmatrix} x_1^0+h_1 \\ x_2^0+h_2 \\ \vdots \\ x_n^0+h_n \end{bmatrix}.$$

Similarly,

DEFINITION 3.6. f *is said to have a local minimum at* $\boldsymbol{x}_1$ *if we can find a spherical* δ*-neighborhood* $\delta(\boldsymbol{x}_1)\subseteq\mathscr{K}$ *about* $\boldsymbol{x}_1$, $\|\boldsymbol{x}-\boldsymbol{x}_1\|<\delta$, *such that* $\mathrm{f}(\boldsymbol{x})\geqslant\mathrm{f}(\boldsymbol{x}_1)$ *for all* $\boldsymbol{x}\in\delta(\boldsymbol{x}_1)$.

Here $\mathrm{f}(\boldsymbol{x})$ is at least as large as $\mathrm{f}(\boldsymbol{x}_1)$ (it may be larger) for all points $\boldsymbol{x}\neq\boldsymbol{x}_1$ within a suitably chosen neighborhood of $\boldsymbol{x}_1$. If $x_i = x_i^1+h_i$, $i = 1, \ldots, n$, then f has a local minimum at $\boldsymbol{x}_1$ if

$$\mathrm{f}(\boldsymbol{x}_1+\boldsymbol{h})-\mathrm{f}(\boldsymbol{x}_1)\geqslant 0 \tag{3.2}$$

when $\|\boldsymbol{h}\|<\delta$ is sufficiently small. In this instance $\boldsymbol{x}_1+\boldsymbol{h}$ is also an $(n\times 1)$ vector and appears as

$$\boldsymbol{x}_1+\boldsymbol{h} = \begin{bmatrix} x_1^1+h_1 \\ x_2^1+h_2 \\ \vdots \\ x_n^1+h_n \end{bmatrix}.$$

With reference to def. 3.5, if $\mathrm{f}(\boldsymbol{x})\leqslant\mathrm{f}(\boldsymbol{x}_0)$ for all $\boldsymbol{x}\in\delta(\boldsymbol{x}_0)$ and $\mathrm{f}(\boldsymbol{x}_0) = \mathrm{f}(\boldsymbol{x})$ for at least one point $\boldsymbol{x}(\neq\boldsymbol{x}_0)\in\delta(\boldsymbol{x}_0)$, then f has a *weak local maximum* at $\boldsymbol{x}_0$. But if $\mathrm{f}(\boldsymbol{x}_0)>\mathrm{f}(\boldsymbol{x})$ for all $\boldsymbol{x}(\neq\boldsymbol{x}_0)\in\delta(\boldsymbol{x}_0)$, then f is said to possess a *strong local maximum* at $\boldsymbol{x}_0$.

Turning to def. 3.6 we note that f has a *weak local minimum at* $\boldsymbol{x}_1$ if $\mathrm{f}(\boldsymbol{x}_1)\leqslant\mathrm{f}(\boldsymbol{x})$ for all $\boldsymbol{x}\in\delta(\boldsymbol{x}_1)$ and $\mathrm{f}(\boldsymbol{x}_1) = \mathrm{f}(\boldsymbol{x})$ for at least one other point $\boldsymbol{x}(\neq\boldsymbol{x}_1)\in\delta(\boldsymbol{x}_1)$. A *strong local minimum* is attained at $\boldsymbol{x}_1$ if $\mathrm{f}(\boldsymbol{x}_1)<\mathrm{f}(\boldsymbol{x})$ for all $\boldsymbol{x}(\neq\boldsymbol{x}_1)\in\delta(\boldsymbol{x}_1)$.

For example, given that $\boldsymbol{x}\in\mathscr{E}$, point C of fig. 3.4 indicates that $\mathrm{f}(x_2) = \mathrm{f}(x)$ for all $x\in\delta_3(x_2)\subset\mathscr{D}_\mathrm{f} = (a, b)$. In this case we say that f possesses a weak local maximum at x_2. However, if we consider the local maximum attained by f and x_0 (point A of fig. 3.4), it is easily seen that $\mathrm{f}(x_0)>\mathrm{f}(x)$ for all $x(\neq x_0)\in\delta_1(x_0)$. Hence, f is said to possess a strong local maximum at x_0.

Likewise, we may say that f possesses a strong local minimum at x_1 (point B in fig. 3.4) since $\mathrm{f}(x_1)<\mathrm{f}(x)$ for all $x(\neq x_1)\in\delta_2(x_1)$ and nowhere within this sub-interval is it the case that $\mathrm{f}(x_1) = \mathrm{f}(x)$. If equality held between $\mathrm{f}(x_1)$ and $\mathrm{f}(x)$ for at least one value of $x(\neq x_1)\in\delta_2(x_1)$, then f would be said to possess a weak local minimum at x_1.

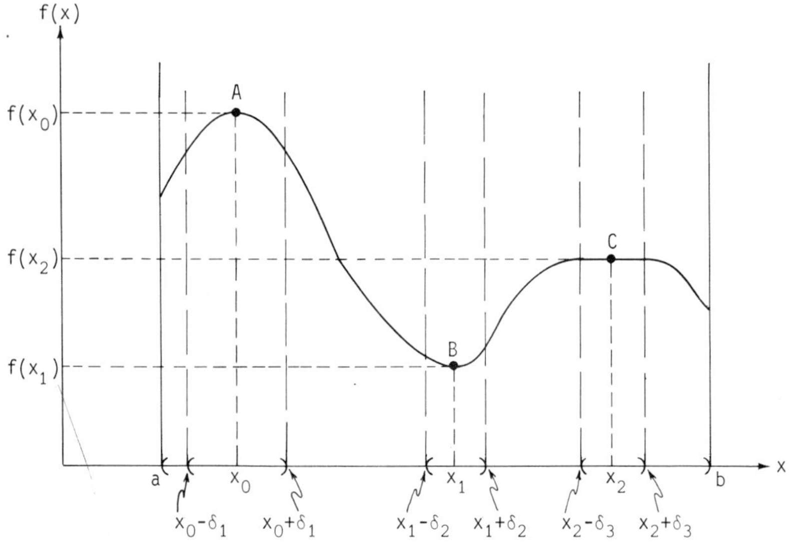

Fig. 3.4.

If f attains a local maximum (whether strong or weak) at the point $\boldsymbol{x}_0 \in \mathscr{K} \subseteq \mathscr{E}^n$, this extremum will be denoted as

$$\mathrm{f}(\boldsymbol{x}_0) = \mathrm{l}\max_{\boldsymbol{x}\in\mathscr{E}^n} \mathrm{f}(\boldsymbol{x}),$$

where it is understood that the extremum is defined relative to a suitably restricted spherical δ-neighborhood about $\boldsymbol{x}_0$. If f happens to possess a local minimum (strong or weak) at $\boldsymbol{x}_1 \in \mathscr{K} \subseteq \mathscr{E}^n$, we write this extremum as

$$\mathrm{f}(\boldsymbol{x}_1) = \mathrm{l}\min_{\boldsymbol{x}\in\mathscr{E}^n} \mathrm{f}(\boldsymbol{x}),$$

where the extremum is also defined relative to a sufficiently small spherical δ-neighborhood surrounding $\boldsymbol{x}_1$.

Example 3.3. Let $y = \mathrm{f}(x) = x^2$ be defined for all real values of $x \in (-\infty, +\infty)$. From fig. 3.5 it is clear that f has a strong local minimum at $x = 0$ since $\mathrm{f}(0) = 0 < \mathrm{f}(x)$ for all $x \in \delta(0)$. That is, from eq. (3.2),

$$\mathrm{f}(x_1 + h) - \mathrm{f}(x_1) = \mathrm{f}(h) - \mathrm{f}(0) = h^2 > 0 \quad \text{for} \quad |h| < \delta.$$

Hence

$$\mathrm{f}(0) = \mathrm{l}\min_{x} \mathrm{f}(x).$$

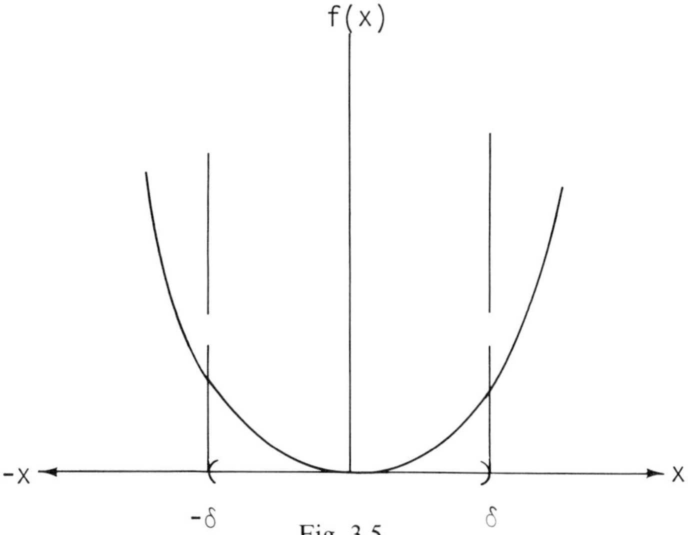

Fig. 3.5.

Example 3.4. Let $y = \mathrm{f}(x) = 10-2(x-3)^2$ for all real $x \in (1, 5)$. As fig. 3.6 shows, f has a strong local maximum at $x = 3$ since $\mathrm{f}(3) = 10 > \mathrm{f}(x)$ for all $x \in \delta(3)$. As eq. (3.1) indicates,

$$\mathrm{f}(x_0+h)-\mathrm{f}(x_0) = \mathrm{f}(3+h)-\mathrm{f}(3) = -2h^2 < 0 \quad \text{for} \quad |h| < \delta.$$

Thus $\mathrm{f}(3) = \mathrm{l}\max_{x} \mathrm{f}(x)$.

Example 3.5. Let the real-valued function $y = \mathrm{f}(\boldsymbol{x}) = x_1^2+x_2^2+2x_1-x_2-3$ be defined throughout the entirety of $\mathscr{E}^2$. Verify that f attains a local minimum at $\boldsymbol{x}_1' = (-1, \frac{1}{2})$. For

$$\boldsymbol{x}_1+\boldsymbol{h} = \begin{bmatrix} x_1^1+h_1 \\ x_2^1+h_2 \end{bmatrix} = \begin{bmatrix} -1+h_1 \\ \frac{1}{2}+h_2 \end{bmatrix}$$

we obtain

$$\begin{aligned} \mathrm{f}(\boldsymbol{x}_1+\boldsymbol{h}) &= (-1+h_1)^2+(\tfrac{1}{2}+h_2)^2+2(-1+h_1)-(\tfrac{1}{2}+h_2)-3 \\ &= h_1^2+h_2^2-\tfrac{17}{4}. \end{aligned}$$

In addition, $\mathrm{f}(\boldsymbol{x}_1) = -\frac{17}{4}$. Then eq. (3.2) yields

$$\mathrm{f}(\boldsymbol{x}_1+\boldsymbol{h})-\mathrm{f}(\boldsymbol{x}_1) = h_1^2+h_2^2.$$

Since this last expression is strictly positive for all $h_1^2+h_2^2 < \delta^2$ sufficiently small, f attains a strong local minimum at $\boldsymbol{x}_1$, i.e.

$$\mathrm{f}(\boldsymbol{x}_1) = \mathrm{l}\min_{\boldsymbol{x}\in\mathscr{E}^2} \mathrm{f}(\boldsymbol{x}).$$

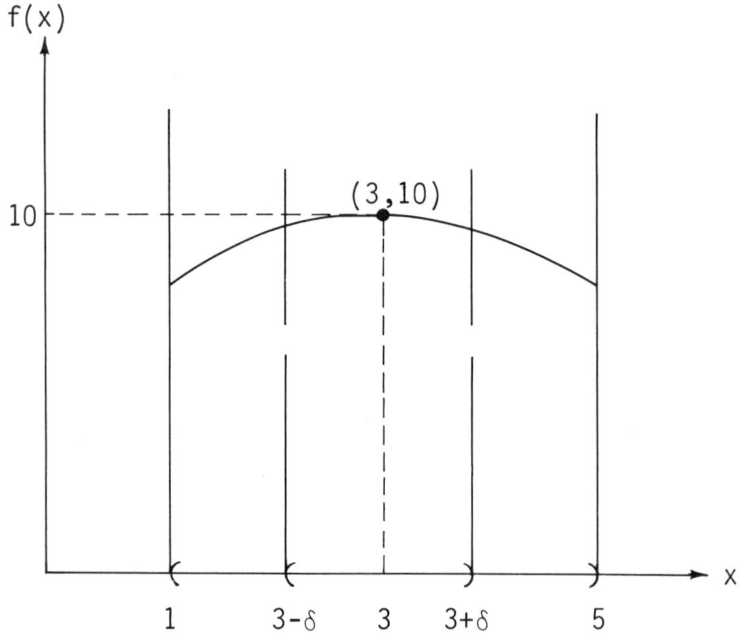

Fig. 3.6.

Furthermore, this extremum is also the strong global minimum of f over its domain since $f(\boldsymbol{x}_1) < f(\boldsymbol{x})$ for all points $\boldsymbol{x} \in \mathscr{D}_f$.

Having specified the basic properties of global and local extrema we may inquire into whether or not these two categories are mutually exclusive, i.e. can an extremum of f be simultaneously classified as global and local? The answer is in the affirmative. If a global extremum occurs at an interior point of a closed region $\mathscr{K} \subseteq \mathscr{E}^n$, it is also a local extremum. Note, however, that the converse of this statement need not necessarily hold, since in the case of a local maximum (minimum), there may exist larger (smaller) values of f outside the implied spherical δ-neighborhood. But if f attains a global extremum at a boundary point of $\mathscr{K}$, then clearly this extremum cannot also be of the local variety. Hence, any global extremum must be either a local extremum or occur at a boundary point of $\mathscr{K}$.

Chapter 4

GLOBAL EXTREMA OF REAL-VALUED FUNCTIONS

4.1. Existence of global extrema

Throughout the discussion which follows we shall assume that the domain of a continuous real-valued function $y = \mathrm{f}(\boldsymbol{x})$, $\boldsymbol{x} \in \mathscr{E}^n$, is a closed bounded region $\mathscr{K} \subseteq \mathscr{E}^n$. In this regard we state

WEIERSTRASS'S THEOREM.[1] *A real-valued function* $y = \mathrm{f}(\boldsymbol{x})$, $\boldsymbol{x} \in \mathscr{E}^n$, *continuous over a non-empty compact (i.e. closed and bounded) region* $\mathscr{K} \subseteq \mathscr{E}^n$ *takes on a least and a greatest value at least once over* $\mathscr{K}$.[2]

This theorem implies that if the domain $\mathscr{D}_\mathrm{f}$ of a continuous function f is compact, then so is its range $\mathscr{R}_\mathrm{f}$. Hence, the range of f is a closed bounded set and, by the completeness axiom, the values of f over $\mathscr{R}_\mathrm{f}$ have a supremum and infimum. Moreover, sup $\mathscr{R}_\mathrm{f}$ and inf $\mathscr{R}_\mathrm{f}$ are themselves elements of $\mathscr{R}_\mathrm{f}$ and thus are respectively the greatest and least elements of $\mathscr{R}_\mathrm{f}$ (see fig. 4.1 for $\boldsymbol{x} \in \mathscr{E}$). That is,

$$\left.\begin{aligned} \sup \mathscr{R}_\mathrm{f} &= \underset{\boldsymbol{x} \in \mathscr{E}^n}{\mathrm{g\,max}}\ \mathrm{f}(\boldsymbol{x}), \\ \inf \mathscr{R}_\mathrm{f} &= \underset{\boldsymbol{x} \in \mathscr{E}^n}{\mathrm{g\,min}}\ \mathrm{f}(\boldsymbol{x}). \end{aligned}\right\} \tag{4.1}$$

In sum, Weierstrass's theorem establishes the fact that a function which is continuous over a finite closed or compact domain attains a global maximum and a global minimum value at some point of the domain.

As mentioned above, the function f was assumed to be bounded over its domain. Let us formalize this notion. Specifically,

DEFINITION 4.1. *A real-valued function* $y = \mathrm{f}(\boldsymbol{x})$, $\boldsymbol{x} \in \mathscr{E}^n$, *is said to be bounded over a region* $\mathscr{K} \subseteq \mathscr{E}^n$ *if and only if there exists a real number* $N > 0$ *such that* $|\mathrm{f}(\boldsymbol{x})| \leqslant N$ *for all* $\boldsymbol{x} \in \mathscr{K}$.

---

[1] For a proof of this theorem the reader may consult either Taylor (1955), p. 102; or, Brand (1955), pp. 94–95.

[2] At first blush it may appear that the requirement that $\mathscr{D}_\mathrm{f}$ be closed *and* bounded is somewhat redundant. However, a set may be closed but not bounded and conversely. For instance, the interval $\mathscr{S} = \{x \mid a \leqslant x < +\infty\}$ is unbounded yet it is closed. This is because an interval (or any set for that matter) is defined as closed if it contains 'all' of its boundary points. Since a is the only boundary point of $\mathscr{S}$ and $a \in \mathscr{S}$, $\mathscr{S}$ is closed. Hence for Weierstrass's theorem to guarantee the existence of global extrema over $\mathscr{D}_\mathrm{f}$, $\mathscr{D}_\mathrm{f}$ must be closed and bounded.

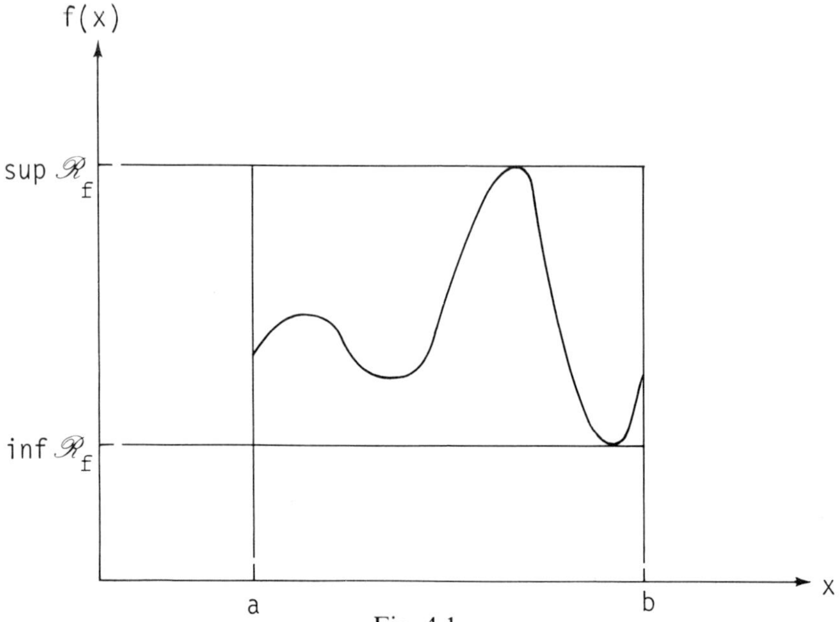

Fig. 4.1.

We note briefly that Weierstrass's theorem guarantees the existence of an $N > 0$ such that $|f(\boldsymbol{x})| \leqslant N$ for all $\boldsymbol{x} \in \mathscr{K}$. This is evident if we choose N to be the larger of $|\text{g max f}|$, $|\text{g min f}|$. Hence, the existence of global extrema provides us with a sufficient condition for f to be bounded on $\mathscr{K}$. However, it is not a necessary condition since f may be bounded even if $\mathscr{R}_f$ does not possess a least and a greatest element (a case in point is provided by example 4.2). Conversely, if f is bounded over $\mathscr{K}$, there must exist numbers inf $\mathscr{R}_f$, sup $\mathscr{R}_f$ such that $\inf \mathscr{R}_f \leqslant f(\boldsymbol{x}) \leqslant \sup \mathscr{R}_f$ for all $\boldsymbol{x} \in \mathscr{K}$. However, as was pointed out in chapter 2, inf $\mathscr{R}_f$, sup $\mathscr{R}_f$ need not be members of $\mathscr{R}_f$. Hence, the boundedness of $\mathscr{R}_f$ is not sufficient to guarantee that f attains a least and a greatest element over its domain. Thus, if f is bounded, we have a necessary condition for the existence of global extrema.

It is interesting to note that, by the use of a suitable transformation, we may express the global minimum of a function in terms of its global maximum. To see this let us explicitly denote $\mathscr{R}_f$ as the closed bounded set of real numbers $\{r | r_1 \leqslant r \leqslant r_2, r \in \mathscr{R}_f\}$. Here $r_1 = \inf \mathscr{R}_f$ and $r_2 = \sup \mathscr{R}_f$. If we take the negative of each real number $r \in \mathscr{R}_f$, we obtain the closed bounded set $\{-r | -r_1 \geqslant -r \geqslant -r_2, r \in \mathscr{R}_f\}$. In this case $-r_1 = \sup \{-r | r \in \mathscr{R}_f\}$ or $r_1 = -\sup \{-r | r \in \mathscr{R}_f\}$. However, r_1 was previously defined as inf $\mathscr{R}_f$.

Hence, we may write

$$\inf \mathscr{R}_{\mathrm{f}} = -\sup \{-r | r \in \mathscr{R}_{\mathrm{f}}\}. \tag{4.2}$$

How may we interpret eq. (4.2)? This relationship indicates that if we desire to obtain the global minimum of a continuous real-valued function f over a closed bounded set, we may do so by taking the negative of the global maximum of $-$f, i.e.

$$\underset{x \in \mathscr{E}^n}{\mathrm{g\,min}}\, \mathrm{f}(\boldsymbol{x}) = -\underset{x \in \mathscr{E}^n}{\mathrm{g\,max}} \{-\mathrm{f}(\boldsymbol{x})\}. \tag{4.3}$$

Weierstrass's theorem has guaranteed the existence of a global maximum and minimum value of f over $\mathscr{K}$. Note, however, that it did not explicitly associate any specific value(s) of $\boldsymbol{x} \in \mathscr{K}$ with sup $\mathscr{R}_{\mathrm{f}}$ and inf $\mathscr{R}_{\mathrm{f}}$. How then can we be sure that we will be able to find at least one $\boldsymbol{x} \in \mathscr{K}$ (say $\boldsymbol{x}_0$) such that f maps $\boldsymbol{x}_0$ into sup $\mathscr{R}_{\mathrm{f}}$? Similarly, is there at least one value of $\boldsymbol{x} \in \mathscr{K}$ (call it $\boldsymbol{x}_1$) such that $\boldsymbol{x}_1$ is mapped by f into inf $\mathscr{R}_{\mathrm{f}}$? As we shall now see, the answer to both questions is 'Yes'. To make the analysis supporting this answer as transparent as possible, let us confine our discussion to $\mathscr{E}$ wherein the plausibility of our argument is evident. In this regard we look to the intermediate-value theorem—which we have tacitly been employing.

INTERMEDIATE-VALUE THEOREM.[3] *Let a and b be real numbers such that $a<b$. In addition, let $y = \mathrm{f}(x)$ be a real-valued function continuous on $[a, b]$ with $\mathrm{f}(a) \neq \mathrm{f}(b)$. Now, if c is any number between $\mathrm{f}(a)$ and $\mathrm{f}(b)$, then there exists at least one number $\bar{x}$ between a and b such that $\mathrm{f}(\bar{x}) = c$.*

That is, as x varies from a to b, f(x) takes on every value between f(a) and f(b). In the light of this, since sup $\mathscr{R}_{\mathrm{f}}$ and inf $\mathscr{R}_{\mathrm{f}}$ are both elements of $\mathscr{R}_{\mathrm{f}}$, we may be certain that there exists at least one point $x_0 \in [a, b]$ where

$$\mathrm{f}(x_0) = \sup \mathscr{R}_{\mathrm{f}} = \underset{x}{\mathrm{g\,max}}\, \mathrm{f}(x);$$

and at least one point $x_1 \in [a, b]$ where

$$\mathrm{f}(x_1) = \inf \mathscr{R}_{\mathrm{f}} = \underset{x}{\mathrm{g\,min}}\, \mathrm{f}(x).$$

(See points A and B in fig. 4.2.) Hence, the intermediate-value theorem insures that we may, in fact, associate at least one $x \in [a, b]$ with sup $\mathscr{R}_{\mathrm{f}}$ and inf $\mathscr{R}_{\mathrm{f}}$.

Example 4.1. Let $y = \mathrm{f}(x) = x^2$ for all real $x \in [a, b]$, $x>0$ (fig. 4.3a). Then $\mathscr{R}_{\mathrm{f}}$ may be depicted as $[a^2, b^2]$. Not only is $\mathscr{R}_{\mathrm{f}}$ a bounded set, but $a^2 = \inf \mathscr{R}_{\mathrm{f}}$

[3] A proof of the intermediate-value theorem may be found in Taylor (1955), pp. 103–104; or Brand, (1955) p. 96.

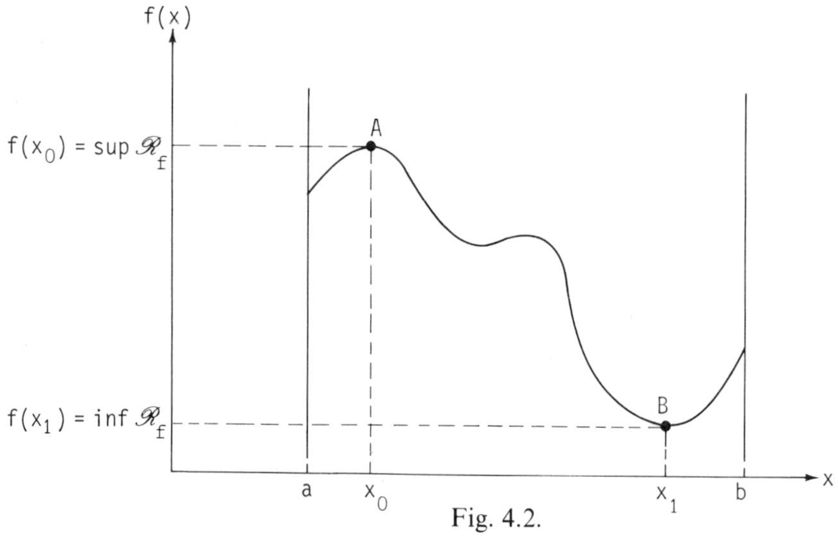

Fig. 4.2.

and $b^2 = \sup \mathscr{R}_f$ are members of $\mathscr{R}_f$. Since a^2 and b^2 are respectively the least and greatest elements of $\mathscr{R}_f$, f has a strong global minimum at a and a strong global maximum at b, i.e.

$$a^2 = \inf \mathscr{R}_f = \underset{x}{\text{g min}}\, f(x),$$

$$b^2 = \sup \mathscr{R}_f = \underset{x}{\text{g max}}\, f(x).$$

If the domain of f is redefined as the open interval (a, b), then its range correspondingly becomes the open interval (a^2, b^2) (fig. 4.3b). In this case $\mathscr{R}_f$ is bounded, but $a^2 = \inf \mathscr{R}_f$ and $b^2 = \sup \mathscr{R}_f$ are not members of $\mathscr{R}_f$. Since $\mathscr{R}_f$ possesses neither a greatest nor a least element, f possesses neither a global maximum nor a global minimum over its domain.

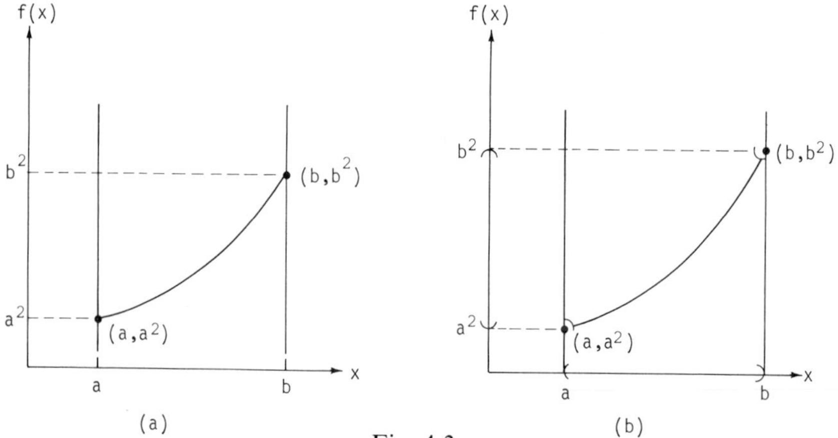

Fig. 4.3.

Example 4.2. Let $y = \mathrm{f}(x)$ be defined as

$$\mathrm{f}(x) = \begin{cases} \frac{1}{2} \text{ when } x = 1, \\ x^2 \text{ for } 1<x<6, \\ 40 \text{ when } x = 6. \end{cases}$$

Here $\mathscr{D}_\mathrm{f}$ is the closed interval $[1, 6]$, while $\mathscr{R}_\mathrm{f}$ is the bounded set

$$\{\tfrac{1}{2}\} \cup \{y \mid 1<y<36\} \cup \{40\} \quad \text{(fig. 4.4a).}$$

Although f is discontinuous at $x = 1$ and $x = 6$, its range possesses a least element and a greatest element since $\frac{1}{2} = \inf \mathscr{R}_\mathrm{f}$ and $40 = \sup \mathscr{R}_\mathrm{f}$ are both members of $\mathscr{R}_\mathrm{f}$. Hence, $\frac{1}{2}$ and 40 are respectively the strong global minimum and strong global maximum of f on $[1, 6]$, i.e.

$$\tfrac{1}{2} = \inf \mathscr{R}_\mathrm{f} = \underset{x}{\mathrm{g\,min}}\, \mathrm{f}(x), \qquad 40 = \sup \mathscr{R}_\mathrm{f} = \underset{x}{\mathrm{g\,max}}\, \mathrm{f}(x).$$

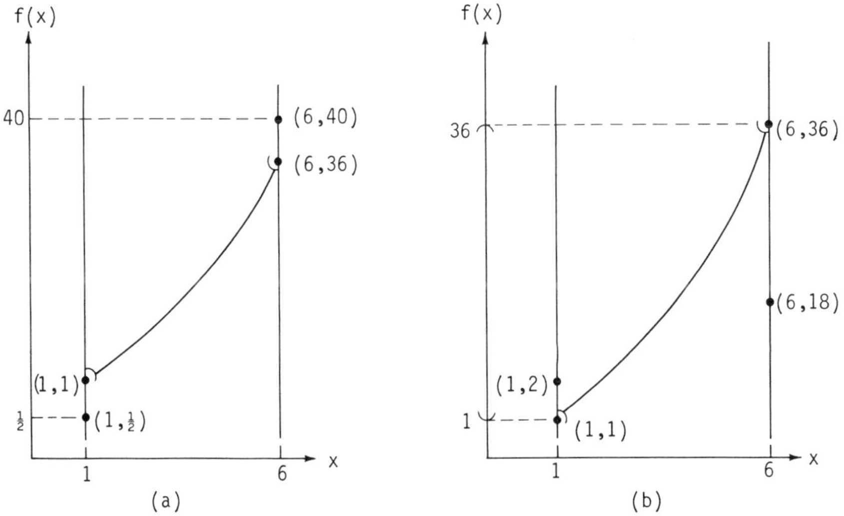

Fig. 4.4.

By redefining f(x) as 2 when $x = 1$ and 18 when $x = 6$ (fig. 4.4b), it is easily seen that f possesses neither a global minimum nor a global maximum over $[1, 6]$ since $\mathscr{R}_\mathrm{f}$, while remaining a bounded set, possesses neither a least nor a greatest element.

Example 4.3. Let $y = \mathrm{f}(x) = x^2$ for $x \in [a, +\infty)$, $x>0$. Since $\mathscr{D}_\mathrm{f}$ is not a bounded (or finite) set, then clearly $\mathscr{R}_\mathrm{f} = \{y \mid a^2 \leqslant y < +\infty\}$ is unbounded also (fig. 4.5). However, $\mathscr{R}_\mathrm{f}$ is bounded below. Moreover, $\inf \mathscr{R}_\mathrm{f} = a^2$ is the least element of $\mathscr{R}_\mathrm{f}$. Hence

$$a^2 = \inf \mathscr{R}_\mathrm{f} = \underset{x}{\mathrm{g\,min}}\, \mathrm{f}(x).$$

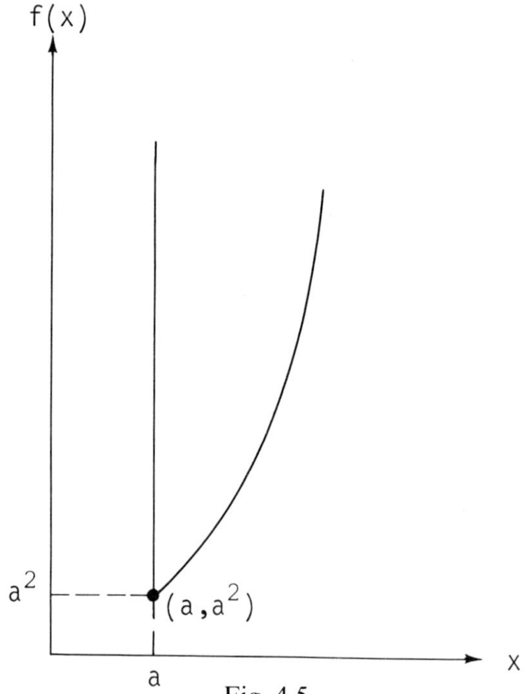

Fig. 4.5.

Thus f possesses a strong global minimum at a; it does not have a global maximum anywhere over its domain.

Generally speaking, these examples indicate that global extrema may not exist either because: (1) $\mathscr{K}$ is bounded but not closed (example 4.1); (2) f is discontinuous at some point(s) of $\mathscr{K}$ (example 4.2); or (3) $\mathscr{K}$ is an unbounded or infinite set (example 4.3). Hence, Weierstrass's theorem is only a sufficient condition for a global extremum, i.e. the theorem makes no mention of the existence or non-existence of global extrema if one or more of its assumptions are not fulfilled. (For instance, we were able to verify the existence of global extrema in the first part of example 4.2 even though f was discontinuous at the endpoints of its domain. But when f was redefined at $x = 1$ and $x = 6$, no such extrema were to be found.) However, one fact is absolutely certain. We can always be sure that a function will enjoy both a global maximum and minimum value if it is continuous over a finite or bounded closed region.

Before discussing the circumstances which underlie the existence and location of local extrema of real-valued functions, consideration will be given to the polynomial approximation of a function at a point within its domain. By employing this mode of representing a function we can greatly enhance our understanding of the motivation behind the derivation of necessary, sufficient, and necessary and sufficient conditions for local extrema.

Chapter 5

POLYNOMIAL APPROXIMATION OF REAL-VALUED FUNCTIONS

5.1. Functions of a single independent variable

In this section the possibility of approximating a given real-valued function $y = \mathrm{f}(x)$ by a polynomial of degree n in x, $P_n(x)$, is considered. Let us address ourselves to the following question. Under what circumstances can we replace a given function $\mathrm{f}(x)$ by its polynomial approximation $P_n(x)$? More specifically, if $P_n(x)$ is of the form

$$P_n(x) = a_0 + a_1(x-x_0) + a_2(x-x_0)^2 + \cdots + a_n(x-x_0)^n, \qquad (5.1)$$

are we at all justified in expressing $\mathrm{f}(x)$ as

$$\mathrm{f}(x) \sim \sum_{k=0}^{n} a_k(x-x_0)^k, \qquad (5.2)$$

i.e. can we act 'as if' $\mathrm{f}(x)$ were a polynomial of degree n, even though it is not, and then treat $P_n(x)$ as though it were the function $\mathrm{f}(x)$ itself?[1] Our answer is provided by

TAYLOR'S THEOREM [1]. *Let the real-valued function $y = \mathrm{f}(x)$ and its first $n+1 (n \geq 0)$ derivatives be continuous throughout a closed interval $[a, b]$ containing the point x_0. Then the value of* f *at any point x near x_0 is*

$$\mathrm{f}(x) = \mathrm{f}(x_0) + \mathrm{f}'(x_0)(x-x_0) + \frac{\mathrm{f}''(x_0)}{2!}(x-x_0)^2 + \cdots + \frac{\mathrm{f}^{(n)}(x_0)}{n!}(x-x_0)^n + R_{n+1}, \qquad (5.3)$$

where R_{n+1} is a remainder term of the form

$$R_{n+1} = \frac{1}{n!}\int_{x_0}^{x} (x-t)^n \mathrm{f}^{(n+1)}(t)\, \mathrm{d}t. \qquad (5.4)$$

[1] Our approximating polynomial has been written in powers of $x - x_0$. This is because we are interested in describing the behavior of f throughout some suitably restricted δ-neighborhood of the point x_0 so that $|x - x_0| < \delta$. When $x_0 = 0$, we seek to approximate f for values of x near zero and thus $P_n(x)$ appears in powers of x alone. In this case, $P_n(x) = \Sigma_{k=0}^{n} a_k x^k$.

Equation (5.3) is known as *Taylor's formula with integral remainder.*

Proof. Let $f'(t)$ be continuous on $[a, b]$. If f is any differentiable function such that $df = f'(t)\, dt$ when $t \in [a, b]$, then

$$\int_{x_0}^{x} f'(t)\, dt = f(x) - f(x_0),$$

$$f(x) = f(x_0) + \int_{x_0}^{x} f'(t)\, dt. \tag{5.5}$$

The second term on the right-hand side of eq. (5.5) may be evaluated using integration by parts.[2] That is, if we set $u = f'(t)$ and $dv = dt$, then $du = f''(t)\, dt$ and $v = t$ plus a constant. For convenience we shall choose $-x$ as our constant term. Then

$$\int_{x_0}^{x} f'(t)\, dt = f'(t)(t-x)\Big|_{x_0}^{x} - \int_{x_0}^{x} (t-x) f''(t)\, dt,$$

and thus

$$f(x) = f(x_0) + f'(x_0)(x - x_0) + \int_{x_0}^{x} (x-t) f''(t)\, dt.$$

By continuing the process of integrating by parts we obtain

$$f(x) = f(x_0) + f'(x_0)(x-x_0) + \frac{f''(x_0)}{2!}(x-x_0)^2$$

$$+ \cdots + \frac{f^{(n)}(x_0)}{n!}(x-x_0)^n + \frac{1}{n!}\int_{x_0}^{x} (x-t)^n f^{(n+1)}(t)\, dt, \tag{5.5.1}$$

where the $(n-1)$st term on the right-hand side of eq. (5.5.1) is the remainder R_{n+1}. Q.E.D.

Not only does Taylor's theorem [1] stipulate the conditions under which a function actually can be approximated by a polynomial, it also shows how the polynomial coefficients a_k are to be determined; that is

$$a_k = \frac{f^{(k)}(x_0)}{k!}, \quad k = 0, 1, 2, \ldots, n. \tag{5.6}$$

How shall we interpret eq. (5.6) in relation to $f(x)$ and $P_n(x)$? Equation (5.5.1) may be written

$$f(x) = \sum_{k=0}^{n} \frac{f^{(k)}(x_0)}{k!}(x-x_0)^k + R_{n+1} = P_n(x) + R_{n+1}. \tag{5.5.2}$$

If we omit R_{n+1} from eq. (5.5.2), then (5.2) holds and

$$f(x) \sim \sum_{k=0}^{n} \frac{f^{(k)}(x_0)}{k!}(x-x_0)^k \tag{5.2.1}$$

[2] This technique may be described as $\int_\alpha^\beta u\, dv = uv \int_\alpha^\beta - \int_\alpha^\beta v\, du$ when dv and $v\, du$ are both integrable. Hence, the product $u\, dv$ is also integrable. For a more elaborate discussion of this method of integration, see Thomas (1960), pp. 365–366.

when R_{n+1} is small. Hence, in choosing the polynomial of degree n that comes closest to approximating f near x_0, eq. (5.2.1) indicates that $P_n(x)$ should pass through f at the point $(x_0, \mathrm{f}(x_0))$ as well as possess the highest possible degree of contact with the function, in the sense that the derivatives of $P_n(x)$, up to and including those of degree n, match the corresponding derivatives of f, at that point. Thus, f and $P_n(x)$ and their derivatives of orders 1, ..., n are to have the same values at x_0.

Example 5.1. If a real-valued function $y = \mathrm{f}(x)$ is a polynomial of degree n in x, the nth-order Taylor expansion of this function about any point x_0 is the original polynomial itself. Let $\mathrm{f}(x) = a_0+a_1x+a_2x^2+a_3x^3$. Then

$$\mathrm{f}'(x) = a_1+2a_2x+3a_3x^2, \qquad \mathrm{f}''(x) = 2a_2+6a_3x,$$
$$\mathrm{f}'''(x) = 6a_3.$$

Evaluating f and its first three derivatives at x_0 gives

$$\mathrm{f}(x_0) = a_0+a_1x_0+a_2x_0^2+a_3x_0^3,$$
$$\mathrm{f}'(x_0) = a_1+2a_2x_0+3a_3x_0^2,$$
$$\mathrm{f}''(x_0) = 2a_2+6a_3x_0, \qquad \mathrm{f}'''(x_0) = 6a_3.$$

A substitution of these values into eq. (5.2.1) yields

$$\begin{aligned}\mathrm{f}(x) &= \mathrm{f}(x_0)+\mathrm{f}'(x_0)(x-x_0)+\frac{\mathrm{f}''(x_0)}{2!}(x-x_0)^2+\frac{\mathrm{f}'''(x_0)}{3!}(x-x_0)^3\\ &= a_0+a_1x+a_2x^2+a_3x^3.\end{aligned}$$

Hence, eq. (5.2.1) holds with strict equality and not just approximately when f is a polynomial.

Example 5.2. Using eq. (5.2.1), compute the nth-order Taylor expansion of the real-valued function $y = \mathrm{f}(x) = \exp(ax)$, $a>0$, about the point $x_0 = 0$. Proceeding as above

$$\mathrm{f}'(x) = a\exp(ax), \qquad \mathrm{f}''(x) = a^2\exp(ax),$$
$$\mathrm{f}'''(x) = a^3\exp(ax), \ldots, \qquad \mathrm{f}^{(n)}(x) = a^n\exp(ax).$$

Evaluating f and its first n derivatives at $x_0 = 0$ yields

$$\mathrm{f}(0) = 1, \quad \mathrm{f}'(0) = a, \quad \mathrm{f}''(0) = a^2, \quad \mathrm{f}'''(0) = a^3, \ldots, \quad \mathrm{f}^{(n)}(0) = a^n.$$

From eq. (5.2.1) we have

$$\begin{aligned}\mathrm{f}(x) &\sim \mathrm{f}(0)+\mathrm{f}'(0)x+\frac{\mathrm{f}''(0)}{2!}x^2+\frac{\mathrm{f}'''(0)}{3!}x^3+\cdots+\frac{\mathrm{f}^{(n)}(0)}{n!}x^n\\ &= 1+ax+\frac{a^2}{2!}x^2+\frac{a^3}{3!}x^3+\cdots+\frac{a^n}{n!}x^n,\end{aligned}$$

or

$$\exp(ax) \sim \sum_{k=0}^{n} \frac{a^k}{k!} x^k.$$

Here, the right-hand side of this equation is just an approximation to f since exp (ax) is not itself a polynomial in x.

As might be expected, the approximation to f gets better as n becomes larger. Hopefully, however, eq. (5.2.1) will hold with a reasonable degree of accuracy for small as well as for large values of n. To see this, let us discuss the behavior of eq. (5.2.1) as n varies between zero and positive integral values.

For $n = 0$, we seek a polynomial of degree zero that gives the closest approximation to f throughout $\delta(x_0)$, i.e. from eq. (5.2.1), $f(x) \sim P_0(x)$ whence $P_0(x) = f(x_0)$, a constant. As fig. 5.1 shows, both f and the approximating polynomial possess the same ordinate value at x_0. Hence, $P_0(x) = f(x_0)$ is a horizontal line passing through point A.

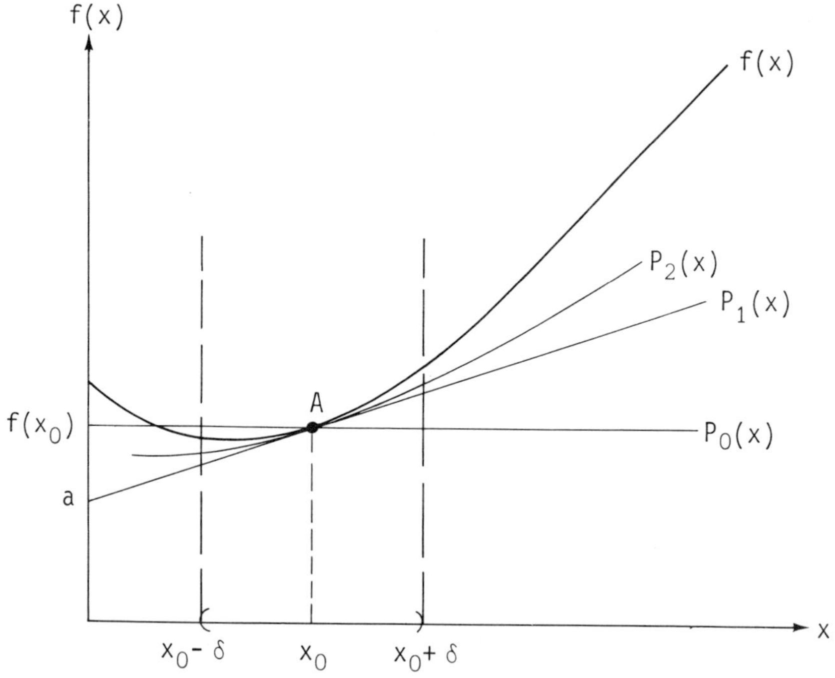

Fig. 5.1.

When $n = 1$, eq. (5.2.1) yields $f(x) \sim P_1(x)$ and our approximating polynomial becomes

$$P_1(x) = f(x_0)+f'(x_0)(x-x_0) = f(x_0)-x_0 f'(x_0)+f'(x_0)x$$
$$= a+f'(x_0)x,$$

where a is constant. Here, $P_1(x)$ is a linear function of x with slope $P'_1(x) = f'(x_0)$ and vertical intercept $a = f(x_0)-x_0 f'(x_0)$. In this case, not only does $P_1(x)$ share the same ordinate value as f at x_0, but their slopes are also equal there, and thus $P_1(x)$ is a tangent to f at A.

For $n = 2$, we have $f(x) \sim P_2(x)$, where

$$P_2(x) = f(x_0)+f'(x_0)(x-x_0)+\frac{f''(x_0)}{2!}(x-x_0)^2$$
$$= b+cx+\frac{f''(x_0)}{2!}x^2$$

with b and c constant. A simple calculation shows that $P''_2(x) = f''(x_0)$. Hence, this second-degree polynomial provides a better approximation yet, since now f and $P_2(x)$ agree with respect to the rate of change of their slopes at x_0.

What about the behavior of eq. (5.2.1) as n increases without bound? It was previously stated that, as n becomes larger, the polynomial approximation to f gets better. We now seek to determine the conditions under which we may secure the best possible approximation to f. This obviously will occur when eq. (5.2.1) holds with strict equality. Let us employ eq. (5.5.2) to pursue this point further.

The remainder term in eq. (5.5.2) may be considered as the error of approximating f—it is the amount by which $P_n(x)$ falls short of f. Hence, the size of R_{n+1} indicates the excellence of the approximation. If R_{n+1} disappears for sufficiently large values of n, then $P_n(x)$ equals f exactly, and not just approximately. In this case, as $R_{n+1} \to 0$ when $n \to \infty$, $P_n(x) \to f(x)$. More specifically, if

$$\lim_{n\to\infty} R_{n+1} = \lim_{n\to\infty}[f(x)-P_n(x)] = 0, \tag{5.7}$$

then

$$f(x) = P_\infty(x) = \sum_{k=0}^{\infty}\frac{f^{(k)}(x_0)}{k!}(x-x_0)^k, \tag{5.8}$$

the *Taylor 'series' expansion of* f *about the point* x_0.[3] In general, eq. (5.8) is

[3] Note that, whereas eq. (5.5.1) has been labeled *Taylor's formula* with integral remainder, eq. (5.8) is known as the Taylor series expansion of f about x_0, i.e. eq. (5.8) is a 'convergent

not always true. However, it will be valid if, for some particular x, eq. (5.7) holds—but this depends upon each particular function f and each particular value of x in question. Even if $P_\infty(x)$ converges for some specific $x \in [a, b]$, this does not necessarily mean that it will actually converge to f. Hence eq. (5.8) holds only if $P_\infty(x)$ converges to f when it does, in fact, converge; and this occurs only when $\lim_{n \to \infty} R_{n+1} = 0$.[4]

5.2. Lagrange's form of the remainder

The term R_{n+1} often appears in a variety of forms. For our purposes we shall use *Lagrange's form of the remainder*; i.e.

$$R_{n+1} = \frac{1}{(n+1)!} f^{(n+1)}(\xi)(x - x_0)^{n+1}, \tag{5.9}$$

where ξ lies between x_0 and x. To derive eq. (5.9) we shall employ the generalized or extended

MEAN-VALUE THEOREM FOR INTEGRALS.[5] *Let* $g(t)$, $h(t)$ *be continuous on* $[\alpha, \beta]$ *with* $h(t) \geqslant 0$ *for all* $t \in [\alpha, \beta]$. *Then, for some* $t = \xi$ *such that* $\alpha < \xi < \beta$,

$$\int_\alpha^\beta g(t)h(t)\,dt = g(\xi)\int_\alpha^\beta h(t)\,dt.$$

Let us set $g(t) = f^{(n+1)}(t)$ and $h(t) = (x-t)^n/n!$ since, for $x_0 \leqslant t \leqslant x$, $x - t \geqslant 0$ and thus $(x-t)/n! \geqslant 0$. We now wish to show that

$$\frac{1}{n!}\int_{x_0}^{x} (x-t)^n f^{(n+1)}(t)\,dt = \frac{1}{(n+1)!} f^{(n+1)}(\xi)\,(x-x_0)^{n+1}, \quad x_0 < \xi < x. \tag{5.10}$$

If m and M are respectively the global minimum and maximum values of

---

infinite (power) series' formula and is essentially different from eq. (5.5.1). If $x_0 = 0$ in eq. (5.8), the resulting expression is called the *Maclaurin 'series' expansion of* f. In this case

$$f(x) = \sum_{k=0}^{\infty} \frac{f^{(k)}(0)}{k!} x^k.$$

[4] For a discussion of the conditions under which $R_{n+1} \to 0$ as $n \to \infty$, see Hirschman (1962), pp. 47–52.

[5] For a proof, see Brand (1955), pp. 266–267.

$f^{(n+1)}(t)$ on $[x_0, x]$, then $m \leqslant f^{(n+1)}(t) \leqslant M$,

$$\frac{m}{n!}(x-t)^n \leqslant \frac{1}{n!} f^{(n+1)}(t)(x-t)^n \leqslant \frac{M}{n!}(x-t)^n,$$

and thus

$$\frac{m}{n!} \int_{x_0}^{x} (x-t)^n \, dt \leqslant \frac{1}{n!} \int_{x_0}^{x} f^{(n+1)}(t)\,(x-t)^n \, dt \leqslant \frac{M}{n!} \int_{x_0}^{x} (x-t)^n \, dt. \tag{5.11}$$

When $(x-t)^n/n! = 0$, eq. (5.10) holds for any ξ. Thus we now consider the case where $(x-t)^n/n! > 0$. Hence, from eq. (5.11), we have

$$m \leqslant \frac{\dfrac{1}{n!} \displaystyle\int_{x_0}^{x} f^{(n+1)}(t)\,(x-t)^n \, dt.}{\dfrac{1}{n!} \displaystyle\int_{x_0}^{x} (x-t)^n \, dt} \leqslant M.$$

As t varies between x_0 and x, $(x-t)^n/n!$ is positive and continuous. Since $f^{(n+1)}(t)$ is continuous on $[x_0, x]$ (by Taylor's theorem [1]), it takes on all values between m and M.[6] Hence, for some $t = \xi \in [x_0, x]$, $f^{(n+1)}(t) = f^{(n+1)}(\xi)$ and

$$f^{(n+1)}(\xi) = \frac{\dfrac{1}{n!} \displaystyle\int_{x_0}^{x} f^{(n+1)}(t)\,(x-t)^n \, dt}{\dfrac{1}{n!} \displaystyle\int_{x_0}^{x} (x-t)^n \, dt} = \frac{R_{n+1}}{\dfrac{1}{n!} \displaystyle\int_{x_0}^{x} (x-t)^n \, dt}.$$

Then

$$R_{n+1} = \frac{1}{n!} f^{(n+1)}(\xi) \int_{x_0}^{x} (x-t)^n \, dt = \frac{1}{(n+1)!} f^{(n+1)}(\xi)\,(x-x_0)^{n+1},$$
$$x_0 < \xi < x.$$

By combining eqs. (5.5.1) and (5.9) we have *Taylor's formula with Lagrange's form of the remainder, i.e.*

$$\begin{aligned} f(x) &= f(x_0) + f'(x_0)\,(x-x_0) + \frac{f''(x_0)}{2!}(x-x_0)^2 \\ &+ \cdots + \frac{f^{(n)}(x_0)}{n!}(x-x_0)^n + \frac{f^{(n+1)}(\xi)}{(n+1)!}(x-x_0)^{n+1}, \\ & x_0 < \xi < x. \end{aligned} \tag{5.12}$$

As eq. (5.9) shows, we can conveniently express R_{n+1} in terms of the function

[6] See the intermediate-value theorem, chapter 4, pp. 79–80, for a brief review of this argument.

f itself. Hence, Taylor's formula with Lagrange's form of the remainder is similar to the polynomial $P_{n+1}(x)$; they differ only with respect to the point at which the highest-order derivative is evaluated.

Example 5.3. Using Taylor's formula with Lagrange's form of the remainder, expand the real-valued function $y = \mathrm{f}(x) = a(1+x)^b$ about the point $x_0 = 0$. Computing the required derivatives gives

$$\begin{aligned}
\mathrm{f}'(x) &= ab(1+x)^{b-1},\\
\mathrm{f}''(x) &= ab(b-1)(1+x)^{b-2},\\
\mathrm{f}'''(x) &= ab(b-1)(b-2)(1+x)^{b-3},\\
&\cdots\cdots\cdots\cdots\cdots\cdots,\\
\mathrm{f}^{(n)}(x) &= ab(b-1)(b-2)\ldots(b-(n-1))(1+x)^{b-n},\\
\mathrm{f}^{(n+1)}(x) &= ab(b-1)(b-2)\ldots(b-(n-1))(b-n)(1+x)^{b-(n+1)}.
\end{aligned}$$

Evaluating f and its first n derivatives at $x_0 = 0$ and $\mathrm{f}^{(n+1)}(x)$ at the value ξ, $0<\xi<x$, we obtain

$$\begin{aligned}
\mathrm{f}(0) &= a, \qquad \mathrm{f}'(0) = ab, \qquad \mathrm{f}''(0) = ab(b-1),\\
\mathrm{f}'''(0) &= ab(b-1)(b-2), \ldots,\\
\mathrm{f}^{(n)}(0) &= ab(b-1)(b-2)\ldots(b-(n-1)), \qquad \mathrm{f}^{(n+1)}(\xi)\\
&= ab(b-1)(b-2)\ldots(b-(n-1))(b-n)(1+\xi)^{b-(n+1)}.
\end{aligned}$$

A substitution of these values into eq. (5.12) yields

$$\begin{aligned}
\mathrm{f}(x) &= a+abx+\frac{ab(b-1)}{2!}x^2+\frac{ab(b-1)(b-2)}{3!}x^3+\ldots\\
&\quad+\frac{ab(b-1)(b-2)\ldots(b-(n-1))}{n!}x^n\\
&\quad+\frac{ab(b-1)(b-2)\ldots(b-(n-1))(b-n)(1+\xi)^{b-(n+1)}}{(n+1)!}x^{n+1},\\
&\quad 0<\xi<x.
\end{aligned}$$

Example 5.4. Using eq. (5.12) approximate the real-valued function $y = \mathrm{f}(x) = \exp(ax)$, $a<0$, near the point $x_0 = 0$. We noted above that

$$\mathrm{f}(0) = 1, \qquad \mathrm{f}'(0) = a, \qquad \mathrm{f}''(0) = a^2, \ldots, \mathrm{f}^{(n)}(0) = a^n.$$

If the $(n+1)$st derivative is evaluated at the point ξ, $0<\xi<x$, we have $\mathrm{f}^{(n+1)}(\xi) = a^{n+1}\exp(a\xi)$. The substitution of these values into eq. (5.12) gives

$$\mathrm{f}(x) = 1+ax+\frac{a^2}{2!}x^2+\ldots+\frac{a^n}{n!}x^n+\frac{a^{n+1}}{(n+1)!}\exp(a\xi)\,x^{n+1},$$
$$0<\xi<x.$$

For our purposes we will usually find it convenient to express eq. (5.12) in a slightly different form. If we set $x = x_0+h$ and $\xi = x_0+\theta h$, $0<\theta<1$, then Taylor's formula with Lagrange's form of the remainder becomes

$$\mathrm{f}(x_0+h) = \mathrm{f}(x_0)+\mathrm{f}'(x_0)h+\frac{\mathrm{f}''(x_0)}{2!}h^2+\ldots+\frac{\mathrm{f}^{(n)}(x_0)}{n!}h^n$$

$$+\frac{\mathrm{f}^{(n+1)}(x_0+\theta h)}{(n+1)!}h^{n+1}, \quad 0<\theta<1. \tag{5.12.1}$$

5.3. A generalization to functions of n independent variables

We now turn to the approximation of the real-valued function $y = \mathrm{f}(\boldsymbol{x})$, $\boldsymbol{x}\in\mathscr{E}^n$, near $\boldsymbol{x}_0$, i.e. throughout some suitably restricted spherical δ-neighborhood of $\boldsymbol{x}_0$. In what follows, extensive use will be made of the notion of the jth-order differential of a function. That is to say, for $\boldsymbol{h} = \boldsymbol{x}-\boldsymbol{x}_0$, an $(n\times 1)$ vector with components $h_i = x_i-x_i^0$, $i = 1, \ldots, n$, the *jth-order differential of* f at a point $\boldsymbol{x}_0$ interior to a closed region $\mathscr{K}\subseteq\mathscr{E}^n$ may be written[7] as

$$\mathrm{d}^j\mathrm{f}(\boldsymbol{x}_0, \boldsymbol{h}) = \left(h_1\frac{\partial}{\partial x_1}+\cdots+h_n\frac{\partial}{\partial x_n}\right)^j_{\boldsymbol{x}_0}\mathrm{f}$$

$$= \sum_{r=1}^{n}\sum_{s=1}^{n}\cdots\sum_{t=1}^{n} h_r h_s \ldots h_t \frac{\partial^j\mathrm{f}(\boldsymbol{x}_0)}{\partial x_r\,\partial x_s\ldots\partial x_t},$$

$$j = 0, 1, \ldots, n. \tag{5.13}$$

Here

$$\mathrm{d}^0\mathrm{f}(\boldsymbol{x}_0, \boldsymbol{h}) = \mathrm{f}(\boldsymbol{x}_0),$$

$$\mathrm{d}^1\mathrm{f}(\boldsymbol{x}_0, \boldsymbol{h}) = \sum_{r=1}^{n} h_r\frac{\partial\mathrm{f}(\boldsymbol{x}_0)}{\partial x_r} = \nabla\mathrm{f}(\boldsymbol{x}_0)'\boldsymbol{h},$$

[7] The differential operator

$$\left(h_1\frac{\partial}{\partial x_1}+\cdots+h_n\frac{\partial}{\partial x_n}\right)^j,$$

a homogeneous polynomial of degree j, may be applied to f according to the multinomial expansion:

$$\left(h_1\frac{\partial}{\partial x_1}+\cdots+h_n\frac{\partial}{\partial x_n}\right)^j = \sum_{j_1+\cdots+j_n=j}\left(\frac{j!}{j_1!\ldots j_n!}\right)h_1^{j_1}\ldots h_n^{j_n}.$$

Then

$$\mathrm{d}^j\mathrm{f}(\boldsymbol{x}_0, \boldsymbol{h}) = \sum_{j_1+\cdots+j_n=j}\left(\frac{j!}{j_1!\ldots j_n!}\right)h_1^{j_1}\ldots h_n^{j_n}\frac{\partial^j\mathrm{f}(\boldsymbol{x}_0)}{\partial x_1^{j_1}\ldots\partial x_n^{j_n}}.$$

$$d^2f(\boldsymbol{x}_0, \boldsymbol{h}) = \sum_{r=1}^{n}\sum_{s=1}^{n} h_r h_s \frac{\partial^2 f(\boldsymbol{x}_0)}{\partial x_r\, \partial x_s} = \boldsymbol{h}'\nabla^2 f(\boldsymbol{x}_0)\boldsymbol{h} = \boldsymbol{h}'\boldsymbol{H}_f(\boldsymbol{x}_0)\boldsymbol{h}, \ldots.$$

If $y = f(\boldsymbol{x})$ is to be represented by a polynomial in $\boldsymbol{x}$ near $\boldsymbol{x}_0$, we may generalize eq. (5.5.2) and write

$$f(\boldsymbol{x}) = P_n(\boldsymbol{x}) + R_{n+1} = \sum_{j=0}^{n} \frac{1}{j!}\, d^j f(\boldsymbol{x}_0, \boldsymbol{h}) + R_{n+1}, \tag{5.14}$$

where R_{n+1} again denotes the $(n+1)$st-order remainder term. The rationalization of eq. (5.14) as the form taken by the approximating polynomial is provided by

TAYLOR'S THEOREM [2]. *Let the real-valued function $y = f(\boldsymbol{x})$, $\boldsymbol{x} \in \mathscr{E}^n$, and its first $n+1 (n \geq 0)$ derivatives be continuous throughout some closed region $\mathscr{K} \subseteq \mathscr{E}^n$ containing the point $\boldsymbol{x}_0$. Then the value of f at any point $\boldsymbol{x}$ near $\boldsymbol{x}_0$, i.e. throughout $\delta(\boldsymbol{x}_0)$, is*

$$f(\boldsymbol{x}) = f(\boldsymbol{x}_0) + df(\boldsymbol{x}_0, \boldsymbol{h}) + \frac{1}{2!}\, d^2 f(\boldsymbol{x}_0, \boldsymbol{h}) + \cdots + \frac{1}{n!}\, d^n f(\boldsymbol{x}_0, \boldsymbol{h}) + R_{n+1}, \tag{5.15}$$

where R_{n+1} is a remainder term of the form

$$\begin{aligned} R_{n+1} &= \frac{1}{(n+1)!}\, d^{n+1} f(\boldsymbol{x}_0 + \theta \boldsymbol{h}, \boldsymbol{h}) \\ &= \frac{1}{(n+1)!} \left(h_1 \frac{\partial}{\partial x_1} + \cdots + h_n \frac{\partial}{\partial x_n} \right)^{n+1}_{\boldsymbol{x}_0 + \theta \boldsymbol{h}} f, \quad 0 < \theta < 1. \end{aligned} \tag{5.16}$$

Proof. Let points $P = \boldsymbol{x}_0$, $Q = \boldsymbol{x}_0 + \boldsymbol{h}$ with coordinates $(x_1^0, \ldots, x_n^0)$, $(x_1^0 + h_1, \ldots, x_n^0 + h_n)$ respectively, be contained within the region $\mathscr{K}$. If $l \in \mathscr{K}$ is the line segment connecting P and Q, then any point $R = \boldsymbol{x}_0 + \boldsymbol{h}t$ on l has coordinates $(x_1^0 + h_1 t, \ldots, x_n^0 + h_n t)$, $0 \leq t \leq 1$ (see fig. 5.2 for the case where $\mathscr{K} \subset \mathscr{E}^2$). Hence the value of f along l is a function of the parameter t since

$$f(\boldsymbol{x}) = f(\boldsymbol{x}_0 + \boldsymbol{h}t) = F(t). \tag{5.17}$$

Applying Taylor's formula with Lagrange's form of the remainder (eq. (5.12.1)) to $F(t)$ for $t = 0$, (i.e. for $\boldsymbol{x} = \boldsymbol{x}_0$) yields

$$\begin{aligned} F(t) = {} & F(0) + F'(0)t + \frac{1}{2!} F''(0)t^2 + \cdots + \frac{1}{n!} F^{(n)}(0)t^n \\ & + \frac{1}{(n+1)!} F^{(n+1)}(\theta t)t^{n+1}, \quad 0 < \theta < 1. \end{aligned} \tag{5.18}$$

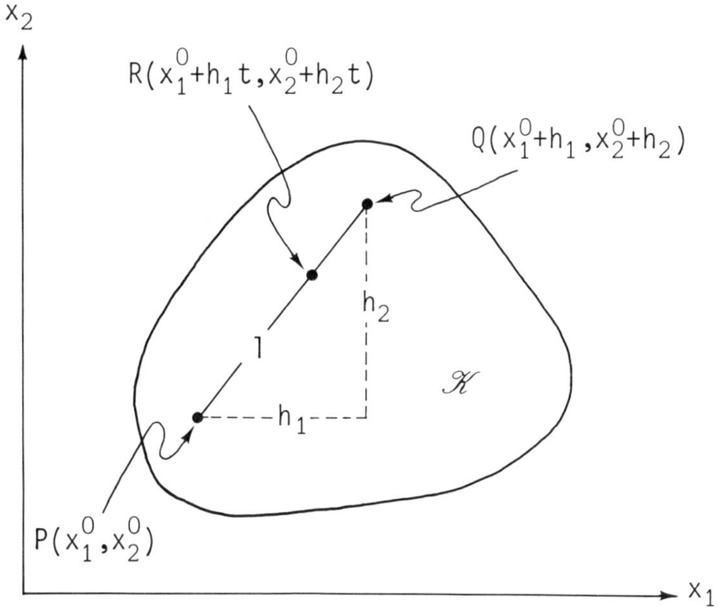

Fig. 5.2.

By employing a chain rule,[8] the derivatives $F^{(j)}(t)$, $j = 0, 1, \ldots, n+1$, indicated in eq. (5.18) may be calculated from eq. (5.17) as

$$F^0(t) = f(\boldsymbol{x}_0 + \boldsymbol{h}t), \qquad F'(t) = \frac{\partial f(\boldsymbol{x}_0 + \boldsymbol{h}t)'}{\partial \boldsymbol{x}} \frac{d\boldsymbol{x}}{dt}$$

$$= f_1(\boldsymbol{x}_0 + \boldsymbol{h}t)h_1 + \cdots + f_n(\boldsymbol{x}_0 + \boldsymbol{h}t)h_n = \nabla f(\boldsymbol{x}_0 + \boldsymbol{h}t)'\boldsymbol{h},$$

$$F''(t) = \frac{\partial(\nabla f(\boldsymbol{x}_0 + \boldsymbol{h}t)'\boldsymbol{h})'}{\partial \boldsymbol{x}} \frac{d\boldsymbol{x}}{dt}$$

$$= \frac{\partial}{\partial x_1}\Big(f_1(\boldsymbol{x}_0 + \boldsymbol{h}t)h_1 + \ldots + f_n(\boldsymbol{x}_0 + \boldsymbol{h}t)h_n\Big)h_1 + \ldots$$

$$+ \frac{\partial}{\partial x_n}\Big((f_1(\boldsymbol{x}_0 + \boldsymbol{h}t)h_1 + \ldots + f_n(\boldsymbol{x}_0 + \boldsymbol{h}t)h_n\Big)h_n$$

$$= \boldsymbol{h}'\boldsymbol{H}_f(\boldsymbol{x}_0 + \boldsymbol{h}t)\boldsymbol{h},$$

. . . .

[8] If $y = f(x_1, \ldots, x_n)$ and $x_i = g^i(t)$, $i = 1, \ldots, n$, then y becomes a composite function of t, $G(t) = f(g^1(t), \ldots, g^n(t))$, and thus $G'(t)$ may be calculated by the chain rule

$$G'(t) = \left(\frac{\partial f}{\partial \boldsymbol{x}}\right)\frac{d\boldsymbol{x}}{dt} = f_1\frac{dx_1}{dt} + \cdots + f_n\frac{dx_n}{dt}.$$

$$\mathrm{F}^{(n)}(t) = \left(h_1 \frac{\partial}{\partial x_1} + \cdots + h_n \frac{\partial}{\partial x_n}\right)^n_{\boldsymbol{x}_0 + \theta \boldsymbol{h} t} \mathrm{f},$$

$$\mathrm{F}^{(n+1)}(\theta t) = \left(h_1 \frac{\partial}{\partial x_1} + \cdots + h_n \frac{\partial}{\partial x_n}\right)^{n+1}_{\boldsymbol{x}_0 + \theta \boldsymbol{h} t} \mathrm{f}, \quad 0<\theta<1.$$

Then eq. (5.18) may be rewritten as

$$\mathrm{F}(t) = \mathrm{f}(\boldsymbol{x}_0) + \mathrm{df}(\boldsymbol{x}_0, \boldsymbol{h})t + \frac{1}{2!}\mathrm{d}^2\mathrm{f}(\boldsymbol{x}_0, \boldsymbol{h})t^2 + \cdots + \frac{1}{n!}\mathrm{d}^n\mathrm{f}(\boldsymbol{x}_0, \boldsymbol{h})t^n + \frac{1}{(n+1)!}\mathrm{d}^{n+1}\mathrm{f}(\boldsymbol{x}_0 + \theta \boldsymbol{h} t, \boldsymbol{h})t^{n+1}, \quad 0<\theta<1. \tag{5.18.1}$$

For $t = 1$, eq. (5.18.1) becomes

$$\mathrm{f}(\boldsymbol{x}) = \mathrm{f}(\boldsymbol{x}_0) + \mathrm{df}(\boldsymbol{x}_0, \boldsymbol{h}) + \frac{1}{2!}\mathrm{d}^2\mathrm{f}(\boldsymbol{x}_0, \boldsymbol{h}) + \cdots + \frac{1}{n!}\mathrm{d}^n\mathrm{f}(\boldsymbol{x}_0, \boldsymbol{h}) + \frac{1}{(n+1)!}\mathrm{d}^{n+1}\mathrm{f}(\boldsymbol{x}_0 + \theta \boldsymbol{h}, \boldsymbol{h}), \quad 0<\theta<1. \quad \text{Q.E.D.} \tag{5.15.1}$$

Here eq. (5.15.1) represents the *Taylor expansion with Lagrange's form of the remainder* of the function $y = \mathrm{f}(\boldsymbol{x})$, $\boldsymbol{x} \in \mathscr{E}^n$, about the point $\boldsymbol{x}_0$.

An important special case of eq. (5.15.1) occurs when $\boldsymbol{x} \in \mathscr{E}^2$. In this instance we obtain[9]

$$\mathrm{f}(x_1, x_2) = \sum_{j=0}^{n} \frac{1}{j!}\left(h_1 \frac{\partial}{\partial x_1} + h_2 \frac{\partial}{\partial x_2}\right)^j_{(x_1^0, x_2^0)} \mathrm{f} + \frac{1}{(n+1)!}\left(h_1 \frac{\partial}{\partial x_1} + h_2 \frac{\partial}{\partial x_2}\right)^{n+1}_{(x_1^0 + \theta h_1, x_2^0 + \theta h_2)} \mathrm{f}, \quad 0<\theta<1. \tag{5.15.2}$$

[9] Here the differential operator

$$\left(h_1 \frac{\partial}{\partial x_1} + h_2 \frac{\partial}{\partial x_2}\right)^j$$

is applied to f via the binomial expansion

$$\left(h_1 \frac{\partial}{\partial x_1} + h_2 \frac{\partial}{\partial x_2}\right)^j \mathrm{f} = \sum_{i=0}^{j} \left(\frac{j}{i}\right)^j h_1^i h_2^{j-i} \frac{\partial^j \mathrm{f}}{\partial x_1^i \, \partial x_2^{j-i}}.$$

Example 5.5. Using eq. (5.15.2) compute the third-order expansion of the real-valued function $y = \mathrm{f}(\boldsymbol{x}) = \exp(2x_1+3x_2)$ about the origin. That is, find

$$\mathrm{f}(x_1, x_2) = \sum_{j=0}^{2} \frac{1}{j!}\left(h_1 \frac{\partial}{\partial x_1} + h_2 \frac{\partial}{\partial x_2}\right)^j_{(0,\,0)} \mathrm{f} + \frac{1}{3!}\left(h_1 \frac{\partial}{\partial x_1} + h_2 \frac{\partial}{\partial x_2}\right)^3_{(\theta h_1,\,\theta h_2)}$$

$$\begin{aligned}\mathrm{f} = {} & \mathrm{f}(0, 0)+\mathrm{f}_1(0, 0)x_1+\mathrm{f}_2(0, 0)x_2 \\ & +\frac{1}{2!}\left[\mathrm{f}_{11}(0, 0)x_1^2+2\mathrm{f}_{12}(0, 0)x_1x_2+\mathrm{f}_{22}(0, 0)x_2^2\right] \\ & +\frac{1}{3!}\left[\mathrm{f}_{111}(\theta h_1, \theta h_2)x_1^3+3\mathrm{f}_{112}(\theta h_1, \theta h_2)x_1^2x_2\right. \\ & \left.+3\mathrm{f}_{122}(\theta h_1, \theta h_2)x_1x_2^2+\mathrm{f}_{222}(\theta h_1, \theta h_2)x_2^3\right], \quad 0<\theta<1.\end{aligned}$$

Calculating the required derivatives yields

$$\begin{aligned} \mathrm{f}_1(x_1, x_2) &= 2\mathrm{f}, & \mathrm{f}_{111}(x_1, x_2) &= 8\mathrm{f}, \\ \mathrm{f}_2(x_1, x_2) &= 3\mathrm{f}, & \mathrm{f}_{112}(x_1, x_2) &= 12\mathrm{f}, \\ \mathrm{f}_{11}(x_1, x_2) &= 4\mathrm{f}, & \mathrm{f}_{122}(x_1, x_2) &= 18\mathrm{f}, \\ \mathrm{f}_{12}(x_1, x_2) &= 6\mathrm{f}, & \mathrm{f}_{222}(x_1, x_2) &= 27\mathrm{f}, \\ \mathrm{f}_{22}(x_1, x_2) &= 9\mathrm{f}. \end{aligned}$$

Evaluating f, f_1, f_2, f_{11}, f_{12}, and f_{22} at the point (0, 0) and f_{111}, f_{112}, f_{122}, and f_{222} at $(\theta h_1, \theta h_2)$ gives

$$\begin{aligned} \mathrm{f}(0, 0) &= 1, & \mathrm{f}_{111}(\theta h_1, \theta h_2) &= 8 \exp(2\theta h_1+3\theta h_2), \\ \mathrm{f}_1(0, 0) &= 2, & \mathrm{f}_{112}(\theta h_1, \theta h_2) &= 12 \exp(2\theta h_1+3\theta h_2), \\ \mathrm{f}_2(0, 0) &= 3, & \mathrm{f}_{122}(\theta h_1, \theta h_2) &= 18 \exp(2\theta h_1+3\theta h_2), \\ \mathrm{f}_{11}(0, 0) &= 4, & \mathrm{f}_{222}(\theta h_1, \theta h_2) &= 27 \exp(2\theta h_1+3\theta h_2). \\ \mathrm{f}_{12}(0, 0) &= 6, \\ \mathrm{f}_{22}(0, 0) &= 9, \end{aligned}$$

From eq. (5.15.2) we have

$$\begin{aligned}\mathrm{f}(x_1, x_2) = {} & 1+2x_1+3x_2+2x_1^2+6x_1x_2+\tfrac{9}{2}x_2^2+(\tfrac{4}{3}x_1^3+6x_1^2x_2 \\ & +9x_1x_2^2+\tfrac{9}{2}x_2^3) \exp(\theta(2h_1+3h_2)).\end{aligned}$$

Example 5.6. Using eq. (5.15), expand the real-valued function $y = \mathrm{f}(\boldsymbol{x}) = 5x_1x_2^2+2x_3^{-1}$ near the point $\boldsymbol{x}_0' = (1, 1, 1)$ for $n = 2$. That is, find

$$\begin{aligned}\mathrm{f}(\boldsymbol{x}) = {} & \sum_{j=0}^{2} \frac{1}{j!} \mathrm{d}^j\mathrm{f}(\boldsymbol{x}_0, \boldsymbol{h})+R_{n+1} = \mathrm{f}(\boldsymbol{x}_0)+\mathrm{d}^1\mathrm{f}(\boldsymbol{x}_0, \boldsymbol{h}) \\ & +\frac{1}{2!} \mathrm{d}^2\mathrm{f}(\boldsymbol{x}_0, \boldsymbol{h})+\frac{1}{3!} \mathrm{d}^3\mathrm{f}(\boldsymbol{x}_0+\theta\boldsymbol{h}, \boldsymbol{h}), \quad 0<\theta<1.\end{aligned}$$

Upon calculating the required differentials and evaluating them at the indicated points we obtain

$$\begin{aligned} \mathrm{f}(\boldsymbol{x}) = {} & 7+5h_1+10h_2-2h_3+10h_1h_2+5h_2^2+2h_3^2 \\ & +5h_1h_2^2-2h_3^3(1+\theta h_3)^{-4}, \quad 0<\theta<1, \end{aligned}$$

as the reader should verify.

Setting $\boldsymbol{x} = \boldsymbol{x}_0+\boldsymbol{h}$, we may rewrite eq. (5.15) as

$$\mathrm{f}(\boldsymbol{x}_0+\boldsymbol{h}) = \sum_{j=0}^{n} \frac{1}{j!}\,\mathrm{d}^j\mathrm{f}(\boldsymbol{x}_0, \boldsymbol{h})+R_{n+1}. \tag{5.15.3}$$

In what follows we shall, for the most part, need only the second-order polynomial

$$\begin{aligned} \mathrm{f}(\boldsymbol{x}_0+\boldsymbol{h}) &= \mathrm{f}(\boldsymbol{x}_0)+\nabla\mathrm{f}(\boldsymbol{x}_0)'\boldsymbol{h}+\frac{1}{2!}\,\boldsymbol{h}'\frac{\partial\nabla\mathrm{f}(\boldsymbol{x}_0+\theta\boldsymbol{h})}{\partial\boldsymbol{x}}\,\boldsymbol{h} \\ &= \mathrm{f}(\boldsymbol{x}_0)+\nabla\mathrm{f}(\boldsymbol{x}_0)'\boldsymbol{h}+\frac{1}{2!}\,\boldsymbol{h}'\boldsymbol{H}_{\mathrm{f}}(\boldsymbol{x}_0+\theta\boldsymbol{h})\boldsymbol{h}, \quad 0<\theta<1. \end{aligned} \tag{5.15.4}$$

Chapter 6

LOCAL EXTREMA OF REAL-VALUED FUNCTIONS

6.1. Functions of a single independent variable

Chapter 3 presented a battery of definitions and descriptions of the various categories of local extrema often encountered in the analysis of real-valued functions. In this chapter we shall endeavor to specify the conditions under which these extrema may be recognized and isolated. We shall first deal with functions of a single independent variable. The general case involving functions of n independent variables follows later.

It will be helpful to introduce initially the notions of increasing and decreasing functions. In this regard we have

DEFINITION 6.1. *Let* $y = \mathrm{f}(x)$ *be a real-valued function defined for all* $x \in [a, b]$. *Then* f *is termed an increasing (decreasing) function over this interval if and only if* $\mathrm{f}(x_1) \leqslant \mathrm{f}(x_2)$ $(\geqslant \mathrm{f}(x_2))$ *when* $a \leqslant x_1 < x_2 \leqslant b$.

If f is increasing or decreasing (but not both) over $[a, b]$, it is said to be *monotonic*. If strict inequality happens to hold in def. 6.1, then f is said to be a *strictly increasing* (*strictly decreasing*) function over $[a, b]$ and thus may be characterized as *strictly monotonic*.

Let us consider the definition of an increasing or decreasing function in a somewhat different light. That is, we shall classify f as increasing or decreasing according to whether its slope is, respectively, non-negative or non-positive. To do so, we must impose upon f conditions which are a little more restrictive than those underlying the above definition. Specifically,

THEOREM 6.1.[1] *Let the real-valued function* $y = \mathrm{f}(x)$ *be continuous over* $[a, b]$ *and differentiable over* (a, b). *Then* f *is an increasing (decreasing) function over* (a, b) *if and only if* $\mathrm{f}'(x) \geqslant 0 (\leqslant 0)$ *for all* $x \in (a, b)$.

Here, also, strict inequality implies that f is *strictly increasing* (*strictly decreasing*) over (a, b). If, under the assumptions of theorem 6.1, $\mathrm{f}'(x) = 0$ for all $x \in (a, b)$, then f is *constant* over (a, b). In this case f may be said to be both increasing and decreasing (though not strictly) over (a, b).

Theorem 6.1 portrayed the behavior of f and its first derivative over the entirety of $\mathscr{D}_\mathrm{f}$. Let us now analyze f and f′ at a specific value of $x \in \mathscr{D}_\mathrm{f}$, namely

[1] For a discussion of the motivation behind the proof of this theorem see Taylor (1955), p. 34.

$\bar{x}$. This case is depicted by

THEOREM 6.2. *Assume that the real-valued function* $y = \mathrm{f}(x)$ *is continuous over* $[a, b]$ *and differentiable over* (a, b). *Let* $\bar{x}$ *be any point interior to* (a, b). *Then, if* $\mathrm{f}'(\bar{x})>0(<0)$:

(*a*) f *is strictly increasing (decreasing) at* $\bar{x}$; *and*

(*b*) *in any* δ-*neighborhood of* $\bar{x}$, $\delta(\bar{x})$, f *takes on values both smaller and larger than* $\mathrm{f}(\bar{x})$. *Furthermore, if* f′ *is continuous at* $\bar{x}$, *then,*

(*c*) *with* $\mathrm{f}'(\bar{x}) \neq 0$, f′ *has the same sign as* $\mathrm{f}'(\bar{x})$ *for all* $x \in \delta(\bar{x})$.

Since part (c) of this theorem will be used extensively in most of the proofs that follow, let us consider a detailed demonstration of its plausibility.[2] The continuity of f′ at $\bar{x}$ means that for any $\varepsilon>0$ we can find $\delta>0$ such that $|\mathrm{f}'(x)-\mathrm{f}'(\bar{x})|<\varepsilon$ when $|x-\bar{x}|<\delta$, or

$$\mathrm{f}'(\bar{x})-\varepsilon<\mathrm{f}'(x)<\mathrm{f}'(\bar{x})+\varepsilon \quad \text{when } \bar{x}-\delta<x<\bar{x}+\delta. \tag{6.1}$$

Let us take $\varepsilon = |\mathrm{f}'(\bar{x})|$. Hence, eq. (6.1) becomes

$$\mathrm{f}'(\bar{x})-|\mathrm{f}'(\bar{x})|<\mathrm{f}'(x)<\mathrm{f}'(\bar{x})+|\mathrm{f}'(\bar{x})| \quad \text{for } x\in\delta(\bar{x}). \tag{6.1.1}$$

With $\mathrm{f}'(\bar{x})>0$ we have, from eq. (6.1.1),

$$0<\mathrm{f}'(x)<2\mathrm{f}'(\bar{x}) \quad \text{for all } x\in\delta(\bar{x}). \tag{6.1.2}$$

If we now assume that $\mathrm{f}'(\bar{x})<0$, eq. (6.1.1) becomes

$$2\mathrm{f}'(\bar{x})<\mathrm{f}'(x)<0 \quad \text{for all } x\in\delta(\bar{x}). \quad \text{Q.E.D.} \tag{6.1.3}$$

From part (a) of theorem 6.2, $\mathrm{f}'(\bar{x})>0(<0)$ is a sufficient but not a necessary condition for f to be strictly increasing (decreasing) at $\bar{x}$, i.e. f may be a strictly increasing or decreasing function at $\bar{x}$, even though $\mathrm{f}'(\bar{x}) = 0$. For instance,

Example 6.1. The real-valued function $y = \mathrm{f}(x) = x^3$, $-\infty<x<+\infty$, is strictly increasing at $\bar{x} = 0$, yet $\mathrm{f}'(0) = 0$ (fig. 6.1).

It is clear from the above discussion that, as f increases when x does, any tangent to f must be positively sloped; and as f decreases when x increases, any tangent to f must be negatively sloped. Let us relate this argument to the behavior of f for values of x within a suitably restricted interval over which f assumes a local extremum. Theorems 6.1 and 6.2 were posited under the assumption that f was continuous over $[a, b]$ and differentiable over (a, b). To tighten our analysis somewhat we shall place an additional restriction upon f. That is, we shall now deem both f and f′ continuous over the closed interval $[a, b]$.

[2] For a proof of part (a) see Brand, (1955), §51, p. 204. A proof of (b) may be found in Taylor (1955), example 4, p. 65.

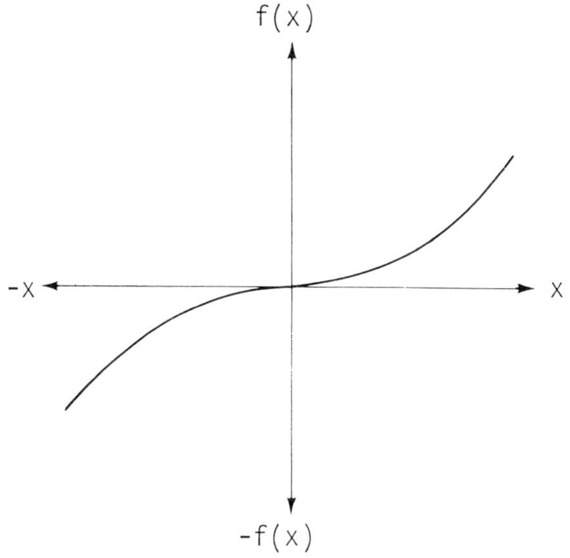

Fig. 6.1.

If it is known that f attains a local maximum at a point $x = x_0 \in (a, b)$, then

$$f(x_0) = l \max_x f(x)$$

(point A in fig. 6.2), and thus f must be increasing for $x_0 - \delta_1 < x < x_0$ and decreasing for $x_0 < x < x_0 + \delta_1$. But this is equivalent to the condition that $f'(x) \geqslant 0$ for all $x \in (x_0 - \delta_1, x_0)$ and $f'(x) \leqslant 0$ for all $x \in (x_0, x_0 + \delta_1)$ (by theorem 6.1). Now, if $f'(x)$ is non-negative for $x_0 - \delta_1 < x < x_0$ and non-positive for $x_0 < x < x_0 + \delta_1$, then $f'(x)$ should equal zero somewhere within the δ-neighborhood $\delta_1(x_0)$. Let us formalize this notion using the following existence theorem, namely

THEOREM 6.3.[3] *If a function, continuous over $[a, b]$, differs in sign at its end-points, it must vanish at some interior point(s).*

Since f' is assumed continuous over $[a, b]$, non-negative for $x_0 - \delta_1 < x < x_0$, and non-positive for $x_0 < x < x_0 + \delta_1$, then clearly $f'(x)$ must vanish for at least one value of $x \in \delta_1(x_0)$. If this were not true, then the sign of f' would change abruptly—going from positive to negative without first equalling

[3] This theorem is actually a consequence of the intermediate-value theorem encountered earlier in chapter 4, pp. 79–80. A proof is provided by Brand (1955), theorem 1, p. 96.

zero. However, the continuity of f′ precludes any such erratic behavior. Similarly, if $x_1 \in (a, b)$ and

$$f(x_1) = 1 \min_x f(x)$$

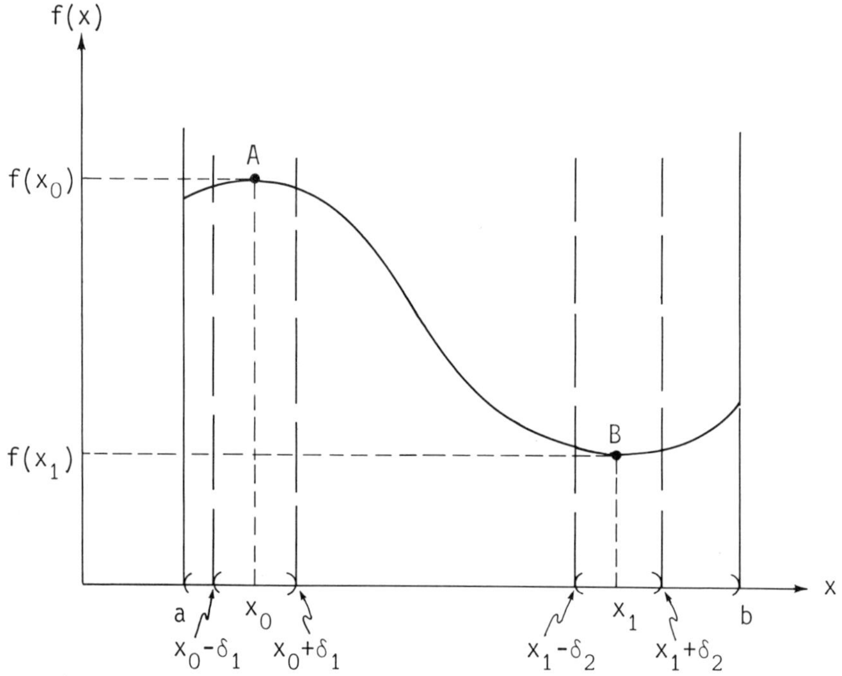

Fig. 6.2.

(point B of fig. 6.2), then f must be decreasing for $x_1 - \delta_2 < x < x_1$ (hence, $f'(x) \leqslant 0$ throughout this sub-interval) and increasing for $x_1 < x < x_1 + \delta_2$ (which means that $f'(x) \geqslant 0$ for all $x \in (x_1, x_1 + \delta_2)$). It is also evident from theorem 6.3 that f′ vanishes at some point(s) interior to $\delta_2(x_1)$.

For which values of $x \in \delta_1(x_0)$ does $f'(x)$ vanish? If $f(x_0)$ is a strong local maximum on (a, b), then f′ vanishes for only one value of $x \in \delta_1(x_0)$, namely, $x = x_0$. Hence, $f'(x_0) = 0$ (point B of fig. 6.3). If f happens to possess a strong local minimum at $x_1 \in \delta_2(x_1) \subseteq (a, b)$, then it is also the case that $f'(x_1) = 0$; and x_1 is the only value of $x \in \delta_2(x_1)$ for which $f'(x)$ vanishes. If f possesses a weak local minimum at $x_1 \in (a, b)$, not only does $f'(x_1) = 0$ (point B in fig. 6.4), but $f'(x)$ vanishes for all other values of $x \in \delta_2(x_1)$. Analogously, if $f(x_0)$ is deemed a weak local maximum on (a, b), then $f'(x)$ equals zero for all $x \in \delta_1(x_0) \subseteq (a, b)$.

Can f enjoy a local extremum at some value of $x \in (a, b)$ without its first derivative vanishing at that point? The answer is in the affirmative. In fig.

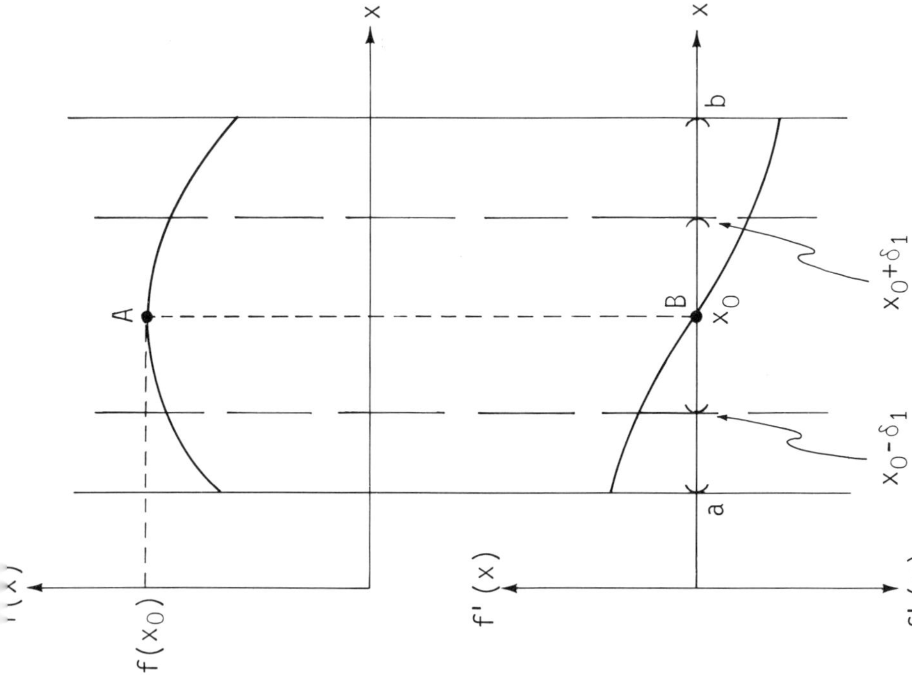

Fig. 6.3.

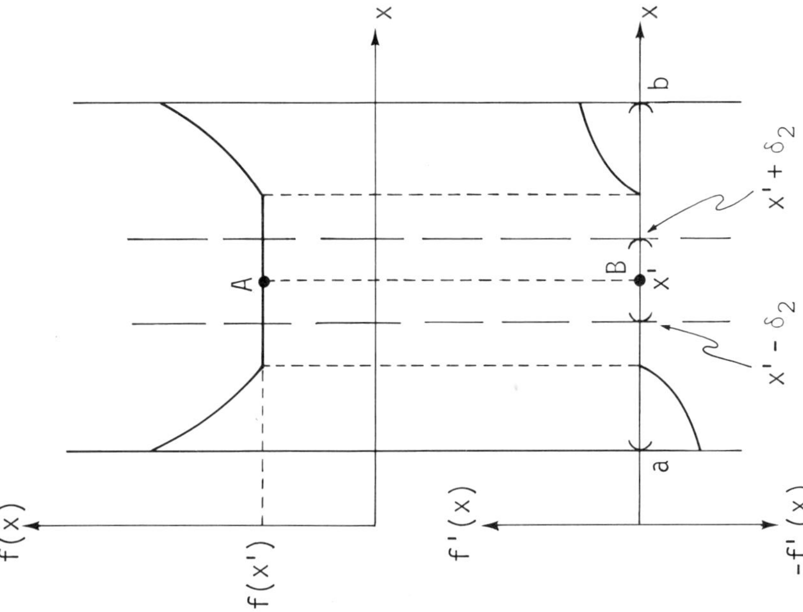

Fig. 6.4.

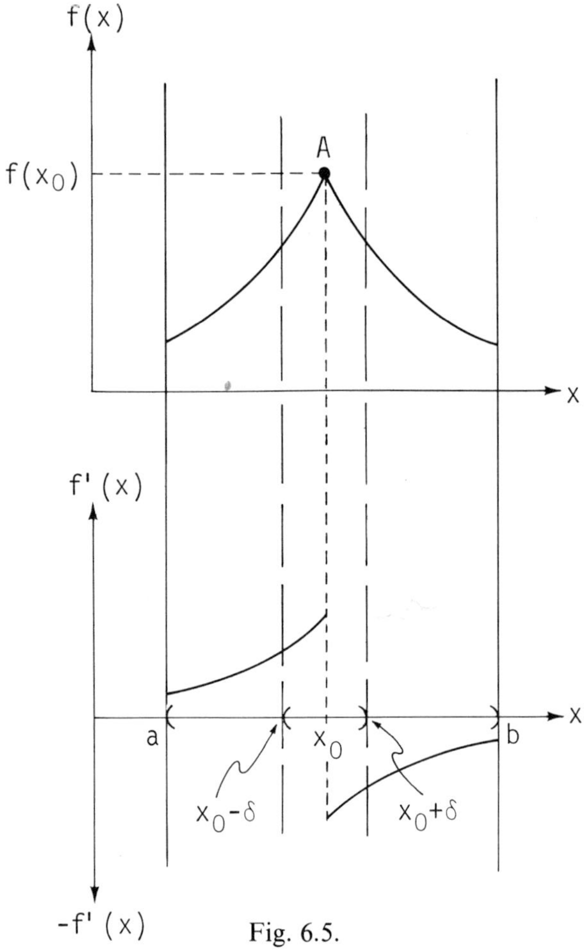

Fig. 6.5.

6.5 (point A), f is defined and continuous at $x = x_0$ and assumes a strong local maximum there, since $f(x_0) > f(x)$ for all $x \in \delta(x_0)$. However, f is not differentiable[4] at x_0, i.e. f′ possesses a (finite) discontinuity at this point, and thus f′ does not even exist at x_0, let alone vanish there.

Let us now introduce some terminology which may be used to categorize a point (or set of points) where the first derivative of a function vanishes or is non-existent on an open interval. First,

---

[4] A function f is differentiable at the point $x = x_0$ if both the right- and left-hand derivatives

$$f'_{+}(x_0) = \lim_{x \to x_0^+} \frac{f(x) - f(x_0)}{x - x_0}, \qquad f'_{-}(x_0) = \lim_{x \to x_0^-} \frac{f(x) - f(x_0)}{x - x_0}$$

exist and $f'_{+}(x_0) = f'_{-}(x_0)$.

DEFINITION 6.2. *The point x' is termed a critical value of $x\in(a, b)$ if*: (*a*) $f'(x')$ *fails to exist; or* (*b*) $f'(x') = 0$.

When $f'(x') = 0$, f is neither increasing nor decreasing. Hence, the value of f at x' is stationary, i.e. the tangent to f at this point is horizontal and thus parallel to the x-axis. Thus, we have

DEFINITION 6.3. *Any point* $(x', f(x'))$ *where* f′ *vanishes will be called a stationary point, while* $f(x')$ *is termed a stationary value of* f.

So if x' is a critical value of $x\in(a, b)$, then either $f'(x') = 0$, and thus $f(x')$ is a stationary value of f on this interval, or $f'(x')$ does not exist. Clearly, point A of fig. 6.5 and points A, B in fig. 6.2 are examples of critical points. However, only points A, B of fig. 6.2 are stationary points.

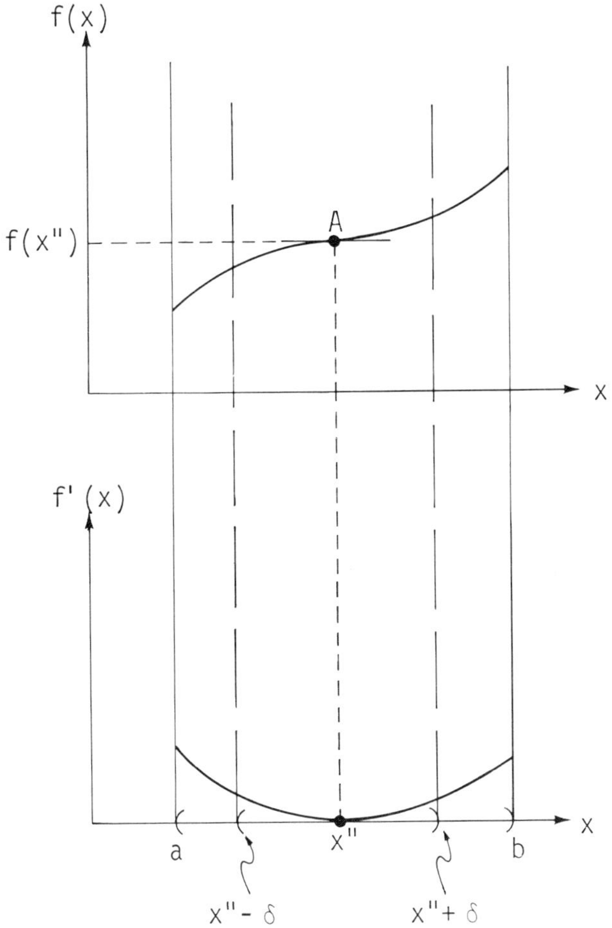

Fig. 6.6.

Can f possess a stationary point which is not a local extremum? To answer this question we need only observe that f may possess a *horizontal point of inflection* for some critical value of $x = x'' \in (a, b)$ (point A in fig. 6.6). At such a point f possesses neither a local maximum nor a local minimum, since it is not the case that $f(x'') \geqslant f(x)$ $(\leqslant f(x))$ for all $x \in \delta(x'')$. As x increases through x'', the curve crosses over its horizontal tangent at $f(x'')$. In this case, although $f'(x'') = 0$, f changes its curvature at x''—going from concave downward to concave upward. Since $f'(x) \geqslant 0$ for all $x \in \delta(x'')$, f may, in fact, be termed strictly increasing over this sub-interval (although it is momentarily stationary at x''). In general,

DEFINITION 6.4. *Any point where a curve crosses over its tangent line (horizontal or not) and changes the direction of its concavity from upward to downward or vice versa is a point of inflection.*

We conclude our classification of critical points by noting: (a) if a function with a continuous first derivative over (a, b) possesses a local extremum, this extreme point is also a stationary point—but not every stationary point is an extreme point; and (b) if f′ fails to exist at a point where f attains a local extremum, this extreme point is not of the stationary variety. These observations are summarized in fig. 6.7.

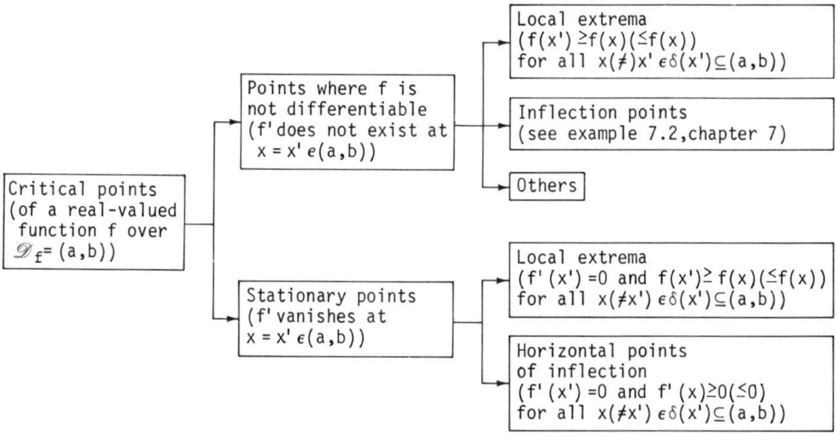

Fig. 6.7.

6.2. A necessary condition for a local extremum

We noted in the previous section that if a function possessing a continuous first derivative assumes a local extremum, this extremum can only occur at a point where the function is momentarily stationary. Hence, if we are to isolate the extreme values of a given function, our search must begin with a systematic examination of its set of stationary points. To aid us in this endeavor we shall, for the remainder of this chapter, concern ourselves with the derivation of necessary, sufficient, and necessary and sufficient conditions which will enable us to locate and identify local extrema. With this end in mind we now look to the following sequence of theorems.

THEOREM 6.4 (a necessary condition). *Let the real-valued function* $y = \mathrm{f}(x)$ *possess a continuous first derivative throughout some* δ*-neighborhood of the point* $x_0 \in (a, b)$*. If* f *has a local extremum at* x_0*, then* $\mathrm{f}'(x_0) = 0$.

Proof. Since this condition is prerequisite, we shall endeavor to demonstrate that a local extremum cannot occur at x_0 if $\mathrm{f}'(x_0) \neq 0$. Hence, there are two cases to consider: (1) $\mathrm{f}'(x_0)>0$; and (2) $\mathrm{f}'(x_0)<0$. Let us assume first that $\mathrm{f}'(x_0)>0$. If we set $n = 0$ in eq. (5.12.1), we obtain Taylor's formula with a remainder of order one. In this case,

$$\mathrm{f}(x_0+h) = \mathrm{f}(x_0)+\mathrm{f}'(x_0+\theta h)h, \quad 0<\theta<1$$

or

$$\mathrm{f}(x_0+h)-\mathrm{f}(x_0) = \mathrm{f}'(x_0+\theta h)h, \quad 0<\theta<1, \tag{6.2}$$

where it is assumed throughout that $|h|<\delta$. From eq. (6.1.2) it can be seen that $\mathrm{f}'(x_0+\theta h)$ will be positive when x, and thus $x_0+\theta h$, is close to x_0. If $x_0<x<x_0+\delta$, then $h>0$. Employing eq. (6.2) it is easily seen that $\mathrm{f}(x_0+h)-\mathrm{f}(x_0)>0$ also, since both $\mathrm{f}'(x_0+\theta h)$ and h are positive. For $x_0-\delta<x<x_0$, $\mathrm{f}'(x_0+\theta h)$ is still positive (by eq. 6.1.2)), but now $\mathrm{f}(x_0+h) -\mathrm{f}(x_0)<0$ since h, and thus $\mathrm{f}'(x_0+\theta h)h$ is negative. In sum, $\mathrm{f}(x_0+h)-\mathrm{f}(x_0)$ is negative for x close to x_0, but smaller; it is positive for x close to x_0, but larger (as anticipated from part (b) of theorem 6.2). However, this cannot happen if a local extremum occurs at x_0. Thus, $\mathrm{f}(x_0)$ is not an extreme value of f on (a, b), since it is not the case that

$$\mathrm{f}(x_0+h)-\mathrm{f}(x_0)\leqslant 0$$

or

$$\mathrm{f}(x_0+h)-\mathrm{f}(x_0)\geqslant 0$$

for $|h|<\delta$ sufficiently small.

If we now assume that $\mathrm{f}'(x_0)<0$, eq. (6.1.3) informs us that $\mathrm{f}'(x_0+\theta h)<0$ also when x is near x_0. In this instance, it is evident that $\mathrm{f}'(x_0+\theta h)h$ is negative for $x_0<x<x_0+\delta$ and positive for $x_0-\delta<x<x_0$. Hence, $\mathrm{f}(x_0)$ is not a local extremum of f on (a, b) since $\mathrm{f}(x_0+h)-\mathrm{f}(x_0)$ is positive for some values of $x \in \delta(x_0)$ and negative for others. Q.E.D.

Whether $\mathrm{f}(x_0)$ is a strong or weak local extremum of f on (a, b), $\mathrm{f}'(x_0) = 0$. If x_0 is the only point where f′ vanishes over $\delta(x_0)$, then clearly this extremum is of the strong variety. It must be stressed that a function does not necessarily have an extremum at every point where its first derivative vanishes (see the discussion on horizontal points of inflection of the previous section and example 6.4 below). However, we can be absolutely certain that if f has a local extremum at some critical value of $x \in \mathscr{D}_f$, f′ vanishes at that point if it exists there.

Example 6.2. Let the real-valued function $y = f(x) = 5+8x-2x^2$ be defined for all $x \in (0, 4)$. From fig. 6.8 it is clear that f attains a strong local maximum at $x = 2$ since $f(2) = 13 > f(x)$, $x \in (0, 4)$. If this is the case, then, by the preceding necessary condition, f should be momentarily stationary at the critical value $x = 2$, i.e. $f'(2) = 0$. With $f'(x) = 8-4x$, it follows that $f'(2) = 0$ as expected.

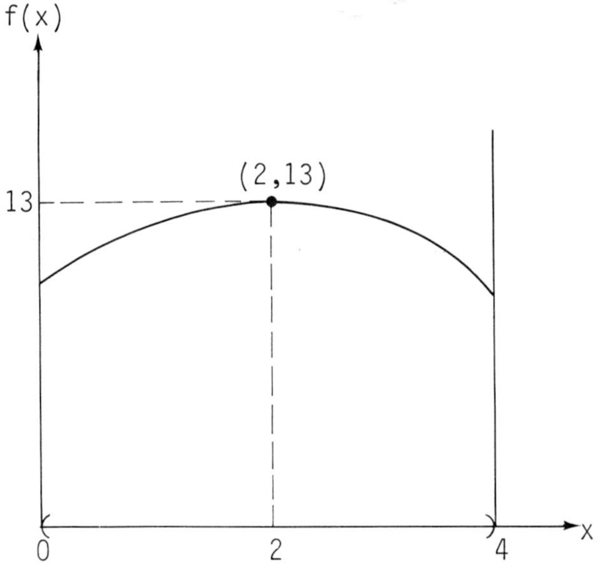

Fig. 6.8.

Example 6.3. Does the real-valued function $y = f(x) = 3-2x+x^2, x \in (-1,4)$, possess a local extremum? To answer this question we must examine the stationary value(s) of f over its domain. Now $f'(x) = -2+2x$. Equating f′ to zero and solving for the implied critical value of x yields $x = 1$. Hence, $f(1) = 2$, the stationary value of f over $\mathscr{D}_f$. Employing eq. (3.2) we find that

$$f(1+h)-f(1) = h^2 > 0, \quad |h| < \delta.$$

Thus, f assumes a strong local minimum at $x = 1$ (fig. 6.9).

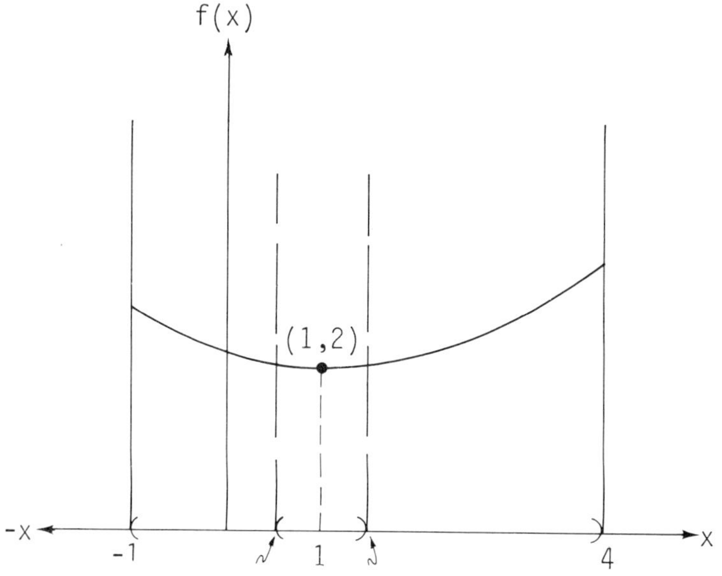

Fig. 6.9.

Example 6.4. Determine whether or not the real-valued function $y = \mathrm{f}(x) = 5-(x-3)^3$, $x \in (1,5)$, attains a local extremum over its domain. Proceeding as in example 6.3 we find that $\mathrm{f}'(3) = 0$. Hence, f is stationary at the critical value $x = 3$. Is $\mathrm{f}(3) = 2$ a local extremum of f over (1, 5)? It is easily shown that

$$\mathrm{f}(3+h)-\mathrm{f}(3)<0 \quad \text{for } h>0, \text{ i.e. for } 3<x<3+h;$$

and

$$\mathrm{f}(3+h)-\mathrm{f}(3)>0 \quad \text{for } h<0, \text{ i.e. for } 3-h<x<3, \ |h|<\delta.$$

Thus, f(3) is not a local extremum of f over the interval (1, 5). The stationary point (3, 2) is, in fact, a horizontal point of inflection, since f turns from being concave upward to concave downward at $x = 3$ (fig. 6.10).

While the above necessary condition provides us with an operational procedure for determining the point(s) at which f is stationary over (a, b), (i.e. we merely set f′ equal to zero and solve for the implied critical value(s) of x),[5] it provides no insight into whether any particular stationary value attained is a maximum, a minimum, or a horizontal point of inflection since

[5] See Appendix A of this chapter for the development of a battery of convenient numerical techniques for isolating the critical values of $\mathrm{f}' = 0$.

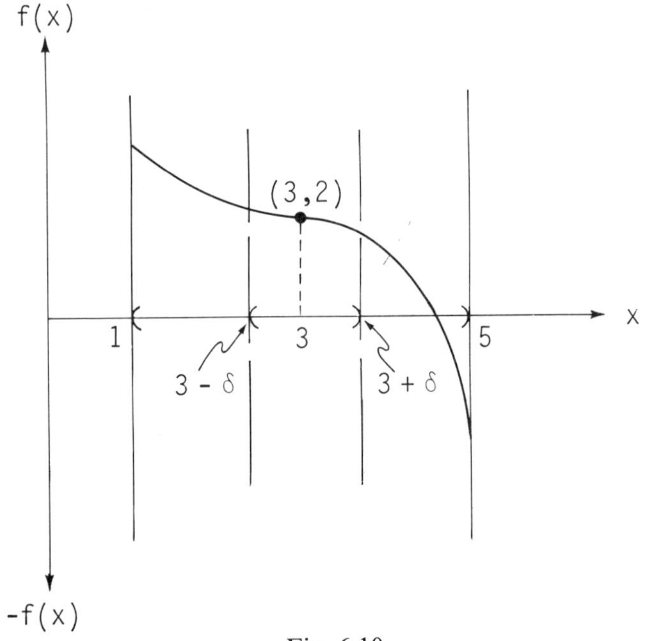

Fig. 6.10.

the vanishing of f′ occurs in each case. To resolve this issue we shall postulate conditions which are either sufficient or necessary and sufficient to identify a local extremum. As will be explained below, a sufficient condition allows us to distinguish a maximum from a minimum, whereas a condition which is necessary and sufficient goes a step further—it enables us to distinguish a maximum from a minimum from a stationary inflectional value. Hence, a necessary and sufficient condition provides us with a complete or exhaustive classification of stationary points. Let us first render consideration to the statement of a sufficient condition. Necessary and sufficient conditions will be developed later. In formulating a sufficient condition for a local extremum, use will be made of the second derivation of the function.

6.3. A sufficient condition for a local extremum

Theorem 6.1 classified a function as increasing or decreasing over a specified interval according to whether its slope was, respectively, non-negative or non-positive. The theorem, however, makes no provision for describing a function as increasing (decreasing) at an increasing rate or at a decreasing rate. We shall extend theorem 6.1 so as to cover these special cases.

THEOREM 6.1.1. *Let* $y = \mathrm{f}(x)$ *be a real-valued function continuous over* $[a, b]$ *and twice differentiable over* (a, b). *Then:*

(*a*) *for* f *increasing at an increasing (decreasing) rate over* (a, b), $\mathrm{f}'(x) > 0$ *and* $\mathrm{f}''(x) > 0 (< 0)$ *for all* $x \in (a, b)$ (*fig. 6.11a, b*); *and*

(*b*) *for* f *decreasing at an increasing (decreasing) rate over* (a, b), $\mathrm{f}'(x) < 0$ *and* $\mathrm{f}''(x) < 0 (> 0)$ *for all* $x \in (a, b)$ (*fig. 6.11c, d*).

It is evident that (a) and (b) implicitly categorize f′ as strictly increasing or decreasing over (a, b) since $\mathrm{f}'' \neq 0$ in each case.

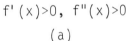

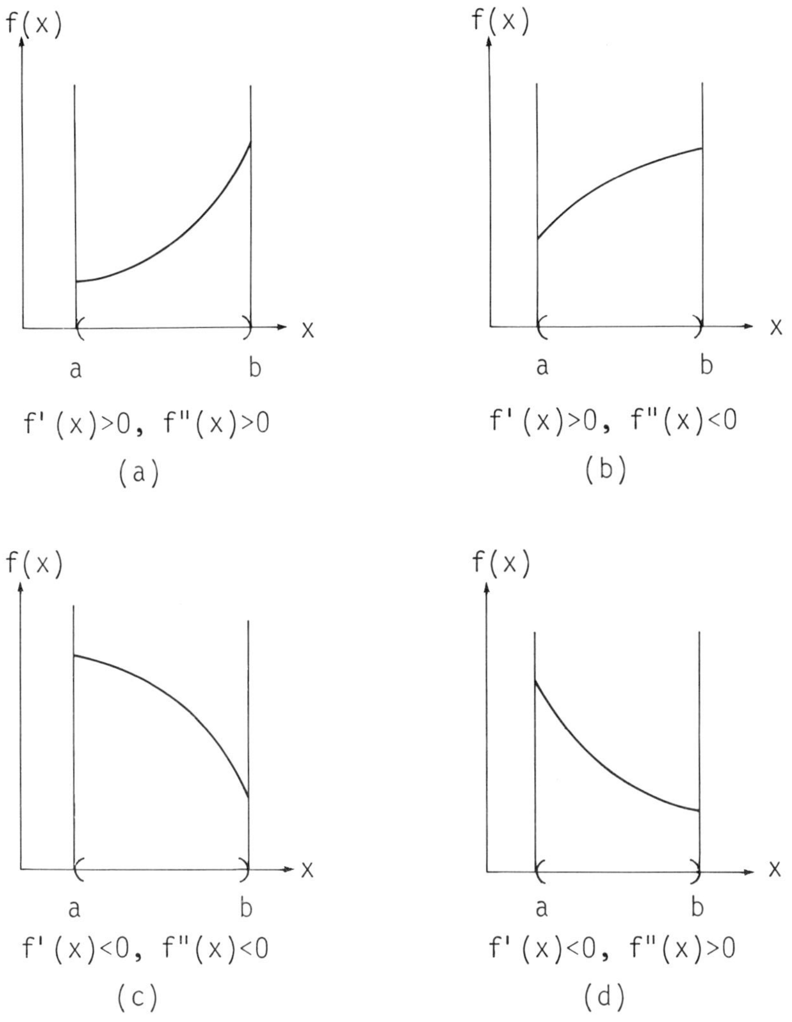

Fig. 6.11.

Let us utilize the observations on f″ incorporated in theorem 6.1.1 as a basis for examining the behavior of f″ near a point where f attains a local

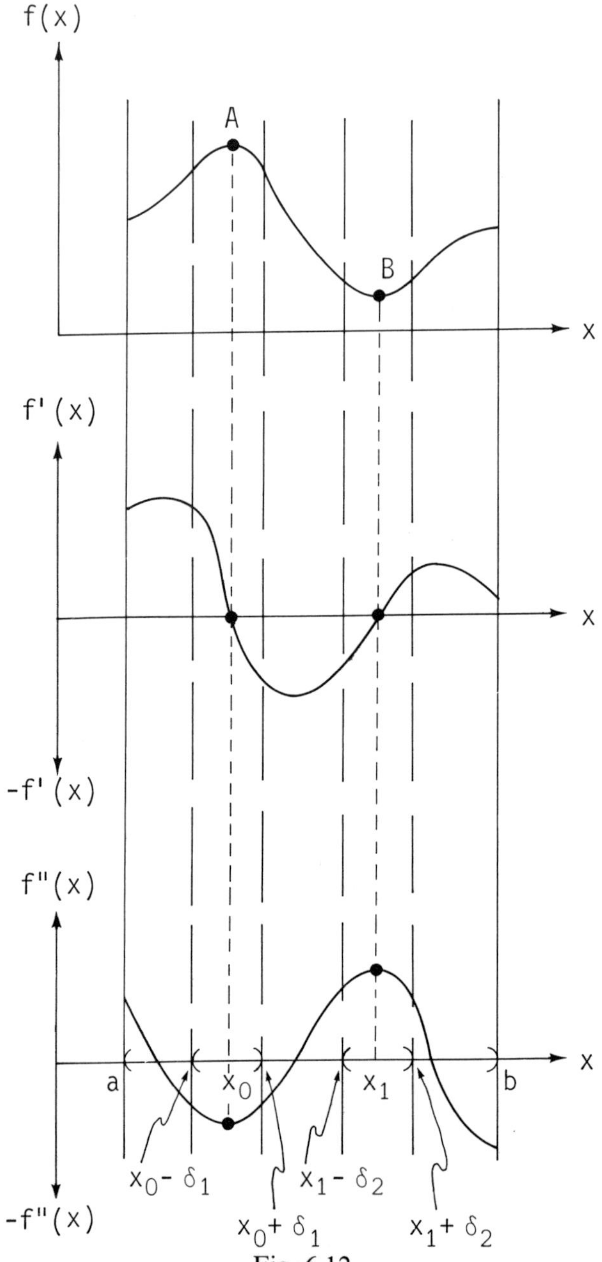

Fig. 6.12.

extremum. To aid us in this undertaking let us plot f′ and f″ directly beneath the graph of some hypothetical function f (fig. 6.12). Now, if f possesses a strong local maximum at $x_0 \in (a, b)$ (point A in fig. 6.12), f is: increasing at a decreasing rate for $x_0 - \delta_1 < x < x_0$ (hence, $f''(x) < 0$ over $(x_0 - \delta_1, x_0)$); stationary at x_0 (with $f''(x_0) < 0$); and decreasing at an increasing rate for $x_0 < x < x_0 + \delta_1$ (with $f''(x)$ still negative over $(x_0, x_0 + \delta_1)$. Hence, $f''(x)$ is negative for all $x \in \delta_1(x_0)$. And if f attains a strong local minimum at $x_1 \in (a, b)$ (point B of fig. 6.12), f: decreases at a decreasing rate when $x_1 - \delta_2 < x < x_1$ (and thus $f''(x) > 0$ throughout $(x_1 - \delta_2, x_1)$); becomes stationary at x_1 (with $f''(x) > 0$); and increases at an increasing rate for $x_1 < x < x_1 + \delta_2$ (with $f''(x)$ also positive on $(x_1, x_1 + \delta_2)$). In this case $f''(x)$ remains positive throughout the entirety of $\delta_2(x_1)$.

It is clear from the preceding discussion that if f attains a strong local extremum over (a, b), strict inequality must hold between the second derivative of f and zero at the point where $f' = 0$. Let us utilize this restriction as a basis for the following theorem. That is, we postulate what we shall call a sufficient condition for a strong local extremum.

THEOREM 6.5 (a sufficient condition). *Let the real-valued function* $y = f(x)$ *possess continuous first and second derivatives throughout some* δ*-neighborhood of the point* $x_0 \in (a, b)$. *If* $f'(x_0) = 0$ *and* $f''(x_0) \neq 0$, *then* f *has a strong local extremum at* x_0. *Moreover: (a) if* $f''(x_0) < 0$, f *has a strong local maximum at* x_0; *and (b) if* $f''(x_0) > 0$, f *has a strong local minimum at* x_0.

Proof. The proof of this theorem follows closely that given in support of theorem 6.4. From eq. (5.12.1) we may write the second-order Taylor expansion of f near x_0 as

$$f(x_0 + h) = f(x_0) + f'(x_0)h + \frac{1}{2!}f''(x_0 + \theta h)h^2, \quad 0 < \theta < 1, |h| < \delta. \quad (6.3)$$

By hypothesis $f'(x_0) = 0$. Hence, eq. (6.3) may be written as

$$f(x_0 + h) - f(x_0) = \frac{1}{2!}f''(x_0 + \theta h)h^2, \quad 0 < \theta < 1, \quad |h| < \delta. \quad (6.3.1)$$

Since f″ is continuous and non-vanishing at x_0, part (c) of theorem 6.2 informs us that we can find an arbitrarily small interval about x_0, $\delta(x_0)$, such that $f''(x)$ has the same sign as $f''(x_0)$ for all $x \in \delta(x_0)$.

If $f''(x_0) < 0$, then, by the preceding argument, $f''(x_0 + \theta h) < 0$ when x, and thus $x_0 + \theta h$, is close to x_0. But this means that the right-hand side of eq. (6.3.1) is negative also since $\frac{1}{2!}h^2 > 0$. Hence, $f(x_0 + h) - f(x_0) < 0$ for all $x \in \delta(x_0)$ and thus f assumes a strong local maximum at x_0. For $f''(x_0) > 0$, $\frac{1}{2!}f''(x_0 + \theta h)h^2 > 0$ since both $f''(x_0 + \theta h)$ and $\frac{1}{2!}h^2$ are positive over the sub-interval $x_0 - \delta < x < x_0 + \delta$. In this case f attains a strong local minimum at x_0 since $f(x_0 + h) - f(x_0) > 0$ when $x \in \delta(x_0)$. Q.E.D.

To enhance our understanding of the significance of this theorem, a few comments pertaining to its interpretation will be advanced. We have seen that the sign of f″ enables us to distinguish a maximum from a minimum at a point where f′ vanishes. But the case where f″ also vanishes at this point is left undecided. Hence, this theorem represents a condition which is only sufficient (and thus incomplete since local extrema may still exist at a point where $f'' = 0$) and not necessary and sufficient to identify a strong local extremum.

Example 6.5. Let the real-valued function $y = f(x) = x^3 - 6x^2 + 20$ be defined for all $x \in (-1, 5)$. Isolate the stationary points of f and determine whether or not they correspond to local extrema over this interval. Setting the first derivative of f equal to zero yields $f'(x) = 3x^2 - 12x = 0$ or $3x(x-4) = 0$. Hence, the critical values of $x \in \mathscr{D}_f$ are 0 and 4. The corresponding stationary values of f are, respectively, $f(0) = 20$, $f(4) = -12$. Does f possess a local maximum or minimum at the stationary points (0, 20), (4, −12)? To apply our sufficient condition we must calculate $f''(x) = 6x - 12$. For $x = 0$, $f''(0) = -12 < 0$; for $x = 4$, $f''(4) = 12 > 0$. Hence, f has a strong local maximum at $x = 0$ and a strong local minimum at $x = 4$ (fig. 6.13).

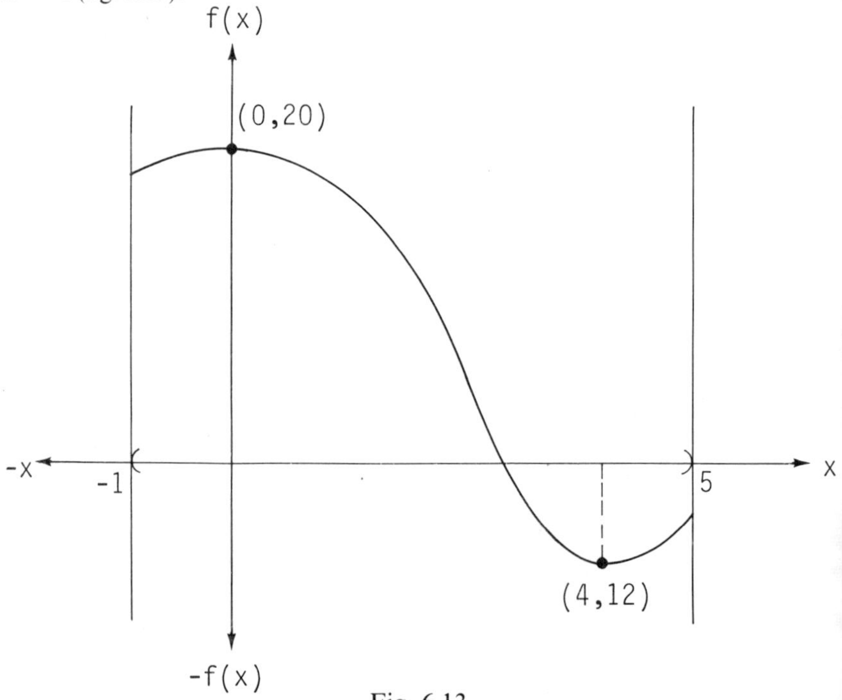

Fig. 6.13.

Example 6.6. In chapter 4 we discovered that the global minimum of a continuous function f on a closed bounded interval could be represented by the negative of the global maximum of $-f$. A similar relationship exists between local extrema, i.e.

$$\underset{x \in \mathscr{E}^n}{\text{l min}} \, f(\boldsymbol{x}) = -\underset{x \in \mathscr{E}^n}{\text{l max}} \{-f(x)\}.$$

For $y = f(x) = x^2+2$, $-\infty < x < +\infty$, demonstrate that this equality is indeed valid. Setting $f'(x) = 2x$ equal to zero yields the critical value $x = 0$. In addition, $f''(x) = 2 > 0$. Hence, f possesses a strong local minimum at $x = 0$ (fig. 6.14). Now, $-f(x) = -x^2-2$ and $-f'(x) = -2x$ also vanishes at $x = 0$. Since $-f''(x) = -2 < 0$, $-f$ attains a strong local maximum at $x = 0$. With

$$f(0) = 2 = \underset{x}{\text{l min}} \, f(x) \quad \text{and} \quad -f(0) = -2 = \underset{x}{\text{l max}} \{-f(x)\},$$

it follows that

$$-\underset{x}{\text{l max}} \{-f(x)\} = -(-f(0)) = -(-2) = \underset{x}{\text{l min}} \, f(x).$$

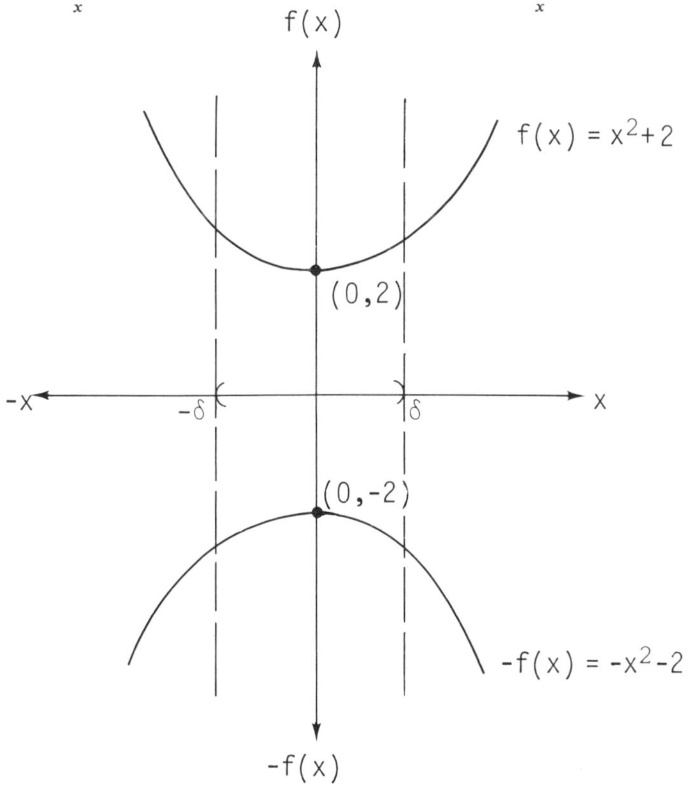

Fig. 6.14.

6.4. A strengthened necessary condition for a local extremum

If we admit the possibility of the second derivative of f vanishing at x_0, our sufficient condition degenerates to a necessary condition. Specifically, by weakening our sufficient condition, i.e. by replacing $f''(x_0) \neq 0$ by $f''(x_0) \leqslant 0 (\geqslant 0)$ we are in effect strengthening theorem 6.4. Hence, we have an alternative necessary condition which is somewhat stronger than the previous one, yet not sufficient (Frisch, 1966, pp. 24–25). We thus posit

THEOREM 6.6 (a strengthened necessary condition). *Let the real-valued function $y = f(x)$ possess continuous first and second derivatives throughout some δ-neighborhood of the point $x_0 \in (a, b)$. If $f'(x_0) = 0$, then: (a) f attains a local maximum at x_0 if $f''(x_0) \leqslant 0$; and (b) f attains a local minimum at x_0 if $f''(x_0) \geqslant 0$.*

Proof. Repeating eq. (6.3.1) we have

$$f(x_0+h)-f(x_0) = \frac{1}{2!} f''(x_0+\theta h)h^2, \quad 0<\theta<1, \quad |h|<\delta.$$

If we now assume that the sign of $f''(x)$ does not change for $x \in \delta(x_0)$, then $f(x_0+h)-f(x_0)$ has the same sign as $f''(x_0+\theta h)$, $|h|<\delta$. So if $f''(x_0+\theta h) \leqslant 0$ throughout $\delta(x_0)$, then $f(x_0+h)-f(x_0) \leqslant 0$ also, and thus f has a local maximum at x_0; and if $f''(x_0+\theta h) \geqslant 0$ throughout $\delta(x_0)$, f attains a local minimum at x_0 since, in this case, $f(x_0+h)-f(x_0) \geqslant 0$, $|h|<\delta$. Q.E.D.

In what sense does this theorem represent a strengthened necessary condition? If $f(x_0)$ is a local maximum, then, in addition to the first derivative of f vanishing at x_0, it is necessary that the condition $f''(x_0)>0$ does not hold. Analogously, if $f(x_0)$ is a local minimum, then, not only does $f'(x_0) = 0$, but it is necessary that we do not have $f''(x_0)<0$. In what sense do we have a weakened sufficient condition? When $f'(x_0) = 0$, it is sufficient for a strong local extremum that we do not have $f''(x_0) = 0$. Hence, the requirement that $f''(x_0) \leqslant 0 (\geqslant 0)$ weakens our sufficient condition for a strong local maximum (minimum). In sum, if $f''(x_0) = 0$, our sufficient condition is inconclusive, i.e. f may or may not have a strong local extremum at x_0. A detailed account of this case appears when we discuss theorem 6.8.

6.5. A necessary and sufficient condition for a local extremum

Let us examine the first derivative of a real-valued function $y = f(x)$ when it is known that the function possesses a strong local extremum at a point $x_0 \in (a, b)$. In what follows it is assumed that f' is continuous over this interval. From fig. 6.3 it is clear that: for $x_0-\delta_1<x<x_0$, $f'(x)>0$; for $x = x_0$,

$f'(x_0) = 0$; and for $x_0 < x < x_0 + \delta_1$, $f'(x) < 0$. Thus when f assumes a strong local maximum at $x_0 \in (a, b)$, f′ changes sign from positive to negative as x increases through x_0, $x \in \delta_1(x_0)$. Similarly, if f attains a strong local minimum at $x' \in (a, b)$, fig. 6.15 indicates that: for $x' - \delta_2 < x < x'$, $f'(x) < 0$; for $x = x'$, $f'(x') = 0$; and for $x' < x < x' + \delta_2$, $f'(x) > 0$. In this case, as x increases through x', $x \in \delta_2(x')$, the sign of f′ changes from negative to positive. If f happens to possess a horizontal point of inflection at $x = x'' \in (a, b)$, figs. 6.6, 6.16 demonstrate that f′ does not change sign as x increases through x'', i.e. from fig. 6.6 (fig. 6.16), $f'(x'') \geq 0 (\leq 0)$ for all $x \in \delta(x'')$. These observations may be consolidated into what we shall call

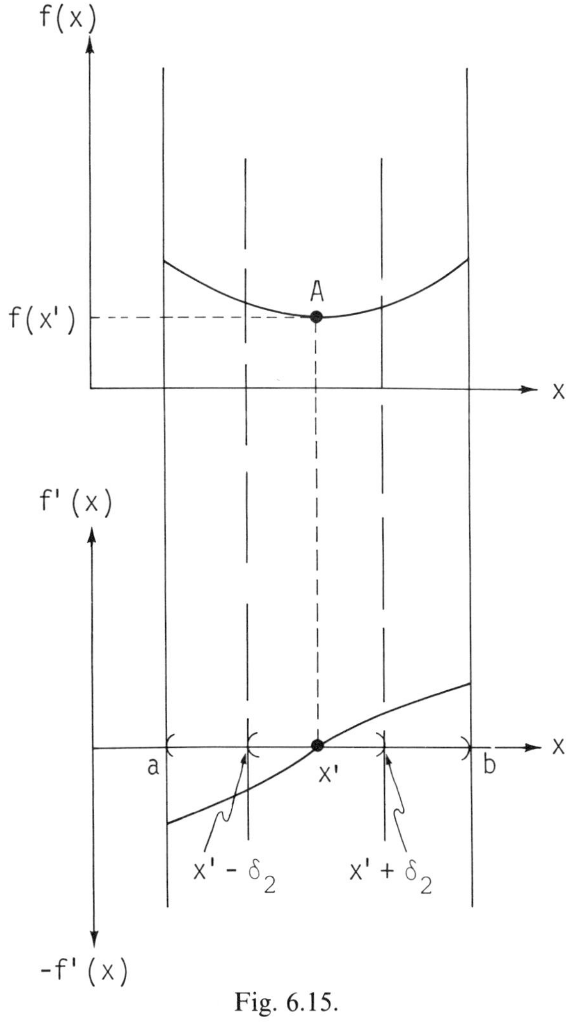

Fig. 6.15.

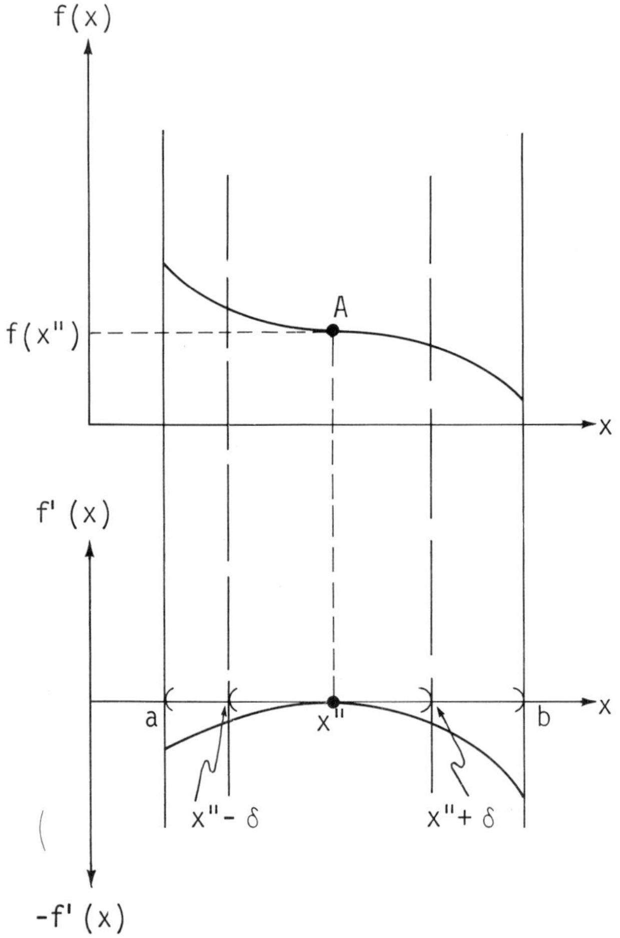

Fig. 6.16.

THEOREM 6.7 (a necessary and sufficient condition). *Let the real-valued function* $y = f(x)$ *and its first derivative be continuous throughout some* δ-*neighborhood of the point* $x_0 \in (a, b)$. *If* $f'(x_0) = 0$ *then, for* $|h| < \delta$ *sufficiently small:*

(*a*) f *has a strong local maximum at* x_0 *if* $f'(x_0+h) > 0$ *for* $h < 0$ *and* $f'(x_0+h) < 0$ *for* $h > 0$;

(*b*) f *has a strong local minimum at* x_0 *if* $f'(x_0+h) < 0$ *when* $h < 0$ *and* $f'(x_0+h) > 0$ *when* $h > 0$; *or*

(*c*) f *has a horizontal point of inflection at* x_0 *if* $f'(x_0+h) > 0 (< 0)$ *for* $h \gtrless 0$.

It is evident that this theorem provides us with a complete set of criteria with which to classify any stationary point(s) which a function may possess. Notice also that it circumvents the use of the second derivative of the function as an aid in classification.

Example 6.7. Let the real-valued function $y = f(x) = x^3 - 6x^2 + 20$ be defined for all $x \in (-1, 5)$. We have seen previously that the stationary points of f are (0, 20) and (4, −12). To determine whether or not they correspond to a maximum or minimum value of f we must apply the above necessary and sufficient condition to $f'(x) = 3x^2 - 12x$ for values of x within a suitably restricted interval about the points 0, 4. Then, for $|h| < \delta$ sufficiently small

$$f'(0+h) = 3(0+h)^2 - 12(0+h) = 3h^2 - 12h > 0 \quad \text{for } h < 0;$$
$$f'(0+h) = 3h^2 - 12h < 0 \quad \text{for } h > 0.$$

A comparison of the signs of these inequalities with part (a) of theorem 6.7 indicates that f assumes a strong local maximum at $x = 0$ (fig. 6.17). A similar set of calculations shows that:

$$f'(4+h) = 3(4+h)^2 - 12(4+h) = 12h + 3h^2 < 0 \quad \text{for } h < 0;$$
$$f'(4+h) = 12h + 3h^2 > 0 \quad \text{for } h > 0.$$

Hence, by part (b) of theorem 6.7, f has a strong local minimum at $x = 4$ (fig. 6.17).

6.6. A generalized necessary and sufficient condition for a local extremum

We noted above that our sufficient condition for a strong local extremum was inconclusive when both f′ and f″ vanished at the critical value $x = x_0 \in (a, b)$. Let us generalize this theorem so as to handle situations of this sort. In doing so we shall again develop criteria with which to simultaneously distinguish a strong local extremum from a horizontal point of inflection. We now postulate

THEOREM 6.8 (a generalized necessary and sufficient condition). *Let* $y = f(x)$ *be a real-valued function possessing continuous derivatives of all orders up to and including n throughout some δ-neighborhood of the point* $x_0 \in (a, b)$. *If* $f'(x_0) = f''(x_0) = \cdots = f^{(n-1)}(x_0) = 0$ *and* $f^{(n)}(x_0) \neq 0$ *then:*

(*a*) f *attains a strong local extremum at* x_0 *if n is even. Moreover:*

(*1*) *if* $f^{(n)}(x_0) < 0$, f *has a strong local maximum at* x_0*; and*

(*2*) *if* $f^{(n)}(x_0) > 0$, f *has a strong local minimum at* x_0.

(*b*) f *attains a horizontal point of inflection at* x_0 *if n is odd.*

Proof. From eq. (5.12.1) we may write the *n*th-order Taylor expansion of

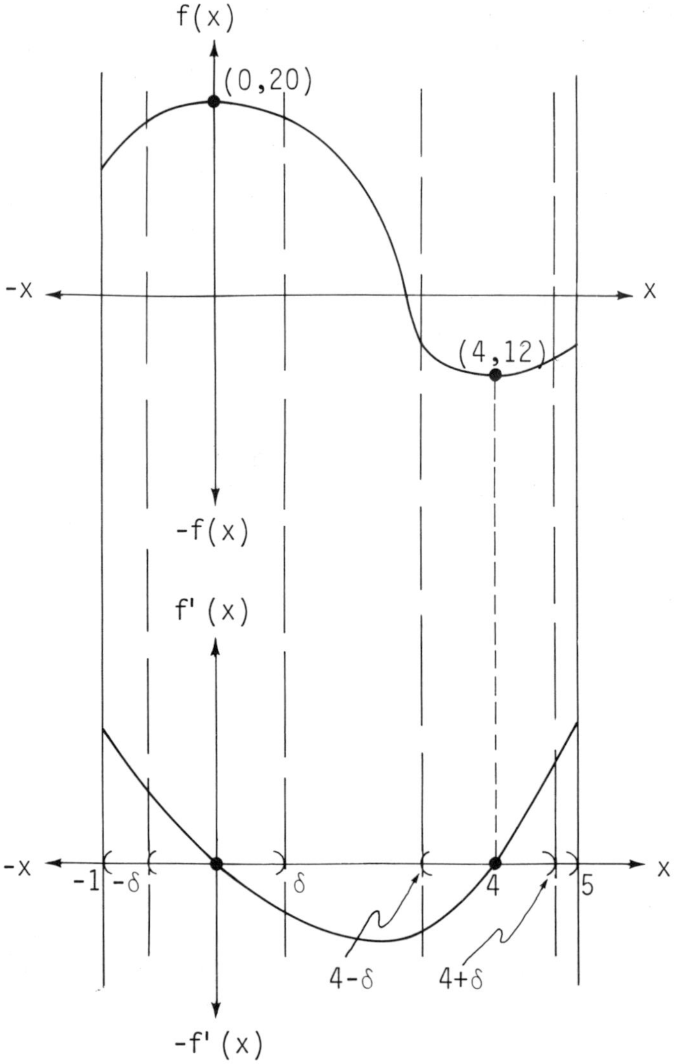

Fig. 6.17.

f near x_0 as

$$f(x_0+h) = f(x_0)+f'(x_0)h+\frac{1}{2!}f''(x_0)h^2+\ldots+\frac{1}{n!}f^{(n)}(x_0+\theta h)h^n,$$
$$0<\theta<1, \quad |h|<\delta. \tag{6.4}$$

By hypothesis $f^{(i)}(x_0) = 0$, $i = 1, \ldots, n-1$. Hence, eq. (6.4) becomes

$$f(x_0+h)-f(x_0) = \frac{1}{n!}f^{(n)}(x_0+\theta h)h^n, \quad 0<\theta<1, \quad |h|<\delta. \tag{6.4.1}$$

Let us first consider the case where n is even (sufficiency). Since $f^{(n)}$ is continuous at x_0 (see Taylor's theorem) and, by assumption, non-vanishing there, we can find an arbitrarily small δ-neighborhood about x_0, $\delta(x_0)$, such that $f^{(n)}(x)$ has the same sign as $f^{(n)}(x_0)$ throughout $\delta(x_0)$ (by part (c) of theorem 6.2). With n even, h^n is positive for $h \gtrless 0$. By the previous argument $f^{(n)}(x_0+\theta h)$ has the same sign as $f^{(n)}(x_0)$ when x, and thus $x_0+\theta h$, is close to x_0. For $f^{(n)}(x_0)<0$,

$$\frac{1}{n!}f^{(n)}(x_0+\theta h)h^n<0$$

since $f^{(n)}(x_0+\theta h)<0$, $|h|<\delta$. Hence, f assumes a strong local maximum at x_0 since, for $|h|<\delta$ sufficiently small, $f(x_0+h)-f(x_0)<0$. When $f^{(n)}(x_0)>0$, $f^{(n)}(x_0+\theta h)>0$ for $x\in\delta(x_0)$. Thus

$$\frac{1}{n!}f^{(n)}(x_0+\theta h)h^n>0$$

for $|h|<\delta$. In this case, f assumes a strong local minimum at x_0 since, with $|h|<\delta$ arbitrarily small, $f(x_0+h)-f(x_0)>0$.

If n is odd (necessity), h^n is negative for $x_0-\delta<x<x_0$ and positive for $x_0<x<x_0+\delta$, while $f^{(n)}(x_0+\theta h)$ is of unchanging sign throughout the entirety of $\delta(x_0)$. However, the sign of

$$\frac{1}{n!}f^{(n)}(x_0+\theta h)h^n$$

changes as x passes through x_0 from left to right since the sign of h^n does. That is, when $f^{(n)}(x_0)<0$, $f^{(n)}(x_0+\theta h)<0$ but

$$\frac{1}{n!}f^{(n)}(x_0+\theta h)h^n$$

is positive for $x_0-\delta<x<x_0$ and negative for $x_0<x<x_0+\delta$. Correspondingly, $f(x_0+h)-f(x_0)$ is positive when $h<0$ and negative when $h>0$ (for instance, see fig. 6.10). Similarly, when $f^{(n)}(x_0)>0$, $f(x_0+h)-f(x_0)$ is negative when $h<0$ and positive when $h>0$ (fig. 6.6). Hence, $f(x_0)$ cannot be a strong local extremum of f; it is, in fact, a horizontal point of inflection. Q.E.D.

Example 6.8. Let the real-valued function $y = f(x) = (x-3)^4+2$ be defined for all $x\in(0, 5)$. Does f possess a local extremum over this interval? Let us apply theorem 6.8. To do so we must calculate

$$f'(x) = 4(x-3)^3, \qquad f''(x) = 12(x-3)^2,$$
$$f'''(x) = 24(x-3), \qquad f^{(iv)}(x) = 24.$$

It is evident that $f'(3) = f''(3) = f'''(3) = 0$ and $f^{(iv)}(3) \neq 0$. Since the order of the first non-vanishing derivative at $x = 3$ is even, part (a) of the above theorem indicates that f attains a strong local extremum at $x = 3$. Also, with $f^{(iv)}(3) = 24>0$, part (a.2) of the theorem tells us that f has a strong local minimum at the point (3, 2) (fig. 6.18).

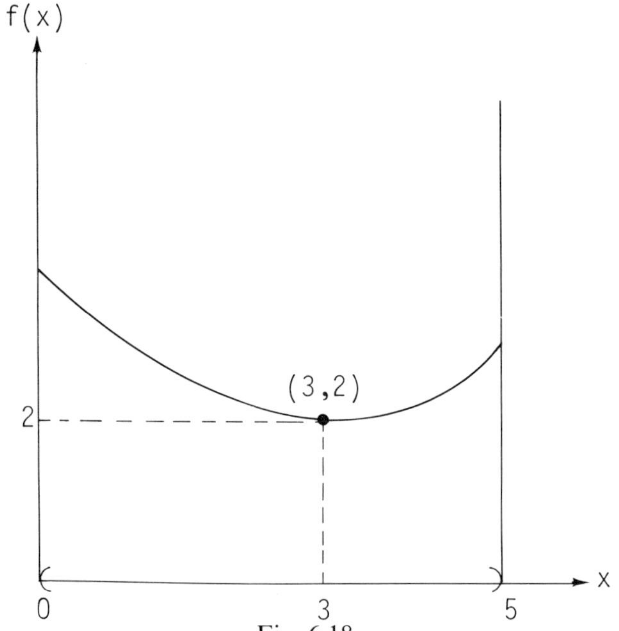

Fig. 6.18.

Example 6.9. We have seen above (example 6.5) that the real-valued function $y = \mathrm{f}(x) = 5-(x-3)^3$, $x \in (-1, 5)$, has a horizontal point of inflection at (3, 2) (fig. 6.10). Let us use theorem 6.8 to verify this result. Now

$$\mathrm{f}'(x) = -3(x-3)^2, \qquad \mathrm{f}''(x) = -6(x-3), \qquad \mathrm{f}'''(x) = -6.$$

When $x = 3$ we have $\mathrm{f}'(3) = \mathrm{f}'(3) = 0$ and $\mathrm{f}'''(3) \neq 0$. Since the first non-vanishing derivative of f at $x = 3$ is of odd order, it is evident that f possesses a horizontal point of inflection there.

Whether the first or second necessary and sufficient condition is applied in actual practice is really a matter of expedience. For some functions the calculation of $\mathrm{f}^{(n)}(x)$ when n is large may be an extremely difficult process. Hence, an application of theorem 6.7 may be warranted. However, one instance, which is by no means uncommon, positively requires the application of theorem 6.7, i.e. theorem 6.8 cannot be used when $\mathrm{f}'(x)$ is not defined at a critical value of $x \in \mathscr{D}_{\mathrm{f}}$. To see this let us consider the following modification of theorem 6.7:

THEOREM 6.9 (a necessary and sufficient condition).[6] *Assume that the real-valued function $y = \mathrm{f}(x)$ is defined at the point $x_0 \in (a, b)$ and $\mathrm{f}'(x_0)$ does not exist. Now, if $\mathrm{f}'(x)$ exists in a suitably restricted deleted δ-neighborhood of x_0, $\delta_{\mathrm{d}}(x_0)$, and has a fixed sign when $x_0-\delta < x < x_0$ and also when $x_0 < x < x_0+\delta$,*

[6] Brand (1955), p. 140.

then, as x *increases through* x_0:

(*a*) $f(x)$ *has a strong local extremum at* x_0 *if the sign of* $f'(x)$ *changes as* x *passes through* x_0. *Specifically*, for $|h|<\delta$ *sufficiently small*,

(*a.1*) f *has a strong local maximum (minimum) at* x_0 *if* $f'(x_0+h)>0(<0)$ *for* $h<0$ *and* $f'(x_0+h)<0(>0)$ *for* $h>0$;

(*b*) $f(x)$ *has a horizontal point of inflection at* x_0 *if the sign of* $f'(x)$ *is invariant throughout* $\delta_d(x_0)$.

Example 6.10. Let $y = f(x) = x^{\frac{3}{5}}+1$ be defined for all real $x\in(-\infty, +\infty)$. Does f possess a local extremum over this interval? We have seen previously that if $f'(x)$ always exists over $\mathscr{D}_f$, then the extreme values of f can only occur where $f'(x) = 0$. A simple calculation shows that $f'(x) = \frac{3}{5}x^{-\frac{2}{5}}$. Although $f'(0)$ does not exist, $f'(x)$ exists for all values of x within a suitably restricted deleted δ-neighborhood of zero. Hence, we must apply theorem 6.9 to $f'(x)$ for values of x throughout this sub-interval. It is easily seen that $f'(x)>0$ for all $x\in\delta_d(0)$. Hence, f does not attain a local extremum at $x = 0$ since the sign of $f'(x)$ does not change as x passes through the origin.

6.7. A note on boundary extrema

In our discussion of local extrema we noted that if a function f and its derivative were continuous and f attained an extremum at a point interior to $[a, b]$, then f′ vanished at that point. But what may we conclude about the behavior of f′ if f assumes an extremum at an endpoint of $[a, b]$? (In this case the extremum is, by definition, of the global variety (see chapter 3 above).) If the one-sided derivatives $f'(a)\,(=f'_+(a))$ and $f'(b)\,(=f'_-(b))$ both exist, then:

(a) for $f(a)>f(x)\,(<f(x))$, $x\in[a, a+\delta)$, $\delta>0$, we may conclude that $f'(a)\leqslant 0(\geqslant 0)$, but not that $f'(a) = 0$ since $f'_-(a)$ is not defined;[7]

(b) for $f(b)>f(x)\,(<f(x))$, $x\in(b-\delta, b]$, $\delta>0$, we may infer that $f'(b)\geqslant 0(\leqslant 0)$, but not that $f'(b) = 0$, since $f'_+(b)$ is undefined.

6.8. The search for global extrema

We noted earlier that a global extremum is either a local extremum or occurs at an endpoint of $[a, b]$. In addition, local extrema may be found among the set of critical values of $x\in(a, b)$. So if global extrema are to be isolated, we must examine: (a) the endpoints of $[a, b]$; (b) points where f has a finite discontinuity (i.e. is undefined); and (c) points where $f' = 0$ or where f′ is undefined. The general search procedure is illustrated in fig. 6.19.

[7] As was indicated earlier, $f'(a) = 0$ if and only if both $f'_+(a)$, $f'_-(a)$ exist and their common value is zero.

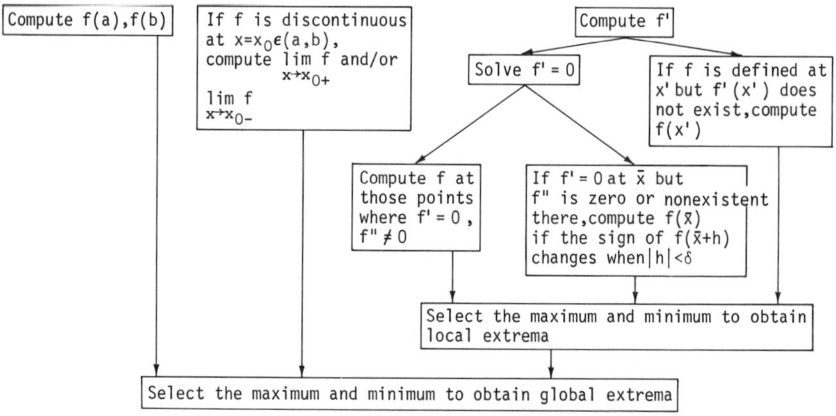

Fig. 6.19.

6.9. Functions of n independent variables

Our initial theorem pertaining to the location of local extrema is

THEOREM 6.10 (a necessary condition). *Let the real-valued function* $y = \mathrm{f}(\boldsymbol{x})$, $\boldsymbol{x} \in \mathscr{E}^n$, *possess continuous first-order partial derivatives throughout some spherical* δ*-neighborhood at the point* $\boldsymbol{x}_0$, $\delta(\boldsymbol{x}_0)$, *contained within an open region* $\mathscr{K} \subseteq \mathscr{E}^n$. *If* f *has a local extremum at* $\boldsymbol{x}_0$, *then* $\nabla \mathrm{f}^0 = \mathbf{0}$.

Proof. Since the vanishing of $\nabla \mathrm{f}$ is a prerequisite for the occurrence of a local extremum at $\boldsymbol{x}_0$, we shall demonstrate that a local extremum cannot occur at that point unless $\nabla \mathrm{f}^0 = \mathbf{0}$. From eq. (5.15.4) we have, for $n = 1$,

$$\mathrm{f}(\boldsymbol{x}_0+\boldsymbol{h})-\mathrm{f}(\boldsymbol{x}_0) = \nabla \mathrm{f}(\boldsymbol{x}_0+\theta\boldsymbol{h})'\boldsymbol{h}, \quad 0<\theta<1. \tag{6.5}$$

Let us assume that the kth partial derivative f_k does not vanish at $\boldsymbol{x}_0$ but that all others are zero there. Then $\mathrm{f}_k(\boldsymbol{x}_0+\theta\boldsymbol{h}) \neq 0$ either since, by part (c) of theorem 6.2, $\mathrm{f}_k(\boldsymbol{x}_0+\theta\boldsymbol{h})$ has the same sign as $\mathrm{f}_k(\boldsymbol{x}_0) \neq 0$ for all points $\boldsymbol{x}$ near $\boldsymbol{x}_0$ with h_k sufficiently small. Then $\nabla \mathrm{f}(\boldsymbol{x}_0+\theta\boldsymbol{h})'\boldsymbol{h} = \mathrm{f}_k(\boldsymbol{x}_0+\theta\boldsymbol{h})h_k \neq 0$ for $|h_k|<\delta$.

If $\mathrm{f}_k(\boldsymbol{x}_0)>0$, then $\mathrm{f}_k(\boldsymbol{x}_0+\theta\boldsymbol{h})>0$ also, and thus $\mathrm{f}(\boldsymbol{x}_0+\boldsymbol{h})-\mathrm{f}(\boldsymbol{x}_0)$ has the same sign as h_k, i.e.

$$\mathrm{f}(\boldsymbol{x}_0+\boldsymbol{h})-\mathrm{f}(\boldsymbol{x}_0) = \mathrm{f}_k(\boldsymbol{x}_0+\theta\boldsymbol{h})h_k \gtrless 0 \quad \text{as } h_k \gtrless 0, \quad 0<\theta<1.$$

Hence f cannot enjoy a local extremum at $\boldsymbol{x}_0$ since the sign of $\mathrm{f}(\boldsymbol{x}_0+\boldsymbol{h})-\mathrm{f}(\boldsymbol{x}_0)$ changes whenever the sign of h_k does, $|h_k|<\delta$.

If $\mathrm{f}_k(x_0)<0$, then $\mathrm{f}_k(\boldsymbol{x}_0+\theta\boldsymbol{h})<0$, and

$$\mathrm{f}(\boldsymbol{x}_0+\boldsymbol{h})-\mathrm{f}(\boldsymbol{x}_0) = \mathrm{f}_k(\boldsymbol{x}_0+\theta\boldsymbol{h})h_k \gtrless 0 \quad \text{as } h_k \gtrless 0, \quad 0<\theta<1.$$

Again we obtain a contradiction, i.e. the sign of $f(\boldsymbol{x}_0+\boldsymbol{h})-f(\boldsymbol{x}_0)$ must be invariant for $|h_k|<\delta$. In sum, f cannot attain a local extremum at $\boldsymbol{x}_0$ if all of its partial derivatives do not vanish there. Q.E.D.

How may we interpret this theorem? It has been demonstrated that if $y = f(\boldsymbol{x})$, $\boldsymbol{x}\in\mathscr{E}^n$, has a local maximum (minimum) at the point $\boldsymbol{x}_0\in\mathscr{K}\subseteq\mathscr{E}^n$, then $\nabla f^0 = \boldsymbol{0}$ and thus, for a suitably restricted variation h from $\boldsymbol{x}_0$ in the $\boldsymbol{e}_i$-direction,

$$f(\boldsymbol{x}_0+h\boldsymbol{e}_i)-f(\boldsymbol{x}_0)\leqslant 0(\geqslant 0), \quad |h|<\delta, \quad i = 1, \dots, n.$$

In addition, when the first partial derivatives of f vanish at $\boldsymbol{x}_0$, the total differential of f, $df = \nabla f'\boldsymbol{h}$, must identically vanish there also. Hence $df^0 = (\nabla f^0)'\boldsymbol{h}\equiv 0$ for any $\boldsymbol{h}$ whatever. So if $(\boldsymbol{x}_0, f^0)$ is known to represent a local maximum (minimum) of f, the function is deemed as having a maximum (minimum) for simultaneous variations $\boldsymbol{h}$ from $\boldsymbol{x}_0$ in 'any' direction or $f(\boldsymbol{x}_0+\boldsymbol{h})-f(\boldsymbol{x}_0)\leqslant 0(\geqslant 0)$ when $\|\boldsymbol{h}\|<\delta$ is sufficiently small.

It must be stressed, however, that the converse of this theorem does not hold since if the gradient of f vanishes at a point interior to $\mathscr{K}$, we cannot conclude that f attains a local extremum there. That is, if $\nabla f^0 = \boldsymbol{0}$, we cannot even be sure that f attains an extremum in any of the $\boldsymbol{e}_i$-directions, $i = 1, \dots, n$, let alone be confident that f attains an extremum for deviations $\boldsymbol{h}$ from $\boldsymbol{x}_0$ in 'all' directions.

When ∇f vanishes at an interior point of an open region $\mathscr{K}\subseteq\mathscr{E}^n$, the value of f at this point is said to be stationary. To further classify such a point we state:

DEFINITION 6.5. *Any point* $(\bar{\boldsymbol{x}}, \bar{f})\in\mathscr{E}^{n+1}$ *where* ∇f *vanishes will be termed a stationary point, while* $\bar{f}$ *is termed a stationary value of* f.

Also,

DEFINITION 6.6. *The point* $\bar{\boldsymbol{x}}\in\mathscr{K}\subseteq\mathscr{E}^n$ *is called a critical point of* $\mathscr{K}$ *if: (a)* $\nabla f(\bar{\boldsymbol{x}}) = \boldsymbol{0}$*; or (b)* $\nabla f(\bar{\boldsymbol{x}})$ *fails to exist.*

So if $\bar{\boldsymbol{x}}\in\mathscr{K}$ is a critical point where ∇f exists, it follows that $\nabla f(\bar{\boldsymbol{x}}) = \boldsymbol{0}$ and $\bar{f}$ is a stationary value of f over $\mathscr{K}$. In this regard, every extreme point where f is differentiable is a stationary point. However, the converse of this statement is not true—as will become evident shortly when we discuss the attainment of saddle values of f over $\mathscr{K}\subseteq\mathscr{E}^2$.

Example 6.11. In example 3.5 we found that the real-valued function $y = f(\boldsymbol{x}) = x_1^2+x_2^2+2x_1-x_2-3$ possessed a strong local minimum at the point $\boldsymbol{x}_0' = (-1, \frac{1}{2})$. If this is the case, then the first partial derivatives must vanish at this point. To verify this result we find $f_1 = 2x_1+2$, $f_2 = 2x_2-1$. Hence, $f_1(\boldsymbol{x}_0) = f_2(\boldsymbol{x}_0) = 0$ as expected.

To apply the above necessary condition in the actual search for stationary values of f we first isolate the critical points in $\mathscr{K} \subseteq \mathscr{E}^n$ at which these values occur. This may be accomplished by setting the gradient of f equal to the null vector and then solving the resulting system of equations $f_i(\boldsymbol{x}) = 0$, $i = 1, \ldots, n$, simultaneously to obtain the implied components of $\boldsymbol{x}$.[8]

Example 6.12. Let the real-valued function

$$y = f(\boldsymbol{x}) = -2x_1^2 - 3x_2^2 + 3x_1x_2 - 2x_1 - x_2 - 4$$

be defined throughout the entirety of $\mathscr{E}^2$. Does f attain a stationary value over $\mathscr{D}_f$? Applying our necessary condition for a local extremum we set $\nabla f = \mathbf{0}$ or $-4x_1 + 3x_2 = 2$, $3x_1 - 6x_2 = 1$. Solving this latter system of equations simultaneously we obtain $\boldsymbol{x}_0' = (-1, -\frac{2}{3})$. Hence, f assumes a stationary value at the critical point $\boldsymbol{x}_0 \in \mathscr{D}_f$.

It has been demonstrated that the vanishing of the first partial derivatives of the function $y = f(\boldsymbol{x})$, $\boldsymbol{x} \in \mathscr{E}^n$, at a point interior to its domain provides us with a necessary condition for the existence of a local extremum. But it was argued above that these partial derivatives may vanish at a point of $\mathscr{D}_f$ even though the point does not yield a local extremum. For example, given that $\boldsymbol{x} \in \mathscr{E}^2$, f may possess a saddle point at $\bar{\boldsymbol{x}} \in \mathscr{D}_f = \mathscr{K}$ (point A of fig. 6.20a). Specifically,

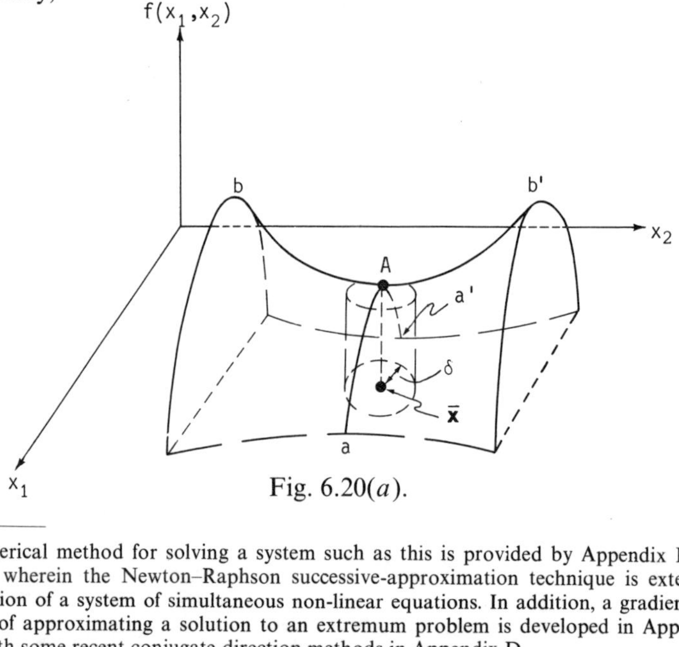

Fig. 6.20(*a*).

[8] A numerical method for solving a system such as this is provided by Appendix B to this chapter, wherein the Newton–Raphson successive-approximation technique is extended to the solution of a system of simultaneous non-linear equations. In addition, a gradient search method of approximating a solution to an extremum problem is developed in Appendix C, along with some recent conjugate-direction methods in Appendix D.

DEFINITION 6.7. *A stationary point* $(\bar{\boldsymbol{x}}, \bar{\mathrm{f}})$, $\bar{\boldsymbol{x}} \in \mathscr{E}^2$, *is termed a saddle point if* $\bar{\mathrm{f}}$ *is simultaneously a strong local maximum in one direction and a strong local minimum in another. Here* $\bar{\mathrm{f}}$ *is called a saddle value or minimax of* f *on* $\mathscr{K} \subseteq \mathscr{E}^n$.

While $\nabla \mathrm{f}(\bar{\boldsymbol{x}}) = \mathbf{0}$, it is not the case that

$$\mathrm{f}(\bar{\boldsymbol{x}}+\boldsymbol{h})-\mathrm{f}(\bar{\boldsymbol{x}}) \leqslant 0 (\geqslant 0), \quad \|\boldsymbol{h}\| < \delta,$$

throughout a suitably restricted circular δ-neighborhood of $\bar{\boldsymbol{x}}$. As fig. 6.20b indicates, f has a strong local maximum along the parabola $a\mathrm{A}a'$ in the $\boldsymbol{e}_1$-direction and a strong local minimum along parabola $b\mathrm{A}b'$ in the $\boldsymbol{e}_2$-direction. Hence

$$\mathrm{f}(\bar{\boldsymbol{x}}+h\boldsymbol{e}_1)-\mathrm{f}(\bar{\boldsymbol{x}}) \leqslant 0$$

but

$$\mathrm{f}(\bar{\boldsymbol{x}}+h\boldsymbol{e}_2)-\mathrm{f}(\bar{\boldsymbol{x}}) \geqslant 0$$

for $|h| < \delta$ sufficiently small.

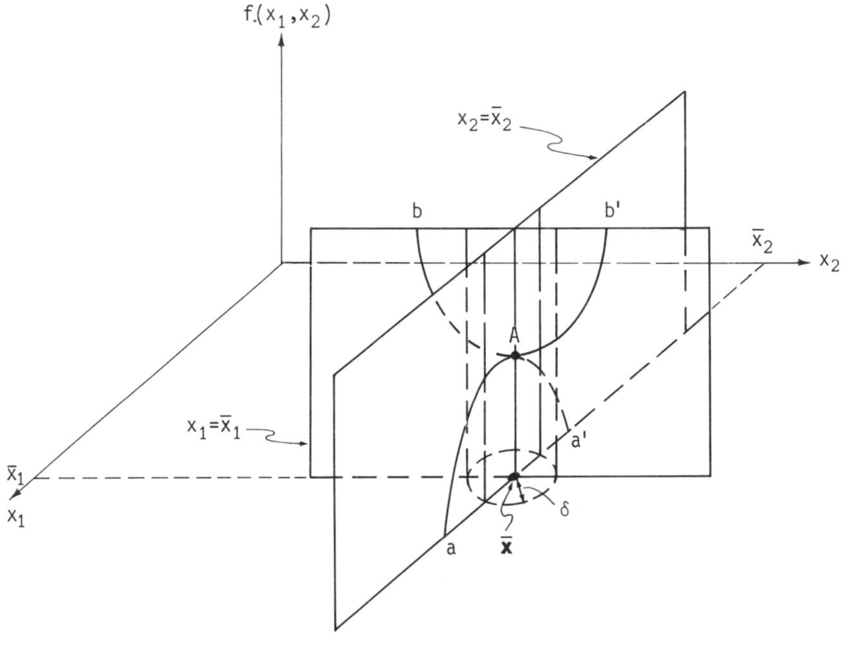

Fig. 6.20(b).

Example 6.13. Does the real-valued function $y = \mathrm{f}(\boldsymbol{x}) = 4x_1x_2-2x_1-2x_2+4$ attain a local extremum anywhere in $\mathscr{K} \subseteq \mathscr{E}^2$? Our answer may be obtained by first isolating the critical points in $\mathscr{K}$ which give rise to stationary values of f and then examining the behavior of f in the immediate vicinity of these points. Setting $\nabla \mathrm{f} = \mathbf{0}$ we obtain the critical point $\boldsymbol{x}_0' = (\frac{1}{2}, \frac{1}{2})$. For $\boldsymbol{x} = \boldsymbol{x}_0+\boldsymbol{h}$,

$$\mathrm{f}(\boldsymbol{x}_0+\boldsymbol{h}) = 4h_1h_2+3.$$

Since $\mathrm{f}(\boldsymbol{x}_0) = 3$,

$$\mathrm{f}(\boldsymbol{x}_0+\boldsymbol{h})-\mathrm{f}(\boldsymbol{x}_0) = 4h_1h_2, \quad \|\boldsymbol{h}\| < \delta.$$

Clearly, this last expression may be either positive, negative, or zero, depending upon the values assigned to the components of $\boldsymbol{h}$ for $\|\boldsymbol{h}\| < \delta$ sufficiently small. Hence, f has a saddle point at $\boldsymbol{x}_0$, f^0). It does not attain a local extremum anywhere over its domain.

Although the above necessary condition allows us to isolate the stationary values of a continuous function over an open region $\mathscr{K} \subseteq \mathscr{E}^n$, it provides no insight into whether any particular critical point yields a local extremum. To determine whether a function actually has a local extremum over its domain, we must employ the second-order partial derivatives of the function. The theorem which follows pertains to the recognition of strong local extrema over $\mathscr{K}$. We look then to

THEOREM 6.11 (a sufficient condition). *Let the real-valued function* $y = \mathrm{f}(\boldsymbol{x})$, $\boldsymbol{x} \in \mathscr{E}^n$, *possess continuous first- and second-order partial derivatives throughout some spherical* δ*-neighborhood of the point* $\boldsymbol{x}_0$, $\delta(\boldsymbol{x}_0)$, *contained within an open region* $\mathscr{K} \subseteq \mathscr{E}^n$. *If* $\nabla \mathrm{f}^0 = \mathbf{0}$ *and the quadratic form*

$$Q(\boldsymbol{h}) = \boldsymbol{h}'\boldsymbol{H}_{\mathrm{f}}(\boldsymbol{x}_0)\boldsymbol{h}$$

is negative (positive) definite for all $\boldsymbol{h} \neq \mathbf{0}$, f *attains a strong local maximum (minimum) at* $\boldsymbol{x}_0$. *That is, if* $\nabla \mathrm{f}^0 = \mathbf{0}$ *and*

$$(a)\ \mathrm{f}^0_{11} < 0, \quad \begin{vmatrix} \mathrm{f}^0_{11} & \mathrm{f}^0_{12} \\ \mathrm{f}^0_{21} & \mathrm{f}^0_{22} \end{vmatrix} > 0, \ldots, (-1)^n|\boldsymbol{H}_{\mathrm{f}}(\boldsymbol{x}_0)| > 0,$$

f *has a strong local maximum at* $\boldsymbol{x}_0$; *while if*

$$(b)\ \mathrm{f}^0_{11} > 0, \quad \begin{vmatrix} \mathrm{f}^0_{11} & \mathrm{f}^0_{12} \\ \mathrm{f}^0_{21} & \mathrm{f}^0_{22} \end{vmatrix} > 0, \ldots, |\boldsymbol{H}_{\mathrm{f}}(\boldsymbol{x}_0)| > 0,$$

f *has a strong local minimum at* $\boldsymbol{x}_0$.

Proof. From eq. (5.15.4) we obtain

$$\mathrm{f}(\boldsymbol{x}_0+\boldsymbol{h})-\mathrm{f}(\boldsymbol{x}_0) = \frac{1}{2!}\boldsymbol{h}'\boldsymbol{H}_{\mathrm{f}}(\boldsymbol{x}_0+\theta\boldsymbol{h})\boldsymbol{h}, \quad 0<\theta<1, \tag{6.6}$$

since, by hypothesis, $\nabla f^0 = \mathbf{0}$. With the second-order partial derivatives of f continuous at $\boldsymbol{x}_0$, the right-hand side of eq. (6.6) approaches $\frac{1}{2!}\boldsymbol{h}'\boldsymbol{H}_f(\boldsymbol{x}_0)\boldsymbol{h}$ when $\theta \to 0$ and $|h_i| < \delta$, $i = 1, \ldots, n$. Hence $f(\boldsymbol{x}_0 + \boldsymbol{h}) - f(\boldsymbol{x}_0)$ has the same sign as $\boldsymbol{h}'\boldsymbol{H}_f(\boldsymbol{x}_0)\boldsymbol{h}$ provided that the partial derivatives f_{ij}, $i, j = 1, \ldots, n$, are not all zero.

When $\boldsymbol{h}'\boldsymbol{H}_f(\boldsymbol{x}_0)\boldsymbol{h} < 0$ for $\boldsymbol{h} \neq \mathbf{0}$, $Q(\boldsymbol{h})$ is negative definite and $f(\boldsymbol{x}_0 + \boldsymbol{h}) - f(\boldsymbol{x}_0) < 0$ for $\|\boldsymbol{h}\|$ small, i.e. f has a strong local maximum at $\boldsymbol{x}_0$. An application of theorem 1.7 indicates that $Q(\boldsymbol{h})$ is negative definite if and only if the naturally ordered principal minors of the Hessian matrix $\boldsymbol{H}_f(\boldsymbol{x}_0)$ alternate in sign, the first being negative.

If $\boldsymbol{h}'\boldsymbol{H}_f(\boldsymbol{x}_0)\boldsymbol{h} > 0$ for $\boldsymbol{h} \neq \mathbf{0}$, $Q(\boldsymbol{h})$ is positive definite and thus $f(\boldsymbol{x}_0 + \boldsymbol{h}) - f(\boldsymbol{x}_0) > 0$ for small $\|\boldsymbol{h}\|$. In this instance f has a strong local minimum at $\boldsymbol{x}_0$. An appeal to theorem 1.6 informs us that $Q(\boldsymbol{h})$ is positive definite if and only if the naturally ordered principal minors of the Hessian matrix $\boldsymbol{H}_f(\boldsymbol{x}_0)$ are all positive. Q.E.D.

What about the instances in which $\nabla f^0 = \mathbf{0}$ and $Q(\boldsymbol{h})$ is indefinite or semi-definite at $\boldsymbol{x}_0$? For $Q(\boldsymbol{h})$ indefinite, i.e. positive for some vectors $\boldsymbol{h}$ and negative for others, $f(\boldsymbol{x}_0 + \boldsymbol{h}) - f(\boldsymbol{x}_0)$ is correspondingly positive for suitably restricted variations $\boldsymbol{h}$ from $\boldsymbol{x}_0$ in one direction and negative for like variations in another. Hence f does not attain a strong local extremum at $\boldsymbol{x}_0$. For $\boldsymbol{x} \in \mathscr{E}^2$, f has a saddle point at $\boldsymbol{x}_0$ if $Q(\boldsymbol{h})$ is indefinite. To see this let $f_{11}^0 \neq 0$, $|\boldsymbol{H}_f(\boldsymbol{x}_0)| = f_{11}^0 f_{22}^0 - (f_{12}^0)^2 < 0$. If $h_2 = 0$ and $h_1 \neq 0$, then $Q(h_1, 0) = h_1^2 f_{11}^0$ has the same sign as f_{11}^0. But if $h_2 \neq 0$ and $h_1 = -h_2 f_{12}^0 / f_{11}^0$, then $Q(\boldsymbol{h}) = (h_2^2 / f_{11}^0)[f_{11}^0 f_{22}^0 - (f_{12}^0)^2]$ has a sign opposite to that of f_{11}^0. A similar argument holds for the case where $f_{22}^0 \neq 0$, $f_{11}^0 f_{22}^0 - (f_{12}^0)^2 < 0$. When $f_{11}^0 = f_{22}^0 = 0$, $f_{11}^0 f_{22}^0 - (f_{12}^0)^2 = -(f_{12}^0)^2 < 0$ implies that $f_{12}^0 \neq 0$. Now, if $h_1 = h_2$, $Q(\boldsymbol{h}) = 2h_2^2 f_{12}^0$ has the same sign as f_{12}^0, while for $h_1 = -h_2$, $Q(-h_2, h_2) = -2h_2^2 f_{12}^0$ has a sign opposite to that of f_{12}^0. In sum, for $f_{11}^0 f_{22}^0 - (f_{12}^0) < 0$, f has a saddle point at $\boldsymbol{x}_0$.

If $Q(\boldsymbol{h})$ is semi-definite, no conclusion about extreme values of f may be reached, since, in this instance, the function may possess a strong local maximum, minimum, or neither at $\boldsymbol{x}_0 \in \mathscr{E}^n$. Since this case is of little practical consequence, an extensive discussion of its details will be omitted.[9] Suffice it to say that when $Q(\boldsymbol{h})$ is semi-definite, our classification scheme is incomplete. Hence, this theorem provides only a sufficient condition for a strong local extremum and not one which is both necessary and sufficient.

Let us now look to the interpretation of theorem 6.11. In our discussion of a necessary condition for a local extremum we made use of the total differential of the function. Let us employ this relationship here. As indicated

[9] The interested reader may consult Taylor (1955), p. 234; Brand (1955), p. 188, and Gue and Thomas (1968), pp. 34–37.

above, $\mathrm{df} = \nabla f' \boldsymbol{h}$. Then

$$\mathrm{d}^2\mathrm{f} = \mathrm{d}(\nabla \mathrm{f}' \boldsymbol{h}) = (\nabla^2 \mathrm{f} \boldsymbol{h})' \boldsymbol{h}, \tag{6.7}$$

where the components of $\boldsymbol{h}$ are measured from the point $\boldsymbol{x}_0 \in \mathscr{K} \subseteq \mathscr{E}^n$. If the partial derivatives in eq. (6.7) are evaluated at $\boldsymbol{x}_0$, then we may write this expression as

$$\mathrm{d}^2\mathrm{f}^0 = Q(\boldsymbol{h}) = \boldsymbol{h}' \boldsymbol{H}_\mathrm{f}(\boldsymbol{x}_0) \boldsymbol{h}, \tag{6.7.1}$$

i.e. $\mathrm{d}^2\mathrm{f}$ is a quadratic form in $\boldsymbol{h}$.[10] Now, if $\mathrm{df}^0 = 0$ (i.e. $\nabla \mathrm{f}^0 = \mathbf{0}$) and $\mathrm{d}^2\mathrm{f}^0 = Q(\boldsymbol{h}) < 0 (> 0)$, $\boldsymbol{h} \neq \mathbf{0}$, then clearly a movement from $\boldsymbol{x}_0$ in 'any' direction must result in a decrease (increase) in f and thus f attains a strong local maximum (minimum) at $\boldsymbol{x}_0$.

It is instructive to consider the interpretation of this theorem in a somewhat different yet equally illuminating light. To make our analysis as transparent as possible, we shall consider the case where $\boldsymbol{x} \in \mathscr{E}^2$. From (a) above we see that a sufficient condition for f to have a strong local maximum at $\boldsymbol{x}_0$ is $\mathrm{f}^0_{11} < 0$ and $\mathrm{f}^0_{11}\mathrm{f}^0_{22} - (\mathrm{f}^0_{12})^2 > 0$; and these inequalities together imply that $\mathrm{f}^0_{22} < 0$. Now when both $\mathrm{f}^0_{11}, \mathrm{f}^0_{22} < 0$, we are provided with a sufficient condition for f to have a strong local maximum at $\boldsymbol{x}_0$ for small variations in both the $\boldsymbol{e}_1$- and $\boldsymbol{e}_2$-directions. But this does not guarantee that f necessarily attains a strong local maximum at $\boldsymbol{x}_0$ for suitably restricted variations in every direction. To insure that f has a strong local maximum at $\boldsymbol{x}_0$ for small variations in 'any' direction, it is sufficient that $\mathrm{f}^0_{11} < 0$ and $\mathrm{f}^0_{11}\mathrm{f}^0_{22} - (\mathrm{f}^0_{12})^2 > 0$. Hence, the inequalities $\mathrm{f}^0_{11} < 0$, $\mathrm{f}^0_{11}\mathrm{f}^0_{22} - (\mathrm{f}^0_{12})^2 > 0$ taken together imply that $Q(\boldsymbol{h}) < 0$ for 'all' $\boldsymbol{h} \neq \mathbf{0}$ and thus $\mathrm{f}(\boldsymbol{x}_0 + \boldsymbol{h}) - \mathrm{f}(\boldsymbol{x}_0) < 0$ when $\|\boldsymbol{h}\| < \delta$ is small.

Recalling (b) above, we have a sufficient condition for a strong local minimum at $\boldsymbol{x}_0$ if both f^0_{11}, $\mathrm{f}^0_{11}\mathrm{f}^0_{22} - (\mathrm{f}^0_{12})^2 > 0$. With these expressions positive it must also be true that $\mathrm{f}^0_{22} > 0$. When f^0_{11}, $\mathrm{f}^0_{22} > 0$, f has a strong local minimum for small variations from $\boldsymbol{x}_0$ in both the $\boldsymbol{e}_1$- and $\boldsymbol{e}_2$-directions. To ensure that f attains a strong local minimum for suitably restricted variations from $\boldsymbol{x}_0$ in 'every' direction, it is sufficient that $\mathrm{f}^0_{11} > 0$ and $\mathrm{f}^0_{11}\mathrm{f}^0_{22} - (\mathrm{f}^0_{12})^2 > 0$. Hence, $Q(\boldsymbol{h}) > 0$ for 'all' $\boldsymbol{h} \neq \mathbf{0}$ and thus $\mathrm{f}(\boldsymbol{x}_0 + \boldsymbol{h}) - \mathrm{f}(\boldsymbol{x}_0) > 0$ when $\|\boldsymbol{h}\| < \delta$ is small.

Example 6.14. Let the real-valued function

$$y = \mathrm{f}(\boldsymbol{x}) = x_1 + x_2 + x_1 x_2 - 2x_1^2 - 3x_2^2$$

---

[10] It is important to remember that in eq. (6.7) the second-order partials and cross-partials of f are variables, while the components in $\boldsymbol{h}$ are constants. However, the reverse of this interpretation holds in eq. (6.7.1), i.e. since all derivatives have been evaluated at $\boldsymbol{x}_0$, they are now the constants, while the h_i, $i = 1, \ldots, n$, are the variables in the quadratic form.

be defined throughout the entirety of $\mathscr{E}^2$. Does f attain a local extremum over its domain? We first set $\nabla f = \mathbf{0}$ or $-4x_1+x_2 = -1$, $x_1-6x_2 = -1$. Solving this latter system of equations simultaneously yields $\boldsymbol{x}_0' = (\frac{7}{23}, \frac{5}{23})$. With $\nabla f(\boldsymbol{x}_0) = \mathbf{0}$ our necessary condition for a local extremum is satisfied. We next find

$$\boldsymbol{H}_f(\boldsymbol{x}_0) = \begin{bmatrix} -4 & 1 \\ 1 & -6 \end{bmatrix}.$$

Now $M_1 = 4<0$ and $M_2 = |\boldsymbol{H}_f(\boldsymbol{x}_0)| = 23>0$. Hence, f attains a strong local maximum at $\boldsymbol{x}_0' = (\frac{7}{23}, \frac{5}{23})$ since the naturally ordered principal minors of the Hessian matrix of f at this critical point alternate in sign, the first being negative.

Example 6.15. Assume that the real-valued function

$$y = f(\boldsymbol{x}) = x_1^3+x_2^2+x_1x_2-x_1-x_2$$

is defined everywhere on $\mathscr{E}^2$. Isolate and identify all stationary points of f over its domain. Employing our necessary condition for a local extremum we set $\nabla f = \mathbf{0}$ or $3x_1^2+x_2 = 1$, $x_1+2x_2 = 1$. Solving for x_2 from the second equation and substituting its value into the first yields $3x_1^2-\frac{1}{2}x_1-\frac{1}{2} = 0$ and thus $x_1 = (\frac{1}{2}\pm\frac{5}{2})/6$. Hence, the critical points within $\mathscr{K}$ at which f attains stationary values are $\boldsymbol{x}_0' = (\frac{1}{2}, \frac{1}{4})$, $\boldsymbol{x}_1' = (-\frac{1}{3}, \frac{2}{3})$. For

$$\boldsymbol{H}_f(\boldsymbol{x}_0) = \begin{bmatrix} 3 & 1 \\ 1 & 2 \end{bmatrix},$$

$M_1 = 3$, $M_2 = 5$. Then f has a strong local minimum at $\boldsymbol{x}_0' = (\frac{1}{2}, \frac{1}{4})$ since the naturally ordered principal minors of the Hessian matrix of f at this point are all positive. With

$$\boldsymbol{H}_f(\boldsymbol{x}_1) = \begin{bmatrix} -2 & 1 \\ 1 & 2 \end{bmatrix},$$

$M_1 = -2$, $M_2 = -5$. In this case f assumes a saddle point at $\boldsymbol{x}_1' = (-\frac{1}{3}, \frac{2}{3})$ since $|\boldsymbol{H}_f(\boldsymbol{x}_1)|<0$.

Example 6.16. Does the real-valued function

$$y = f(\boldsymbol{x}) = x_1-3x_2+\tfrac{1}{2}x_3-x_4+4x_1^2+5x_2^2+3x_3^2+x_4^2$$

attain a local extremum anywhere within $\mathscr{E}^4$? Setting $\nabla f = \mathbf{0}$ we find that a possible candidate for a local extremum is the critical point

$$\boldsymbol{x}_0' = (-\tfrac{1}{8}, \tfrac{3}{10}, -\tfrac{1}{12}, \tfrac{1}{2}).$$

Since the naturally ordered principal minors of the Hessian matrix

$$H_f(x_0) = \begin{bmatrix} 8 & 0 & 0 & 0 \\ 0 & 10 & 0 & 0 \\ 0 & 0 & 6 & 0 \\ 0 & 0 & 0 & 2 \end{bmatrix}$$

are all positive, we may conclude that f has a strong local minimum at $\boldsymbol{x}_0$.

If we weaken the above sufficient condition somewhat, i.e. if we replace $\nabla f^0 = \mathbf{0}$, $\boldsymbol{h}'\boldsymbol{H}_f(\boldsymbol{x}_0)\boldsymbol{h} < 0 (> 0)$ by $\nabla f^0 = \mathbf{0}$, $\boldsymbol{h}'\boldsymbol{H}_f(\boldsymbol{x}_0)\boldsymbol{h} \leqslant 0 (\geqslant 0)$, thus obtaining a strengthened necessary condition, then we may state

THEOREM 6.12 (a strengthened necessary condition). *Let the real-valued function $y = f(\boldsymbol{x})$, $\boldsymbol{x} \in \mathscr{E}^n$, possess continuous first- and second-order partial derivatives throughout some spherical δ-neighborhood of the point $\boldsymbol{x}_0$ contained within an open region $\mathscr{K} \subseteq \mathscr{E}^n$. If $\nabla f^0 = \mathbf{0}$, then:*

(*a*) f *attains a local maximum at $\boldsymbol{x}_0$ if $\boldsymbol{h}'\boldsymbol{H}_f(\boldsymbol{x}_0)\boldsymbol{h} \leqslant 0$; and*

(*b*) f *attains a local minimum at $\boldsymbol{x}_0$ if $\boldsymbol{h}'\boldsymbol{H}_f(\boldsymbol{x}_0)\boldsymbol{h} \geqslant 0$.*

Accordingly, if f^0 is a local maximum (minimum), in addition to the requirement that $\nabla f^0 = \mathbf{0}$, it is necessary that the condition $\boldsymbol{h}'\boldsymbol{H}_f(\boldsymbol{x}_0)\boldsymbol{h} > 0 (< 0)$ does not hold. Hence we obtain a strengthened necessary condition. When $\nabla f^0 = \mathbf{0}$, it is sufficient for a strong local extremum that we do not have $\boldsymbol{h}'\boldsymbol{H}_f(\boldsymbol{x}_0)\boldsymbol{h} = 0$. Hence, the requirement that $\boldsymbol{h}'\boldsymbol{H}_f(\boldsymbol{x}_0)\boldsymbol{h} \leqslant 0 (\geqslant 0)$ weakens our sufficient condition for a strong local maximum (minimum).

6.10. Contour maps of real-valued functions

A convenient mode of representing a local or global extremum or saddle value of a continuous real-valued function $y = f(\boldsymbol{x})$, $\boldsymbol{x} \in \mathscr{E}^2$, is to depict it as a point within the functions *contour map* or *system of level curves*. In fig. 6.21 let us cut the surface f by the plane $f = n$ (=constant) which is horizontal and thus parallel to the x_1, x_2-plane. We then project the resulting curve of intersection downward into the x_1, x_2-plane, thereby obtaining what we shall call level curve n. Specifically,

DEFINITION 6.8. *A level curve or contour of the real-valued function $y = f(\boldsymbol{x})$, $\boldsymbol{x} \in \mathscr{E}^2$, is the locus of combinations of points $\boldsymbol{x}$ within $\mathscr{D}_f$ for which* f = *constant.*

If we now cut f with a series of parallel planes and project each curve of intersection into the x_1, x_2-plane, there is generated a whole system of level curves—the contour map of f in $\mathscr{D}_f$. Note that a contour map admits an infinite number of contours since f is assumed continuous over $\mathscr{D}_f$. Hence the contours are said to be *everywhere dense* within $\mathscr{D}_f$, since between

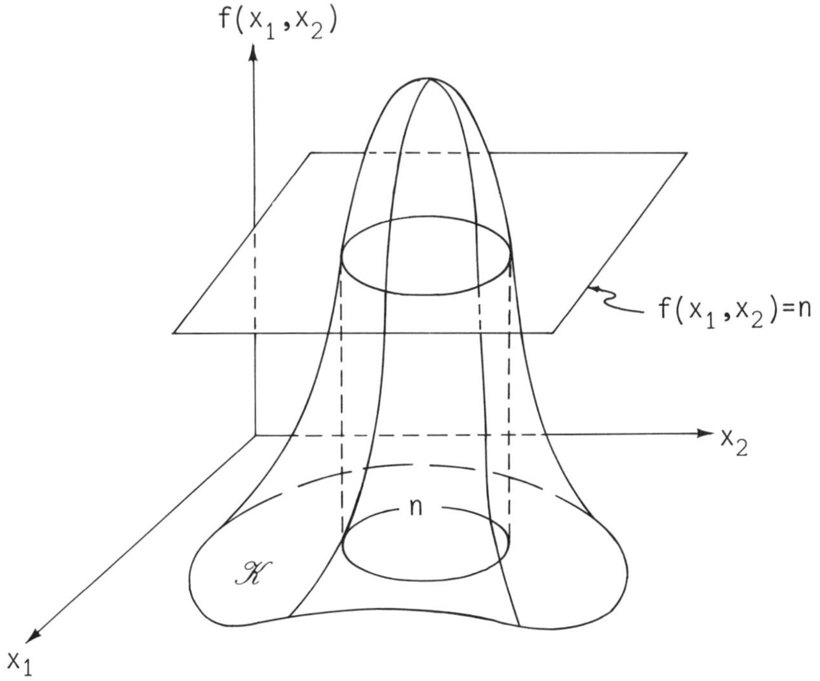

Fig. 6.21.

any two of them one can find another. Under what conditions may we obtain the contour map of f in $\mathscr{D}_f$? To answer this question we state the following existence theorem:

THEOREM 6.13. *Let the real-valued function* $y = f(\boldsymbol{x})$, $\boldsymbol{x} \in \mathscr{E}^2$, *be defined throughout a region* $\mathscr{K} \subseteq \mathscr{E}^2$. *If* $\nabla f \not\equiv \mathbf{0}$ *in* $\mathscr{K}$, *then the level curves* f = *constant are well defined throughout this region.*

This theorem provides us with a sufficient condition for the existence of a set of contours (since if $\nabla f \equiv \mathbf{0}$, f is constant for all $\boldsymbol{x} \in \mathscr{K}$), with one passing through each point of $\mathscr{K}$. For instance, if f attains a strong global maximum at $\boldsymbol{x}_0 \in \mathscr{K}$, then the contour map representing this extremum may be depicted as a system of concentric level curves with $f(\boldsymbol{x}_0) = n > n - 1 > n - 2 > \ldots$ (fig. 6.22a).

Example 6.17. If the real-valued function $y = f(\boldsymbol{x})$, $\boldsymbol{x} \in \mathscr{E}^2$, hypothetically attains a strong global minimum at the point $\boldsymbol{x}_0' = (2, 2) \in \mathscr{K} \subseteq \mathscr{E}^2$ and

$$f(\boldsymbol{x}_0) = 5 = \underset{\boldsymbol{x} \in \mathscr{E}^2}{\mathrm{g\,min}}\, f(\boldsymbol{x}),$$

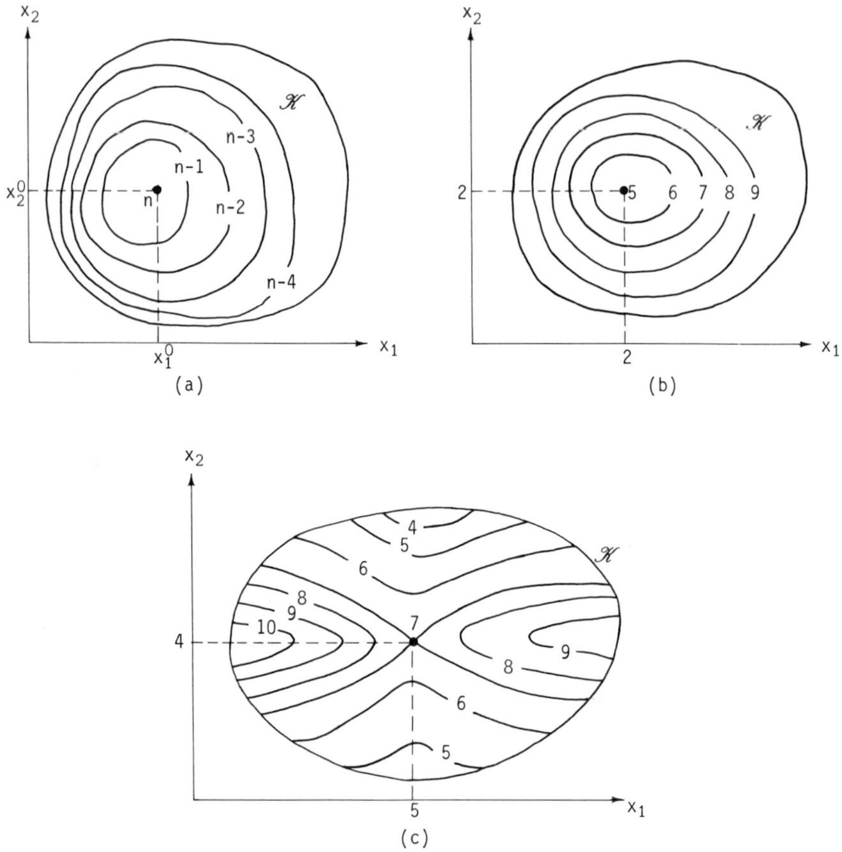

Fig. 6.22.

fig. 6.22b may be conceived as representing its contour map. And if a function hypothetically assumes a saddle value at the point $\mathbf{x}'_1 = (5, 4) \in \mathscr{K}$, with

$$f(\mathbf{x}_1) = 7 = g \max_{x_2} f(5, x_2) = g \min_{x_1} f(x_1, 4),$$

the implied contour map may look something like the one in fig. 6.22c.

6.11. Appendix A: The Newton–Raphson, secant, and false position methods

Throughout chapter 6 we examined a variety of rather simple and straightforward examples involving the application of various theorems designed to identify and isolate local extrema. For the most part, we may refer to these contrived examples as 'classroom exercises' whose singular purpose is pedagogic exposition, rather than the development of computational prowess. However, the vast majority of functions that one usually encounters do not lend themselves to any such clear-cut analysis. That is, we are usually not fortunate enough in most applications to compute f′, equate it to zero, and then find that we are faced with simply solving a linear or quadratic equation for the critical value(s) of x which give rise to local extrema. Indeed, one may have to solve a polynomial of rather high order or even an equation of a more complex nature. How are we to handle such contingencies? In this section we shall explore three common methods of finding the roots of non-linear equations: the Newton–Raphson method; the secant method; and the method of false position.

Basically, each of the said techniques for computing the root(s)[11] of a non-linear equation involves a process of successive approximations, i.e. each is an iterative procedure. As with any iterative technique, we begin the various rounds of iteration by choosing an initial point (near the desired solution) from which a new point is computed by an appropriate algorithm or computational rule. The process is continued (until the desired degree of accuracy is attained) by successively calculating additional points that yield improved approximations to the solution.

To see exactly how the *Newton–Raphson method* works, let us assume that we have taken the first derivative of the real-valued function $y = f(x)$ and we desire to find a value of x, x^*, for which it vanishes. That is, we desire to find a root x^* of $f'(x) = 0$. Without loss of generality, let us further assume that f attains a strong local minimum at $x = x^*$ (fig. A.1). If we choose an initial estimate of x^*, x_0, to the right (or left) of x^* (with $|x^* - x_0|$ small) and approximate f′ at the point $(x_0, f'(x_0))$ by the linear portion of Taylor's expansion of a function (eq. (5.12)), we obtain

$$f'(x) = f'(x_0) + f''(x_0)(x - x_0). \tag{A.1}$$

Here, eq. (A.1) represents the equation of the line tangent to f′ at $(x_0, f'(x_0))$. It crosses the x-axis at the point $(x_1, 0)$. A substitution of the coordinates of this point into eq. (A.1) yields

$$0 = f'(x_0) + f''(x_0)(x_1 - x_0)$$

or

$$x_1 = x_0 - f'(x_0)/f''(x_0),$$

[11] By a *root* of the real-valued function $y = f(x) = 0$ is meant a real number r such that, when r is substituted into f for the unknown, the equation is satisfied. That is, $f(x) = 0$ reduces to the identity $0 \equiv 0$ for $x = r$.

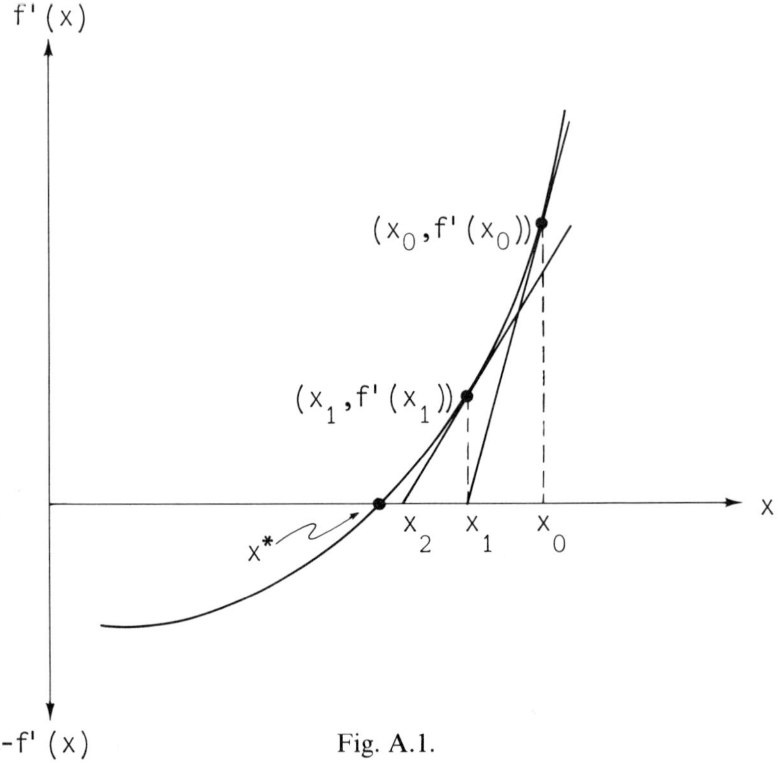

Fig. A.1.

where x_1 represents our second approximation to x^*. (Note that x_1 is closer to x^* than is x_0.) This completes the first round or iteration of the Newton–Raphson technique. To start the second iteration we again approximate f′ by Taylor's expansion, but this time at the point $(x_1, f'(x_1))$. Then

$$f'(x) = f'(x_1)+f''(x_1)(x-x_1). \tag{A.2}$$

In this instance the tangent to f′ at $(x_1, f'(x_1))$(A.2) intersects the x-axis at a point even closer to x^* than before, namely x_2. Our third approximation to x^*, x_2, is obtained by substituting the coordinates of this new point $(x_2, 0)$ into eq. (A.2). Hence

$$\begin{aligned} 0 &= f'(x_1)+f''(x_1)(x_2-x_1), \\ x_2 &= x_1-f'(x_1)/f''(x_1). \end{aligned}$$

Our second iteration is now complete. This successive-approximation technique may be repeated until the difference $|x_i-x_{i-1}|$ is as small as one desires. In general, after i iterations,

$$x_i = x_{i-1} - \frac{f'(x_{i-1})}{f''(x_{i-1})}, \quad i = 1, 2, \ldots. \tag{A.3}$$

A summary of the various steps involved in implementing the Newton–Raphson method proceeds as follows:

(1) draw a graph of $f'(x) = 0$;

(2) choose an initial estimate x_0 near the point x^* where the curve crosses the x-axis;

(3) from x_0 move vertically to $f'(x_0)$;

(4) construct the tangent to f' at $(x_0, f'(x_0))$;

(5) find the point where the tangent to f' at $(x_0, f'(x_0))$ crosses the x-axis. This yields

$$x_1 = x_0 - f'(x_0)/f''(x_0);$$

(6) repeat the process, involving steps (1)–(5) i times in succession to obtain

$$x_i = x_{i-1} - f'(x_{i-1})/f''(x_{i-1}).$$

We note briefly that, with the Newton–Raphson (or any) successive-approximation technique, a proof of convergence to the desired solution and an estimate of the error incurred upon completing the ith iteration are needed. In addition, one must demonstrate the existence and uniqueness of the solution (see Saaty and Bram, 1964, pp. 58–62).

Example A.1. Determine the extreme values of the real-valued function

$$y = f(x) = \tfrac{1}{4}x^4 - \tfrac{2}{3}x^3 - x^2 - 5x + 2$$

over the x-axis. Setting $f'(x) = 0$ we obtain

$$x^3 - 2x^2 - 2x - 5 = 0.$$

A graph of f' (fig. A.2) indicates that this function possesses a critical root x^* somewhere between $x = 3$ and $x = 4$. To find it let us approximate x^* by the Newton–Raphson method for $i = 1, 2, 3$. From eq. (A.3) we have, for $x_0 = 3.5$,

$$x_1 = x_0 - \frac{f'(x_0)}{f''(x_0)} = 3.5000 - \frac{f'(3.5000)}{f''(3.5000)} = 3.1900,$$

$$x_2 = x_1 - \frac{f'(x_1)}{f''(x_1)} = 3.1900 - \frac{f'(3.1900)}{f''(3.1900)} = 3.1440,$$

$$x_3 = x_2 - \frac{f'(x_2)}{f''(x_2)} = 3.1440 - \frac{f'(3.1440)}{f''(3.1440)} = 3.1427.$$

Since $f''(3.1427) > 0$, f has a strong local minimum at $x^* \sim 3.1427$.

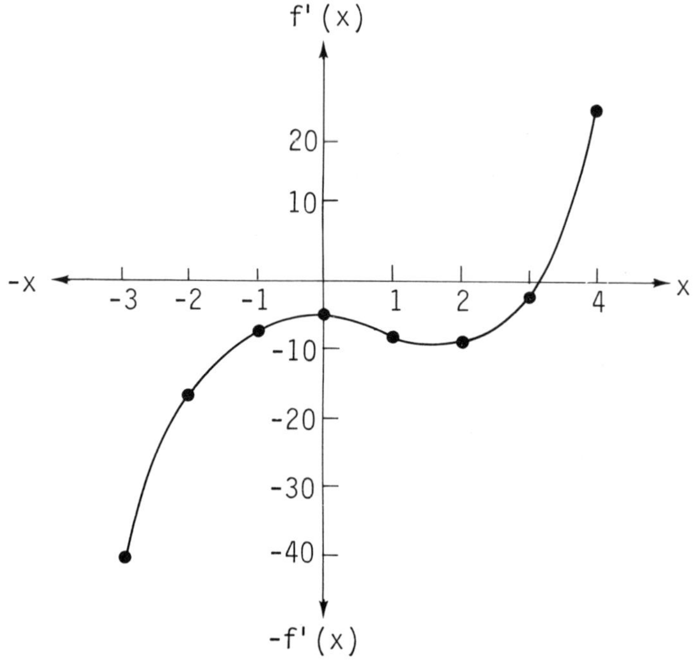

Fig. A.2.

The Newton–Raphson method may be modified for computational convenience by replacing $f''(x_{i-1})$ in eq. (A.3) by $f''(x_0)$ (Saaty and Bram, 1964, p. 62). This substitution enables us to avoid computing $f''(x_{i-1})$ at each round of the process. Hence, the iterations are now described by

$$x_i = x_{i-1} - \frac{f'(x_{i-1})}{f''(x_0)}, \quad i = 1, 2, \ldots \tag{A.3.1}$$

Example A.2. Using $f' = 0$ from example A.1 above, demonstrate that, for $x_0 = 3.5$, the successive terms of the modified Newton–Raphson process described by eq. (A.3.1) approach 3.1427 for $i = 1, \ldots, 6$. In this case

$$x_1 = x_0 - \frac{f'(x_0)}{f''(x_0)} = 3.19000, \qquad x_4 = x_3 - \frac{f'(x_3)}{f''(x_0)} = 3.14360,$$

$$x_2 = x_1 - \frac{f'(x_1)}{f''(x_0)} = 3.15000, \qquad x_5 = x_4 - \frac{f'(x_4)}{f''(x_0)} = 3.14290,$$

$$x_3 = x_2 - \frac{f'(x_2)}{f''(x_0)} = 3.14600, \qquad x_6 = x_5 - \frac{f'(x_5)}{f''(x_0)} = 3.14274.$$

Note that while eq. (A.3.1) is easier to handle from a computational viewpoint than eq. (A.3), the rapidity of convergence is substantially greater for eq. (A.3) than for eq. (A.3.1).

At times it may be desirable to further modify the Newton–Raphson process (eq. (A.3)) so as to accelerate convergence to x^*. One such modification, leading to what is called the *generalized Newton–Raphson method*, is developed as follows. If eq. (A.1) is replaced by

$$f'(x) = f'(x_0)+\tau f''(x_0)(x+x_0), \quad \tau \neq 1. \tag{A.1.1}$$

(Here eq. (A.1.1) represents the equation of a line through $(x_0, f'(x_0))$ which intersects the x-axis at a point closer to x^* than the previously specified x_1 value in fig. A.1.), then it is easily shown that

$$x_1 = x_0 - \frac{1}{\tau}\,\frac{f'(x_0)}{f''(x_0)}, \quad \tau \neq 1.$$

In general, the ith iteration is determined from

$$x_i = x_{i-1} - \lambda\frac{f'(x_{i-1})}{f''(x_{i-1})}, \quad i = 1, 2, \ldots, \tag{A.3.2}$$

where $\lambda = 1/\tau$. As an exercise the reader should rework example A.1 using eq. (A.3.2) with $\tau = 0.90$.

It is important to note that the sequences described by eqs. (A.3), (A.3.1), and (A.3.2) may not converge if x_0 is not chosen sufficiently close to x^*. Moreover, if they do, in fact, converge to some number $x \in \mathscr{D}_{f'}$, this number may not be the correct root.

The Newton–Raphson technique requires first- as well as second-order information about a function, i.e. it utilizes both first and second derivatives in its implementation. A modification of the Newton–Raphson method which uses only first-order information is the *secant method*, so named because f″ in eq. (A.3) is replaced by its finite difference approximation

$$f''(x_{i-1}) \sim \frac{f'(x_{i-1})-f'(x_{i-2})}{x_{i-1}-x_{i-2}}, \tag{A.4}$$

where the difference quotient on the right-hand side of eq. (A.4) is simply the slope of the secant line between the two points

$$(x_{i-1}, f'(x_{i-1})), \qquad (x_{i-2}, f'(x_{i-2}))$$

on f′ (fig. A.3) and x_{i-1}, x_{i-2} are any 'two' initial approximations to the root x^*. Upon substituting eq. (A.4) into (A.3) we obtain

$$\begin{aligned} x_i &= x_{i-1} - f'(x_{i-1})\frac{x_{i-1}-x_{i-2}}{f'(x_{i-1})-f'(x_{i-2})} \\ &= \frac{x_{i-2}f'(x_{i-1})-x_{i-1}f'(x_{i-2})}{f'(x_{i-1})-f'(x_{i-2})}, \quad i = 2, 3, \ldots. \end{aligned} \tag{A.5}$$

What is the geometric interpretation of eq. (A.5)? Given the two initial

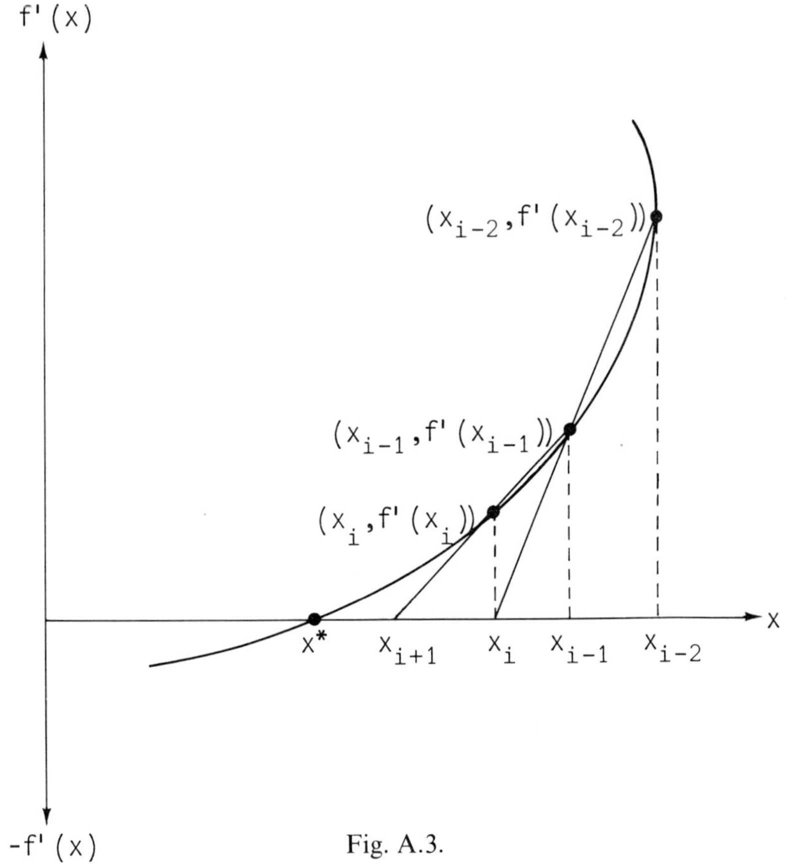

Fig. A.3.

approximations x_{i-1}, x_{i-2} to x^*, the next approximation x_i corresponds to the intersection of the chord joining points $(x_{i-1}, f'(x_{i-1}))$, $(x_{i-2}, f'(x_{i-2}))$ with the x-axis. Once x_i is obtained, x_{i+1} is determined in a similar fashion, i.e. by finding the intersection of the chord joining points

$$(x_i, f'(x_i)), \qquad (x_{i-1}, f'(x_{i-1}))$$

with the x-axis. The process is repeated until the desired degree of accuracy, in terms of $|x_i - x_{i-1}|$, is achieved.

A variation of the secant method is the *method of false position.* Let us choose the two initial approximations x_{i-2}, x_{i-1} to x^* in a fashion such that $f'(x_{i-2})$, $f'(x_{i-1})$ are of opposite sign, i.e. $f'(x_{i-2})f'(x_{i-1}) < 0$. Then x^* must lie between x_{i-2}, x_{i-1} so that if we connect points $(x_{i-1}, f'(x_{i-1}))$, $(x_{i-2}, f'(x_{i-2}))$ (fig. A.4) by a secant line, x_i in eq. (A.5) represents the intersection of this line with the x-axis. To obtain x_{i+1}, let us, in general, proceed in the following fashion:

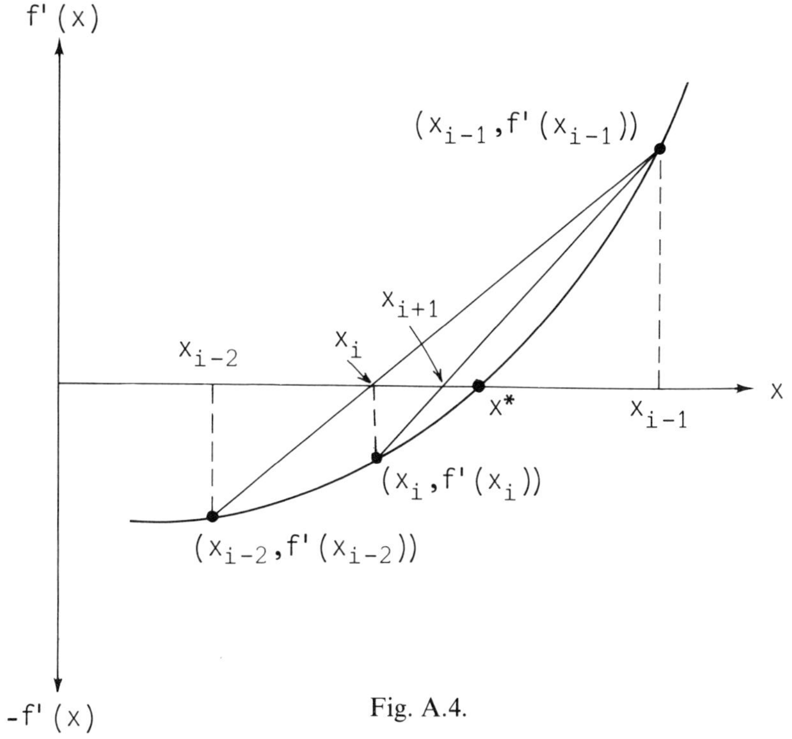

Fig. A.4.

(a) If $f'(x_{i-2})$, $f'(x_i)$ are opposite in sign ($f'(x_{i-2})f'(x_i)<0$), replace x_{i-1} by x_i (x_{i-2} is unchanged) and obtain the next approximation from eq. (A.5). (Geometrically, x_{i+1} is just the intersection of the chord joining $(x_{i-2}, f'(x_{i-2}))$, $(x_i, f'(x_i))$ and the x-axis.)
(b) Otherwise, replace x_{1-2} by x_i(x_{i-1} is invariant) and again use eq. (A.5) to determine a new approximation. (In terms of fig. A.4, if $(x_i, f'(x_i))$, $(x_{i-1}, f'(x_{i-1}))$ are connected by a secant line, the new estimate, x_{i+1}, is again taken to be the intersection of this line with the x-axis.) As always, the process is repeated until the desired degree of accuracy obtains.

When should these various iterative schemes be employed? If f″ is easily computed, the standard Newton–Raphson technique is preferred, the reason being that it converges faster to x^* than the other two methods. (In this case, the Newton–Raphson technique is said to possess *second-order convergence* or to *converge quadratically*, i.e. the error incurred at any iteration is proportional to the square of the error of the previous iteration so that, asymptotically, the number of places of accuracy doubles with each succeeding iteration beyond the first few.) Next, if the information provided by f″ is difficult to obtain, the secant method should be used. Finally, the method of false position can be utilized if the previous two methods fail to converge to the desired critical value of x. As an exercise the reader should rework example A.1 using both the secant method and the method of false position.

6.12. Appendix B: The Newton-Raphson method, $x \in \mathscr{E}^n$

We noted above that a necessary condition for the real-valued function $y = \mathrm{f}(\boldsymbol{x})$, $\boldsymbol{x} \in \mathscr{E}^n$, to assume a local extremum at a point $\boldsymbol{x}_*$ contained within an open region $\mathscr{K} \subseteq \mathscr{E}^n$ is that $\nabla \mathrm{f}^* = \mathbf{0}$. If $\nabla \mathrm{f} = \mathbf{0}$ gives rise to a non-linear system of equations, then $\boldsymbol{x}_*$ may be found by a series of successive approximations using the Newton–Raphson technique. As in Appendix A, our strategy will be to obtain a series of successive approximations to $\boldsymbol{x}_*$, with each iteration yielding an improved solution.

That is, if we choose the point $\boldsymbol{x}_0$ as our initial estimate of $\boldsymbol{x}_*$, with $\|\boldsymbol{x}_0 - \boldsymbol{x}_*\|$ sufficiently small, and approximate $\nabla \mathrm{f}$ at $\boldsymbol{x}_0$ by the linear portion of Taylor's expansion of a function (eq. (5.15)), we obtain

$$\left.\begin{aligned} \nabla \mathrm{f} &= \nabla \mathrm{f}^0 + \left(\frac{\partial \nabla \mathrm{f}^0}{\partial \boldsymbol{x}}\right)\boldsymbol{h} \\ &= \nabla \mathrm{f}^0 + \boldsymbol{H}_\mathrm{f}(\boldsymbol{x}_0)\,(\boldsymbol{x} - \boldsymbol{x}_0) \end{aligned}\right\} \text{ or } \left\{\begin{aligned} \mathrm{f}_1(\boldsymbol{x}) &= \mathrm{f}_1^0 + \sum_{j=1}^{n} \mathrm{f}_{1j}^0 (x_j - x_j^0), \\ \mathrm{f}_2(\boldsymbol{x}) &= \mathrm{f}_2^0 + \sum_{j=1}^{n} \mathrm{f}_{2j}^0 (x_j - x_j^0), \\ &\cdots\cdots\cdots\cdots\cdots\cdots \\ \mathrm{f}_n(\boldsymbol{x}) &= \mathrm{f}_n^0 + \sum_{j=1}^{n} \mathrm{f}_{nj}^0 (x_j - x_j^0). \end{aligned}\right. \tag{B.1}$$

To undertake our first iteration let us set $\boldsymbol{x} = \boldsymbol{x}_1$ in system (B.1) and equate $\nabla \mathrm{f}(\boldsymbol{x}_1)$ to the null vector. Then eq. (B.1) becomes

$$\mathbf{0} = \nabla \mathrm{f}^0 + \boldsymbol{H}_\mathrm{f}(\boldsymbol{x}_0)(\boldsymbol{x}_1 - \boldsymbol{x}_0) \text{ or } \left\{\begin{aligned} 0 &= \mathrm{f}_1^0 + \sum_{j=1}^{n} \mathrm{f}_{1j}^0 (x_j^1 - x_j^0), \\ 0 &= \mathrm{f}_2^0 + \sum_{j=1}^{n} \mathrm{f}_{2j}^0 (x_j^1 - x_j^0), \\ &\cdots\cdots\cdots\cdots\cdots\cdots \\ 0 &= \mathrm{f}_n^0 + \sum_{j=1}^{n} \mathrm{f}_{nj}^0 (x_j^1 - x_j^0), \end{aligned}\right.$$

or, upon transposing,

$$H_f(x_0)x_1 = H_f(x_0)x_0 - \nabla f^0. \tag{B.2}$$

Here $H_f(x_0)$ is the nth-order Hessian matrix of f evaluated at x_0, and ∇f^0 is the $(n \times 1)$ gradient vector of f at x_0. If $H_f(x_0)$ is non-singular, we obtain, from eq. (B.2)

$$x_1 = x_0 - H_f^{-1}(x_0)\,(\nabla f^0).$$

Round one of this iterative procedure is now complete.

In general, after i iterations,

$$x_i = x_{i-1} - H_f^{-1}(x_{i-1})\,(\nabla f(x_{i-1})), \quad i = 1, 2, \ldots \tag{B.3}$$

provided $H_f(x_{i-1})$ is non-singular. Additionally, this process converges to a strong local maximum (minimum) provided $H_f(x_{i-1})$ is negative (positive) definite and the change in the function is less than some predetermined limit η, i.e. $|f(x_i) - f(x_{i-1})| < \eta$ for several successive values of i.

Example B.1. Does the real-valued function

$$y = f(x) = -x_1^4 + 2x_1x_2 - 3x_2^3 + 3x_1 + x_2 - 6$$

attain a local extremum over $\mathscr{E}^2$? Setting $\nabla f = \mathbf{0}$ we obtain the system

$$\begin{aligned} -4x_1^3 + 2x_2 + 3 &= 0, \\ 2x_1 - 9x_2^2 + 1 &= 0, \end{aligned}$$

which must be solved simultaneously to find the critical point $x_* \in \mathscr{E}^2$ where $\nabla f^* = \mathbf{0}$. We first find

$$H_f(x) = \begin{bmatrix} -12x_1^2 & 2 \\ 2 & -18x_2 \end{bmatrix}.$$

Then, from eq. (B.3) we have, for $i = 1, 2$ and $x_0' = (1, 1)$,

$$\begin{aligned} x_1 &= x_0 - H_f^{-1}(x_0)\,(\nabla f(x_0)) \\ &= \begin{bmatrix} 1 \\ 1 \end{bmatrix} - \begin{bmatrix} -0.0849 & -0.0094 \\ -0.0094 & -0.0566 \end{bmatrix} \begin{bmatrix} 1 \\ -6 \end{bmatrix} = \begin{bmatrix} 1.0285 \\ 0.6698 \end{bmatrix}, \end{aligned}$$

$$\begin{aligned} x_2 &= x_1 - H_f^{-1}(x_1)\,(\nabla f(x_1)) \\ &= \begin{bmatrix} 1.0285 \\ 0.6698 \end{bmatrix} - \begin{bmatrix} -0.0809 & -0.0131 \\ -0.0131 & -0.0831 \end{bmatrix} \begin{bmatrix} -0.0120 \\ -0.9804 \end{bmatrix} = \begin{bmatrix} 1.0147 \\ 0.5881 \end{bmatrix}. \end{aligned}$$

Hence, $x_*' \sim (1.0147, 0.5881)$. Since the naturally ordered principal minors of the Hessian matrix alternate in sign (the first being negative) at x_*, f assumes a strong local maximum there, i.e.

$$M_1 = -12.35 < 0, \qquad M_2 = |H_f(1.0147, 0.5881)| = 130.27 > 0.$$

6.13. Appendix C: The method of steepest ascent

The Newton–Raphson iteration technique may be described as an 'indirect method' of determining an extremum of a real-valued function, i.e. its implementation involves the application of a set of supplemental (necessary) conditions which must be satisfied at the maximum or minimum of the function. An alternative technique involves what may be described as a 'direct method'. This process makes use of an initial estimate from which information about the behavior of the function is used to determine locally a direction in which the function increases or decreases. The direct method which we shall consider here may generally be characterized as a process involving 'gradient search'. Specifically, it is Cauchy's *method of steepest ascent (descent)*. In what follows we shall attempt to maximize the real-valued function $y = \mathrm{f}(\boldsymbol{x})$, $\boldsymbol{x}\in\mathscr{K}\subseteq\mathscr{E}^n$, by the method of steepest ascent. That is to say, we seek to approximate the coordinates of a point $\boldsymbol{x}_*\in\mathscr{K}$ such that $\mathrm{f}(\boldsymbol{x}_*)\geqslant\mathrm{f}(\boldsymbol{x})$, $\boldsymbol{x}\in\delta(\boldsymbol{x}_*)$. The modification for handling minimization problems is obvious and will not be presented in detail.

We noted previously that the gradient vector $\nabla\mathrm{f}$ points locally in the direction of maximum increase of f. Hence we may: (1) start at some initial point $\boldsymbol{x}_0\in\mathscr{K}$ and compute $\nabla\mathrm{f}^0$; (2) take a step in the direction of steepest ascent $\nabla\mathrm{f}^0$, using a step length λ_0, to obtain a new point $\boldsymbol{x}_1$ (here the search parameter λ_0 is interpreted as some scalar multiple of $\nabla\mathrm{f}^0$); and (3) repeat the process until the desired degree of accuracy to our approximation of $\boldsymbol{x}_*$ is obtained. The iteration scheme may thus be described as

$$\boldsymbol{x}_i = \boldsymbol{x}_{i-1}+\lambda_{i-1}\nabla\mathrm{f}(\boldsymbol{x}_{i-1}),\quad i = 1, 2, \ldots, \tag{C.1}$$

with the process converging to a strong local maximum if the λ_{i-1} are chosen so that $\mathrm{f}(\boldsymbol{x}_i)>\mathrm{f}(\boldsymbol{x}_{i-1})$, i.e. the function is made to increase with each step. Since f is increasing locally in the direction of $\nabla\mathrm{f}(\boldsymbol{x}_{i-1})$, we can be sure that there always exists a $\lambda_{i-1}>0$ such that $\mathrm{f}(\boldsymbol{x}_i)>\mathrm{f}(\boldsymbol{x}_{i-1})$. The process is then stopped when the change in the function is less than some predetermined limit η or $|\mathrm{f}(\boldsymbol{x}_i)-\mathrm{f}(\boldsymbol{x}_{i-1})|<\eta$ for several successive values of i. Since our direction of movement throughout $\mathscr{K}$ is specified by the gradient of f at $\boldsymbol{x}_{i-1}$, it thus remains to determine λ_{i-1}.

Utilizing eq. (5.15) we may write the quadratic approximation of f at $\boldsymbol{x}_{i-1}$ as

$$\mathrm{f}(\boldsymbol{x}) = \mathrm{f}(\boldsymbol{x}_{i-1})+\nabla\mathrm{f}(\boldsymbol{x}_{i-1})'\boldsymbol{h}+\frac{1}{2!}\boldsymbol{h}'\boldsymbol{H}_\mathrm{f}(\boldsymbol{x}_{i-1})\boldsymbol{h}, \tag{C.2}$$

where $\boldsymbol{h} = \boldsymbol{x}-\boldsymbol{x}_{i-1}$. In light of the iteration scheme described by eq. (C.1) let us set

$$x = \boldsymbol{x}_i = \boldsymbol{x}_{i-1}+\lambda_{i-1}\nabla\mathrm{f}(\boldsymbol{x}_{i-1})$$

in eq. (C.2), thus obtaining, for

$$\begin{aligned} \boldsymbol{h} &= \boldsymbol{x}_i - \boldsymbol{x}_{i-1} = \lambda_{i-1}\nabla \mathrm{f}(\boldsymbol{x}_{i-1}), \\ \mathrm{f}(\boldsymbol{x}_i) &= \mathrm{f}(\boldsymbol{x}_{i-1}) + \lambda_{i-1}\nabla \mathrm{f}(\boldsymbol{x}_{i-1})'\nabla \mathrm{f}(\boldsymbol{x}_{i-1}) \\ &\quad + \frac{\lambda_{i-1}^2}{2!}\nabla \mathrm{f}(\boldsymbol{x}_{i-1})'\boldsymbol{H}_\mathrm{f}(\boldsymbol{x}_{i-1})\nabla \mathrm{f}(\boldsymbol{x}_{i-1}). \end{aligned} \tag{C.3}$$

How should λ_{i-1} be chosen? Since we require a λ_{i-1} for which $\mathrm{f}(\boldsymbol{x}_i) - \mathrm{f}(\boldsymbol{x}_{i-1}) > 0$ is as large as possible, let us determine λ_{i-1} according to the criterion

$$\mathrm{f}(\boldsymbol{x}_{i-1} + \lambda_{i-1}\nabla \mathrm{f}(\boldsymbol{x}_{i-1})) = \max_{\lambda} \mathrm{f}(\boldsymbol{x}_{i-1} + \lambda\nabla \mathrm{f}(\boldsymbol{x}_{i-1})), \tag{C.4}$$

i.e. λ_{i-1} is chosen by maximizing f along the $\nabla \mathrm{f}(\boldsymbol{x}_{i-1})$ direction. Then

$$\left.\frac{\mathrm{d}\mathrm{f}(\boldsymbol{x}_{i-1} + \lambda\nabla \mathrm{f}(\boldsymbol{x}_{i-1}))}{\mathrm{d}\lambda}\right|_{\lambda=\lambda_{i-1}}$$
$$= \nabla \mathrm{f}(\boldsymbol{x}_{i-1})'\nabla \mathrm{f}(\boldsymbol{x}_{i-1}) + \lambda_{i-1}\nabla \mathrm{f}(\boldsymbol{x}_{i-1})'\boldsymbol{H}_\mathrm{f}(\boldsymbol{x}_{i-1})\nabla \mathrm{f}(\boldsymbol{x}_{i-1}) = 0$$

or

$$\lambda_{i-1} = -\frac{\nabla \mathrm{f}(\boldsymbol{x}_{i-1})'\nabla \mathrm{f}(\boldsymbol{x}_{i-1})}{\nabla \mathrm{f}(\boldsymbol{x}_{i-1})'\boldsymbol{H}_\mathrm{f}(\boldsymbol{x}_{i-1})\nabla \mathrm{f}(\boldsymbol{x}_{i-1})}.$$

Additionally, $\mathrm{f}(\boldsymbol{x}_{i-1} + \lambda\nabla \mathrm{f}(\boldsymbol{x}_{i-1}))$ will attain a maximum if

$$\frac{\mathrm{d}^2\mathrm{f}(\boldsymbol{x}_{i-1} + \lambda\nabla \mathrm{f}(\boldsymbol{x}_{i-1}))}{\mathrm{d}\lambda^2} = \nabla \mathrm{f}(\boldsymbol{x}_{i-1})'\boldsymbol{H}_\mathrm{f}(\boldsymbol{x}_{i-1})\nabla \mathrm{f}(\boldsymbol{x}_{i-1}) < 0,$$

i.e. if $\boldsymbol{H}_\mathrm{f}(\boldsymbol{x}_{i-1})$ is negative definite.

In general, the various iterations in the method of steepest ascent may be described as

$$\boldsymbol{x}_i = \boldsymbol{x}_{i-1} + \lambda_{i-1}\nabla \mathrm{f}(\boldsymbol{x}_{i-1}), \quad i = 1, 2, \ldots, \quad \text{(steepest ascent)} \tag{C.5}$$

where

$$\lambda_{i-1} = -\frac{\nabla \mathrm{f}(\boldsymbol{x}_{i-1})'\nabla \mathrm{f}(\boldsymbol{x}_{i-1})}{\nabla \mathrm{f}(\boldsymbol{x}_{i-1})'\boldsymbol{H}_\mathrm{f}(\boldsymbol{x}_{i-1})\nabla \mathrm{f}(\boldsymbol{x}_{i-1})}$$

is chosen to maximize f along $\nabla \mathrm{f}(\boldsymbol{x}_{i-1})$. Moreover, convergence to a strong local maximum of f is assured if $\boldsymbol{H}_\mathrm{f}(\boldsymbol{x}_{i-1})$ is negative definite.

If we desire to minimize f over $\mathscr{K}$, then we must employ the method of steepest descent. The modification is straightforward. Since $-\nabla \mathrm{f}$ points locally in the direction of maximum decrease of f, $-\nabla \mathrm{f}(\boldsymbol{x}_{i-1})$ replaces $\nabla \mathrm{f}(\boldsymbol{x}_{i-1})$ in eq. (C.1). Hence the various rounds of the method of steepest descent may be characterized as

$$\boldsymbol{x}_i = \boldsymbol{x}_{i-1} - \lambda_{i-1}\nabla \mathrm{f}(\boldsymbol{x}_{i-1}), \quad i = 1, 2, \ldots, \quad \text{(steepest descent)} \quad \text{(C.5.1)}$$

where

$$\lambda_{i-1} = \frac{\nabla \mathrm{f}(\boldsymbol{x}_{i-1})'\nabla \mathrm{f}(\boldsymbol{x}_{i-1})}{\nabla \mathrm{f}(\boldsymbol{x}_{i-1})'\boldsymbol{H}_{\mathrm{f}}(\boldsymbol{x}_{i-1})\nabla \mathrm{f}(\boldsymbol{x}_{i-1})}$$

is chosen to minimize f along $-\nabla \mathrm{f}(\boldsymbol{x}_{i-1})$.[12] In this instance the process will converge to a strong local minimum of f if $\boldsymbol{H}_{\mathrm{f}}(\boldsymbol{x}_{i-1})$ is positive definite.

Example C.1. Given $y = \mathrm{f}(\boldsymbol{x})$, $\boldsymbol{x}_0' = (1, 1)$, from example B.1, p. 141, find $\boldsymbol{x}_3$ using the method of steepest ascent (eq. (C.5)). Since

$$\lambda_0 = -\frac{\nabla \mathrm{f}(\boldsymbol{x}_0)'\nabla \mathrm{f}(\boldsymbol{x}_0)}{\nabla \mathrm{f}(\boldsymbol{x}_0)'\boldsymbol{H}_{\mathrm{f}}(\boldsymbol{x}_0)\nabla \mathrm{f}(\boldsymbol{x}_0)} = -\frac{(1, -6)\begin{bmatrix}1\\-6\end{bmatrix}}{(1, -6)\begin{bmatrix}-12 & 2\\ 2 & -18\end{bmatrix}\begin{bmatrix}1\\-6\end{bmatrix}}$$

$$= 0.0551,$$

it follows that

$$\boldsymbol{x}_1 = \boldsymbol{x}_0 + \lambda_0\nabla \mathrm{f}(\boldsymbol{x}_0) = \begin{bmatrix}1\\1\end{bmatrix} + 0.0551\begin{bmatrix}1\\-6\end{bmatrix} = \begin{bmatrix}1.0551\\0.6694\end{bmatrix}.$$

With

$$\lambda_1 = -\frac{\nabla \mathrm{f}(\boldsymbol{x}_1)'\nabla \mathrm{f}(\boldsymbol{x}_1)}{\nabla \mathrm{f}(\boldsymbol{x}_1)'\boldsymbol{H}_{\mathrm{f}}(\boldsymbol{x}_1)\nabla \mathrm{f}(\boldsymbol{x}_1)}$$

$$= -\frac{(-0.3592, 0.9227)\begin{bmatrix}-0.3592\\0.9227\end{bmatrix}}{(-0.3592, 0.9227)\begin{bmatrix}-13.3584 & 2\\ 2 & -12.0492\end{bmatrix}\begin{bmatrix}-0.3592\\0.9227\end{bmatrix}}$$

$$= 0.0737,$$

$$\boldsymbol{x}_2 = \boldsymbol{x}_1 + \lambda_1\nabla \mathrm{f}(\boldsymbol{x}_1) = \begin{bmatrix}1.0551\\0.6694\end{bmatrix} + 0.0737\begin{bmatrix}-0.3592\\0.9227\end{bmatrix} = \begin{bmatrix}1.0286\\0.7374\end{bmatrix}.$$

Also, with

$$\lambda_2 = -\frac{\nabla \mathrm{f}(\boldsymbol{x}_2)'\nabla \mathrm{f}(\boldsymbol{x}_2)}{\nabla \mathrm{f}(\boldsymbol{x}_2)'\boldsymbol{H}_{\mathrm{f}}(\boldsymbol{x}_2)\nabla \mathrm{f}(\boldsymbol{x}_2)}$$

---

[12] For a discussion on the conditions underlying the existence of a solution to an extremum problem via this method with a variety of proofs of convergence to the same, see Saaty and Bram (1964), pp. 76–88.

$$= -\frac{(0.1216,\ -1.8370)\begin{bmatrix}0.1216\\-1.8370\end{bmatrix}}{(0.1216,\ -1.8370)\begin{bmatrix}-12.6960 & 2\\ 2 & -13.2732\end{bmatrix}\begin{bmatrix}0.1216\\-1.8370\end{bmatrix}}$$

$$= 0.0739,$$

$$\boldsymbol{x}_3 = \boldsymbol{x}_2+\lambda_2\nabla \mathrm{f}(\boldsymbol{x}_2) = \begin{bmatrix}1.0286\\0.7374\end{bmatrix}+0.0739\begin{bmatrix}0.1216\\-1.8370\end{bmatrix} = \begin{bmatrix}1.0376\\0.6016\end{bmatrix}.$$

Notice that for this particular example the successive steps of the steepest ascent method tend to be somewhat erratic, i.e. an inefficient zigzag pattern unfolds because the contours of f are non-spherical. In such instances the direction of the gradient is not coincident with the direction to the maximum (minimum) with the result that convergence is slow.

What is the relationship between the Newton–Raphson and steepest ascent methods? A glance at eqs. (B.3) and (C.5) indicates that both these equations are actually special cases of the more general expression

$$\boldsymbol{x}_i = \boldsymbol{x}_{i-1}+\lambda_{i-1}\boldsymbol{M}(\boldsymbol{x}_{i-1})\nabla \mathrm{f}(\boldsymbol{x}_{i-1}), \quad i = 1, 2, \ldots, \tag{C.6}$$

where $\boldsymbol{M}(\boldsymbol{x}_{i-1})$ is termed an nth-order *deflection matrix* which serves to modify or deflect the gradient to a direction which leads to a greater total increase in the function than would be attained simply by moving locally in the direction of the gradient. In this regard, if $\boldsymbol{M}(\boldsymbol{x}_{i-1})$ equals the identity matrix $\boldsymbol{I}_n$ for all values of i, then eq. (C.5) obtains, while if $\lambda_{i-1} = 1$ for all i and $\boldsymbol{M}(\boldsymbol{x}_{i-1}) = -\boldsymbol{H}_{\mathrm{f}}^{-1}(\boldsymbol{x}_{i-1})$, eq. (B.3) results. Hence it can be seen that the Newton–Raphson method is essentially a modified steepest ascent technique.[13]

[13] The preceding discussion has hinted at a procedure which may be used to generalize the Newton–Raphson technique (eq. (B.3)). If in eq. (C.6) we let $\boldsymbol{M}(\boldsymbol{x}_{i-1}) = -\boldsymbol{H}_{\mathrm{f}}^{-1}(\boldsymbol{x}_{i-1})$, then, starting at some initial point $\boldsymbol{x}_0$, we may take a step in the direction $-\boldsymbol{H}_{\mathrm{f}}^{-1}(\boldsymbol{x}_0)\nabla \mathrm{f}(\boldsymbol{x}_0)$, using a step length λ_0 which is chosen to maximize f along $-\boldsymbol{H}_{\mathrm{f}}^{-1}(\boldsymbol{x}_0)\nabla \mathrm{f}(\boldsymbol{x}_0)$, to obtain a new point

$$\boldsymbol{x}_1 = \boldsymbol{x}_0-\lambda_0\boldsymbol{H}_{\mathrm{f}}^{-1}(\boldsymbol{x}_0)\nabla \mathrm{f}(\boldsymbol{x}_0).$$

In general, the ith iteration is determined as

$$\boldsymbol{x}_i = \boldsymbol{x}_{i-1}-\lambda_{i-1}\boldsymbol{H}_{\mathrm{f}}^{-1}(\boldsymbol{x}_{i-1})\nabla \mathrm{f}(\boldsymbol{x}_{i-1}), \quad i = 1, 2, \ldots,$$

where λ_{i-1} is chosen so that

$$\mathrm{f}(\boldsymbol{x}_{i-1}-\lambda_{i-1}\boldsymbol{H}_{\mathrm{f}}^{-1}(\boldsymbol{x}_{i-1})\nabla \mathrm{f}(\boldsymbol{x}_{i-1})) = \max_{\lambda} \mathrm{f}(\boldsymbol{x}_{i-1}-\lambda\boldsymbol{H}_{\mathrm{f}}^{-1}(\boldsymbol{x}_{i-1})\nabla \mathrm{f}(\boldsymbol{x}_{i-1})).$$

6.14. Appendix D: Conjugate direction methods

6.14.1. The Fletcher–Powell (variable-metric) method

An extremely efficient deflected-gradient technique is the method of Fletcher and Powell (Fletcher and Powell, 1963, pp. 163–168). To gain some insight into the motivation underlying their technique, let us re-examine the Newton–Raphson and gradient schemes depicted by eqs. (B.3) and (C.5) respectively. Note that in these two processes the Hessian of f is computed at each iteration, a task which may at times require a considerable amount of effort. Moreover, once a particular iteration is executed, the information provided by such a calculation is discarded, i.e. none of the information previously obtained regarding the behavior of f near an extremum is stored and then used to implement further iterations which may hasten convergence to the desired critical value of $\boldsymbol{x}$. To improve upon these shortcomings Fletcher and Powell have developed a modified or accelerated steepest ascent method which relies solely upon first-order information, as generated by the gradients of f at several different points, to construct a second-order approximation to f in the neighborhood of the extreme point, i.e. a quadratic approximation to f at the said point is obtained without explicitly calculating the Hessian of f there.[14] Fletcher and Powell develop their technique for the case where the function to be maximized is quadratic in $\boldsymbol{x}$, the reason being that if an iterative process can be found which possesses quadratic convergence, i.e. it quickly and efficiently maximizes a quadratic function in a finite number of steps, then that same technique should work well on a general function which behaves like (can be closely approximated by) a quadratic in the vicinity of the extremum.

Let us assume then that the real-valued function $y = \mathrm{f}(\boldsymbol{x}), \boldsymbol{x} \in \mathscr{E}^n$, is differentiable over an open region $\mathscr{K} \subseteq \mathscr{E}^n$ and quadratic in $\boldsymbol{x}$. Then

$$\mathrm{f}(\boldsymbol{x}) = a + \boldsymbol{b}'\boldsymbol{x} + \tfrac{1}{2}\boldsymbol{x}'\boldsymbol{Q}\boldsymbol{x},$$

where $\boldsymbol{b}$ is an $(n \times 1)$ vector and the $(n \times n)$ Hessian matrix $\boldsymbol{Q}$ is taken to be negative definite and non-singular. At an arbitrary point $\boldsymbol{x}_0 \in \mathscr{K}$, $\nabla \mathrm{f}(\boldsymbol{x}_0) = \boldsymbol{b} + \boldsymbol{Q}\boldsymbol{x}_0$. Then $\boldsymbol{x}_0 = \boldsymbol{Q}^{-1}(\nabla \mathrm{f}(\boldsymbol{x}_0) - \boldsymbol{b})$. If f attains a strong local maximum at $\boldsymbol{x}_* \in \mathscr{K}$, then $\nabla \mathrm{f}(\boldsymbol{x}_*) = \boldsymbol{0}$ so that $\boldsymbol{x}_* = -\boldsymbol{Q}^{-1}\boldsymbol{b}$. Upon subtracting $\boldsymbol{x}_0$ from $\boldsymbol{x}_*$ we obtain

$$\boldsymbol{x}_* - \boldsymbol{x}_0 = -\boldsymbol{Q}^{-1}\nabla \mathrm{f}(\boldsymbol{x}_0). \tag{D.1}$$

Here the difference $\boldsymbol{x}_* - \boldsymbol{x}_0$ simply depicts the single step traversed to the

[14] An iterative technique which does not rely upon first-order information and which performs almost as well as the Fletcher–Powell method is that developed by Powell (1964), pp. 155–162.

maximum of f from an arbitrary point x_0 at which the gradient of f is known. Let us now assume that the inverse of the Hessian Q^{-1} is unknown so that eq. (D.1) cannot be applied directly. What we would like to do is to piece together information about the curvature of f which yields something like eq. (D.1). But first let us consider

DEFINITION D.1. *Given an* $(n \times n)$ *negative-definite matrix* Q, *the directions* $s_i \in \mathscr{E}^n$, $i = 0, 1, \ldots, n-1$, *are mutually* Q*-conjugate if they are non-null and*

$$s_i' Q s_j = 0, \quad i \neq j, \quad i, j = 0, 1, \ldots, n-1. \tag{D.2}$$

In addition, an important property of such directions is stated in

THEOREM D.1. *Let* Q *be an* $(n \times n)$ *negative-definite matrix. If n non-null directions* s_i, $i = 0, 1, \ldots, n-1$, *are mutually* Q*-conjugate, then they are also linearly independent.*

Proof. Let us assume to the contrary that the s_i are linearly dependent. Then some particular s_i, say the kth, is expressible as a linear combination of the remaining s_i's, i.e.

$$s_k = \sum_{\substack{i=0 \\ i \neq k}}^{n-1} \theta_i s_i,$$

where at least one of the θ_i's, say the jth, is different from zero. Since the s_i are mutually Q-conjugate, $s_j' Q s_k = 0$. Then

$$s_j' Q s_k = s_j' Q \left(\sum_{\substack{i=0 \\ i \neq k}}^{n-1} \theta_i s_i \right) = \theta_j s_j' Q s_j \neq 0.$$

Since the expressions $s_j' Q s_k = 0$, $s_j' Q s_k \neq 0$ are contradictory, the s_i must be linearly independent. Q.E.D.

In this regard, the Fletcher–Powell method maximizes a quadratic function of n variables in exactly n iterations by generating a sequence of n mutually conjugate directions $s_0, s_1, \ldots, s_{n-1}$, the rationalization being that if we search locally in the s_k-direction and find a point x_k which maximizes f, and then search locally in the conjugate direction s_{k+1} and determine a point x_{k+1} which does the same, then the value of f at x_{k+1} cannot be increased by searching again in the s_k-direction. Hence we need search locally along each of the directions s_i, $i = 0, 1, \ldots, n-1$, only once.

Let us begin by considering the iteration scheme depicted by eq. (C.6), namely

$$x_i = x_{i-1} + \lambda_{i-1} M(x_{i-1}) \nabla f(x_{i-1}), \quad i = 1, 2, \ldots, n$$

or

$$\boldsymbol{x}_i = \boldsymbol{x}_{i-1} + \lambda_{i-1}\boldsymbol{s}_{i-1}, \quad i = 1, 2, \ldots, n,$$

where the directions $\boldsymbol{s}_{i-1} = \boldsymbol{M}(\boldsymbol{x}_{i-1})\nabla \mathrm{f}(\boldsymbol{x}_{i-1})$ satisfy eq. (D.2). From some initial estimate of $\boldsymbol{x}_*$, $\boldsymbol{x}_0$, we construct a direction $\boldsymbol{s}_0 = -\boldsymbol{H}_0 \nabla \mathrm{f}(\boldsymbol{x}_0)$, where the $(n \times n)$ matrix $\boldsymbol{H}_0$ is chosen to be symmetric and negative definite so that movement locally along $\boldsymbol{s}_0$ yields an increase in f. Hence the role of $\boldsymbol{H}_0$ is simply to supply the current direction of motion. (Note that if $-\boldsymbol{H}_0$ is the identity matrix, then our initial step is in the direction of steepest ascent. In all other instances $\boldsymbol{H}_0$ serves to deflect the direction of ascent to a path different from that of the gradient.) Thus $\boldsymbol{x}_1$ is determined as

$$\boldsymbol{x}_1 = \boldsymbol{x}_0 + \lambda_0 \boldsymbol{s}_0, \qquad \boldsymbol{s}_0 = -\boldsymbol{H}_0 \nabla \mathrm{f}(\boldsymbol{x}_0),$$

with the search parameter λ_0 chosen to maximize $\mathrm{f}(\boldsymbol{x}_1)$ along $\boldsymbol{s}_0$, i.e.

$$\mathrm{f}(\boldsymbol{x}_0 + \lambda_0 \boldsymbol{s}_0) = \max_{\lambda} \mathrm{f}(\boldsymbol{x}_0 + \lambda \boldsymbol{s}_0).$$

With $\boldsymbol{H}_0$ negative definite,

$$\frac{\mathrm{d}}{\mathrm{d}\lambda} \mathrm{f}(\boldsymbol{x}_0 + \lambda \boldsymbol{s}_0) \bigg|_{\lambda=0} = -\nabla \mathrm{f}(\boldsymbol{x}_0)' \boldsymbol{H}_0 \nabla \mathrm{f}(\boldsymbol{x}_0) > 0.$$

Hence we are assured that f actually increases locally in the direction of $\boldsymbol{s}_0$.

In general, the ith iteration is determined as

$$\boldsymbol{x}_i = \boldsymbol{x}_{i-1} + \lambda_{i-1}\boldsymbol{s}_{i-1}, \quad i = 1, 2, \ldots, n, \tag{D.3}$$

where the directions $\boldsymbol{s}_{i-1} = -\boldsymbol{H}_{i-1} \nabla \mathrm{f}(\boldsymbol{x}_{i-1})$ are mutually $\boldsymbol{Q}$ conjugate, $\boldsymbol{H}_{i-1}$ is symmetric and negative definite, and, starting at $\boldsymbol{x}_{i-1}$, λ_{i-1} is chosen so that

$$\mathrm{f}(\boldsymbol{x}_{i-1} + \lambda_{i-1}\boldsymbol{s}_{i-1}) = \max_{\lambda} \mathrm{f}(\boldsymbol{x}_{i-1} + \lambda \boldsymbol{s}_{i-1}). \tag{D.4}$$

As far as the quadratic convergence of eq. (D.3) to the maximum of f is concerned, we shall demonstrate that if eq. (D.2) is satisfied, $\nabla \mathrm{f}(\boldsymbol{x}_n)$ vanishes so that the maximum is attained at the nth step. From eq. (D.3) it is easily shown that $\boldsymbol{x}_n = \boldsymbol{x}_0 + \Sigma_{i=0}^{n-1} \lambda_i \boldsymbol{s}_i$ or, for our purposes,

$$\boldsymbol{x}_n = \boldsymbol{x}_j + \sum_{i=j}^{n-1} \lambda_i \boldsymbol{s}_i = \boldsymbol{x}_j + \lambda_j \boldsymbol{s}_j + \sum_{i=j+1}^{n-1} \lambda_i \boldsymbol{s}_i, \quad j = 0, 1, \ldots, n-1.$$

Upon substituting this latter expression into $\nabla \mathrm{f}(\boldsymbol{x}) = \boldsymbol{b} + \boldsymbol{Q}\boldsymbol{x}$ we obtain

$$\nabla \mathrm{f}(\boldsymbol{x}_n) = \boldsymbol{b} + \boldsymbol{Q}(\boldsymbol{x}_j + \lambda_j \boldsymbol{s}_j) + \sum_{i=j+1}^{n-1} \lambda_i \boldsymbol{Q}\boldsymbol{s}_i = \nabla \mathrm{f}(\boldsymbol{x}_{j+1}) + \sum_{i=j+1}^{n-1} \lambda_i \boldsymbol{Q}\boldsymbol{s}_i,$$

$$j = 0, 1, \ldots, n-1.$$

Then

$$s_j'\nabla f(x_n) = s_j'\nabla f(x_{j+1}) + \sum_{i=j+1}^{n-1} \lambda_i s_j Q s_i = \sum_{i=j+1}^{n-1} \lambda_i s_j Q s_i$$

since successive steps are mutually orthogonal, i.e. at the maximum indicated by eq. (D.4),

$$\left.\frac{\mathrm{d}f(x_{i-1}+\lambda s_{i-1})}{\mathrm{d}\lambda}\right|_{\lambda=\lambda_{i-1}} = s_{i-1}' \nabla f(x_i) = 0, \quad i = 1, 2, \ldots, n.$$

If the directions s_i, $i = 0, 1, \ldots, n-1$, satisfy eq. (D.2), then $s_j'\nabla f(x_n) = 0$. Since the s_i, $i = 0, 1, \ldots, n-1$, are linearly independent, $\nabla f(x_n)$ is orthogonal to s_i, $i = 0, 1, \ldots, n-1$, only if $\nabla f(x_n) \equiv 0$. Hence the maximum of f is attained at the nth iteration when we search along a set of n mutually Q-conjugate directions.

Since the iterative process described by eq. (D.3) is to converge to something which resembles eq. (D.1) in n steps, we must have $H_n = Q^{-1}$. To see exactly how the sequence of deflection matrices H_i, $i = 1, \ldots, n$, actually converges to Q^{-1}, let us consider the matrix difference equation

$$H_i = H_{i-1} + A_i + B_i, \quad i = 1, \ldots, n, \tag{D.5}$$

where it is stipulated that $H_n = Q^{-1}$. We first form the sum

$$\sum_{i=1}^{n} H_i = \sum_{i=1}^{n} H_{i-1} + \sum_{i=1}^{n} A_i + \sum_{i=1}^{n} B_i$$

or

$$H_n = H_0 + \sum_{i=1}^{n} A_i + \sum_{i=1}^{n} B_i$$

so that

$$Q^{-1} = H_0 + \sum_{i=1}^{n} A_i + \sum_{i=1}^{n} B_i. \tag{D.5.1}$$

As we shall now see, the role of eq. (D.5) is twofold. As our iterations progress we desire: (1) to improve our initial estimate of Q^{-1}, H_0, by continually updating the information regarding the curvature of f at x_* obtained at each successive step; and (2) to cancel out the effects of a poor choice of H_0. If we set

$$\sum_{i=1}^{n} B_i = -H_0, \tag{D.6}$$

then

$$\sum_{i=1}^{n} A_i = Q^{-1}. \tag{D.7}$$

Thus the matrices $\boldsymbol{A}_i$, $i = 1, \ldots, n$, scrve to systematically generate $\boldsymbol{Q}^{-1}$ in n steps according to eq. (D.7), whereas the $\boldsymbol{B}_i$, $i = 1, \ldots, n$, matrices tend to gradually eliminate the influence of $\boldsymbol{H}_0$ by virtue of eq. (D.6).

Our final step is to determine how the $\boldsymbol{A}_i$, $\boldsymbol{B}_i$ matrices are computed. We indicated earlier that a second-order approximation of f at $\boldsymbol{x}_*$ would be achieved by piecing together information about the curvature of f obtained from its gradients at two successive points. To this end let us form the gradient difference vector

$$\boldsymbol{d}_i = \nabla f(\boldsymbol{x}_i) - \nabla f(\boldsymbol{x}_{i-1}), \quad i = 1, \ldots, n. \tag{D.8}$$

From our initial expression for $f(\boldsymbol{x})$ we obtain $\nabla f(\boldsymbol{x}) = \boldsymbol{b} + \boldsymbol{Q}\boldsymbol{x}$. Coupling this result with eq. (D.8) for $\boldsymbol{x} = \boldsymbol{x}_i, \boldsymbol{x}_{i-1}$ yields

$$\boldsymbol{d}_i = \boldsymbol{Q}(\boldsymbol{x}_i - \boldsymbol{x}_{i-1}) = \boldsymbol{Q}\boldsymbol{\sigma}_i, \tag{D.8.1}$$

where $\boldsymbol{\sigma}_i = \lambda_{i-1}\boldsymbol{s}_{i-1}$ (eq. (D.3)). In addition, from eqs. (D.7) and (D.8),

$$\boldsymbol{\sigma}_i = \boldsymbol{Q}^{-1}\boldsymbol{Q}\boldsymbol{\sigma}_i = \sum_{k=1}^{n} \boldsymbol{A}_k\boldsymbol{d}_i = \boldsymbol{A}_i\boldsymbol{d}_i \tag{D.9}$$

(here $\boldsymbol{A}_k\boldsymbol{d}_i = 0$, $k \neq i$. For a proof on this account, see Fletcher and Powell (1963), p. 165). Then

$$\boldsymbol{\sigma}_i = \boldsymbol{\sigma}_i\left(\frac{\boldsymbol{\sigma}_i'\boldsymbol{d}_i}{\boldsymbol{\sigma}_i'\boldsymbol{d}_i}\right) = \left(\frac{\boldsymbol{\sigma}_i'\boldsymbol{\sigma}_i}{\boldsymbol{\sigma}_i'\boldsymbol{d}_i}\right)\boldsymbol{d}_i$$

and thus, from eq. (D.9),

$$\boldsymbol{A}_i = (\boldsymbol{\sigma}_i\boldsymbol{\sigma}_i')/(\boldsymbol{\sigma}_i'\boldsymbol{d}_i). \tag{D.10}$$

We now obtain, from eqs. (D.5), (D.8.1), and (D.9),

$$\boldsymbol{H}_i\boldsymbol{Q}\boldsymbol{\sigma}_i = \boldsymbol{H}_i\boldsymbol{d}_i = \boldsymbol{H}_{i-1}\boldsymbol{d}_i + \boldsymbol{\sigma}_i + \boldsymbol{B}_i\boldsymbol{d}_i. \tag{D.11}$$

Since the directions $\boldsymbol{s}_i$, $i = 0, 1, \ldots, n-1$, are linearly independent, successive directions are related to $\boldsymbol{H}_i$ by $\boldsymbol{H}_i\boldsymbol{Q}\boldsymbol{\sigma}_i = \boldsymbol{\sigma}_i$, $i = 1, 2, \ldots, n$ (Fletcher and Powell, 1963, p. 165). Hence, eq. (D.11) becomes

$$\boldsymbol{B}_i\boldsymbol{d}_i = -\boldsymbol{H}_i\boldsymbol{d}_i = -\boldsymbol{H}_{i-1}\boldsymbol{d}_i\left(\frac{\boldsymbol{d}_i'\boldsymbol{H}_{i-1}\boldsymbol{d}_i}{\boldsymbol{d}_i'\boldsymbol{H}_{i-1}\boldsymbol{d}_i}\right) = -\left(\frac{\boldsymbol{H}_{i-1}\boldsymbol{d}_i\boldsymbol{d}_i'\boldsymbol{H}_{i-1}}{\boldsymbol{d}_i'\boldsymbol{H}_{i-1}\boldsymbol{d}_i}\right)\boldsymbol{d}_i,$$

whence

$$\boldsymbol{B}_i = -\frac{\boldsymbol{H}_{i-1}\boldsymbol{d}_i\boldsymbol{d}_i'\boldsymbol{H}_{i-1}}{\boldsymbol{d}_i'\boldsymbol{H}_{i-1}\boldsymbol{d}_i}. \tag{D.12}$$

The Fletcher–Powell method is now completely defined and successive iterations may be carried out as follows:

(1) to maximize f, choose an initial point $\boldsymbol{x}_0$ and a negative-definite

matrix $\boldsymbol{H}_0$ (for convenience, let $\boldsymbol{H}_0 = -\boldsymbol{I}_n$);
(2) compute $\nabla f(\boldsymbol{x}_0)$;
(3) calculate a direction in which to move $\boldsymbol{s}_0 = -\boldsymbol{H}_0 \nabla f(\boldsymbol{x}_0)$;
(4) to move along $\boldsymbol{s}_0$, compute a step length λ_0 so that

$$f(\boldsymbol{x}_0 + \lambda_0 \boldsymbol{s}_0) = \max_{\lambda} f(\boldsymbol{x}_0 + \lambda \boldsymbol{s}_0);$$

(5) compute $\boldsymbol{\sigma}_1 = \lambda_0 \boldsymbol{s}_0$, $\boldsymbol{x}_1 = \boldsymbol{x}_0 + \boldsymbol{\sigma}_1$;
(6) compute $\nabla f(\boldsymbol{x}_1)$, $\boldsymbol{d}_1 = \nabla f(\boldsymbol{x}_1) - \nabla f(\boldsymbol{x}_0)$;
(7) compute

$$\boldsymbol{A}_1 = \frac{\boldsymbol{\sigma}_1 \boldsymbol{\sigma}_1'}{\boldsymbol{\sigma}_1' \boldsymbol{d}_1}, \qquad \boldsymbol{B}_1 = -\frac{\boldsymbol{H}_0 \boldsymbol{d}_1 \boldsymbol{d}_1' \boldsymbol{H}_0}{\boldsymbol{d}_1' \boldsymbol{H}_0 \boldsymbol{d}_1},$$

and thus

$$\boldsymbol{H}_1 = \boldsymbol{H}_0 + \boldsymbol{A}_1 + \boldsymbol{B}_1;$$

(8) repeat steps (1)–(7), increasing each subscript by 1 at the beginning of each round until $|f(\boldsymbol{x}_i) - f(\boldsymbol{x}_{i-1})| < \eta$, where η is set at some predetermined level.

If the minimum of f is to be determined, $\boldsymbol{H}_0$ is chosen as positive definite ($\boldsymbol{H}_0 = \boldsymbol{I}_n$ will do) and we minimize in step (4) rather than maximize.

When the Fletcher–Powell method is applied to a general function, convergence to the desired extremum will not occur in exactly n steps as in the pure quadratic case. In this instance the process should be thought of as one involving the generation of conjugate directions for a quadratic approximation of f. As the iterations progress and the sequence of $\boldsymbol{H}_n$ matrices yield increasingly better estimates of the curvature of f at the extremum, the rate of convergence accelerates as soon as the process gets reasonably close to a second-order approximation.

Example D.1. Let the real-valued function

$$y = f(\boldsymbol{x}) = \boldsymbol{b}'\boldsymbol{x} + \tfrac{1}{2}\boldsymbol{x}'\boldsymbol{Q}\boldsymbol{x}$$

be defined for all $\boldsymbol{x} \in \mathscr{E}^2$, where

$$\boldsymbol{b} = \begin{bmatrix} 5 \\ 4 \end{bmatrix}, \qquad \boldsymbol{Q} = \begin{bmatrix} -1 & 0 \\ 0 & -1.5 \end{bmatrix}.$$

Maximize f using the Fletcher–Powell technique given that $\boldsymbol{x}_0' = (1, 1)$, $\boldsymbol{H}_0 = -\boldsymbol{I}_2$. We first find

$$\nabla f(\boldsymbol{x}_0) = \boldsymbol{b} + \boldsymbol{Q}\boldsymbol{x}_0 = \begin{bmatrix} 4 \\ 2.5 \end{bmatrix}, \qquad \boldsymbol{s}_0 = -\boldsymbol{H}_0 \nabla f(\boldsymbol{x}_0) = \begin{bmatrix} 4 \\ 2.5 \end{bmatrix}.$$

To determine λ_0, lct us maximize

$$\begin{aligned} f(\boldsymbol{x}_0+\lambda \boldsymbol{s}_0) &= \boldsymbol{b}'(\boldsymbol{x}_0+\lambda \boldsymbol{s}_0)+\tfrac{1}{2}(\boldsymbol{x}_0+\lambda \boldsymbol{s}_0)'\boldsymbol{Q}(\boldsymbol{x}_0+\lambda \boldsymbol{s}_0) \\ &= 7.75+22.25\lambda-12.6875\lambda^2. \end{aligned}$$

From

$$\frac{df(\boldsymbol{x}_0+\lambda \boldsymbol{s}_0)}{d\lambda} = 22.25-25.375\lambda = 0$$

we obtain $\lambda_0 = 0.87$ and thus

$$\boldsymbol{\sigma}_1 = \lambda_0 \boldsymbol{s}_0 = \begin{bmatrix} 3.480 \\ 2.175 \end{bmatrix}, \quad \boldsymbol{x}_1 = \boldsymbol{x}_0+\boldsymbol{\sigma}_1 = \begin{bmatrix} 4.480 \\ 3.175 \end{bmatrix}.$$

To initiate the next iteration we compute

$$\begin{aligned} \nabla f(\boldsymbol{x}_1) &= \boldsymbol{b}+\boldsymbol{Q}\boldsymbol{x}_1 = \begin{bmatrix} 0.5200 \\ -0.7625 \end{bmatrix}, \\ \boldsymbol{d}_1 &= \nabla f(\boldsymbol{x}_1)-\nabla f(\boldsymbol{x}_0) = \begin{bmatrix} -3.4800 \\ -3.2625 \end{bmatrix}. \end{aligned}$$

From

$$\begin{aligned} \boldsymbol{A}_1 &= \frac{\boldsymbol{\sigma}_1\boldsymbol{\sigma}_1'}{\boldsymbol{\sigma}_1'\boldsymbol{d}_1} = \begin{bmatrix} -0.6305 & -0.3941 \\ -0.3941 & -0.2463 \end{bmatrix}, \\ \boldsymbol{B}_1 &= -\frac{\boldsymbol{H}_0\boldsymbol{d}_1\boldsymbol{d}_1'\boldsymbol{H}_0}{\boldsymbol{d}_1'\boldsymbol{H}_0\boldsymbol{d}_1} = \begin{bmatrix} 0.5322 & 0.4990 \\ 0.4990 & 0.4678 \end{bmatrix} \end{aligned}$$

we obtain

$$\begin{aligned} \boldsymbol{H}_1 &= \boldsymbol{H}_0+\boldsymbol{A}_1+\boldsymbol{B}_1 = \begin{bmatrix} -1.0983 & 0.1049 \\ 0.1049 & -0.7785 \end{bmatrix}, \\ \boldsymbol{s}_1 &= -\boldsymbol{H}_1\nabla f(\boldsymbol{x}_1) = \begin{bmatrix} 0.6510 \\ -0.6481 \end{bmatrix}. \end{aligned}$$

We next compute λ_1 by maximizing

$$\begin{aligned} f(\boldsymbol{x}_1+\lambda \boldsymbol{s}_1) &= \boldsymbol{b}'(\boldsymbol{x}_1+\lambda \boldsymbol{s}_1)+\tfrac{1}{2}(\boldsymbol{x}_1+\lambda \boldsymbol{s}_1)'\boldsymbol{Q}(\boldsymbol{x}_1+\lambda \boldsymbol{s}_1) \\ &= -0.913+1.0025\lambda-1.0538\lambda^2. \end{aligned}$$

To this end we have

$$\frac{df(\boldsymbol{x}_1+\lambda \boldsymbol{s}_1)}{d\lambda} = 1.0025-2.1076\lambda = 0$$

or $\lambda_1 = 0.48$ and thus

$$\boldsymbol{\sigma}_2 = \lambda_1 \boldsymbol{s}_1 = \begin{bmatrix} 0.3125 \\ -0.3111 \end{bmatrix}, \quad \boldsymbol{x}_2 = \boldsymbol{x}_1+\boldsymbol{\sigma}_2 = \begin{bmatrix} 4.7925 \\ 2.8639 \end{bmatrix} \sim \boldsymbol{x}_*.$$

The next example is designed to provide the reader with a convenient numerical procedure for determining the value of the search parameter λ in situations where the function to be maximized or minimized is not quadratic in $\boldsymbol{x}$.

Example D.2. Minimize the real-valued function

$$y = \mathrm{f}(\boldsymbol{x}) = x_1^2 x_2 + x_2^2 + x_1 x_2, \quad \boldsymbol{x} \in \mathscr{E}^2,$$

using the Fletcher–Powell method. Upon choosing $\boldsymbol{x}_0' = (1, 1)$, $\boldsymbol{H}_0 = \boldsymbol{I}_2$, we first obtain

$$\nabla \mathrm{f}(\boldsymbol{x}_0) = \begin{bmatrix} 3 \\ 4 \end{bmatrix}, \qquad \boldsymbol{s}_0 = -\boldsymbol{H}_0 \nabla \mathrm{f}(\boldsymbol{x}_0) = \begin{bmatrix} -3 \\ -4 \end{bmatrix}.$$

Our next step is to minimize $\mathrm{f}(\boldsymbol{x}_0 + \lambda \boldsymbol{s}_0)$. Since f is not quadratic in $\boldsymbol{x}$, let us approximate $\mathrm{f}(\boldsymbol{x}_0 + \lambda \boldsymbol{s}_0)$ by a second-order polynomial in λ. Setting

$$\mathrm{f}(\boldsymbol{x}_0 + \lambda \boldsymbol{s}_0) = \mathrm{g}(\lambda) = a + b\lambda + c\lambda^2,$$

we have, for $\lambda = 0$,

$$\mathrm{g}(0) = a = \mathrm{f}(\boldsymbol{x}_0) = 3.$$

Additionally,

$$\left.\frac{\mathrm{d}\mathrm{g}}{\mathrm{d}\lambda}\right|_{\lambda=0} = b = \left(\left.\frac{\partial \mathrm{f}}{\partial \boldsymbol{x}}\right|_{\lambda=0}\right)' \frac{\mathrm{d}\boldsymbol{x}}{\mathrm{d}\lambda} = \nabla \mathrm{f}(\boldsymbol{x}_0)' \boldsymbol{s}_0 = -25.$$

To obtain c, let us arbitrarily set $\lambda = 1$. Then

$$\mathrm{g}(1) = \mathrm{f}(\boldsymbol{x}_0 + \boldsymbol{s}_0) = 3 = 3 - 25 + c \quad \text{or} \quad c = 25.$$

Hence

$$\mathrm{f}(\boldsymbol{x}_0 + \lambda \boldsymbol{s}_0) = 3 - 25\lambda + 25\lambda^2,$$

$$\frac{\mathrm{d}\mathrm{f}(\boldsymbol{x}_0 + \lambda \boldsymbol{s}_0)}{\mathrm{d}\lambda} = -25 + 50\lambda = 0$$

and thus $\lambda_0 = 0.5$. Then

$$\boldsymbol{\sigma}_1 = \lambda_0 \boldsymbol{s}_0 = \begin{bmatrix} -1.5 \\ -2 \end{bmatrix}, \qquad \boldsymbol{x}_1 = \boldsymbol{x}_0 + \boldsymbol{\sigma}_1 = \begin{bmatrix} -0.5 \\ -1 \end{bmatrix}.$$

To start the next round of calculations we first determine

$$\nabla \mathrm{f}(\boldsymbol{x}_1) = \begin{bmatrix} 0 \\ -2.25 \end{bmatrix}, \qquad \boldsymbol{d}_1 = \nabla \mathrm{f}(\boldsymbol{x}_1) - \nabla \mathrm{f}(\boldsymbol{x}_0) = \begin{bmatrix} -3 \\ -6.25 \end{bmatrix}.$$

Then

$$A_1 = \frac{\sigma_1 \sigma_1'}{\sigma_1' d_1} = \begin{bmatrix} 0.1324 & 0.1765 \\ 0.1765 & 0.2353 \end{bmatrix},$$

$$B_1 = -\frac{H_0 d_1 d_1' H_0}{d_1' H_0 d_1} = \begin{bmatrix} -0.2043 & -0.3901 \\ -0.3901 & -0.8127 \end{bmatrix}$$

and thus

$$H_1 = H_0 + A_1 + B_1 = \begin{bmatrix} 0.9283 & -0.2136 \\ -0.2136 & 0.4226 \end{bmatrix},$$

$$s_1 = -H_1 \nabla f(x_1) = \begin{bmatrix} -0.4806 \\ 0.9506 \end{bmatrix}.$$

We will now minimize $f(x_1 + \lambda s_1)$. Again a quadratic approximation to $f(x_1 + \lambda s_1) = g(\lambda)$ is in order. For $\lambda = 0$,

$$g(0) = a = f(x_1) = 1.25.$$

Furthermore,

$$\left.\frac{dg}{d\lambda}\right|_{\lambda=0} = b = \nabla f(x_1)' s_1 = -2.1389.$$

Finally, for $\lambda = 1$,

$$g(1) = f(x_1 + s_1) = 0.0033 = 1.25 - 2.1389 + c \quad \text{or} \quad c = 0.8922.$$

Then

$$f(x_1 + \lambda s_1) = 1.25 - 2.1389\lambda + 0.8922\lambda^2,$$

$$\frac{df(x_1 + \lambda s_1)}{d\lambda} = -2.1389 + 1.7844\lambda = 0$$

and thus $\lambda_1 = 1.1987$. Hence

$$\sigma_2 = \lambda_1 s_1 = \begin{bmatrix} -0.5761 \\ 1.1395 \end{bmatrix}, \qquad x_2 = x_1 + \sigma_2 = \begin{bmatrix} -1.0761 \\ 0.1398 \end{bmatrix}.$$

The above process is repeated until the successive iterations converge to x_*.

6.14.2. The Fletcher–Reeves (conjugate gradient) method

We noted in the previous section that to undertake the various rounds of the Fletcher–Powell technique an $(n \times n)$ symmetric negative-definite matrix H_i had to be computed and updated at the next iteration to insure that $H_n = Q^{-1}$. From the viewpoint of economizing on time and effort, a method which does not store any such information but simply locates the maximum may at times be preferred. Such a process is that provided by

Fletcher and Reeves. If the function to be maximized is quadratic in $\boldsymbol{x}$, their method will also locate the extremum in n steps by generating a sequence of mutually conjugate directions.

Thus, in what follows we shall attempt to find the maximum of the differentiable real-valued function

$$y = \mathrm{f}(\boldsymbol{x}) = a+\boldsymbol{b}'\boldsymbol{x}+\tfrac{1}{2}\boldsymbol{x}'\boldsymbol{Q}\boldsymbol{x}, \quad \boldsymbol{x}\in\mathscr{E}^n,$$

over an open region $\mathscr{K}\subseteq\mathscr{E}^n$. Given the iteration scheme depicted by

$$\boldsymbol{x}_i = \boldsymbol{x}_{i-1}+\lambda_{i-1}\boldsymbol{s}_{i-1}, \quad i = 1, 2, \ldots, n,$$

let us start from an arbitrary estimate of the critical point $\boldsymbol{x}_*$, $\boldsymbol{x}_0$, and search initially in the direction of steepest ascent. Then $\boldsymbol{x}_1$ is obtained as

$$\boldsymbol{x}_1 = \boldsymbol{x}_0+\lambda_0\boldsymbol{s}_0, \qquad \boldsymbol{s}_0 = \nabla\mathrm{f}(\boldsymbol{x}_0),$$

where λ_0 is determined by maximizing $\mathrm{f}(\boldsymbol{x}_1)$ along $\boldsymbol{s}_0$, i.e.

$$\mathrm{f}(\boldsymbol{x}_0+\lambda_0\boldsymbol{s}_0) = \max_{\lambda} \mathrm{f}(\boldsymbol{x}_0+\lambda\boldsymbol{s}_0).$$

At the implied maximum

$$\boldsymbol{s}_0'\nabla\mathrm{f}(\boldsymbol{x}_1) = \boldsymbol{s}_0'(\boldsymbol{b}+\boldsymbol{Q}(\boldsymbol{x}_0+\lambda_0\boldsymbol{s}_0)) = 0$$

or

$$\lambda_0 = -\frac{\boldsymbol{s}_0'(\boldsymbol{b}+\boldsymbol{Q}\boldsymbol{x}_0)}{\boldsymbol{s}_0'\boldsymbol{Q}\boldsymbol{s}_0} = -\frac{\boldsymbol{s}_0'\nabla\mathrm{f}(\boldsymbol{x}_0)}{\boldsymbol{s}_0'\boldsymbol{Q}\boldsymbol{s}_0}.$$

To execute succeeding iterations the search directions $\boldsymbol{s}_i$, $i>0$, are chosen to equal the gradient at $\boldsymbol{x}_i$, $i>0$, plus an appropriate linear combination of the previous directions. Hence the directions $\boldsymbol{s}_i$, $i = 0, 1, \ldots, n-1$, will satisfy eq. (D.2) if $\boldsymbol{s}_0 = \nabla\mathrm{f}(\boldsymbol{x}_0)$ and

$$\boldsymbol{s}_i = \nabla\mathrm{f}(\boldsymbol{x}_i)+\beta_{i-1}\boldsymbol{s}_{i-1}, \quad i = 1, 2, \ldots, n-1,$$

where, by the orthogonality of successive gradients,[15]

$$\beta_{i-1} = \frac{\nabla\mathrm{f}(\boldsymbol{x}_i)'\nabla\mathrm{f}(\boldsymbol{x}_i)}{\nabla\mathrm{f}(\boldsymbol{x}_{i-1})'\nabla\mathrm{f}(\boldsymbol{x}_{i-1})}, \quad i = 1, 2, \ldots, n-1.$$

In general, the various rounds of the Fletcher–Reeves method may be carried out as follows:

(1) to maximize f, choose an arbitrary point $\boldsymbol{x}_0$;
(2) compute $\nabla\mathrm{f}(\boldsymbol{x}_0)$;

[15] A detailed development of these last two expressions is provided by Beckman (1964), pp. 62–72, and Zangwill (1969), pp. 139–144.

(3) choose as the initial direction $\boldsymbol{s}_0 = \nabla \mathrm{f}(\boldsymbol{x}_0)$;

(4) to move along $\boldsymbol{s}_0$, compute the step length λ_0 so that

$$\mathrm{f}(\boldsymbol{x}_0+\lambda_0\boldsymbol{s}_0) = \max_{\lambda} \mathrm{f}(\boldsymbol{x}_0+\lambda\boldsymbol{s}_0),$$

that is,

$$\lambda_0 = -\frac{\boldsymbol{s}_0'\nabla \mathrm{f}(\boldsymbol{x}_0)}{\boldsymbol{s}_0'\boldsymbol{Q}\boldsymbol{s}_0};$$

(5) compute $\boldsymbol{x}_1 = \boldsymbol{x}_0+\lambda_0\nabla \mathrm{f}(\boldsymbol{x}_0)$;

(6) for $i = 1, 2, \ldots, n-1$, choose λ_i so that

$$\mathrm{f}(\boldsymbol{x}_i+\lambda_i\boldsymbol{s}_i) = \max_{\lambda} \mathrm{f}(\boldsymbol{x}_i+\lambda\boldsymbol{s}_i),$$

that is,

$$\lambda_i = -\frac{\boldsymbol{s}_i'\nabla \mathrm{f}(\boldsymbol{x}_i)}{\boldsymbol{s}_i'\boldsymbol{Q}\boldsymbol{s}_i},$$

where

$$s_i = \nabla \mathrm{f}(\boldsymbol{x}_i)+\beta_{i-1}\boldsymbol{s}_{i-1}, \qquad \beta_{i-1} = \frac{\nabla \mathrm{f}(\boldsymbol{x}_i)'\nabla \mathrm{f}(\boldsymbol{x}_i)}{\nabla \mathrm{f}(\boldsymbol{x}_{i-1})'\nabla \mathrm{f}(\boldsymbol{x}_{i-1})};$$

(7) compute

$$\boldsymbol{x}_i = \boldsymbol{x}_{i-1}+\lambda_{i-1}\boldsymbol{s}_{i-1}, \quad i = 2, 3, \ldots, n;$$

(8) after the first iteration is completed, repeat steps (6) and (7) until $\nabla \mathrm{f}(\boldsymbol{x}_i) = \boldsymbol{0}$.

To minimize f, choose $\boldsymbol{s}_0 = -\nabla \mathrm{f}(\boldsymbol{x}_0)$, $\boldsymbol{s}_i = -\nabla \mathrm{f}(\boldsymbol{x}_i)+\beta_{i-1}\boldsymbol{s}_{i-1}$, and minimize in steps (4) and (6) rather than maximize.[16]

If the function to be maximized or minimized is not quadratic in $\boldsymbol{x}$, the desired extremum will not be located in exactly n steps. In this instance Fletcher and Reeves suggest restarting the process in the direction of steepest ascent or descent after every $n+1$ iterations. As an exercise the reader is asked to rework example D.2 using the algorithm developed in this section.

---

[16] For an evaluation of the relative performance of the Fletcher–Powell, Fletcher–Reeves techniques, among others, see Box (1966), pp. 67–77; Pearson (1969), pp. 171–178; Fiacco and McCormick (1968), pp. 162–165.

Chapter 7

INFLECTION POINTS OF REAL-VALUED FUNCTIONS

7.1. Classification of inflection points

In chapter 6 we defined the notion of a horizontal point of inflection of the real-valued function $y = f(x)$. However, inflectional values may occur at a point where the tangent to the curve is not horizontal. In the ensuing discussion we shall identify two broad classes of points of inflection. Specifically, points of inflection occur where a curve crosses over its tangent and:

(CLASS I) changes the direction of its concavity from upward to downward (fig. 7.1a, b); or
(CLASS II) changes the direction of its concavity from downward to upward (fig. 7.1c, d).

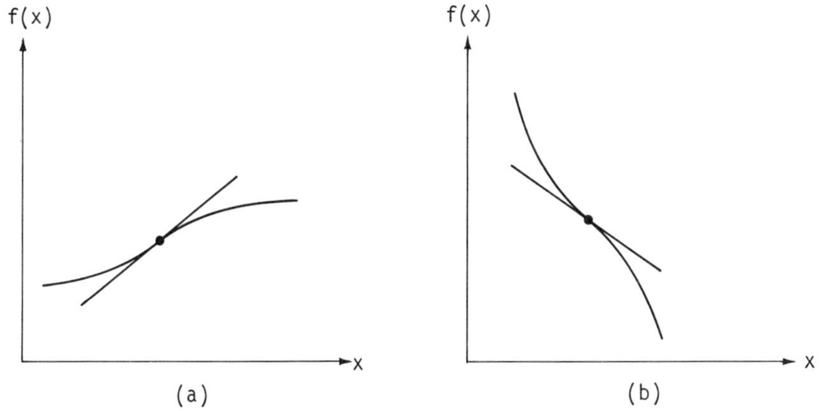

Fig. 7.1.

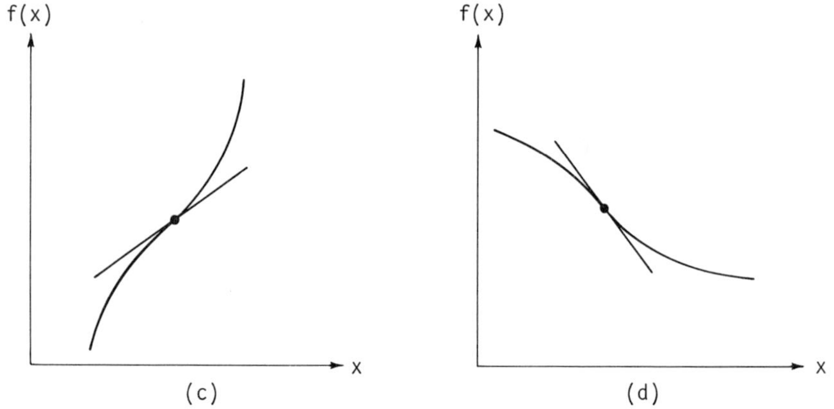

Fig. 7.1.

Two limiting cases of the above classification scheme occur when a curve crosses over its horizontal or vertical tangent and thus changes the direction of its concavity from upward to downward or conversely.

No matter what variety of inflectional value a continuous real-valued function $y = f(x)$ attains over its domain, it always occurs at a point where the first derivative of f assumes an extreme value. For instance, if f has a point of inflection of the first class at $x_0 \in (a, b)$, then fig. 7.2a depicts f as increasing at an increasing rate for $x < x_0$, reaching a point of inflection at x_0, and then increasing at a decreasing rate for $x > x_0$. Hence, f′ increases when $x < x_0$, reaches a strong local maximum at x_0, and then decreases for values of $x > x_0$. However, when f′ is at a maximum, its slope is zero there, and thus $f''(x_0) = 0$. If f has a point of inflection of the second class at $x' \in (a, b)$, fig. 7.2b indicates that f increases at a decreasing rate when $x < x'$, attains a point of inflection at x', and, for $x > x'$, increases at an increasing rate. Thus, f′ decreases for $x < x'$, assumes a strong local minimum at x', and then increases as x does beyond x'. So with f′ at a minimum at x', $f''(x') = 0$. In sum, at a point of inflection of the first (second) class, f′ assumes a maximum (minimum) value and thus $f'' = 0$.

The above observations may be consolidated into what will be called a necessary condition for the occurrence of a point of inflection of f interior to its domain.

THEOREM 7.1 (a necessary condition).[1] *Let the real-valued function* $y = f(x)$ *possess a continuous second derivative throughout some* δ*-neighborhood of the*

[1] The proof of this theorem follows closely that given in support of theorem 6.4, chapter 6, pp. 105–106, and consequently will not be duplicated here. Suffice it to say that what must be demonstrated is that a point of inflection cannot occur if $f'' \neq 0$.

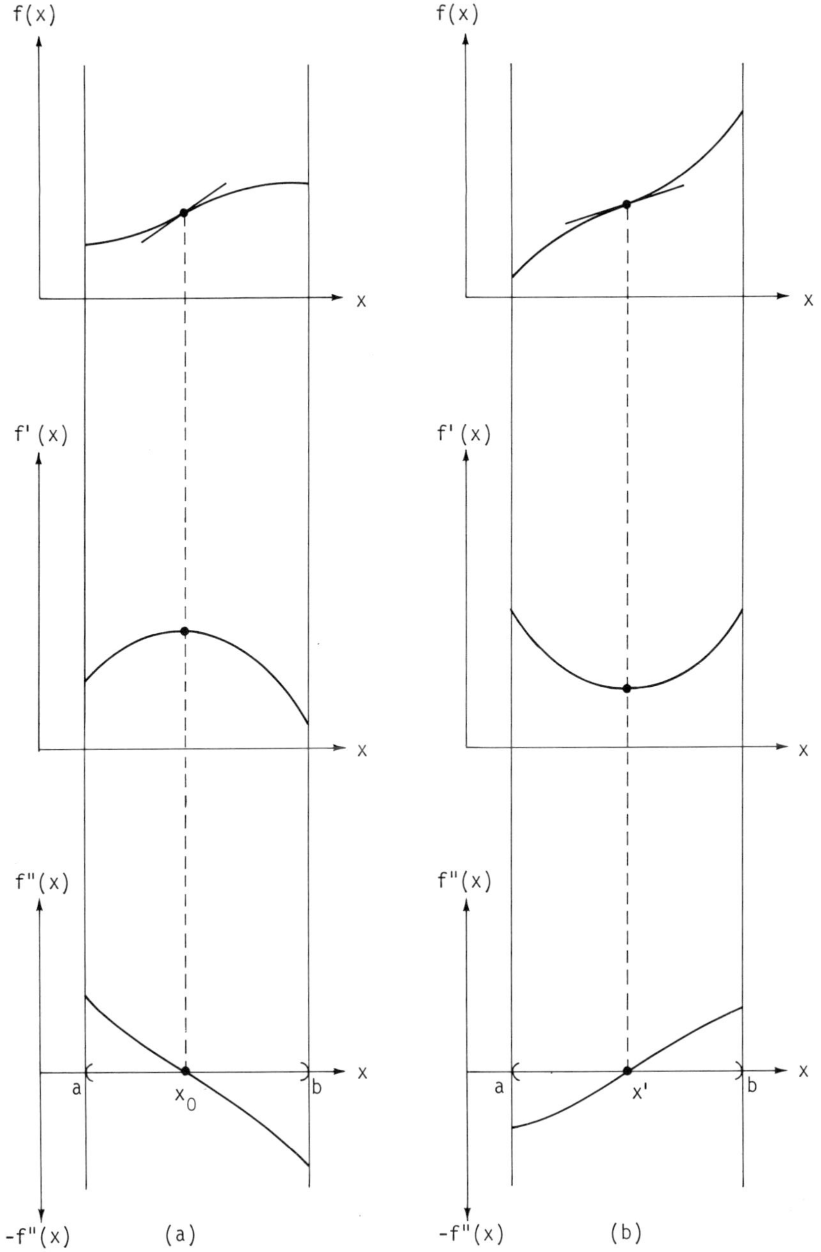

Fig. 7.2.

point $x_0 \in (a, b)$. *If* f *has a point of inflection (i.e.* f′ *has a strong local extremum) at* x_0, *then* $f''(x_0) = 0$.

It is obvious that the converse of this theorem does not hold true since, if $f'' = 0$, f may or may not possess a point of inflection.

Throughout this discussion we have been assuming that f′ was differentiable at a point where f assumed an inflectional value. However, it is imperative to note that a point of inflection can occur where f″ fails to exist (see example 7.2 below).

Example 7.1. Let the real-valued function $y = f(x) = -x^3+x^2+x$ be defined for all $x \in (-1, 2)$ (fig. 7.3). Verify that f assumes an inflectional value at $x = \frac{1}{3}$. Employing our necessary condition for a point of inflection we find that $f''(x) = -6x+2$ vanishes at $x = \frac{1}{3}$ as expected. Is this a point of inflection of the first or second class? To answer this question we must determine whether f′ attains a maximum or a minimum at $x = \frac{1}{3}$. Employing the sufficient condition (theorem 6.5) for a strong local extremum developed in chapter 6 we find that

$$\frac{d}{dx} f''(x) = -6 < 0.$$

Hence, f′ has a strong local maximum at $x = \frac{1}{3}$ and thus the point of inflection is of the first class.

Example 7.2. Let the real-valued function $y = f(x) = x^{\frac{1}{3}}+1$ be defined throughout the entirety of the x-axis. Does f assume a point of inflection over its domain? A glance at fig. 7.4 indicates that it has a vertical point of inflection of the first class at $x = 0$. Does f″ vanish there? A simple calculation shows that $f''(x) = -\frac{2}{9}x^{-\frac{5}{3}}$ is not defined at $x = 0$. Hence, f may assume a point of inflection over its domain even if f″ is non-existent there.

Example 7.1 intimated a procedure for determining inflectional values of a function by applying the sufficient condition for a strong local extremum to f′. Let us incorporate this suggestion in a theorem which may be used to distinguish a point of inflection of the first class from one of the second class.

THEOREM 7.2 (a sufficient condition).[2] *Let the real-valued function* $y = f(x)$ *possess a continuous third derivative throughout a* δ*-neighborhood of the point* $x_0 \in (a, b)$. *If* $f''(x_0) = 0$ *and* $f'''(x_0) \neq 0$, *then* f *attains a point of inflection (*f′ *attains a strong local extremum) at* x_0. *Moreover: (a) if* $f'''(x_0) < 0$, f *has*

[2] The proof of this theorem parallels that of the sufficient condition (theorem 6.5) for a strong local extremum presented in chapter 6, pp. 111–112.

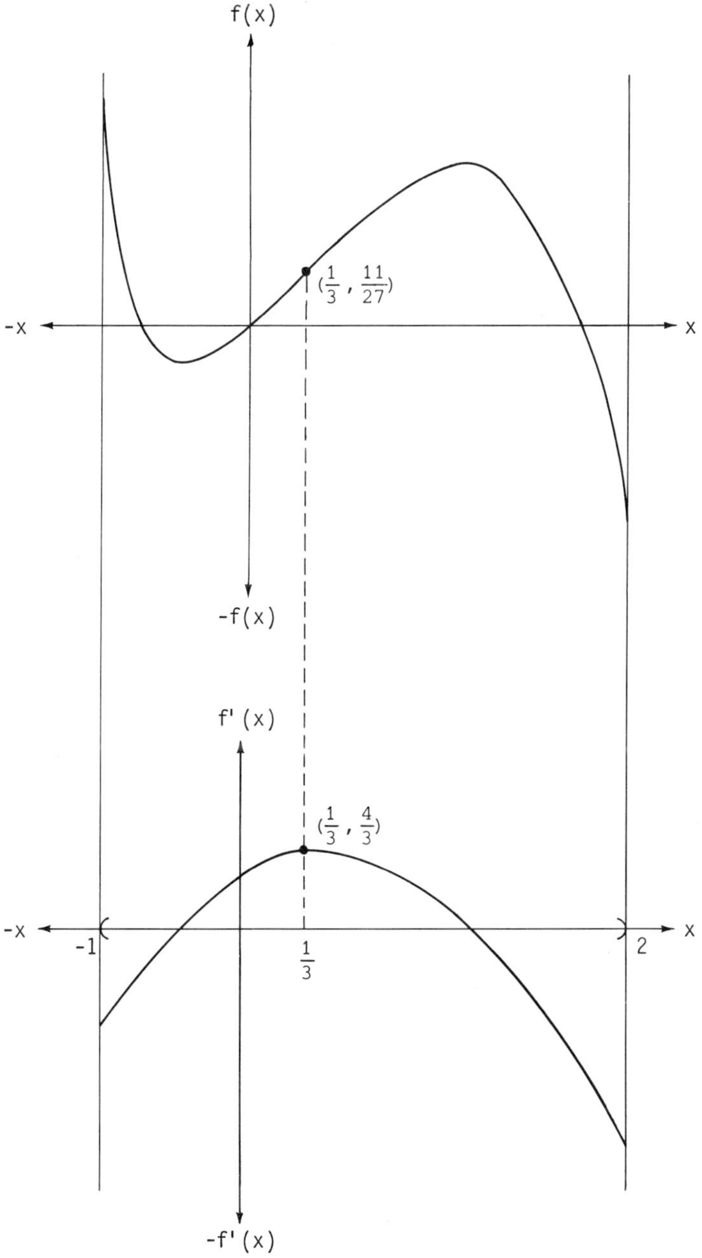

Fig. 7.3.

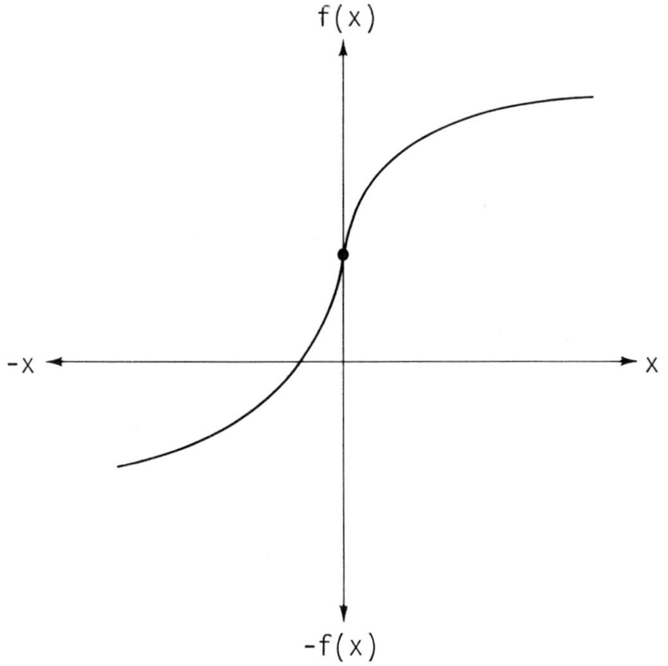

Fig. 7.4.

a point of inflection of the first class (i.e. f′ *has a strong local maximum) at* x_0*;* (*b*) *if* $f'''(x_0) > 0$, f *has a point of inflection of the second class (i.e.* f′ *is at its strong local minimum) at* x_0.

Example 7.3. Demonstrate that the real-valued function $y = f(x) = x^3 + 6$, $x \in (-2, 2)$, assumes a point of inflection over its domain. Applying our sufficient condition for a point of inflection we find that:

$$f'(x) = 3x^2, \qquad f''(x) = 6x, \qquad f'''(x) = 6 \neq 0.$$

Hence, for $x = 0$, $f'' = 0$ while f''' is positive there. Thus, f has a point of inflection of the second class at $x = 0$. In addition, since $f' = 0$ for $x = 0$, the said point of inflection is of the horizontal variety.

If both the second and third derivatives of f vanish at $x_0 \in \mathscr{D}_f$, the above sufficient condition for the existence of a point of inflection breaks down; i.e. the case where $f'' = f''' = 0$ is left undecided. To handle contingencies of this sort we must rely upon a condition which is simultaneously necessary and sufficient to identify a point of inflection.

Let us reproduce the bottom panel of fig. 6.2a, b below (fig. 7.6a, b) and consider the behavior of f″ throughout some δ-neighborhood about the

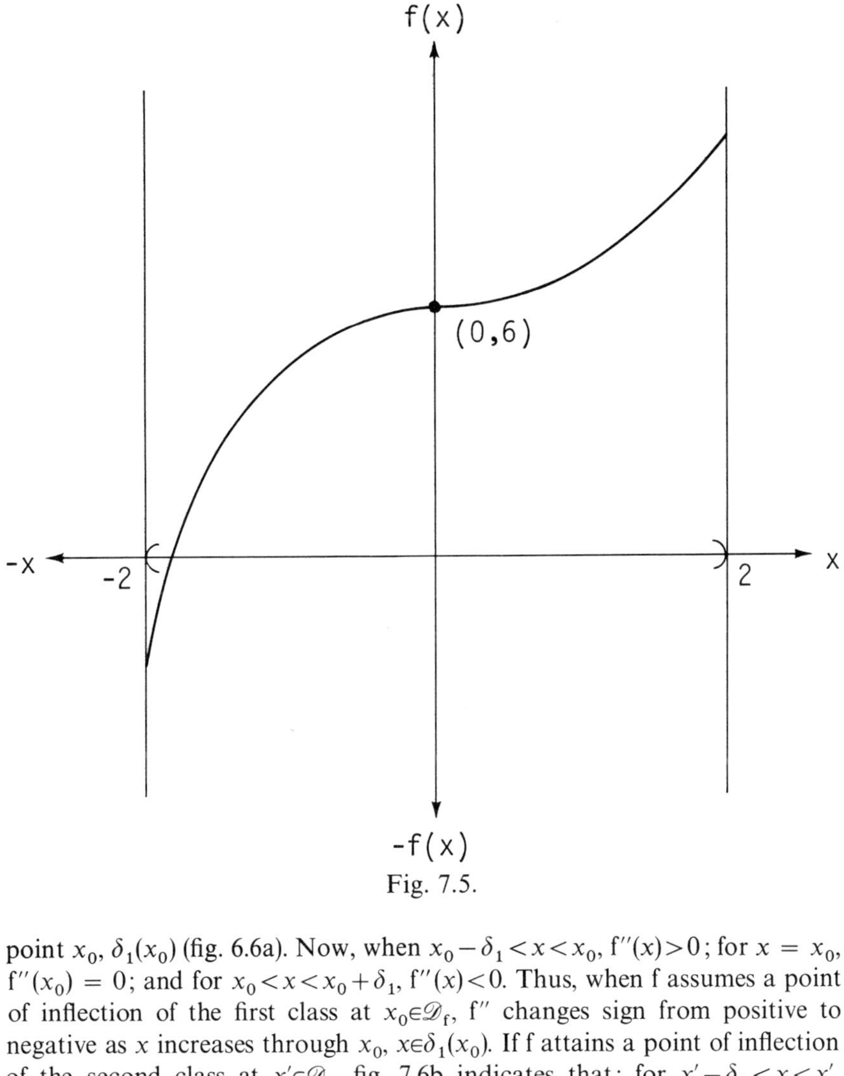

Fig. 7.5.

point x_0, $\delta_1(x_0)$ (fig. 6.6a). Now, when $x_0-\delta_1<x<x_0$, $f''(x)>0$; for $x = x_0$, $f''(x_0) = 0$; and for $x_0<x<x_0+\delta_1$, $f''(x)<0$. Thus, when f assumes a point of inflection of the first class at $x_0 \in \mathscr{D}_f$, f'' changes sign from positive to negative as x increases through x_0, $x \in \delta_1(x_0)$. If f attains a point of inflection of the second class at $x' \in \mathscr{D}_f$, fig. 7.6b indicates that: for $x'-\delta_2<x<x'$, $f''(x)<0$; for $x = x'$, $f''(x') = 0$; while for $x'<x<x'+\delta_2$, $f''(x)>0$. In this case, as x increases through x', $x \in \delta_2(x')$, the sign of f'' changes from negative to positive. These observations are incorporated in

THEOREM 7.3 (a necessary and sufficient condition). *Let the real-valued function* $y = f(x)$ *possess a continuous second derivative throughout a* δ-*neighborhood of the point* $x_0 \in (a, b)$. *If* $f''(x_0) = 0$ *then, for* $|h|<\delta$ *sufficiently small:* (*a*) f *has a point of inflection of the first class* (*i.e.* f' *has a strong local*

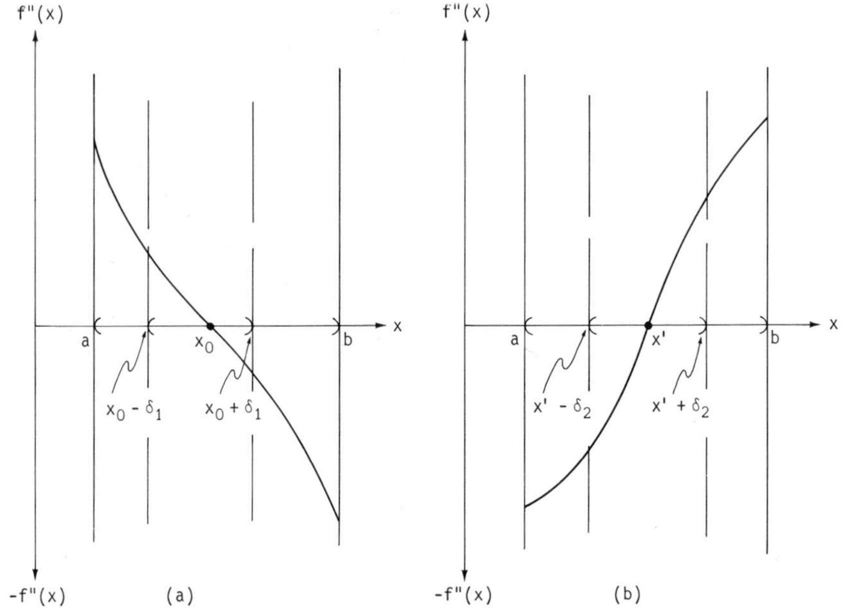

Fig. 7.6.

maximum) at x_0 *if* $f''(x_0+h)>0$ *when* $h<0$ *and* $f''(x_0+h)<0$ *when* $h>0$; (*b*) f *has a point of inflection of the second class (i.e.* f′ *has a strong local minimum) at* x_0 *if* $f''(x_0+h)<0$ *for* $h<0$ *and* $f''(x_0+h)>0$ *for* $h>0$.

In short, this theorem provides us with a complete set of criteria with which to identify points of inflection.

It must be mentioned that if f″ is not defined at x_0 when f is, we may modify this necessary and sufficient condition somewhat and consider the behavior of f″ throughout some suitably restricted deleted δ-neighborhood of x_0. The modification is left as an exercise to the reader.

Example 7.4. Let the real-valued function $y = f(x) = x^3-6x^2+4$ be defined for all $x \in (-1, 2)$. Using the above necessary and sufficient condition demonstrate that f assumes a point of inflection of the second class at $x = 2$. Now

$$f''(x) = 3x^2-12x, \qquad f''(x) = 6x-12.$$

Clearly, $f''(2) = 0$. For $|h|<\delta$ sufficiently small,

$$f''(2+h) = 6(2+h)-12 = 6h \gtrless 0 \quad \text{for } h \gtrless 0.$$

Hence, part (b) of the necessary and sufficient condition holds, and thus our demonstration is complete.

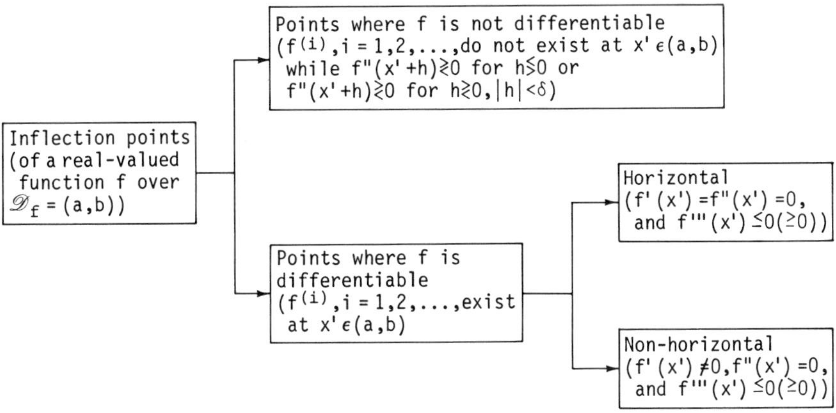

Fig. 7.7.

Example 7.5. In example 7.2 we found that $f''(x) = -\frac{2}{9}x^{-\frac{5}{3}}$ did not exist at $x = 0$. Yet f has a point of inflection of the first class there since, for values of x within a suitably restricted deleted δ-neighborhood of zero, $\delta_d(0)$,

$$f''(0+h) = -\tfrac{2}{9}h^{-\frac{5}{3}} \lesseqgtr 0 \quad \text{when } h \lesseqgtr 0,\ |h| < \delta,$$

as anticipated by part (a) of the above necessary and sufficient condition.

Our classification of points of inflection is summarized in fig. 7.7.

Chapter 8

CONVEX AND CONCAVE REAL-VALUED FUNCTIONS

8.1. Convex sets

In this chapter we seek to describe the attainment of global and local extrema of two broad classes of real-valued functions which are of paramount importance in many areas of analysis, namely, those functions which are classified as either convex or concave over a convex domain. Before doing so, however, it is helpful to consider the following special case of definition 1.43, i.e. for $m = 2$ we have

DEFINITION 8.1. *A region $\mathscr{K} \subseteq \mathscr{E}^n$ is termed convex if for any two points $\boldsymbol{x}_1, \boldsymbol{x}_2 \in \mathscr{K}$, the line segment joining them is also in $\mathscr{K}$, i.e. the internal average (or convex combination) of $\boldsymbol{x}_1, \boldsymbol{x}_2$, $\boldsymbol{x}_c = \theta \boldsymbol{x}_2 + (1-\theta)\boldsymbol{x}_1$, $0 \leqslant \theta \leqslant 1$, is also a member of $\mathscr{K}$, where*

$$\boldsymbol{x}_c' = (x_1^c, \ldots, x_n^c) = (\theta x_1^2 + (1-\theta)x_1^1, \ldots, \theta x_n^2 + (1-\theta)x_n^1).$$

Note that the components of $\boldsymbol{x}_c$ are themselves convex combinations of the components of $\boldsymbol{x}_1, \boldsymbol{x}_2$. Here, $\boldsymbol{x}_c$ represents, for a given value of θ, a point on the line segment joining $\boldsymbol{x}_1, \boldsymbol{x}_2$. That is, for $\theta = 0$, $\boldsymbol{x}_c = \boldsymbol{x}_1$, while for $\theta = 1$, $\boldsymbol{x}_c = \boldsymbol{x}_2$; and as θ increases in value from 0 to 1, the point $\boldsymbol{x}_c$ travels along the line segment joining $\boldsymbol{x}_1$ and $\boldsymbol{x}_2$ from $\boldsymbol{x}_1$ to $\boldsymbol{x}_2$. By convention we shall classify a set containing but a single element or point as convex.

Let us apply this definition to the real-line $\mathscr{E}$. It is easily seen that the real line is itself a convex set since, for any points $x_1, x_2 \in \mathscr{E}$, $x_c = \theta x_2 + (1-\theta)x_1 \in \mathscr{E}$, $0 \leqslant \theta \leqslant 1$. Hence, x_c lies between x_1 and x_2 (fig. 8.1). It is

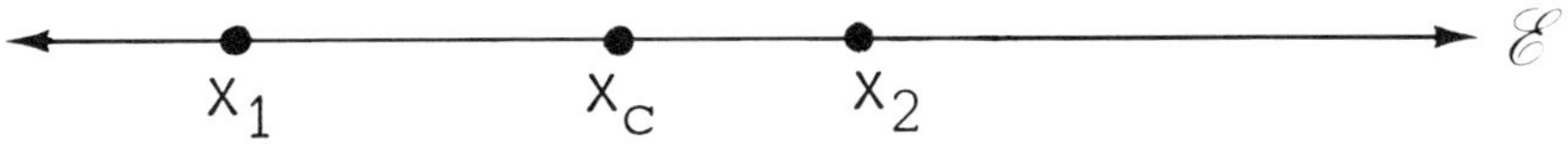

Fig. 8.1.

evident that any open or closed interval in $\mathscr{E}$ is also a convex set. Additionally, for $\boldsymbol{x} \in \mathscr{E}^2$, $\boldsymbol{x}_c$ is depicted as a point on the line connecting $\boldsymbol{x}_1$ and $\boldsymbol{x}_2$ (fig. 8.2a).

Often a convex set is alternatively depicted as one which is *non-re-entrant*, e.g. as fig. 8.2b indicates, the region $\mathscr{K}$ is not convex since the variable point $\boldsymbol{x}_c$ on the line segment connecting $\boldsymbol{x}_1, \boldsymbol{x}_2$ leaves and then re-enters $\mathscr{K}$ as θ steadily increases in value from 0 to 1.

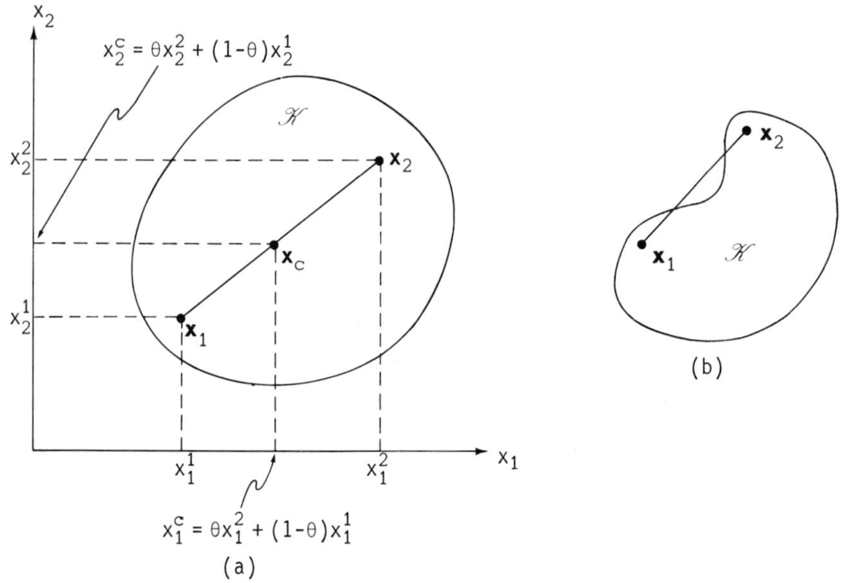

Fig. 8.2.

8.2. Convex and concave real-valued functions

We next turn to the definition of functions which may be classified as convex or concave over their domain. In this regard, we present

DEFINITION 8.2. *A real-valued function* $y = \mathrm{f}(\boldsymbol{x})$, $\boldsymbol{x} \in \mathscr{E}^n$, *is convex (concave) over a convex region* $\mathscr{K} \subseteq \mathscr{E}^n$ *if linear interpolation between any two points on (the hypersurface)* f *never underestimates (overestimates) the value of* f *at the point of interpolation.*

That is, if f is defined throughout the entirety of a convex region $\mathscr{K} \subseteq \mathscr{E}^n$, then f is termed convex in $\mathscr{K}$ if and only if, for any two points $\boldsymbol{x}_1, \boldsymbol{x}_2 \in \mathscr{K}$,

$$\mathrm{f}(\boldsymbol{x}_c) \leqslant \theta \mathrm{f}(\boldsymbol{x}_2) + (1-\theta)\mathrm{f}(\boldsymbol{x}_1), \quad 0 \leqslant \theta \leqslant 1. \tag{8.1}$$

If f is concave over $\mathscr{K} \subseteq \mathscr{E}^n$, the inequality in eq. (8.1) is reversed. In this case f is said to be concave over $\mathscr{K}$ if and only if, for $\boldsymbol{x}_1, \boldsymbol{x}_2 \in \mathscr{K}$,

$$\mathrm{f}(\boldsymbol{x}_c) \geqslant \theta \mathrm{f}(\boldsymbol{x}_2) + (1-\theta)\mathrm{f}(\boldsymbol{x}_1), \quad 0 \leqslant \theta \leqslant 1. \tag{8.2}$$

We shall term f *strictly convex (concave)* over $\mathscr{K}$ if and only if, for $\boldsymbol{x}_1 \neq \boldsymbol{x}_2$ and $0 < \theta < 1$, strict inequality holds in eqs. (8.1) ((8.2)).

Let us illustrate eqs. (8.1) and (8.2) geometrically for $\boldsymbol{x} \in \mathscr{E}$. In fig. 8.3a, b, $x_c = \theta x_2 + (1-\theta)x_1 \in \mathscr{D}_\mathrm{f} = [a, b]$, $0 \leqslant \theta \leqslant 1$, is our point of interpolation. Hence, linear interpolation of f at $\boldsymbol{x}_c$ is represented as $\theta \mathrm{f}(x_2) + (1-\theta)\mathrm{f}(x_1)$

$$f(x_c) \le \theta f(x_2) + (1-\theta)f(x_1)$$
(a)

$$f(x_c) \ge \theta f(x_2) + (1-\theta)f(x_1)$$
(b)

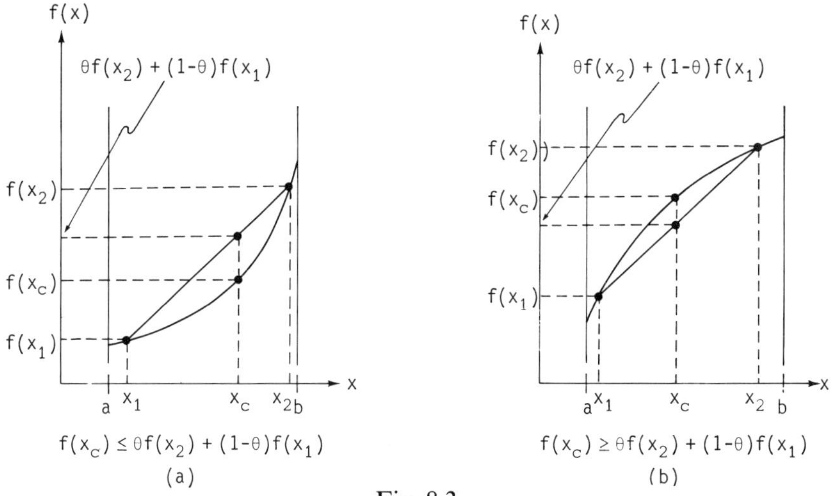

Fig. 8.3.

(i.e. linear interpolation of f between x_1, x_2 is represented as a point on the straight line between $f(x_1)$ and $f(x_2)$) while the value of f at x_c is $f(\theta x_2+(1-\theta)x_1)$. Now, if eq. (8.1) is to hold so that f is convex, the line segment joining $f(x_1)$, $f(x_2)$ must lie on or above the curve (fig. 8.3a). If eq. (8.2) holds, for f concave, the line segment connecting $f(x_1)$ and $f(x_2)$ must lie on or below the function (fig. 8.3b). If f is strictly concave (convex) over $[a, b]$, the line segment joining $f(x_1)$ and $f(x_2)$ lies totally below (above) f for all values of $x \in (x_1, x_2)$ since, in this case, $0 < \theta < 1$.

We note briefly the circumstance under which eqs. (8.1) and (8.2) are equivalent. If a real-valued function f is linear over $\mathcal{K} \subseteq \mathcal{E}^n$, then $f(x_c) = \theta f(x_2)+(1-\theta)f(x_1)$ for all $x \in \mathcal{K}$, and thus eqs. (8.1) and (8.2) hold simultaneously. Accordingly, any linear function is both convex and concave (though not strictly) over a convex domain.

Example 8.1. Let the real-valued function $y = f(x) = x^2$ be defined for all $x \in [a, b]$, $0 < a < b$. From fig. 8.4 it is clear that f is convex over $[a, b]$. Let us verify this observation. To demonstrate that f is convex, we must show that eq. (8.1) holds, i.e. that $f(x_c)-\theta f(x_2)-(1-\theta)f(x_1) \le 0$, $0 \le \theta \le 1$. For $x_1, x_2 \in [a, b]$, $f(x_1) = x_1^2$, $f(x_2) = x_2^2$. Let $x_c = \theta x_2+(1-\theta)x_1$. Then

$$f(x_c) = (\theta x_2+(1-\theta)x_1)^2 = \theta^2 x_2^2+2\theta(1-\theta)x_1 x_2+(1-\theta)^2 x_1^2.$$

From eq. (8.1) we have

$$\theta^2 x_2^2+2\theta(1-\theta)x_1 x_2+(1-\theta)^2 x_1^2-\theta x_2^2-(1-\theta)x_1^2 \le 0$$

or

$$\theta(\theta-1)x_2^2+\theta(\theta-1)x_1^2-2\theta(\theta-1)x_1 x_2 \le 0, \quad 0 \le \theta \le 1.$$

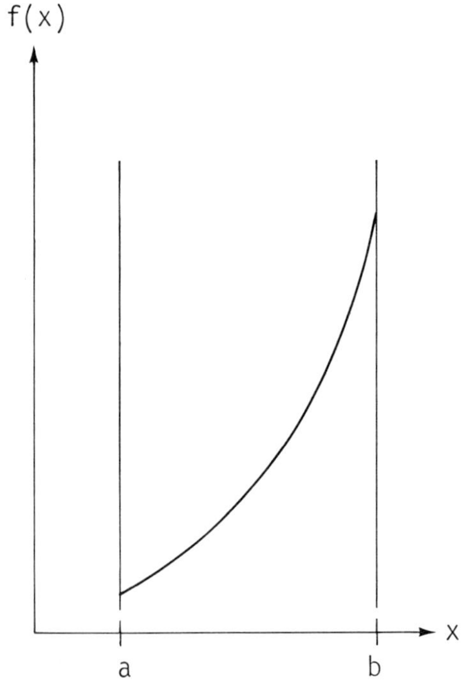

Fig. 8.4.

For $\theta = 0, 1$ this last expression reduces trivially to zero, while for $0<\theta<1$ this inequality simplifies to $(x_1 - x_2)^2 \geqslant 0$. Hence f is convex. If $x_1 \neq x_2$, f is strictly convex since $(x_1 - x_2)^2 > 0$.

In example 8.1 let us multiply the indicated function by a minus one. Hence, the negative of f becomes $-\mathrm{f}(x) = -x^2$, $x \in [a, b]$, $0<a<b$. It is easily verified that this new function is concave over its domain. In general, if a real-valued function $y = \mathrm{f}(\boldsymbol{x})$, $\boldsymbol{x} \in \mathscr{E}^n$, is convex over a convex domain, then $-\mathrm{f}(\boldsymbol{x})$ is concave over that same domain and conversely.

8.3. Differentiable convex and concave real-valued functions

Our previous discussion on convex and concave functions made no use of the concept of differentiability. We now turn to the consideration of convex and concave real-valued functions which are differentiable and twice-differentiable over a convex domain.

If f is differentiable over an open convex domain $\mathscr{K} \subseteq \mathscr{E}^n$, then a necessary condition for such a function to be convex (concave) on $\mathscr{K}$ is

THEOREM 8.1. *Let the real-valued function* $y = \mathrm{f}(\boldsymbol{x})$, $\boldsymbol{x} \in \mathscr{E}^n$, *be differentiable at the point* $\boldsymbol{x}_0$ *contained within an open convex region* $\mathscr{K} \subseteq \mathscr{E}^n$. *If* f *is convex at* $\boldsymbol{x}_0$, *then*

$$\mathrm{f}(\boldsymbol{x}) \geqslant \mathrm{f}(\boldsymbol{x}_0) + \nabla \mathrm{f}(\boldsymbol{x}_0)'(\boldsymbol{x} - \boldsymbol{x}_0), \quad \boldsymbol{x} \in \mathscr{K}; \tag{8.3}$$

if f *is concave at* $\boldsymbol{x}_0$, *then*

$$\mathrm{f}(\boldsymbol{x}) \geqslant \mathrm{f}(\boldsymbol{x}_0) + \nabla \mathrm{f}(\boldsymbol{x}_0)'(\boldsymbol{x} - \boldsymbol{x}_0), \quad \boldsymbol{x} \in \mathscr{K}. \tag{8.4}$$

Here eqs. (8.3) *and* (8.4) *depict the linearization of* f *at* $\boldsymbol{x}_0$.

Proof. Let f be concave at $\boldsymbol{x}_0$ (a similar proof holds for f convex at $\boldsymbol{x}_0$). Then

$$\mathrm{f}(\theta \boldsymbol{x} + (1-\theta)\boldsymbol{x}_0) \geqslant \theta \mathrm{f}(\boldsymbol{x}) + (1-\theta)\mathrm{f}(\boldsymbol{x}_0),$$

and, for $\boldsymbol{h} = \boldsymbol{x} - \boldsymbol{x}_0$, $0 \leqslant \theta \leqslant 1$,

$$\frac{\mathrm{f}(\boldsymbol{x}_0 + \theta \boldsymbol{h}) - \mathrm{f}(\boldsymbol{x}_0)}{\theta} \geqslant \mathrm{f}(\boldsymbol{x}) - \mathrm{f}(\boldsymbol{x}_0).$$

From eq. (5.15),

$$\mathrm{f}(\boldsymbol{x}_0 + \theta \boldsymbol{h}) = \mathrm{f}(\boldsymbol{x}_0) + \theta \nabla \mathrm{f}(\boldsymbol{x}_0 + \tau \theta \boldsymbol{h})'\boldsymbol{h}, \quad 0 < \tau < 1.$$

A substitution of this expression into the previous one yields

$$\nabla \mathrm{f}(\boldsymbol{x}_0 + \tau \theta \boldsymbol{h})'\boldsymbol{h} \geqslant \mathrm{f}(\boldsymbol{x}) - \mathrm{f}(\boldsymbol{x}_0).$$

Then

$$\lim_{\theta \to 0} \nabla \mathrm{f}(\boldsymbol{x}_0 + \tau \theta \boldsymbol{h})'\boldsymbol{h} = \nabla \mathrm{f}(\boldsymbol{x}_0)'\boldsymbol{h} \geqslant \mathrm{f}(\boldsymbol{x}) - \mathrm{f}(\boldsymbol{x}_0)$$

or

$$\mathrm{f}(\boldsymbol{x}) \leqslant \mathrm{f}(\boldsymbol{x}_0) + \nabla \mathrm{f}(\boldsymbol{x}_0)'(\boldsymbol{x} - \boldsymbol{x}_0). \quad \text{Q.E.D.}$$

If f is strictly convex (concave) at $\boldsymbol{x}_0 \in \mathscr{K}$, then eq. (8.3) ((8.4)) holds with strict inequality for $\boldsymbol{x}(\neq \boldsymbol{x}_0) \in \mathscr{K}$.

As indicated in our previous discussion, eq. (8.1) ((8.2)) characterizes a function f as convex (concave) in a convex domain $\mathscr{K}$ if linear interpolation between $\boldsymbol{x}_1, \boldsymbol{x}_2 \in \mathscr{K}$ never underestimates (overestimates) f at the point of interpolation $\boldsymbol{x}_c$. However, eqs. (8.3) and (8.4) respectively stipulate that if f is convex (concave) on $\mathscr{K}$, a linear approximation to f at $\boldsymbol{x}_0$ always underestimates (overestimates) the function, i.e. for f convex (concave), f lies everywhere above (below) its tangent hyperplane. For $x \in \mathscr{E}$, eqs. (8.3) and (8.4) simply depict the equation of the line tangent to f at x_0 (see fig. 8.5a, b, respectively). Hence f is convex (concave) at x_0 if it lies everywhere above (below) or on its tangent line at that point.

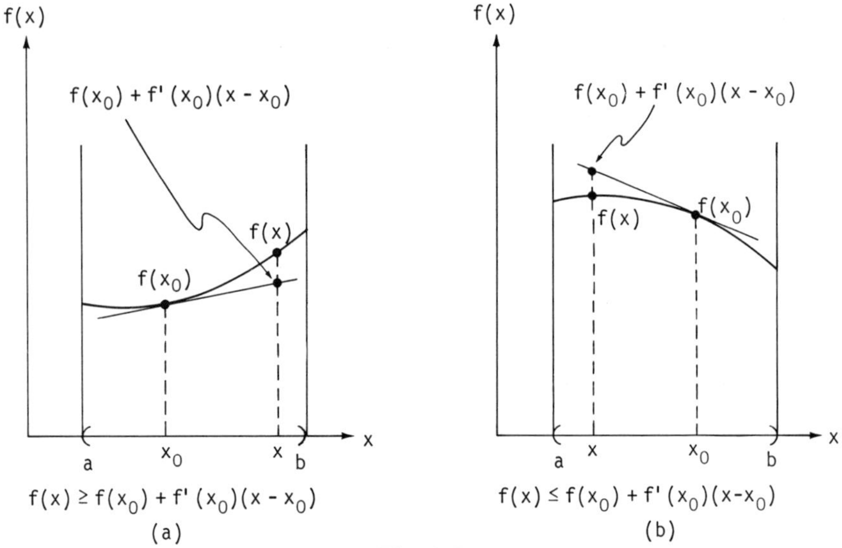

Fig. 8.5.

A necessary and sufficient condition for a differentiable function to be convex or concave over an open convex domain $\mathscr{K} \subseteq \mathscr{E}^n$ is

THEOREM 8.2. *Let the real-valued function* $y = \mathrm{f}(\boldsymbol{x})$, $\boldsymbol{x} \in \mathscr{E}^n$, *be differentiable over an open convex region* $\mathscr{K} \subseteq \mathscr{E}^n$. *Then* f *is convex over* $\mathscr{K}$ *if and only if*

$$\mathrm{f}(\boldsymbol{x}_2) - \mathrm{f}(\boldsymbol{x}_1) \geqslant \nabla \mathrm{f}(\boldsymbol{x}_1)'(\boldsymbol{x}_2 - \boldsymbol{x}_1) \quad \textit{for any } \boldsymbol{x}_1, \boldsymbol{x}_2 \in \mathscr{K}; \tag{8.5}$$

f *is concave over* $\mathscr{K}$ *if and only if*

$$\mathrm{f}(\boldsymbol{x}_2) - \mathrm{f}(\boldsymbol{x}_1) \leqslant \nabla \mathrm{f}(\boldsymbol{x}_1)'(\boldsymbol{x}_2 - \boldsymbol{x}_1) \quad \textit{for any } \boldsymbol{x}_1, \boldsymbol{x}_2 \in \mathscr{K}. \tag{8.6}$$

Proof (necessity). If f is convex (concave) at each $\boldsymbol{x}_1 \in \mathscr{K}$, this portion of the proof proceeds as in the above theorem. (Sufficiency.) For $\boldsymbol{x}_1$, $\boldsymbol{x}_2 \in \mathscr{K}$, $\boldsymbol{x}_c = \theta \boldsymbol{x}_2 + (1-\theta)\boldsymbol{x}_1 \in \mathscr{K}$, $0 \leqslant \theta \leqslant 1$. From eq. (8.6),

$$\mathrm{f}(\boldsymbol{x}_1) - \mathrm{f}(\boldsymbol{x}_c) \leqslant \theta \nabla \mathrm{f}(\boldsymbol{x}_c)'(\boldsymbol{x}_1 - \boldsymbol{x}_c),$$
$$\mathrm{f}(\boldsymbol{x}_2) - \mathrm{f}(\boldsymbol{x}_c) \leqslant -(1-\theta) \nabla \mathrm{f}(\boldsymbol{x}_c)'(\boldsymbol{x}_1 - \boldsymbol{x}_c).$$

Weighting the first inequality by $(1-\theta)$, the second by θ, and summing yields

$$\theta \mathrm{f}(\boldsymbol{x}_2) + (1-\theta)\mathrm{f}(\boldsymbol{x}_1) - \mathrm{f}(\boldsymbol{x}_c) \leqslant 0.$$

Hence f is concave on $\mathscr{K}$. A symmetric proof utilizing eq. (8.5) indicates that f is convex over $\mathscr{K}$. Q.E.D.

Additionally, f is strictly convex (concave) over $\mathscr{K}$ if and only if eq. (8.5) ((8.6)) holds with strict inequality for any $\boldsymbol{x}_1$, $\boldsymbol{x}_2 \in \mathscr{K}$, $\boldsymbol{x}_1 \neq \boldsymbol{x}_2$.

For $\boldsymbol{x} \in \mathscr{E}$, eq. (8.5) ((8.6)) implies that

$$[f(x_2)-f(x_1)]/(x_2-x_1) \geqslant f'(x_1)\ (\leqslant f'(x_1)), \quad x_1 < x_2,$$

i.e. for f convex (concave), the slope of f at x_1 is less than or equal to (greater than or equal to) the slope of the secant line through the points $(x_1, f(x_1))$, $(x_2, f(x_2))$ (fig. 8.6a, b, respectively).

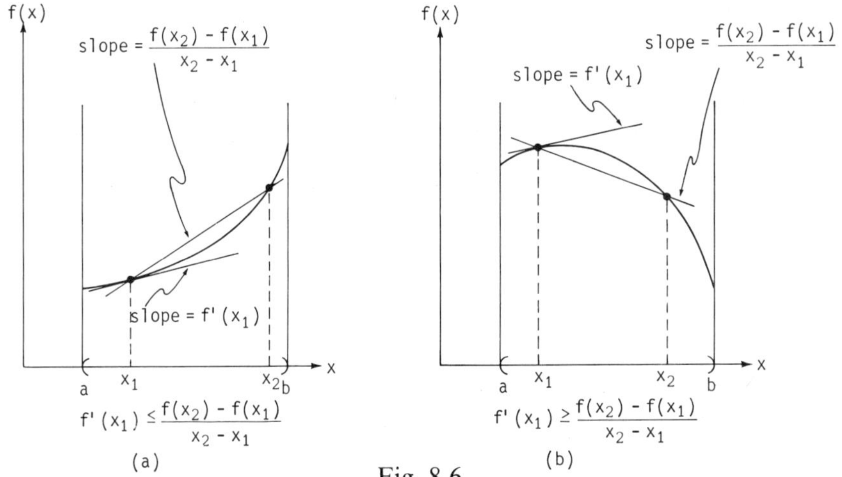

Fig. 8.6.

We next turn to an important property of twice-differentiable convex and concave functions which may serve to identify them. In particular, it is a condition which is necessary and sufficient for a twice-differentiable function to be convex or concave over an open convex domain $\mathscr{K} \subseteq \mathscr{E}^n$. In this regard we have

THEOREM 8.3. *Let the real-valued function* $y = f(\boldsymbol{x})$, $\boldsymbol{x} \in \mathscr{E}^n$, *possess continuous second-order partial derivatives throughout an open convex region* $\mathscr{K} \subseteq \mathscr{E}^n$. *Then* f *is convex (concave) over* $\mathscr{K}$ *if and only if the quadratic form*

$$Q(\boldsymbol{h}) = \sum_{r=1}^{n} \sum_{s=1}^{n} h_r h_s\ \partial^2 f(\boldsymbol{x})/\partial x_r\ \partial x_s = \boldsymbol{h}' \boldsymbol{H}_f(\boldsymbol{x}) \boldsymbol{h}$$

is positive (negative) semi-definite for all $\boldsymbol{h}$ *and all points* $\boldsymbol{x} \in \mathscr{K}$. *Here* $\boldsymbol{h}$ *is an* $(n \times 1)$ *vector with elements* h_i, $i = 1, \ldots, n$, *and* $\boldsymbol{H}_f(\boldsymbol{x})$ *is the Hessian matrix of* f *at* $\boldsymbol{x}$.

Proof. By employing eq. (5.15) we may approximate f near $\boldsymbol{x}_c = \theta \boldsymbol{x}_2 + (1-\theta)\boldsymbol{x}_1 \in \mathscr{K}$, $0 \leqslant \theta \leqslant 1$, as

$$f(\boldsymbol{x}) = f(\boldsymbol{x}_c) + \nabla f(\boldsymbol{x}_c)' \boldsymbol{h} + \frac{1}{2!} \boldsymbol{h}' \boldsymbol{H}_f(\boldsymbol{x}_c + \eta \boldsymbol{h}) \boldsymbol{h}, \quad 0 < \eta < 1. \tag{8.7}$$

(Necessity.) Let f be concave (convex) over $\mathscr{K}$. From eq. (8.7),

$$\mathrm{f}(\boldsymbol{x})-\mathrm{f}(\boldsymbol{x}_c)-\nabla\mathrm{f}(\boldsymbol{x}_c)'\boldsymbol{h} = \frac{1}{2!}\boldsymbol{h}'\boldsymbol{H}_\mathrm{f}(\boldsymbol{x}_c+\eta\boldsymbol{h})\boldsymbol{h}, \quad 0<\eta<1. \tag{8.7.1}$$

With f concave (convex) over $\mathscr{K}$, the left-hand side of eq. (8.7.1), and thus its right-hand side, is non-positive (non-negative) by eq. (8.4) ((8.3)). Hence $\boldsymbol{h}'\boldsymbol{H}_\mathrm{f}(\boldsymbol{x}_c+\eta\boldsymbol{h})\boldsymbol{h}\leqslant 0(\geqslant 0)$.

(Sufficiency.) Upon substituting $\boldsymbol{x} = \boldsymbol{x}_1, \boldsymbol{x}_2\in\mathscr{K}$ into eq. (8.7) we obtain

$$\mathrm{f}(\boldsymbol{x}_j) = \mathrm{f}(\boldsymbol{x}_c)+\nabla\mathrm{f}(\boldsymbol{x}_c)'\boldsymbol{h}_j+\frac{1}{2!}\boldsymbol{h}_j'\boldsymbol{H}_\mathrm{f}(\boldsymbol{x}_c+\eta_j\boldsymbol{h}_j)\boldsymbol{h}_j,$$
$$0<\eta_j<1, \quad j = 1, 2,$$

where $\boldsymbol{h}_j$, $j = 1, 2$, denotes an $(n\times 1)$ vector with elements $h_1^j, \ldots, h_n^j$. Weighting $\mathrm{f}(\boldsymbol{x}_2)$ by θ, $\mathrm{f}(\boldsymbol{x}_1)$ by $(1-\theta)$, $0\leqslant\theta\leqslant 1$, and summing, yields

$$\begin{aligned}\theta\mathrm{f}(\boldsymbol{x}_2)+(1-\theta)\mathrm{f}(\boldsymbol{x}_1) = {}& \mathrm{f}(\boldsymbol{x}_c)+\theta\nabla\mathrm{f}(\boldsymbol{x}_c)'\boldsymbol{h}_2+(1-\theta)\nabla\mathrm{f}(\boldsymbol{x}_c)'\boldsymbol{h}_1\\ &+\frac{\theta}{2!}\boldsymbol{h}_2'\boldsymbol{H}_\mathrm{f}(\boldsymbol{x}_c+\eta_2\boldsymbol{h}_2)\boldsymbol{h}_2\\ &+\frac{(1-\theta)}{2!}\boldsymbol{h}_1'\boldsymbol{H}_\mathrm{f}(\boldsymbol{x}_c+\eta_1\boldsymbol{h}_1)\boldsymbol{h}_1,\\ &0<\eta_j<1, \quad j = 1, 2.\end{aligned} \tag{8.8}$$

Since $\theta\nabla\mathrm{f}(\boldsymbol{x}_c)'\boldsymbol{h}_2+(1-\theta)\nabla\mathrm{f}(\boldsymbol{x}_c)'\boldsymbol{h}_1 = \nabla\mathrm{f}(\boldsymbol{x}_c)'[\theta\boldsymbol{h}_2+(1-\theta)\boldsymbol{h}_1] = 0$ (here $\theta h_i^2+(1-\theta)h_i^1 = 0, i = 1, \ldots, n$), eq. (8.8) becomes

$$\begin{aligned}\theta\mathrm{f}(\boldsymbol{x}_2)+(1-\theta)\mathrm{f}(\boldsymbol{x}_1) = {}& \mathrm{f}(\boldsymbol{x}_c)+\frac{\theta}{2!}\boldsymbol{h}_2'\boldsymbol{H}_\mathrm{f}(\boldsymbol{x}_c+\eta_2\boldsymbol{h}_2)\boldsymbol{h}_2\\ &+\frac{(1-\theta)}{2!}\boldsymbol{h}_1'\boldsymbol{H}_\mathrm{f}(\boldsymbol{x}_c+\eta_1\boldsymbol{h}_1)\boldsymbol{h}_1,\\ &0<\eta_j<1, \quad j = 1, 2.\end{aligned} \tag{8.8.1}$$

Now, if the quadratic forms $\boldsymbol{h}_j'\boldsymbol{H}_\mathrm{f}(\boldsymbol{x}_c+\eta_j\boldsymbol{h}_j)\boldsymbol{h}_j\geqslant 0(\leqslant 0)$ (i.e. are positive (negative) semi-definite), $j = 1, 2$, then $\theta\mathrm{f}(\boldsymbol{x}_2)+(1-\theta)\mathrm{f}(\boldsymbol{x}_1)\geqslant\mathrm{f}(\boldsymbol{x}_c)$ $(\leqslant\mathrm{f}(\boldsymbol{x}_c))$. Thus f is convex (concave) over $\mathscr{K}$. Q.E.D.

If $Q(\boldsymbol{h}) = \boldsymbol{h}'\boldsymbol{H}_\mathrm{f}(\boldsymbol{x})\boldsymbol{h}>0$ (<0) (i.e. is positive (negative) definite) for $\boldsymbol{h}\neq\boldsymbol{0}$ and all points $\boldsymbol{x}\in\mathscr{K}$, then f is strictly convex (concave) over $\mathscr{K}$. But if f is strictly convex (concave) on $\mathscr{K}$, then $\boldsymbol{h}'\boldsymbol{H}_\mathrm{f}(\boldsymbol{x})\boldsymbol{h}\geqslant 0$ $(\leqslant 0)$ for all $\boldsymbol{x}\in\mathscr{K}$, i.e. we may not conclude that $\boldsymbol{h}'\boldsymbol{H}_\mathrm{f}(\boldsymbol{x})\boldsymbol{h}>0$ (<0), $\boldsymbol{x}\in\mathscr{K}$.

For $\boldsymbol{x}\in\mathscr{E}$, theorem 8.3 indicates that $y = \mathrm{f}(x)$ is convex (concave) over $\mathscr{D}_\mathrm{f} = (a, b)$ if and only if $\mathrm{f}''(x)\geqslant 0$ $(\leqslant 0)$. If $\mathrm{f}''(x)>0$ (<0) for all $x\in(a, b)$, f is strictly convex (concave) on (a, b). But if f is strictly convex (concave) over (a, b), it is not necessarily the case that $\mathrm{f}''(x)>0(<0)$ for all $x\in(a, b)$, i.e. if f is strictly convex (concave) over (a, b), we may only conclude that $\mathrm{f}''(x)\geqslant 0$ $(\leqslant 0)$.

Example 8.2. From fig. 8.7 we see that the real-valued function $y = \mathrm{f}(x) = x^4-3x+1$, $x\in(-1, 1)$, is strictly convex over its domain with $\mathrm{f}''(x) = 12x^2$. However, $\mathrm{f}''(0) = 0$, hence $\mathrm{f}''(x)\geqslant 0$ over $(-1, 1)$.

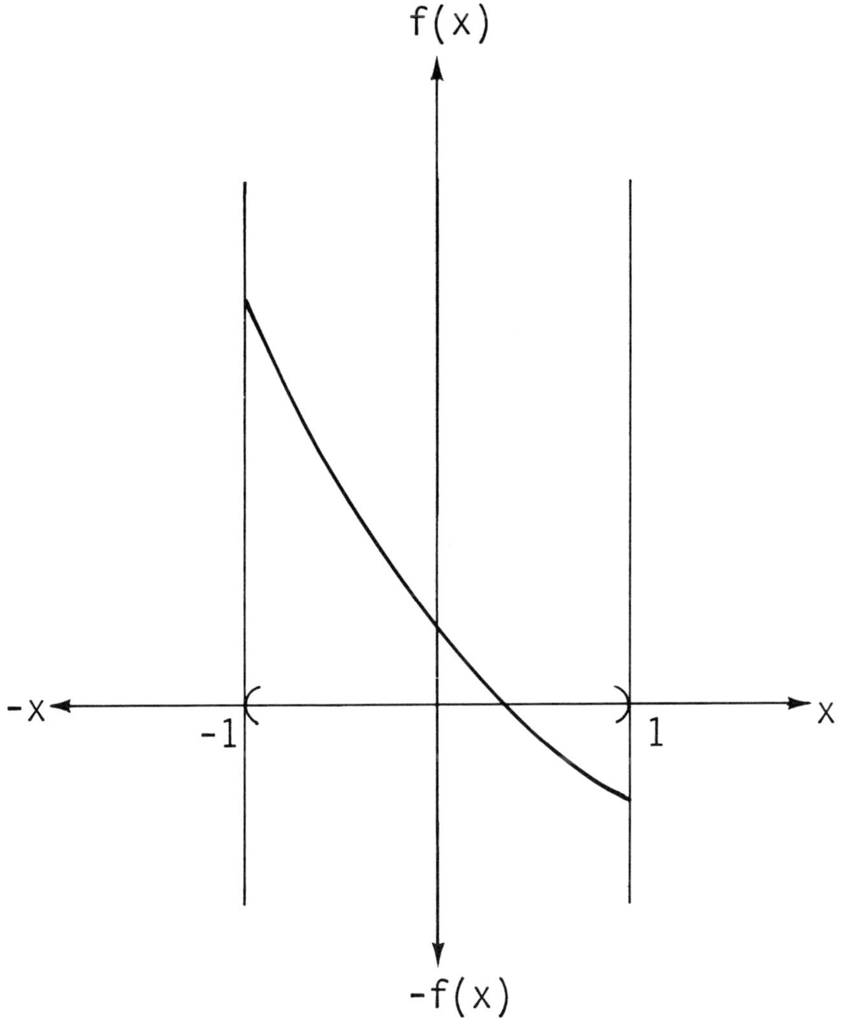

Fig. 8.7.

Example 8.3. Is the real-valued function $y = \mathrm{f}(\boldsymbol{x}) = (x_1 x_2)^{\frac{1}{2}}$ convex or concave for all $\boldsymbol{x} \geqslant \boldsymbol{0}$? By theorem 1.9 we see that $Q(\boldsymbol{h}) = \boldsymbol{h}'\boldsymbol{H}_{\mathrm{f}}\boldsymbol{h} \leqslant 0$ for all $\boldsymbol{h}$ and all points $\boldsymbol{x} \geqslant \boldsymbol{0}$ since the naturally ordered principal minors of the Hessian matrix $\boldsymbol{H}_{\mathrm{f}}(\boldsymbol{x})$ are all non-positive. That is, $\boldsymbol{h}'\boldsymbol{H}_{\mathrm{f}}(\boldsymbol{x})\boldsymbol{h}$ is negative semi-definite since

$$\mathrm{f}_{11} = \tfrac{1}{4} x_1^{-\frac{3}{2}} x_2^{\frac{1}{2}} \leqslant 0, \quad \boldsymbol{x} \geqslant \boldsymbol{0},$$

$$\begin{vmatrix} \mathrm{f}_{11} & \mathrm{f}_{12} \\ \mathrm{f}_{21} & \mathrm{f}_{22} \end{vmatrix} = (16 x_1 x_2)^{-1} - (16 x_1 x_2)^{-1} = 0.$$

Hence, f is concave over the non-negative orthant of $\mathscr{E}^2$.

Example 8.4. Let the real-valued function $y = \mathrm{f}(\boldsymbol{x}) = x_1^2+x_1x_2+2x_2^2$ be defined throughout the entirety of $\mathscr{E}^2$. Since

$$\mathrm{f}_{11} = 2>0, \qquad \begin{vmatrix} \mathrm{f}_{11} & \mathrm{f}_{12} \\ \mathrm{f}_{21} & \mathrm{f}_{22} \end{vmatrix} = 7>0,$$

it is evident that $Q(\boldsymbol{h}) = \boldsymbol{h}'\boldsymbol{H}_{\mathrm{f}}(\boldsymbol{x})\boldsymbol{h}>0$ (theorem 1.6) for all $\boldsymbol{h} \neq \boldsymbol{0}$ and all points $\boldsymbol{x}$. In this instance $\boldsymbol{h}'\boldsymbol{H}_{\mathrm{f}}(\boldsymbol{x})\boldsymbol{h}$ is positive definite and thus f is strictly convex over its domain.

Example 8.5. Let the real-valued function $y = \mathrm{f}(\boldsymbol{x}) = 2x_1^2-x_2^2$ be defined for all values of $\boldsymbol{x}$. Is f concave or convex over $\mathscr{E}^2$? Since $|\boldsymbol{H}_{\mathrm{f}}(\boldsymbol{x})| = -8<0$, $\boldsymbol{h}'\boldsymbol{H}_{\mathrm{f}}(\boldsymbol{x})\boldsymbol{h}$ is indefinite. Hence, f is neither convex nor concave. The surface is, in fact, saddle-shaped over its domain.

Example 8.6. Is the real-valued function

$$y = \mathrm{f}(\boldsymbol{x}) = -2x_1^{-2}+x_1x_3-x_2^2+x_2x_3+x_2x_4-x_3^2-x_4^{-2}$$

concave at $\boldsymbol{x}_0' = (1, 0, 0, 1)$? Upon calculating

$$\begin{array}{llll} \mathrm{f}_{11}^0 = -12, & \mathrm{f}_{12}^0 = 0, & \mathrm{f}_{23}^0 = 1, & \mathrm{f}_{34}^0 = 0, \\ \mathrm{f}_{22}^0 = -2, & \mathrm{f}_{13}^0 = 1, & \mathrm{f}_{24}^0 = 1, & \\ \mathrm{f}_{33}^0 = -2, & \mathrm{f}_{14}^0 = 0, & & \\ \mathrm{f}_{44}^0 = -6 & & & \end{array}$$

we obtain the Hessian matrix

$$\begin{bmatrix} -12 & 0 & 1 & 0 \\ 0 & -2 & 1 & 1 \\ 1 & 1 & -2 & 0 \\ 0 & 1 & 0 & -6 \end{bmatrix}.$$

Since the naturally ordered principal minors of this matrix alternate in sign (i.e. form the sequence -12, 24, -34, 93), theorem 1.7 informs us that the Hessian is negative definite and thus f is strictly concave.

An alternative (and equivalent) characterization of a concave (convex) function over a convex domain $\mathscr{K} \subseteq \mathscr{E}^n$ is that its second differential,

$$\mathrm{d}^2\mathrm{f} = \boldsymbol{h}'\boldsymbol{H}_{\mathrm{f}}(\boldsymbol{x})\boldsymbol{h} = Q(\boldsymbol{h}),$$

is negative (positive) semi-definite for all $\boldsymbol{h}$ and all $\boldsymbol{x}\in\mathscr{K}$. If $\mathrm{d}^2\mathrm{f}<0(>0)$ (i.e. is negative (positive) definite) for all $\boldsymbol{h} \neq \boldsymbol{0}$ and all $\boldsymbol{x}\in\mathscr{K}$, then f is strictly concave (convex) over $\mathscr{K}$.

8.4. Extrema of convex and concave real-valued functions

As one may have anticipated, the most important cases involving the attainment of global or local extrema by convex or concave real-valued functions occur when the functions are strictly convex or concave over their domain. In these instances the extrema are exclusively of the strong variety—and it is on an analysis of their properties that our energy will be spent. Hence, the following sequence of theorems deals exclusively with the strict case. We begin with

THEOREM 8.4. *Let the real-valued function* $y = \mathrm{f}(\boldsymbol{x})$, $\boldsymbol{x} \in \mathscr{E}^n$, *be strictly concave over a closed convex set* $\mathscr{K} \subset \mathscr{E}^n$. *Then* f *assumes a strong global maximum somewhere over its domain.*

Moreover, this extremum is unique and occurs either at an interior point of $\mathscr{K}$ (hence, it is also a strong local maximum) or on the boundary of $\mathscr{K}$. (For $\boldsymbol{x} \in \mathscr{E}$, these cases are respectively illustrated by fig. 8.8a, b). The global minimum of a strictly concave function always occurs on the boundary of $\mathscr{K}$, and may or may not be unique (as indicated respectively by fig. 8.9a, b when $\boldsymbol{x} \in \mathscr{E}$). Hence, a strictly concave function never assumes a local minimum over its domain. Next, we present

THEOREM 8.5. *Let the real-valued function* $y = \mathrm{f}(\boldsymbol{x})$, $\boldsymbol{x} \in \mathscr{E}^n$, *be strictly convex over a closed convex set* $\mathscr{K} \subset \mathscr{E}^n$. *Then* f *assumes a strong global minimum somewhere over its domain.*

It is also true that this extremum is unique and occurs at an interior point of $\mathscr{K}$ (hence, it is also a strong local minimum) or at one of its boundary

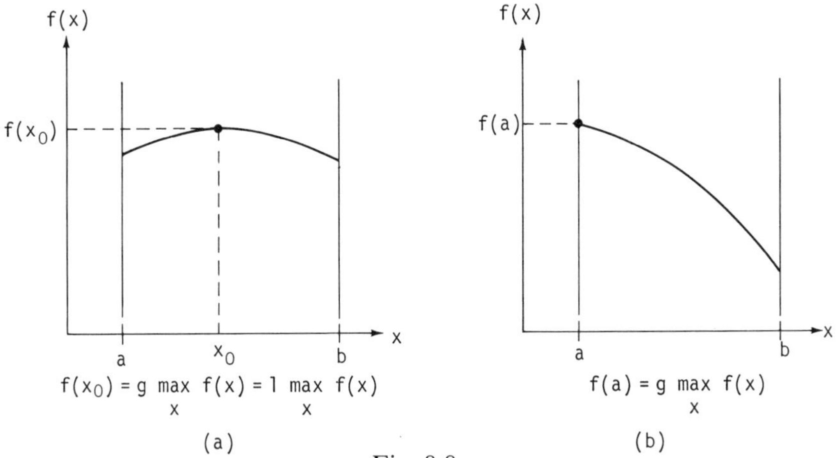

Fig. 8.8.

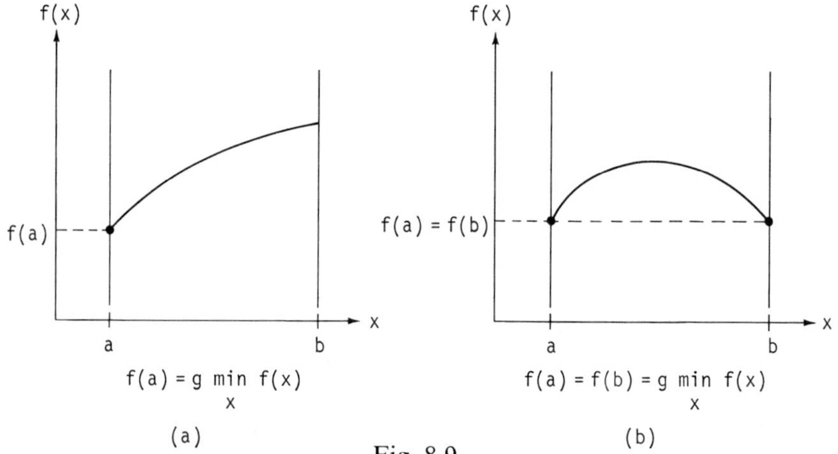

Fig. 8.9.

points (see fig. 8.10a, b, respectively for $x \in \mathscr{E}$). The global maximum of a strictly convex function must occur at a boundary point of $\mathscr{K}$. It may or may not be unique. In this light, a strictly convex function never attains a local maximum anywhere over its domain.

Let us now look to the development of operational criteria with which to determine the maximum (minimum) of a strictly concave (convex) function. To do so we must first consider the following special case of theorems 8.4 and 8.5.

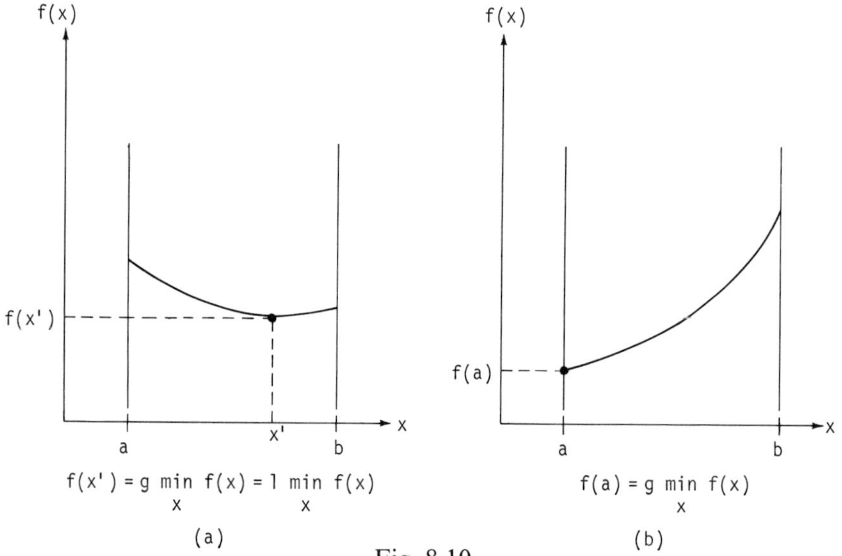

Fig. 8.10.

THEOREM 8.6. *Let the real-valued function* $y = \mathrm{f}(\boldsymbol{x})$, $\boldsymbol{x} \in \mathscr{E}^n$, *be strictly concave (convex) over a closed convex region* $\mathscr{K} \subset \mathscr{E}^n$. *Then any local maximum (minimum) is also the strong global maximum (minimum) of* f *over* $\mathscr{K}$.

Proof. We shall assume to the contrary of the theorem that f is strictly concave (a symmetric proof holds for f strictly convex) on $\mathscr{K}$ and attains a strong global maximum at $\boldsymbol{x}_0$ and a strong local maximum at $\boldsymbol{x}_1$ with $\mathrm{f}(\boldsymbol{x}_0) > \mathrm{f}(\boldsymbol{x}_1)$ (fig. 8.11 illustrates the case when $\boldsymbol{x} \in \mathscr{E}$). Since f is strictly concave over $\mathscr{K}$,

$$\mathrm{f}(\theta\boldsymbol{x}_0 + (1-\theta)\boldsymbol{x}_1) > \theta\mathrm{f}(\boldsymbol{x}_0) + (1-\theta)\mathrm{f}(\boldsymbol{x}_1), \quad 0 < \theta < 1,$$

and thus

$$\mathrm{f}(\theta\boldsymbol{x}_0 + (1-\theta)\boldsymbol{x}_1) > \theta\mathrm{f}(\boldsymbol{x}_1) + (1-\theta)\mathrm{f}(\boldsymbol{x}_1) = \mathrm{f}(\boldsymbol{x}_1), \quad 0 < \theta < 1. \tag{8.9}$$

Let us now consider an open spherical δ-neighborhood about $\boldsymbol{x}_1$, $\delta(\boldsymbol{x}_1)$,

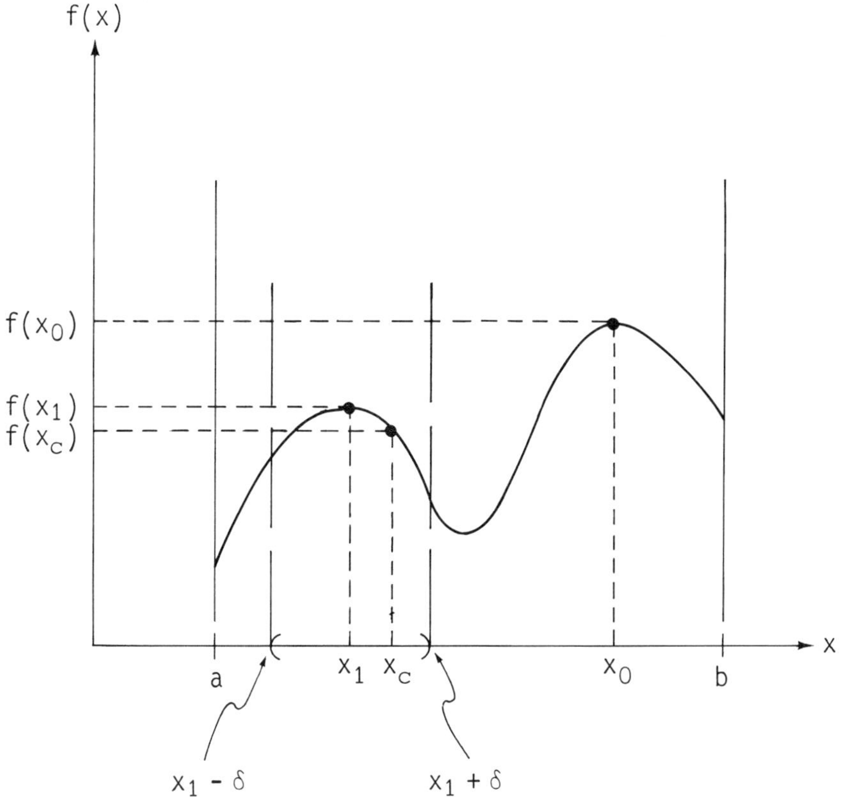

Fig. 8.11.

which is sufficiently small to exclude $\boldsymbol{x}_0$, i.e. take $\delta < \|\boldsymbol{x}_1 - \boldsymbol{x}_0\|$. Then

$$\frac{\delta}{\|\boldsymbol{x}_1 - \boldsymbol{x}_0\|} < 1$$

and, for

$$0 < \theta = \frac{\delta}{\|\boldsymbol{x}_1 - \boldsymbol{x}_0\|} < 1,$$

$$\boldsymbol{x}_c = \frac{\delta}{\|\boldsymbol{x}_1 - \boldsymbol{x}_0\|} \boldsymbol{x}_0 + \left(1 - \frac{\delta}{\|\boldsymbol{x}_1 - \boldsymbol{x}_0\|}\right) \boldsymbol{x}_1 \in \delta(\boldsymbol{x}_1).$$

Hence eq. (8.9) becomes

$$\mathrm{f}(\theta \boldsymbol{x}_0 + (1-\theta)\boldsymbol{x}_1) = \mathrm{f}(\boldsymbol{x}_c) > \mathrm{f}(\boldsymbol{x}_1), \quad 0 < \theta = \frac{\delta}{\|\boldsymbol{x}_1 - \boldsymbol{x}_0\|} < 1.$$

But $\mathrm{f}(\boldsymbol{x}_c) > \mathrm{f}(\boldsymbol{x}_1)$, $\boldsymbol{x}_c \in \delta(\boldsymbol{x}_1)$ violates the assumption that $\mathrm{f}(\boldsymbol{x}_1)$ is a strong local maximum of f. For a contradiction not to occur it must be true that $\boldsymbol{x}_1 = \boldsymbol{x}_0$, in which case the strong local and thus strong global maximum is unique. Q.E.D.

In this regard, if we can isolate any local extremum of f on $\mathscr{K}$, we have determined its strong global extremum since f is assumed to be strictly convex or concave. Since this extremum is unique, we can be sure that if we find one point where $\nabla \mathrm{f} = \mathbf{0}$ for $\mathscr{K}$ open, then we have in fact found the strong global maximum (for f concave) or minimum (when f is convex) of f over $\mathscr{K}$ closed. We may formalize these comments in

THEOREM 8.7. *Let the real-valued function $y = \mathrm{f}(\boldsymbol{x})$, $\boldsymbol{x} \in \mathscr{E}^n$, be strictly concave (convex) over a closed convex region $\mathscr{K} \subset \mathscr{E}^n$ and differentiable at a point $\boldsymbol{x}_0$ interior to $\mathscr{K}$. Then f has a strong global maximum (minimum) at $\boldsymbol{x}_0$ if and only if $\nabla \mathrm{f}^0 = \mathbf{0}$.*

Proof (sufficiency). For f strictly concave at $\boldsymbol{x}_0$, eq. (8.4) informs us that

$$\mathrm{f}(\boldsymbol{x}) < \mathrm{f}(\boldsymbol{x}_0) + \nabla \mathrm{f}(\boldsymbol{x}_0)'(\boldsymbol{x} - \boldsymbol{x}_0), \quad \boldsymbol{x}(\neq \boldsymbol{x}_0) \in \mathscr{K}, \tag{8.4.1}$$

i.e. f lies everywhere below its tangent hyperplane (see fig. 8.12a for $\boldsymbol{x} \in \mathscr{E}$). If $\nabla \mathrm{f}(\boldsymbol{x}_0) = \mathbf{0}$, eq. (8.4.1) becomes $\mathrm{f}(\boldsymbol{x}) < \mathrm{f}(\boldsymbol{x}_0)$ for all $\boldsymbol{x}(\neq \boldsymbol{x}_0) \in \mathscr{K}$. Hence, f has a strong local maximum which is also the strong global maximum of f at $\boldsymbol{x}_0$. If f is strictly convex at $\boldsymbol{x}_0$, the function lies everywhere above its tangent hyperplane (fig. 8.12b) so that

$$\mathrm{f}(\boldsymbol{x}) > \mathrm{f}(\boldsymbol{x}_0) + \nabla \mathrm{f}(\boldsymbol{x}_0)'(\boldsymbol{x} - \boldsymbol{x}_0), \quad \boldsymbol{x}(\neq \boldsymbol{x}_0) \in \mathscr{K}, \tag{8.3.1}$$

whereupon setting $\nabla \mathrm{f}(\boldsymbol{x}_0) = \mathbf{0}$ implies $\mathrm{f}(\boldsymbol{x}) < \mathrm{f}(\boldsymbol{x}_0)$, $\boldsymbol{x}(\neq \boldsymbol{x}_0) \in \mathscr{K}$. In this instance f has a strong local and thus strong global minimum at $\boldsymbol{x}_0$.

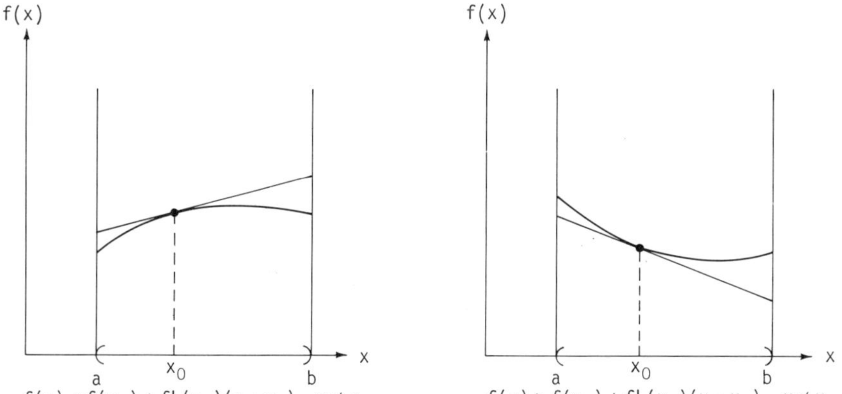

$f(x) < f(x_0) + f'(x_0)(x - x_0),\ x \neq x_0$

(a)

$f(x) > f(x_0) + f'(x_0)(x - x_0),\ x \neq x_0$

(b)

Fig. 8.12.

(Necessity.) With $\nabla f(\boldsymbol{x}_0) \neq \mathbf{0}$, the above necessary condition for a local extremum (theorem 6.10) informs us that $f(\boldsymbol{x}_0)$ is not an extreme value of f over $\mathscr{K}$. Q.E.D.

How does theorem 8.7 compare with the necessary and sufficient conditions for an extremum developed earlier? In chapter 6 we discovered that, under an appropriate set of assumptions, the vanishing of the gradient vector of a function was a necessary condition for the existence of a local extremum (theorem 6.10). There, no reference to the concepts of convexity or concavity was made. However, theorem 8.7 now incorporates the assumption that a function is strictly convex or concave over its domain. In this case the vanishing of the gradient becomes a necessary and sufficient condition for the existence of a strong local extremum (and thus for a strong global extremum—by theorem 8.6), i.e. the property of strict concavity (convexity) replaces the usual sufficient condition for a strong local maximum (minimum) as given in chapter 6 (theorem 6.11). This is evident if we remember that theorem 8.3 characterized a function as being strictly concave (convex) over $\mathscr{K}$ if its associated quadratic form $\boldsymbol{h}'\boldsymbol{H}_f(\boldsymbol{x})\boldsymbol{h}$ is negative (positive) definite for all $\boldsymbol{h} \neq \mathbf{0}$, $\boldsymbol{x} \in \mathscr{K}$. But this is equivalent to the sufficient condition for a strong local extremum per theorem 6.11. Hence, the ordinary sufficient condition for a strong local extremum over $\mathscr{K}$ and the notions of strict convexity and concavity over this region are one and the same.

Chapter 9

CONSTRAINED OPTIMIZATION: A SINGLE EQUALITY CONSTRAINT

9.1. Constrained extrema of real-valued functions of *n* independent variables

Throughout the preceding portions of the text problems pertaining to the optimization (maximization or minimization) of real-valued functions involving n independent variables were dealt with. That is, in attempting to find any (strong) local extrema associated with a real-valued function $y = \mathrm{f}(\boldsymbol{x})$, $\boldsymbol{x} \in \mathscr{E}^n$, all variables x_i, $i = 1, \ldots, n$, were 'free' to assume any value whatever within a region $\mathscr{K} \subseteq \mathscr{E}^n$, with the selection of a value of one variable in no way restricting our choice of any other. In what follows, our discussion now centers around the problem of optimizing f given that the variables are confined to a specific mode of behavior within $\mathscr{K}$. In this regard, if f has a strong local maximum at $\boldsymbol{x}_0 \in \mathscr{K} \subseteq \mathscr{E}^n$ (see fig. 9.1a for $\mathscr{K} \subseteq \mathscr{E}^2$), then, if the variables x_i, $i = 1, \ldots, n$, are not restricted to follow any particular path interior to $\mathscr{K}$, we may move throughout $\mathscr{K}$ in any manner whatever in our search for the maximum. But what if we must maximize or minimize f subject to a side relation involving $\boldsymbol{x}$, namely, $\mathrm{g}(\boldsymbol{x}) = b$, $\boldsymbol{x} \in \mathscr{E}^n$, where b is constant? In this instance the variables x_i, $i = 1, \ldots, n$, are obviously not free to assume any value within $\mathscr{K}$. Such a problem will be referred to quite generally as a 'constrained optimization problem involving an equality constraint'. Before attempting to generate a solution to such a problem let us examine the constraint function g itself.

Our first efforts will be directed toward determining the nature of $\mathrm{g} = b$ or, as it is usually written, $\hat{\mathrm{g}} = b - \mathrm{g} = 0$. As we shall now see, $\hat{\mathrm{g}} = 0$ is an implicit function of $\boldsymbol{x}$. That is

DEFINITION 9.1. *If the real-valued function* $\hat{\mathrm{g}}(\boldsymbol{x}) = 0$, $\boldsymbol{x} \in \mathscr{E}^n$, *defines* x_n *as a function of* $\hat{\boldsymbol{x}}' = (x_1, \ldots, x_{n-1}) \in \mathscr{E}^{n-1}$, $x_n = \zeta(\hat{\boldsymbol{x}})$, *so that* $\hat{\mathrm{g}}(\hat{\boldsymbol{x}}, \zeta(\hat{\boldsymbol{x}})) = 0$, *then* $x_n = \zeta(\hat{\boldsymbol{x}})$ *is defined implicitly as* $\hat{\mathrm{g}}(\boldsymbol{x}) = 0$.

Under what conditions does $\hat{\mathrm{g}}(\boldsymbol{x}) = 0$ define a unique implicit function? That is to say, can we find a function $x_n = \zeta(\hat{\boldsymbol{x}})$ such that $\hat{\mathrm{g}}(\boldsymbol{x}) = 0$ is satisfied? The answer to whether ζ exists or not is provided by an existence or implicit function theorem, namely

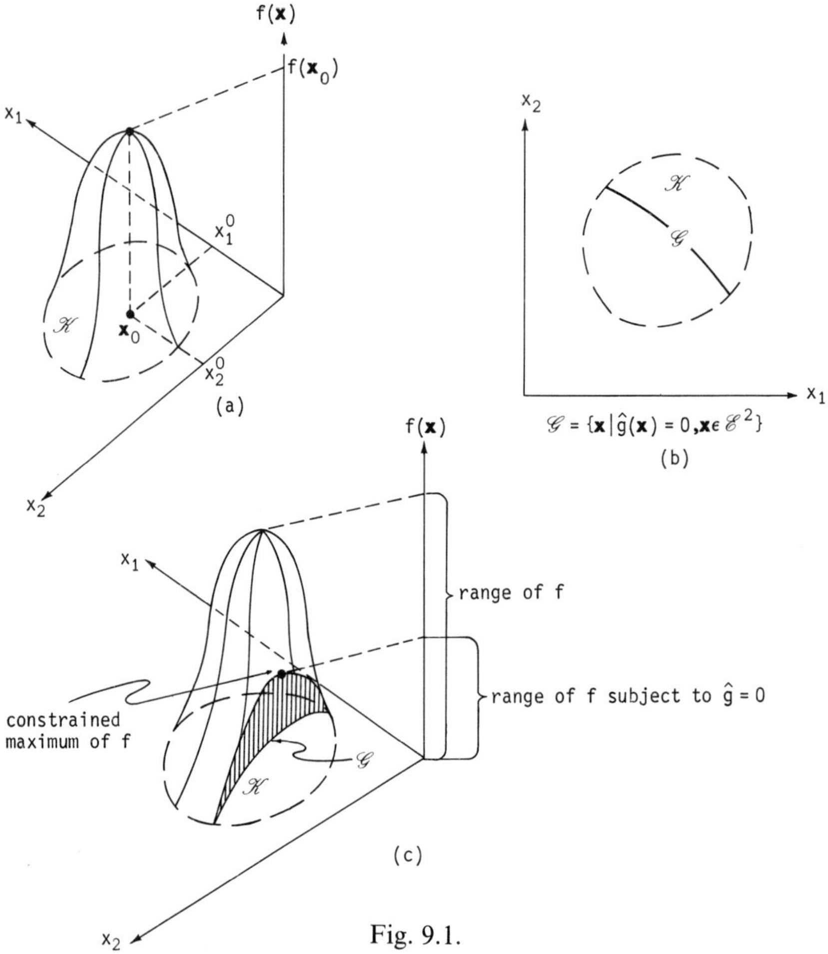

Fig. 9.1.

THEOREM 9.1 (implicit function theorem).[1] *Let the real-valued function* $\hat{g}(\boldsymbol{x}) = 0$, $\boldsymbol{x} \in \mathscr{E}^n$, *be defined over a region* $\mathscr{K} \subseteq \mathscr{E}^n$ *and let* $\mathbf{x}_0$ *be an interior point of* $\mathscr{K}$. *If:*

(*1*)$\hat{g}(\boldsymbol{x}_0) = 0$,

(*2*)$\hat{g}_i$, $i = 1, \ldots, n$, *are continuous within some spherical* δ-*neighborhood of* $\boldsymbol{x}_0$, $\delta(\boldsymbol{x}_0)$, *and*

(*3*)$\hat{g}_n(\boldsymbol{x}_0) \neq 0$, *then*

(*4*)*there is some spherical* ε-*neighborhood of* $\hat{\boldsymbol{x}}'_0 = (x_1^0, \ldots, x_{n-1}^0) \in \mathscr{E}^{n-1}$, $\varepsilon(\hat{\boldsymbol{x}}_0)$, *throughout which there exists for every* $\hat{\boldsymbol{x}} \in \varepsilon(\hat{\boldsymbol{x}}_0)$ *a unique differentiable function* $x_n = \zeta(\hat{\boldsymbol{x}})$ *such that:* $x_n^0 = \zeta(\hat{\boldsymbol{x}}_0)$; $\hat{g}(\hat{\boldsymbol{x}}, \zeta(\hat{\boldsymbol{x}})) = 0$; *and which*

[1] See Taylor (1955), pp. 244–245.

possesses continuous first partial derivatives $\zeta_i = -\hat{g}_i/\hat{g}_n$, $i = 1, \ldots, n-1$.

In sum, this theorem states the circumstances under which we can solve $\hat{g}(\boldsymbol{x}) = 0$ for x_n in terms of x_i, $i = 1, \ldots, n-1$, $x_n = \zeta(\hat{\boldsymbol{x}})$. For example, the contour $\mathscr{G} = \{\boldsymbol{x} \mid \hat{g}(\boldsymbol{x}) = 0, \boldsymbol{x} \in \mathscr{E}^2\} \subset \mathscr{K} \subseteq \mathscr{E}^2$ is illustrated in fig. 9.2. For $\boldsymbol{x}_0 \in \mathscr{G}$, there exists a unique differentiable function $x_2 = \zeta(x_1)$ for all $x_1 \in \varepsilon(x_1^0)$ such that part (4) of the implicit function theorem is satisfied, that is: $x_2^0 = \zeta(x_1^0)$; $\hat{g}(x_1, \zeta(x_1)) = 0$; and $dx_2/dx_1 = -\hat{g}_1/\hat{g}_2$. The graph of ζ is depicted as the shaded portion of $\mathscr{G}$.

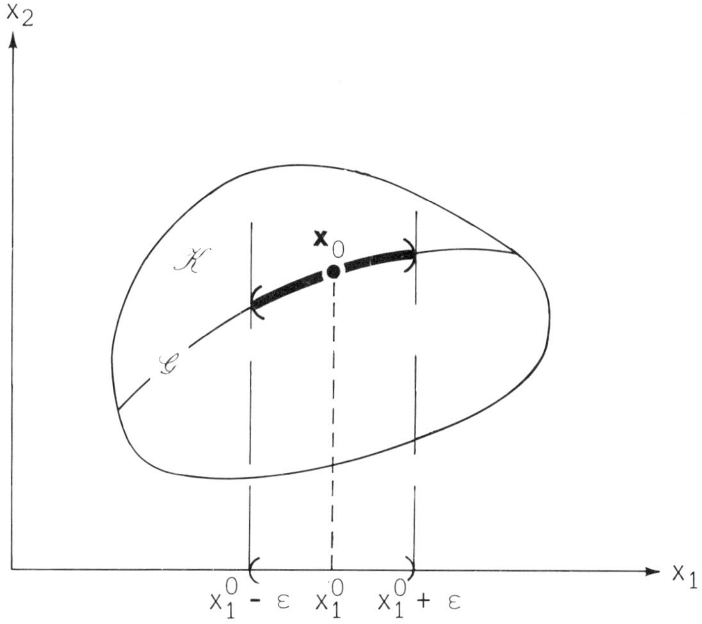

Fig. 9.2.

Let us now explicitly incorporate the constraint function $\hat{g}(\boldsymbol{x}) = 0$ into our analysis. As will become evident shortly, the consequence of introducing $\hat{g} = 0$ is twofold. First, since we must maximize (or minimize) $f(\boldsymbol{x})$ subject to $\hat{g}(\boldsymbol{x}) = 0$, the immediate effect is to reduce the size of the domain of f. That is, whereas $\mathscr{K}$ was the domain of f in our unconstrained problem (e.g. see fig. 9.1a), the domain in our constrained problem is only some subset $\mathscr{G}$ of $\mathscr{K}$, namely, the set of points of $\mathscr{K}$ which satisfy $\hat{g}(\boldsymbol{x}) = 0$ (for $\mathscr{G} \subset \mathscr{E}^2$, see fig. 9.1b). Second, since the domain of f is restricted, then so is its range. In this regard, one should expect that the effect of introducing a constraint is to reduce the set of values which constitutes the range of f (e.g. see fig. 9.1c).

At this point we may now proceed to classify the various types of constrained extrema which we shall later encounter. As was the case for unconstrained extrema, constrained extrema are of the global and local varieties. First, let $y = \mathrm{f}(\boldsymbol{x})$, $\hat{\mathrm{g}}(\boldsymbol{x}) = b - \mathrm{g}(\boldsymbol{x}) = 0$, $\boldsymbol{x} \in \mathscr{E}^n$, be real-valued functions defined on a closed region $\mathscr{K} \subset \mathscr{E}^n$ and let $\boldsymbol{x}_0 \in \mathscr{G} \cap \mathscr{K}$, where $\mathscr{G} = \{\boldsymbol{x} | \hat{\mathrm{g}}(\boldsymbol{x}) = 0, \boldsymbol{x} \in \mathscr{E}^n\}$. Then, we have

DEFINITION 9.2. *The real-valued function* $y = \mathrm{f}(\boldsymbol{x})$ (*subject to* $\hat{\mathrm{g}}(\boldsymbol{x}) = 0$) *has a constrained global maximum (minimum) at* $\boldsymbol{x}_0 \in \mathscr{G} \cap \mathscr{K}$ *if* $\mathrm{f}(\boldsymbol{x}_0) \geqslant \mathrm{f}(\boldsymbol{x})$ $(\leqslant \mathrm{f}(\boldsymbol{x}))$ *for all points* $\boldsymbol{x}(\neq \boldsymbol{x}_0) \in \mathscr{G} \cap \mathscr{K}$.

When $\mathrm{f}(\boldsymbol{x}_0) \geqslant \mathrm{f}(\boldsymbol{x})$ $(\leqslant \mathrm{f}(\boldsymbol{x}))$ and equality holds between $\mathrm{f}(\boldsymbol{x}_0)$ and $\mathrm{f}(\boldsymbol{x})$ for at least one point $\boldsymbol{x}(\neq \boldsymbol{x}_0) \in \mathscr{G} \cap \mathscr{K}$, f has a *constrained weak global maximum (minimum)* at $\boldsymbol{x}_0$. Alternatively, f attains a *constrained strong global maximum (minimum)* at $\boldsymbol{x}_0$ if $\mathrm{f}(\boldsymbol{x}_0) > \mathrm{f}(\boldsymbol{x})$ $(< \mathrm{f}(\boldsymbol{x}))$ for all $\boldsymbol{x}(\neq \boldsymbol{x}_0) \in \mathscr{G} \cap \mathscr{K}$. Next, for $\mathscr{K} \subseteq \mathscr{E}^n$ an open region, we have

DEFINITION 9.3. *The real-valued function* $y = \mathrm{f}(\boldsymbol{x})$ (*subject* $\hat{\mathrm{g}}(\boldsymbol{x}) = 0$) *has a constrained local maximum (minimum) at* $\boldsymbol{x}_0 \in \mathscr{G} \cap \mathscr{K}$ *if there is some spherical* δ*-neighborhood about* $\boldsymbol{x}_0$, $\delta(\boldsymbol{x}_0)$, *such that* $\mathrm{f}(\boldsymbol{x}_0) \geqslant \mathrm{f}(\boldsymbol{x})$ $(\leqslant \mathrm{f}(\boldsymbol{x}))$ *for all points* $\boldsymbol{x} \in \delta(\boldsymbol{x}_0) \cap \mathscr{G} \cap \mathscr{K}$.

If $\mathrm{f}(\boldsymbol{x}_0) \geqslant \mathrm{f}(\boldsymbol{x})$ $(\leqslant \mathrm{f}(\boldsymbol{x}))$ and $\mathrm{f}(\boldsymbol{x}_0) = \mathrm{f}(\boldsymbol{x})$ for at least one point $\boldsymbol{x}(\neq \boldsymbol{x}_0) \in \delta(\boldsymbol{x}_0) \cap \mathscr{G} \cap \mathscr{K}$, f has a *constrained weak local maximum (minimum)* at $\boldsymbol{x}_0$, while if $\mathrm{f}(\boldsymbol{x}_0) > \mathrm{f}(\boldsymbol{x})$ $(< \mathrm{f}(\boldsymbol{x}))$ for all $\boldsymbol{x}(\neq \boldsymbol{x}_0) \in \delta(\boldsymbol{x}_0) \cap \mathscr{G} \cap \mathscr{K}$, then f is said to have a *constrained strong local maximum (minimum)* at $\boldsymbol{x}_0$.

How may we describe the attainment of an extreme value of f when x_i, $i = 1, \ldots, n$, are not independent variables but are connected by a side relation? It is evident from fig. 9.3 that if we are to, let us say, maximize the real-valued function $y = \mathrm{f}(\boldsymbol{x})$, $\boldsymbol{x} \in \mathscr{E}^2$, subject to $\hat{\mathrm{g}}(\boldsymbol{x}) = 0$, then we can do so only by choosing, as possible candidates for a maximum, one of those points $\boldsymbol{x}$ which satisfy the constraint. That is, we must, in effect, move along $\hat{\mathrm{g}}(\boldsymbol{x}) = 0$ from A to B (B to A) so as to reach the 'highest possible' contour of f. It is obvious that this extremum occurs at the point $\boldsymbol{x}_0$ since, if we deviate from $\boldsymbol{x}_0$ (to either the left or right along $\hat{\mathrm{g}}(\boldsymbol{x}) = 0$) ever so slightly, the value of f decreases since we are now on a 'lower' level curve. So, to maximize (minimize) $\mathrm{f}(\boldsymbol{x})$ subject to $\hat{\mathrm{g}}(\boldsymbol{x}) = 0$, we must choose the point $\boldsymbol{x}_0 \in \mathscr{G}$ where a contour of f is just tangent to the level curve $\hat{\mathrm{g}}(\boldsymbol{x}) = 0$.

Let us now look to the circumstances under which a unique point of tangency will occur between the contours of f, g by considering some observations on the concept of functional dependence. To this end we state

THEOREM 9.2. *Let the real-valued functions* $y = \mathrm{f}(\boldsymbol{x})$, $w = \mathrm{g}(\boldsymbol{x})$, $\boldsymbol{x} \in \mathscr{E}^2$, *be defined throughout a region* $\mathscr{K} \subseteq \mathscr{E}^2$. *Additionally, assume that:* (1) $\nabla \mathrm{f}, \nabla \mathrm{g} \not\equiv \mathbf{0}$ *in* $\mathscr{K}$ *so that both* f, g *have well-defined level curves there; and* (2) *there exists a function* $\phi(y, w) = 0$ *such that* $\phi(\mathrm{f}(\boldsymbol{x}), \mathrm{g}(\boldsymbol{x})) \equiv 0$. *Then* f, g *are functionally*

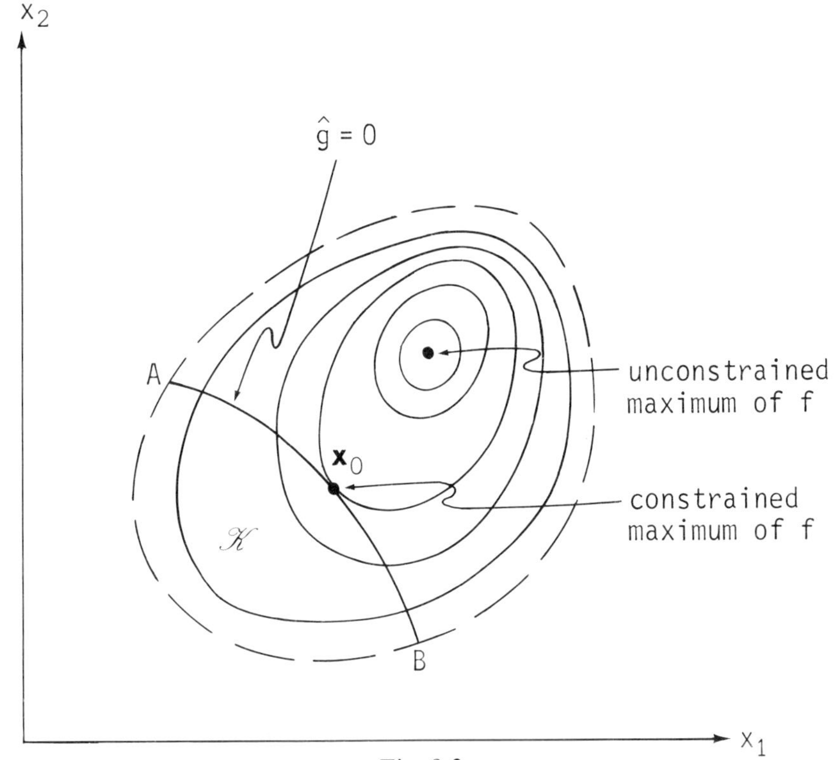

Fig. 9.3.

dependent[2] *throughout* $\mathscr{K}$ *if and only if the Jacobian determinant of* f, g *identically vanishes at each point of* $\mathscr{K}$, i.e.

$$\left|\frac{\partial(f, g)}{\partial(x_1, x_2)}\right| = \begin{vmatrix} f_1 & f_2 \\ g_1 & g_2 \end{vmatrix} \equiv 0.$$

The consequence of this theorem is that if the Jacobian determinant of f, g is identically zero for all points $\boldsymbol{x} \in \mathscr{K} \subseteq \mathscr{E}^2$, the level curves of f, g coincide, i.e. each level curve of f is a level curve of g and conversely, although their labeling may conceivably differ.

Example 9.1. Are the real-valued functions

$$y = f(\boldsymbol{x}) = x_1^2 + x_2^2 \quad \text{and} \quad w = g(\boldsymbol{x}) = (x_1^2 + x_2^2)^{\frac{3}{2}}$$

---

[2] If y, w are functionally dependent and either $f_1 \neq 0$ or $f_2 \neq 0$, then $f = \alpha(g)$ and quite possibly $y = cw$ (where c is some constant), $y = w^n$, $y = w/(1+w)$, etc. And if $g_1 \neq 0$ or $g_2 \neq 0$, then $g = \beta(f)$. For a more elaborate discussion on this account see Taylor (1955), pp. 276–277.

functionally dependent throughout $\mathscr{E}^2$? Since

$$\left|\frac{\partial(\mathrm{f}, \mathrm{g})}{\partial(x_1, x_2)}\right| = \begin{vmatrix} 2x_1 & 2x_2 \\ 3(x_1^2+x_2^2)^{\frac{1}{2}}x_1 & 3(x_1^2+x_2^2)^{\frac{1}{2}}x_2 \end{vmatrix} \equiv 0$$

for all points $\boldsymbol{x}$, the answer is yes. In fact, $w = y^{\frac{3}{2}}$ for $\boldsymbol{x}' \neq (0, 0)$.

The implication of theorem 9.2 for constrained optimization problems is that if $|\partial(\mathrm{f}, \hat{\mathrm{g}})/\partial(x_1, x_2)| \equiv 0$ throughout $\mathscr{K} \subseteq \mathscr{E}^2$, no unique tangency point (such as at $\boldsymbol{x}_0$ in fig. 9.3) between the contours of f and $\hat{\mathrm{g}} = 0$ is discernible. With this background in mind, let us now look to the generation of a solution to our constrained optimization problem. In what follows we shall develop necessary as well as sufficient conditions for the existence of a constrained local extremum of f over $\mathscr{K} \subseteq \mathscr{E}^n$. We state first

THEOREM 9.3 (a necessary condition). *Let the real-valued functions* $y = \mathrm{f}(\boldsymbol{x})$, $\hat{\mathrm{g}}(\boldsymbol{x}) = 0$, $\boldsymbol{x} \in \mathscr{E}^n$, *be defined over an open region* $\mathscr{K} \subseteq \mathscr{E}^n$ *and differentiable throughout some spherical* δ*-neighborhood of the point* $\boldsymbol{x}_0 \in \mathscr{K}$. *If* f *has a local extremum subject to* $\hat{\mathrm{g}} = 0$ *at* $\boldsymbol{x}_0$, *then*

$$\left|\frac{\partial(\mathrm{f}, \hat{\mathrm{g}})}{\partial(x_i, x_n)}\right|_{\boldsymbol{x}_0} = \begin{vmatrix} \mathrm{f}_i(\boldsymbol{x}_0) & \mathrm{f}_n(\boldsymbol{x}_0) \\ \hat{\mathrm{g}}_i(\boldsymbol{x}_0) & \hat{\mathrm{g}}_n(\boldsymbol{x}_0) \end{vmatrix} = 0$$

or

$$\frac{\mathrm{f}_i(\boldsymbol{x}_0)}{\mathrm{f}_n(\boldsymbol{x}_0)} = \frac{\hat{\mathrm{g}}_i(\boldsymbol{x}_0)}{\hat{\mathrm{g}}_n(\boldsymbol{x}_0)}, \quad i = 1, \ldots, n-1. \tag{9.1}$$

Proof. Let $\hat{\mathrm{g}}(\boldsymbol{x}_0) = 0$. Additionally, let $\hat{\mathrm{g}}$ be differentiable throughout a spherical δ-neighborhood of $\boldsymbol{x}_0$, $\delta(\boldsymbol{x}_0)$, with $\hat{\mathrm{g}}_n(\boldsymbol{x}_0) \neq 0$. Then by the implicit function theorem, there exists a spherical ε-neighborhood of $\hat{\boldsymbol{x}}_0$, $\varepsilon(\hat{\boldsymbol{x}}_0)$, such that for every $\hat{\boldsymbol{x}} \in \varepsilon(\hat{\boldsymbol{x}}_0)$, $x_n = \zeta(\hat{\boldsymbol{x}})$. Since $(\hat{\boldsymbol{x}}, \zeta(\hat{\boldsymbol{x}})) \in \mathscr{K}$, f has a local extremum subject to $\hat{\mathrm{g}} = 0$ at $\boldsymbol{x}_0$ if and only if $\mathrm{F}(\hat{\boldsymbol{x}}) = \mathrm{f}(\hat{\boldsymbol{x}}, \zeta(\hat{\boldsymbol{x}}))$ has an unconstrained local extremum at $\hat{\boldsymbol{x}}_0$. In this regard, we first find

$$\mathrm{F}_i = \mathrm{f}_i + \mathrm{f}_n\zeta_i, \quad i = 1, \ldots, n-1.$$

Then if a local extremum of F occurs at $\hat{\boldsymbol{x}}_0$,

$$\mathrm{F}_i(\hat{\boldsymbol{x}}_0) = \mathrm{f}_i(\boldsymbol{x}_0) + \mathrm{f}_n(\boldsymbol{x}_0)\zeta_i(\hat{\boldsymbol{x}}_0) = 0, \quad i = 1, \ldots, n-1. \tag{9.2}$$

Since we must restrict our movements throughout $\mathscr{K}$ to those values of $\boldsymbol{x}$ which satisfy $\mathrm{G}(\hat{\boldsymbol{x}}) = \hat{\mathrm{g}}(\hat{\boldsymbol{x}}, \zeta(\hat{\boldsymbol{x}})) = 0$, it follows that

$$\mathrm{G}_i = \hat{\mathrm{g}}_i + \hat{\mathrm{g}}_n\zeta_i = 0, \quad i = 1, \ldots, n-1. \tag{9.3}$$

Then eq. (9.3) yields, at $\hat{\boldsymbol{x}}_0$,

$$\zeta_i(\hat{\boldsymbol{x}}_0) = -\frac{\hat{\mathrm{g}}_i(\boldsymbol{x}_0)}{\hat{\mathrm{g}}_n(\boldsymbol{x}_0)}, \quad \hat{\mathrm{g}}_n(\boldsymbol{x}_0) \neq 0, i = 1, \ldots, n-1.$$

Upon substituting this derivative into eq. (9.2) we obtain

$$\mathrm{f}_i(\boldsymbol{x}_0)+\mathrm{f}_n(\boldsymbol{x}_0)\left(-\frac{\hat{\mathrm{g}}_i(\boldsymbol{x}_0)}{\hat{\mathrm{g}}_n(\boldsymbol{x}_0)}\right)=0 \quad \text{or} \quad \frac{\mathrm{f}_i(\boldsymbol{x}_0)}{\mathrm{f}_n(\boldsymbol{x}_0)}=\frac{\hat{\mathrm{g}}_i(\boldsymbol{x}_0)}{\hat{\mathrm{g}}_n(\boldsymbol{x}_0)}, \quad i=1,\ldots,n-1.$$

This last equality describes a point of tangency between a contour of f and $\hat{\mathrm{g}}=0$ at (x_i^0, x_n^0) in x_i, x_n-space. Q.E.D.

To summarize: a necessary condition for f subject to $\hat{\mathrm{g}}=0$ to have a local extremum at $\boldsymbol{x}_0 \in \mathscr{E}^n$ is that the sequence of Jacobians $[\partial(\mathrm{f}, \hat{\mathrm{g}})/\partial(x_i, x_n)]_{\boldsymbol{x}_0}$, $i=1,\ldots,n-1$, is singular, i.e. eq. (9.1) holds. In this regard, the coordinates of $\boldsymbol{x}_0$ may be obtained from the simultaneous solution of the system

$$\left.\begin{aligned} &\left|\frac{\partial(\mathrm{f}, \hat{\mathrm{g}})}{\partial(x_i, x_n)}\right|=0, \quad i=1,\ldots,n-1, \\ &\hat{\mathrm{g}}=0. \end{aligned}\right\} \tag{9.4}$$

Given that $\boldsymbol{x}\in\mathscr{E}^2$, if the Jacobian determinant $|\partial(\mathrm{f}, \hat{\mathrm{g}})/\partial(x_1, x_2)|$ is not identically zero, then we may equate it to zero so as to locate a unique point of tangency between a level curve of f and $\hat{\mathrm{g}}=0$. As indicated above, the coordinates of such a point may then be obtained from the simultaneous solution of

$$\left.\begin{aligned} &\left|\frac{\partial(\mathrm{f}, \hat{\mathrm{g}})}{\partial(x_1, x_2)}\right|=\begin{vmatrix} \mathrm{f}_1 & \mathrm{f}_2 \\ \hat{\mathrm{g}}_1 & \hat{\mathrm{g}}_2 \end{vmatrix} \\ &\hat{\mathrm{g}}=0. \end{aligned}\right\} \tag{9.4.1}$$

How may we determine whether any constrained extremum actually attained corresponds to a maximum or minimum of f? Before answering this question, let us develop a bit of terminology and a couple of supporting theorems.

DEFINITION 9.4. *Let the real-valued functions $y=\mathrm{f}(\boldsymbol{x})$, $w=\mathrm{g}(\boldsymbol{x})$, $\boldsymbol{x}\in\mathscr{E}^n$, be defined over a region $\mathscr{K}\subseteq\mathscr{E}^n$. The $(n+1)$st-order bordered Hessian matrix of* f *is represented, at those points* $\boldsymbol{x}$ *where* g *is differentiable and* f *is twice differentiable, as*

$$\boldsymbol{H}_{\mathrm{f}}^{\mathrm{g}}(\boldsymbol{x})=\begin{bmatrix} \mathrm{f}_{11} & \mathrm{f}_{12} & \cdots & \mathrm{f}_{1n} & \mathrm{g}_1 \\ \mathrm{f}_{21} & \mathrm{f}_{22} & \cdots & \mathrm{f}_{2n} & \mathrm{g}_2 \\ \vdots & \vdots & & \vdots & \vdots \\ \mathrm{f}_{n1} & \mathrm{f}_{n2} & \cdots & \mathrm{f}_{nn} & \mathrm{g}_n \\ \mathrm{g}_1 & \mathrm{g}_2 & \cdots & \mathrm{g}_n & 0 \end{bmatrix} \begin{bmatrix} \boldsymbol{H}_{\mathrm{f}} & \vdots & \nabla\mathrm{g} \\ \cdots & \vdots & \cdots \\ \nabla\mathrm{g}' & \vdots & 0 \end{bmatrix}.$$

Here the Hessian matrix of f has been 'bordered' by the first partial derivatives of g. It is obvious that the bordered Hessian matrix is symmetric, i.e. $\boldsymbol{H}_{\mathrm{f}}^{\mathrm{g}}(\boldsymbol{x})=\boldsymbol{H}_{\mathrm{f}}^{\mathrm{g}}(\boldsymbol{x})'$ since $\mathrm{f}_{ij}=\mathrm{f}_{ji}$, $i\neq j$. We next state a necessary and sufficient condition for the sign definiteness of a quadratic form $Q(\boldsymbol{x})$ subject to a linear constraint in $\boldsymbol{x}$.[3] In this regard, if the symmetric matrix A is of order $(n \times n)$, $\boldsymbol{B}$ is of order $(n \times 1)$, $\boldsymbol{x}$ is an $(n \times 1)$ vector, and $\boldsymbol{B}'\boldsymbol{x} = 0$ is a linear side relation to which the variables of Q must conform, then

THEOREM 9.4. *The quadratic form* $\boldsymbol{x}'\boldsymbol{A}\boldsymbol{x}$ *subject to* $\boldsymbol{B}'\boldsymbol{x} = 0$ *is positive definite* (>0) *for every* $\boldsymbol{x} \neq \boldsymbol{0}$ *if and only if*

$$\Delta_r = \begin{vmatrix} \boldsymbol{A}_{rr} & \vdots & \boldsymbol{B}_r \\ \cdots & \vdots & \cdots \\ \boldsymbol{B}_r' & \vdots & 0 \end{vmatrix} < 0, \quad r = 2, \ldots, n. \tag{9.5}$$[4]

Also,

THEOREM 9.5. *The quadratic form* $\boldsymbol{x}'\boldsymbol{A}\boldsymbol{x}$ *subject to* $\boldsymbol{B}'\boldsymbol{x} = 0$ *is negative definite* (<0) *for every* $\boldsymbol{x} \neq \boldsymbol{0}$ *if and only if*

$$\Delta_r = (-1)^r \begin{vmatrix} \boldsymbol{A}_{rr} & \vdots & \boldsymbol{B}_r \\ \cdots & \vdots & \cdots \\ \boldsymbol{B}_r' & \vdots & 0 \end{vmatrix} > 0, \quad r = 2, \ldots, n. \tag{9.5.1}$$

Example 9.2. Determine the sign definiteness of $\boldsymbol{x}'\boldsymbol{A}\boldsymbol{x}$ subject to $\boldsymbol{B}'\boldsymbol{x} = 3x_1 + 2x_2 + x_3 = 0$ when

$$\boldsymbol{A} = \begin{bmatrix} 1 & 4 & 0 \\ 2 & 1 & 2 \\ 1 & 0 & 1 \end{bmatrix}.$$

Given that

$$\begin{vmatrix} \boldsymbol{A}_{22} & \vdots & \boldsymbol{B}_2 \\ \cdots & \vdots & \cdots \\ \boldsymbol{B}_2' & \vdots & 0 \end{vmatrix} = \begin{vmatrix} 1 & 4 & 3 \\ 2 & 1 & 2 \\ 3 & 2 & 0 \end{vmatrix} = 23, \quad \begin{vmatrix} \boldsymbol{A}_{33} & \vdots & \boldsymbol{B}_3 \\ \cdots & \vdots & \cdots \\ \boldsymbol{B}_3' & \vdots & 0 \end{vmatrix} = \begin{vmatrix} 1 & 4 & 0 & 3 \\ 2 & 1 & 2 & 2 \\ 1 & 0 & 1 & 1 \\ 3 & 2 & 1 & 0 \end{vmatrix} = -7,$$

it follows from eq. (9.5.1.) that $\Delta_2 = 23 > 0$, $\Delta_3 = 7 > 0$ so that $\boldsymbol{x}'\boldsymbol{A}\boldsymbol{x}$ subject to $\boldsymbol{B}'\boldsymbol{x} = 0$ is negative definite.

Let us now endeavor, accordingly, to answer our previous question by stating

THEOREM 9.6 (a sufficient condition). *Let the real-valued functions* $y = \mathrm{f}(\boldsymbol{x})$, $\hat{\mathrm{g}}(\boldsymbol{x}) = 0$, $\boldsymbol{x} \in \mathscr{E}^n$, *possess continuous first- and second-order partial derivatives*

---

[3] The two theorems given immediately below are based on the work of Debreu (1952), pp. 597–607.

[4] Here $\boldsymbol{B}_r$ is obtained from $\boldsymbol{B}$ by retaining only the first r components of $\boldsymbol{B}$, while $\boldsymbol{A}_{rr}$ is obtained from $\boldsymbol{A}$ by keeping just the first r rows and columns of $\boldsymbol{A}$, $r = 2, \ldots, n$.

throughout some spherical δ-neighborhood of the point $\boldsymbol{x}_0$ contained within an open region $\mathscr{K} \subseteq \mathscr{E}^n$. If

$$\left|\frac{\partial(\mathrm{f}, \hat{\mathrm{g}})}{\partial(x_i, x_n)}\right|_{\boldsymbol{x}_0} = 0, \quad i = 1, \ldots, n-1, \quad \textit{and} \quad \begin{vmatrix} \boldsymbol{H}_{\mathrm{f}+\lambda\hat{\mathrm{g}}}(\boldsymbol{x}_0)_{rr} & \nabla\hat{\mathrm{g}}(\boldsymbol{x}_0)_r \\ \nabla\hat{\mathrm{g}}(\boldsymbol{x}_0)'_r & 0 \end{vmatrix}$$

$$\neq 0, \quad r = 2, \ldots, n,$$

then f *subject to* $\hat{\mathrm{g}} = 0$ *has a strong local extremum at* $\boldsymbol{x}_0$. *Moreover:*

(*a*) *if*

$$\Delta_r = (-1)^r \begin{vmatrix} \boldsymbol{H}_{\mathrm{f}+\lambda\hat{\mathrm{g}}}(\boldsymbol{x}_0)_{rr} & \nabla\hat{\mathrm{g}}(\boldsymbol{x}_0)_r \\ \nabla\hat{\mathrm{g}}(\boldsymbol{x}_0)'_r & 0 \end{vmatrix} > 0, \quad r = 2, \ldots, n, \tag{9.6}$$

then f *subject to* $\hat{\mathrm{g}} = 0$ *has a strong local maximum at* $\boldsymbol{x}_0$, *but*

(*b*) *if*

$$\Delta_r = \begin{vmatrix} \boldsymbol{H}_{\mathrm{f}+\lambda\hat{\mathrm{g}}}(\boldsymbol{x}_0)_{rr} & \nabla\hat{\mathrm{g}}(\boldsymbol{x}_0)_r \\ \nabla\hat{\mathrm{g}}(\boldsymbol{x}_0)'_r & 0 \end{vmatrix} < 0, \quad r = 2, \ldots, n, \tag{9.6.1}$$

then f *subject to* $\hat{\mathrm{g}} = 0$ *has a strong local minimum at* $\boldsymbol{x}_0$.

Proof. Let $\hat{\mathrm{g}}(\boldsymbol{x}_0) = 0$. Additionally, let $\hat{\mathrm{g}}$ be differentiable throughout a spherical δ-neighborhood of $\boldsymbol{x}_0$, $\delta(\boldsymbol{x}_0)$, with $\hat{\mathrm{g}}_n(\boldsymbol{x}_0) \neq 0$. Then, by the implicit function theorem, there exists a spherical ε-neighborhood of $\hat{\boldsymbol{x}}_0$, $\varepsilon(\hat{\boldsymbol{x}}_0)$, such that for every $\hat{\boldsymbol{x}} \in \varepsilon(\hat{\boldsymbol{x}}_0)$, $x_n = \zeta(\hat{\boldsymbol{x}})$. We first form $\mathrm{F}(\hat{\boldsymbol{x}}) = \mathrm{f}(\hat{\boldsymbol{x}}, \zeta(\hat{\boldsymbol{x}}))$. Then, from eq. (5.15.4), the second-order Taylor expansion of F near $\hat{\boldsymbol{x}}_0$ is

$$\mathrm{F}(\hat{\boldsymbol{x}}_0 + \boldsymbol{h}) = \mathrm{F}(\hat{\boldsymbol{x}}_0) + \nabla\mathrm{F}(\hat{\boldsymbol{x}}_0)'\boldsymbol{h} + \tfrac{1}{2!}\boldsymbol{h}'\boldsymbol{H}_{\mathrm{F}}(\hat{\boldsymbol{x}}_0 + \theta\boldsymbol{h})\boldsymbol{h}, \quad 0 < \theta < 1, \tag{9.7}$$

where the ith component of $\nabla\mathrm{F} = \nabla\mathrm{f} + \mathrm{f}_n\nabla\zeta$ is $\mathrm{F}_i = \mathrm{f}_i + \mathrm{f}_n\zeta_i$, $i = 1, \ldots, n-1$, and the element within the ith row and jth column of $\boldsymbol{H}_{\mathrm{F}}$ is

$$\mathrm{F}_{ij} = \mathrm{f}_{ij} + \mathrm{f}_{in}\zeta_j + \zeta_i(\mathrm{f}_{nj} + \mathrm{f}_{nn}\zeta_j) + \mathrm{f}_n\zeta_{ij}, \quad i, j = 1, \ldots, n-1.$$

Also, for $\mathrm{G}(\hat{\boldsymbol{x}}) = \hat{\mathrm{g}}(\hat{\boldsymbol{x}}, \zeta(\hat{\boldsymbol{x}})) = 0$, $\mathrm{G}_i = 0$ or $\hat{\mathrm{g}}_i + \hat{\mathrm{g}}_n\zeta_i = 0$, $i = 1, \ldots, n-1$, and thus

$$\mathrm{G}_{ij} = \hat{\mathrm{g}}_{ij} + \hat{\mathrm{g}}_{in}\zeta_j + \zeta_i(\hat{\mathrm{g}}_{nj} + \hat{\mathrm{g}}_{nn}\zeta_j) + \hat{\mathrm{g}}_n\zeta_{ij} = 0, \quad i, j = 1, \ldots, n-1,$$

so that

$$\zeta_{ij} = -\frac{\hat{\mathrm{g}}_{ij} + \hat{\mathrm{g}}_{in}\zeta_j + \zeta_i(\hat{\mathrm{g}}_{nj} + \hat{\mathrm{g}}_{nn}\zeta_j)}{\hat{\mathrm{g}}_n}, \quad \hat{\mathrm{g}}_n \neq 0, \; i, j = 1, \ldots, n-1. \tag{9.8}$$

Upon substituting eq. (9.8) into F_{ij} above we obtain

$$\mathrm{F}_{ij} = (\mathrm{f}_{ij} + \lambda\hat{\mathrm{g}}_{ij}) + (\mathrm{f}_{in} + \lambda\hat{\mathrm{g}}_{in})\zeta_j + (\mathrm{f}_{nj} + \lambda\hat{\mathrm{g}}_{nj})\zeta_i + (\mathrm{f}_{nn} + \lambda\hat{\mathrm{g}}_{nn})\zeta_i\zeta_j,$$
$$i, j = 1, \ldots, n-1,$$

where $\lambda = -\mathrm{f}_n/\hat{\mathrm{g}}_n$, $\hat{\mathrm{g}}_n \neq 0$. In this light,

$$\begin{aligned} \boldsymbol{h}'\boldsymbol{H}_{\mathrm{F}}\boldsymbol{h} &= \sum_{i=1}^{n-1}\sum_{j=1}^{n-1} \mathrm{F}_{ij}h_i h_j = \sum_{i=1}^{n-1}\sum_{j=1}^{n-1} (\mathrm{f}_{ij}+\lambda\hat{\mathrm{g}}_{ij})h_i h_j \\ &\quad + \sum_{i=1}^{n-1} (\mathrm{f}_{in}+\lambda\hat{\mathrm{g}}_{in})h_i \sum_{j=1}^{n-1} \zeta_j h_j + \sum_{j=1}^{n-1} (\mathrm{f}_{nj}+\lambda\hat{\mathrm{g}}_{nj})h_j \sum_{i=1}^{n-1} \zeta_i h_i \\ &\quad +(\mathrm{f}_{nn}+\lambda\hat{\mathrm{g}}_{nn}) \sum_{i=1}^{n-1} \zeta_i h_i \sum_{j=1}^{n-1} \zeta_j h_j. \end{aligned}$$

Since $\boldsymbol{x}$ is restricted to the set of vectors for which $\hat{\mathrm{g}}(\boldsymbol{x}) = 0$, $\mathrm{d}\hat{\mathrm{g}} = \nabla\hat{\mathrm{g}}'\boldsymbol{h} = 0$ and thus

$$h_n = -\sum_{k=1}^{n-1} \hat{\mathrm{g}}_k h_k/\hat{\mathrm{g}}_n = \sum_{k=1}^{n-1} \zeta_k h_k, \quad \hat{\mathrm{g}}_n \neq 0.$$

Substituting this expression into the preceding quadratic form yields

$$\begin{aligned} \boldsymbol{h}'\boldsymbol{H}_{\mathrm{F}}\boldsymbol{h} &= \sum_{i=1}^{n}\sum_{j=1}^{n} (\mathrm{f}_{ij}+\lambda\hat{\mathrm{g}}_{ij})h_i h_j = \boldsymbol{h}'\boldsymbol{H}_{\mathrm{f}+\lambda\hat{\mathrm{g}}}\boldsymbol{h} \\ &= \boldsymbol{h}'\begin{bmatrix} \mathrm{f}_{11}+\lambda\hat{\mathrm{g}}_{11} & \mathrm{f}_{12}+\lambda\hat{\mathrm{g}}_{12} & \cdots & \mathrm{f}_{1n}+\lambda\hat{\mathrm{g}}_{1n} \\ \mathrm{f}_{21}+\lambda\hat{\mathrm{g}}_{21} & \mathrm{f}_{22}+\lambda\hat{\mathrm{g}}_{22} & \cdots & \mathrm{f}_{2n}+\lambda\hat{\mathrm{g}}_{2n} \\ \vdots & \vdots & & \vdots \\ \mathrm{f}_{n1}+\lambda\hat{\mathrm{g}}_{n1} & \mathrm{f}_{n2}+\lambda\hat{\mathrm{g}}_{n2} & \cdots & \mathrm{f}_{nn}+\lambda\hat{\mathrm{g}}_{nn} \end{bmatrix}\boldsymbol{h}. \end{aligned}$$

Since the first- and second-order partial derivatives of f, $\hat{\mathrm{g}}$ are continuous throughout $\delta(\boldsymbol{x}_0)$,

$$\boldsymbol{H}_{\mathrm{F}}(\hat{\boldsymbol{x}}_0+\theta\boldsymbol{h})\rightarrow\boldsymbol{H}_{\mathrm{F}}(\hat{\boldsymbol{x}}_0) \quad \text{as} \quad \theta\rightarrow 0, \quad \|\boldsymbol{h}\|<\delta.$$

Thus eq. (9.7) may be rewritten as

$$\mathrm{F}(\hat{\boldsymbol{x}}_0+\boldsymbol{h})\sim\mathrm{F}(\hat{\boldsymbol{x}}_0)+\nabla\mathrm{F}(\hat{\boldsymbol{x}}_0)'\boldsymbol{h}+\tfrac{1}{2!}\boldsymbol{h}'\boldsymbol{H}_{\mathrm{f}+\lambda\hat{\mathrm{g}}}(\hat{\boldsymbol{x}}_0)\boldsymbol{h}. \tag{9.7.1}$$

By hypothesis

$$\begin{aligned} |\partial(\mathrm{f},\hat{\mathrm{g}})/\partial(x_i,x_n)|_{\boldsymbol{x}_0} &= \mathrm{F}_i(\hat{\boldsymbol{x}}_0) = \mathrm{f}_i(\boldsymbol{x}_0)+\mathrm{f}_n(\boldsymbol{x}_0)\,(-\hat{\mathrm{g}}_i(\boldsymbol{x}_0)/\hat{\mathrm{g}}_n(\boldsymbol{x}_0)\,) \\ &= 0, \quad i = 1, \ldots, n-1, \end{aligned}$$

so that $\nabla\mathrm{F}(\hat{\boldsymbol{x}}_0) = \mathbf{0}$. Hence eq. (9.7.1) becomes

$$\mathrm{F}(\hat{\boldsymbol{x}}_0+\boldsymbol{h})-\mathrm{F}(\hat{\boldsymbol{x}}_0)\sim\tfrac{1}{2!}\boldsymbol{h}'\boldsymbol{H}_{\mathrm{f}+\lambda\hat{\mathrm{g}}}(\hat{\boldsymbol{x}}_0)\boldsymbol{h}. \tag{9.7.2}$$

Now $\mathrm{F}(\hat{\boldsymbol{x}}_0+\boldsymbol{h})-\mathrm{F}(\hat{\boldsymbol{x}}_0)<0(>0)$ as $\boldsymbol{h}'\boldsymbol{H}_{\mathrm{f}+\lambda\hat{\mathrm{g}}}(\boldsymbol{x}_0)\boldsymbol{h}<0(>0)$ provided that not all the elements within this Hessian vanish. However, the arguments of this quadratic form are not independent, i.e. they must satisfy $\nabla\hat{\mathrm{g}}(\boldsymbol{x}_0)'\boldsymbol{h} = 0$. Hence we must ultimately determine the sign definiteness of $\boldsymbol{h}'\boldsymbol{H}_{\mathrm{f}+\lambda\hat{\mathrm{g}}}(\boldsymbol{x}_0)\boldsymbol{h}$ subject to $\nabla\hat{\mathrm{g}}(\boldsymbol{x}_0)'\boldsymbol{h} = 0$. In this regard, theorem 9.5 (9.4) informs us that if eq. (9.6) ((9.6.1)) holds, then $\mathrm{F}(\hat{\boldsymbol{x}}_0+\boldsymbol{h})-\mathrm{F}(\hat{\boldsymbol{x}}_0)<0(>0)$ so that F has a strong local unconstrained maximum (minimum) at $\hat{\boldsymbol{x}}_0$. But, as noted earlier, this is a necessary and sufficient condition for f subject to $\hat{g} = 0$ to attain a strong local maximum (minimum) at $\hat{\boldsymbol{x}}_0$. Q.E.D.

How are we to interpret eqs. (9.6) and (9.6.1)? It is evident that both of these equations represent a sequence of signed, bordered, principal minors of the $(n+1)$st-order bordered Hessian matrix

$$\boldsymbol{H}^{\hat{g}}_{f+\lambda\hat{g}}(\boldsymbol{x}_0) = \begin{bmatrix} f_{11}+\lambda\hat{g}_{11} & f_{12}+\lambda\hat{g}_{12} & \cdots & f_{1n}+\lambda\hat{g}_{1n} & \hat{g}_1 \\ f_{21}+\lambda\hat{g}_{21} & f_{22}+\lambda\hat{g}_{22} & \cdots & f_{2n}+\lambda\hat{g}_{2n} & \hat{g}_2 \\ \vdots & \vdots & & \vdots & \vdots \\ f_{n1}+\lambda\hat{g}_{n1} & f_{n2}+\lambda\hat{g}_{n2} & \cdots & f_{nn}+\lambda\hat{g}_{nn} & \hat{g}_n \\ \hat{g}_1 & \hat{g}_2 & \cdots & \hat{g}_n & 0 \end{bmatrix}$$

(where it is to be understood that all the partial derivatives within $\boldsymbol{H}^{\hat{g}}_{f+\lambda\hat{g}}$ are evaluated at $\boldsymbol{x}_0$). For a strong local minimum, we require that each of the determinants

$$\hat{\Delta}_r = \begin{vmatrix} \boldsymbol{H}_{f+\lambda\hat{g}}(\boldsymbol{x}_0)_{rr} & \nabla\hat{g}(\boldsymbol{x}_0)_r \\ \nabla\hat{g}(\boldsymbol{x}_0)'_r & 0 \end{vmatrix}, \quad r = 2, \ldots, n,$$

have a negative sign. For a strong local maximum, the sequence of determinants $\hat{\Delta}_r$, $r = 2, \ldots, n$, should alternate in sign, beginning with a positive sign for $\hat{\Delta}_2$. Since these conditions are only sufficient and not simultaneously necessary and sufficient for a strong local constrained extremum, f subject to $\hat{g} = 0$ may still possess a strong local maximum or minimum even if some of the determinants $\hat{\Delta}_r$ vanish.

For $\boldsymbol{x} \in \mathscr{E}^2$, a sufficient condition for f subject to $\hat{g} = 0$ to attain a strong local maximum at a point interior to $\mathscr{K} \subseteq \mathscr{E}^2$ is

$$\left|\frac{\partial(f, \hat{g})}{\partial(x_1, x_2)}\right| = \begin{vmatrix} f_1 & f_2 \\ \hat{g}_1 & \hat{g}_2 \end{vmatrix} = 0$$

and

$$|\boldsymbol{H}^{\hat{g}}_{f+\lambda\hat{g}}| = \begin{vmatrix} f_{11}+\lambda\hat{g}_{11} & f_{12}+\lambda\hat{g}_{12} & \hat{g}_1 \\ f_{21}+\lambda\hat{g}_{21} & f_{22}+\lambda\hat{g}_{22} & \hat{g}_2 \\ \hat{g}_1 & \hat{g}_2 & 0 \end{vmatrix} > 0, \tag{9.6.2}$$

where $\lambda = -f_2/\hat{g}_2$, $\hat{g}_2 \neq 0$. For a strong local minimum of f subject to $\hat{g} = 0$ at such a point, it is sufficient that

$$\left|\frac{\partial(f, \hat{g})}{\partial(x_1, x_2)}\right| = \begin{vmatrix} f_1 & f_2 \\ \hat{g}_1 & \hat{g}_2 \end{vmatrix} = 0$$

and

$$|\boldsymbol{H}^{\hat{g}}_{f+\lambda\hat{g}}| = \begin{vmatrix} f_{11}+\lambda\hat{g}_{11} & f_{12}+\lambda\hat{g}_{12} & \hat{g}_1 \\ f_{21}+\lambda\hat{g}_{21} & f_{22}+\lambda\hat{g}_{22} & \hat{g}_2 \\ \hat{g}_1 & \hat{g}_2 & 0 \end{vmatrix} < 0, \tag{9.6.3}$$

where again $\lambda = -\mathrm{f}_2/\hat{\mathrm{g}}_2$, $\hat{\mathrm{g}}_2 \neq 0$. In either instance the coordinates of the implied constrained optimum point are provided by eq. (9.4.1).

We note briefly that if $|\partial(\mathrm{f}, \hat{\mathrm{g}})/\partial(x_i, x_n)|_{x_0} = 0$, $i = 1, \ldots, n-1$, and $\boldsymbol{h}'\boldsymbol{H}_{\mathrm{f}+\lambda\hat{\mathrm{g}}}(\boldsymbol{x}_0)\boldsymbol{h} \leqslant 0(\geqslant 0)$ for all $\boldsymbol{h}$ satisfying $\nabla\hat{\mathrm{g}}(\boldsymbol{x}_0)'\boldsymbol{h} = 0$, then we have a weakened sufficient or strengthened necessary condition for f subject to $\hat{\mathrm{g}} = 0$ to have a local maximum (minimum) at $\boldsymbol{x}_0 \in \mathscr{K} \subseteq \mathscr{E}^n$.

We now consider two special cases of eqs. (9.6) and (9.6.1). First, if f is non-linear but $\hat{\mathrm{g}} = 0$ is linear in $\boldsymbol{x}$, then $\mathrm{g}_{ij} = 0$, $i, j = 1, \ldots, n$. Hence, eqs. (9.6) and (9.6.1) become, respectively,

$$\Delta_r = (-1)^r \begin{vmatrix} \boldsymbol{H}_{\mathrm{f}}(\boldsymbol{x}_0)_{rr} & \nabla\hat{\mathrm{g}}(\boldsymbol{x}_0)_r \\ \nabla\hat{\mathrm{g}}(\boldsymbol{x}_0)'_r & 0 \end{vmatrix} > 0, \quad r = 2, \ldots, n, \tag{9.6.4}$$

$$\Delta_r = \begin{vmatrix} \boldsymbol{H}_{\mathrm{f}}(\boldsymbol{x}_0)_{rr} & \nabla\hat{\mathrm{g}}(\boldsymbol{x}_0)_r \\ \nabla\hat{\mathrm{g}}(\boldsymbol{x}_0)'_r & 0 \end{vmatrix} < 0, \quad r = 2, \ldots, n. \tag{9.6.5}$$

Next, for f linear but $\hat{\mathrm{g}} = 0$ non-linear in $\boldsymbol{x}$, $\mathrm{f}_{ij} = 0$, $i, j = 1, \ldots, n$. In this instance eqs. (9.6) and (9.6.1) simplify, respectively, to

$$\Delta_r = (-1)^r \begin{vmatrix} \lambda\boldsymbol{H}_{\hat{\mathrm{g}}}(\boldsymbol{x}_0)_{rr} & \nabla\hat{\mathrm{g}}(\boldsymbol{x}_0)_r \\ \nabla\hat{\mathrm{g}}(\boldsymbol{x}_0)'_r & 0 \end{vmatrix} > 0, \quad r = 2, \ldots, n, \tag{9.6.6}$$

$$\Delta_r = \begin{vmatrix} \lambda\boldsymbol{H}_{\hat{\mathrm{g}}}(\boldsymbol{x}_0)_{rr} & \nabla\hat{\mathrm{g}}(\boldsymbol{x}_0)_r \\ \nabla\hat{\mathrm{g}}(\boldsymbol{x}_0)'_r & 0 \end{vmatrix} < 0, \quad r = 2, \ldots, n, \tag{9.6.7}$$

since $\boldsymbol{H}_{\lambda\hat{\mathrm{g}}} = \lambda\boldsymbol{H}_{\hat{\mathrm{g}}}$.

In actual practice how may we obtain an extremum of the real-valued function $y = \mathrm{f}(\boldsymbol{x})$ subject to $\hat{\mathrm{g}}(\boldsymbol{x}) = 0$, $\boldsymbol{x} \in \mathscr{E}^n$? The process is illustrated by the following set of examples.

Example 9.3. Does the real-valued function $y = \mathrm{f}(\boldsymbol{x}) = 2x_1^2 + x_2^2$ possess an extremum over $\mathscr{E}^2$ when x_1, x_2 are connected by a side relation of the form $\hat{\mathrm{g}}(\boldsymbol{x}) = 6 - x_1 - x_2 = 0$? From $\hat{\mathrm{g}} = 0$ we obtain $x_2 = \zeta(x_1) = 6 - x_1$. Forming $\mathrm{F}(x_1) = \mathrm{f}(x_1, \zeta(x_1)) = 2x_1^2 + (6 - x_1)^2$ and differentiating yields $\mathrm{F}' = 6x_1 - 12$. Upon setting $\mathrm{F}' = 0$ we obtain the critical value $x_1 = 2$. Hence, $x_2 = 6 - x_1 = 4$. Since $\mathrm{F}'' = 6 > 0$, F attains a strong local unconstrained minimum at $x_1^0 = 2$, and thus the constrained minimum of f is at $\boldsymbol{x}'_0 = (2, 4)$ with $\mathrm{f}(\boldsymbol{x}_0) = 24$ (compared with an unconstrained minimum of $\mathrm{f}(0, 0) = 0$, as the reader may easily verify).

This example indicates that if we can solve for $x_2 = \zeta(x_1)$ given $\hat{\mathrm{g}}(\boldsymbol{x}) = 0$, we may transform a constrained optimization problem into one without any restraint on x_1, x_2 by finding the extremes of $F(x_1) = f(x_1, \zeta(x_1)$. While this procedure is quite straightforward from a computational viewpoint, it depends upon our being able to find ζ. However, this may at times be a difficult, if not impossible, task. The next three examples demonstrate that we may find the extremes of f subject to $\hat{g} = 0$ without first solving for ζ. In this regard, we shall rely upon the necessary as well as the sufficient condition developed above.

Example 9.4. Find an extremum of the real-valued function $y = f(\boldsymbol{x}) = x_1^2 + 2x_1x_2 + 3x_2$ subject to $\hat{g}(\boldsymbol{x}) = 1 - 3x_1 - x_2 = 0$ over $\mathscr{E}^2$. Employing the necessary condition for a constrained extremum (eq. (9.4.1)) we have

$$\begin{vmatrix} f_1 & f_2 \\ \hat{g}_1 & \hat{g}_2 \end{vmatrix} = \begin{vmatrix} 2x_1 + 2x_2 & 2x_1 + 3 \\ -3 & -1 \end{vmatrix} = 0 \quad \text{or} \quad 4x_1 - 2x_2 + 9 = 0,$$
$$1 - 3x_1 - x_2 = 0.$$

Solving this system simultaneously yields $\boldsymbol{x}_0' = (-0.7, 3.1)$. Additionally, our sufficient condition for a constrained extremum yields (since $\hat{g} = 0$ is linear)

$$|\boldsymbol{H}_f^{\hat{g}}(\boldsymbol{x}_0)| = \begin{vmatrix} 2 & 2 & -3 \\ 2 & 0 & -1 \\ -3 & -1 & 0 \end{vmatrix} = 10 > 0.$$

Hence, from eq. (9.6.3), f has a strong local constrained maximum at the critical point $\boldsymbol{x}_0$ since the bordered Hessian determinant of f is positive.

Example 9.5. Does the real-valued function $y = f(\boldsymbol{x}) = x_1^2 + x_2^2$ subject to $\hat{g}(\boldsymbol{x}) = 3 - x_1^2 - x_2 = 0$ attain an extremum over $\mathscr{E}^2$? From eq. (9.4.1) or

$$\begin{vmatrix} f_1 & f_2 \\ \hat{g}_1 & \hat{g}_2 \end{vmatrix} = \begin{vmatrix} 2x_1 & 2x_2 \\ -2x_1 & -1 \end{vmatrix} = 2x_1(2x_2 - 1) = 0,$$
$$3 - x_1^2 - x_2 = 0$$

we obtain the critical points $\boldsymbol{x}_0' = (0, 3)$, $\boldsymbol{x}_1' = (\sqrt{\tfrac{5}{2}}, \tfrac{1}{2})$, and $\boldsymbol{x}_2' = (-\sqrt{\tfrac{5}{2}}, \tfrac{1}{2})$. Do these points give rise to constrained extrema? To answer this question let us look to our sufficient condition for a constrained maximum or minimum of f. That is, we must determine the sign of

$$|\boldsymbol{H}_{f+\lambda\hat{g}}^{\hat{g}}| = \begin{vmatrix} f_{11} + \lambda\hat{g}_{11} & f_{12} + \lambda\hat{g}_{12} & \hat{g}_1 \\ f_{21} + \lambda\hat{g}_{21} & f_{22} + \lambda\hat{g}_{22} & \hat{g}_2 \\ \hat{g}_1 & \hat{g}_2 & 0 \end{vmatrix} = \begin{vmatrix} 2 - 4x_2 & 0 & -2x_1 \\ 0 & 2 & -1 \\ -2x_1 & -1 & 0 \end{vmatrix}$$
$$= -2 + 4x_2 - 8x_1^2,$$

where $\lambda = +2x_2$. Since the value of this expression is 10 at $\boldsymbol{x}_0$ and -20

at $\boldsymbol{x}_1$, $\boldsymbol{x}_2$, it is easily seen from eqs. (9.6.2) and (9.6.3) respectively that f assumes a strong local constrained maximum at $\boldsymbol{x}_0$ and a strong local constrained minimum at $\boldsymbol{x}_1$, $\boldsymbol{x}_2$.

Example 9.6. Determine an extremum of the real-valued function $y = \mathrm{f}(\boldsymbol{x}) = x_1 x_3 + 3x_2^2$ when the variables are connected by a side relation of the form $g(\boldsymbol{x}) = x_1 + 4x_2 + 3x_3 = 2$. From eq. (9.4),

$$\begin{vmatrix} \mathrm{f}_1 & \mathrm{f}_3 \\ \hat{\mathrm{g}}_1 & \hat{\mathrm{g}}_3 \end{vmatrix} = \begin{vmatrix} x_3 & x_1 \\ -1 & -3 \end{vmatrix} = -3x_3 + x_1 = 0,$$

$$\begin{vmatrix} \mathrm{f}_2 & \mathrm{f}_3 \\ \hat{\mathrm{g}}_2 & \hat{\mathrm{g}}_3 \end{vmatrix} = \begin{vmatrix} 6x_2 & x_1 \\ -4 & -3 \end{vmatrix} = -18x_2 + 4x_1 = 0,$$

$$2 - x_1 - 4x_2 - 3x_3 = 0.$$

Solving this system simultaneously yields $\boldsymbol{x}_0' = (\frac{9}{13}, \frac{2}{13}, \frac{3}{13})$. In addition,

$$\hat{\Delta}_2 = \begin{vmatrix} \boldsymbol{H}_\mathrm{f}(\boldsymbol{x}_0)_{22} & \nabla\hat{\mathrm{g}}(\boldsymbol{x}_0)_2 \\ \nabla\hat{\mathrm{g}}(\boldsymbol{x}_0)_2' & 0 \end{vmatrix} = \begin{vmatrix} 0 & 0 & -1 \\ 0 & 6 & -4 \\ -1 & -4 & 0 \end{vmatrix} = -6,$$

$$\hat{\Delta}_3 = \begin{vmatrix} \boldsymbol{H}_\mathrm{f}(\boldsymbol{x}_0)_{33} & \nabla\hat{\mathrm{g}}(\boldsymbol{x}_0)_3 \\ \nabla\hat{\mathrm{g}}(\boldsymbol{x}_0)_3' & 0 \end{vmatrix} = \begin{vmatrix} 0 & 0 & 1 & -1 \\ 0 & 6 & 0 & -4 \\ 1 & 0 & 0 & -3 \\ -1 & -4 & -3 & 0 \end{vmatrix} = -4.$$

Hence, from eq. (9.6.5), f subject to $\hat{\mathrm{g}} = 0$ has a strong local minimum at $\boldsymbol{x}_0$.

9.2. Geometric interpretation of the sufficient condition

To make our analysis in this section as transparent as possible, let us assume that $\boldsymbol{x} \in \mathscr{E}^2$. We noted above that for f to have a strong local extremum subject to $\hat{\mathrm{g}} = 0$ at a point $\boldsymbol{x} \in \mathscr{E}^2$ where $|\partial(\mathrm{f}, \hat{\mathrm{g}})/\partial(x_1, x_2)| = 0$, it was sufficient that $|\boldsymbol{H}^{\hat{\mathrm{g}}}_{\mathrm{f}+\lambda\hat{\mathrm{g}}}| \neq 0$. In terms of the properties of the functions f and $\hat{\mathrm{g}} = 0$, how may we interpret this inequality?

Expanding $|\boldsymbol{H}^{\hat{\mathrm{g}}}_{\mathrm{f}+\lambda\hat{\mathrm{g}}}|$ we obtain

$$\begin{vmatrix} \mathrm{f}_{11} + \lambda\hat{\mathrm{g}}_{11} & \mathrm{f}_{12} + \lambda\hat{\mathrm{g}}_{12} & \hat{\mathrm{g}}_1 \\ \mathrm{f}_{21} + \lambda\hat{\mathrm{g}}_{21} & \mathrm{f}_{22} + \lambda\hat{\mathrm{g}}_{22} & \hat{\mathrm{g}}_2 \\ \hat{\mathrm{g}}_1 & \hat{\mathrm{g}}_2 & 0 \end{vmatrix} = -(\mathrm{f}_{11} + \lambda\hat{\mathrm{g}}_{11})\hat{\mathrm{g}}_2^2$$

$$+ 2(\mathrm{f}_{12} + \lambda\hat{\mathrm{g}}_{12})\hat{\mathrm{g}}_1\hat{\mathrm{g}}_2 - (\mathrm{f}_{22} + \lambda\hat{\mathrm{g}}_{22})\hat{\mathrm{g}}_1^2.$$

By hypothesis

$$|\partial(\mathrm{f}, \hat{\mathrm{g}})/\partial(x_1, x_2)| = 0 \quad \text{or} \quad \hat{\mathrm{g}}_1 = \hat{\mathrm{g}}_2(\mathrm{f}_1/\mathrm{f}_2).$$

A substitution of this expression into the above determinant yields

$$\begin{aligned}|\boldsymbol{H}^{\hat{g}}_{f+\lambda\hat{g}}| = & -(\hat{g}_2/f_2)\,[(f_{11}f_2^2-2f_{12}f_1f_2+f_{22}f_1^2)\\ & +\lambda(\hat{g}_{11}f_2^2-2\hat{g}_{12}f_1f_2+\hat{g}_{22}f_1^2)].\end{aligned} \tag{9.9}$$

Let us now consider the rate of change of the slope of the contour $f = f^0$. Since

$$df = f_1dx_1+f_2dx_2 = 0 \quad \text{or} \quad dx_2/dx_1 = -f_1/f_2,$$

it follows that

$$\begin{aligned}\left(\frac{d^2x_2}{dx_1^2}\right)^{f=f^0} &= -\frac{d}{dx_1}\left(\frac{f_1}{f_2}\right) = -\left[\frac{\partial}{\partial x_1}\left(\frac{f_1}{f_2}\right)+\frac{\partial}{\partial x_2}\left(\frac{f_1}{f_2}\right)\frac{dx_2}{dx_1}\right] \\ &= -\frac{1}{f_2^3}(f_{11}f_2^2-2f_{12}f_1f_2+f_{22}f_1^2).\end{aligned} \tag{9.10}$$

A similar calculation for $\hat{g} = \hat{g}^0$ yields

$$\left(\frac{d^2x_2}{dx_1^2}\right)^{\hat{g}=\hat{g}^0} = -\frac{1}{\hat{g}_2^3}\,(\hat{g}_{11}\hat{g}_2^2-2\hat{g}_{12}\hat{g}_1\hat{g}_2+\hat{g}_{22}\hat{g}_1^2) \tag{9.11}$$

or, for $\hat{g}_1 = \hat{g}_2(f_1/f_2)$,

$$\left(\frac{d^2x_2}{dx_1^2}\right)^{\hat{g}=\hat{g}^0} = -\frac{1}{\hat{g}_2f_2^2}\,(\hat{g}_{11}f_2^2-2\hat{g}_{12}f_1f_2+\hat{g}_{22}f_1^2). \tag{9.11.1}$$

In view of eqs. (9.10) and (9.11.1), it is easily demonstrated that eq. (9.9) becomes, for $\lambda = -f_2/\hat{g}_2$,

$$|\boldsymbol{H}^{\hat{g}}_{f+\lambda\hat{g}}| = f_2\hat{g}_2^2\left[\left(\frac{d^2x_2}{dx_1^2}\right)^{f=f^0}-\left(\frac{d^2x_2}{dx_1^2}\right)^{\hat{g}=\hat{g}^0}\right]. \tag{9.12}$$

A moment's reflection concerning the sign of d^2x_2/dx_1^2 indicates that if it is negative, a curve in $\mathscr{E}^2$ becomes steeper as x_1 gets larger (fig. 9.4a) while if the sign of d^2x_2/dx_1^2 is positive, the curve becomes less steep as x_1 increases (fig. 9.4b).

As is noted above, a sufficient condition for f to attain a strong local maximum (minimum) subject to $\hat{g} = 0$ at a point $\boldsymbol{x}_0\in\mathscr{E}^2$ where $|\partial(f,\hat{g})/\partial(x_1,x_2)|_{\boldsymbol{x}_0} = 0$ is that $|\boldsymbol{H}^{\hat{g}}_{f+\lambda\hat{g}}(\boldsymbol{x}_0)|>0(<0)$ or, from eq. (9.12),

$$\left(\frac{d^2x_2}{dx_1^2}\right)^{f=f^0}_{\boldsymbol{x}_0}-\left(\frac{d^2x_2}{dx_1^2}\right)^{\hat{g}=\hat{g}^0}_{\boldsymbol{x}_0}>0(<0), \tag{9.12.1}$$

provided that $f_2^0>0$, i.e. the rate of change of the slope of f must exceed (be less than) that of $\hat{g}$ at $\boldsymbol{x}_0$. For example, using eq. (9.12.1), let us consider the various sub-cases characterizing the attainment of a strong local constrained maximum at $\boldsymbol{x}_0$ (the reader should trace through the symmetric argument involving the conditions under which eq. (9.12.1) is negative):

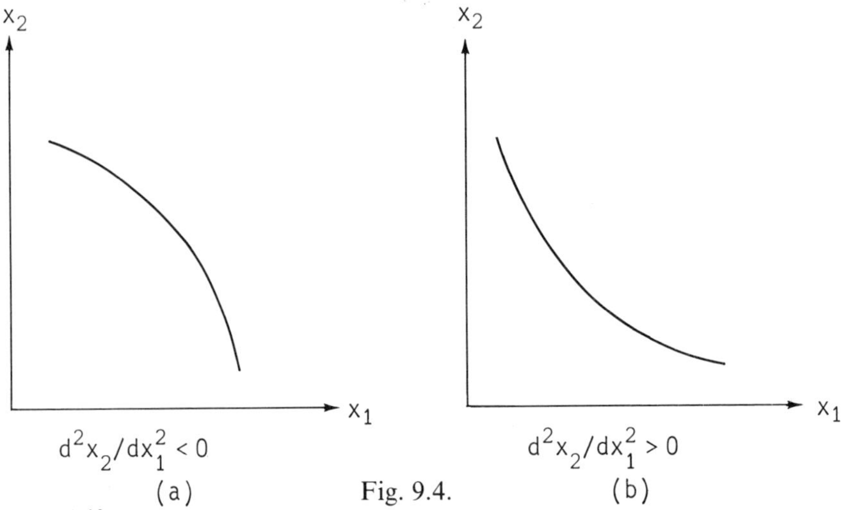

Fig. 9.4.

(a) if

$$\left(\frac{d^2x_2}{dx_1^2}\right)_{x_0}^{f=f^0} \geqslant 0, \qquad \left(\frac{d^2x_2}{dx_1^2}\right)_{x_0}^{\hat{g}=\hat{g}^0} < 0,$$

then clearly their difference is positive and the sufficient condition for a constrained maximum of f at $\boldsymbol{x}_0$ holds (fig. 9.5a, b);

(b) if

$$\left(\frac{d^2x_2}{dx_1^2}\right)_{x_0}^{f=f^0} > 0, \qquad \left(\frac{d^2x_2}{dx_1^2}\right)_{x_0}^{\hat{g}=\hat{g}^0} = 0,$$

the difference between these second derivatives is also positive at $\boldsymbol{x}_0$ and thus condition (9.12.1) is met (fig. 9.5c);

(c) if

$$\left(\frac{d^2x_2}{dx_1^2}\right)_{x_0}^{f=f^0} > \left(\frac{d^2x_2}{dx_1^2}\right)_{x_0}^{\hat{g}=\hat{g}^0} > 0,$$

i.e. both f, $\hat{g} = 0$ become less steep as x_1 increases but the slope of f changes slightly faster than that of $\hat{g} = 0$ at $\boldsymbol{x}_0$, their difference is positive and eq. (9.12.1) again holds (fig. 9.5d);

(d) if

$$\left(\frac{d^2x_2}{dx_1^2}\right)_{x_0}^{\hat{g}=\hat{g}^0} < \left(\frac{d^2x_2}{dx_1^2}\right)_{x_0}^{f=f^0} < 0,$$

i.e. both f, $\hat{g} = 0$ become steeper as x_1 increases but the slope of $\hat{g} = 0$ changes faster than that of f at $\boldsymbol{x}_0$, the sufficient condition for a constrained maximum is fulfilled (fig. 9.5e).

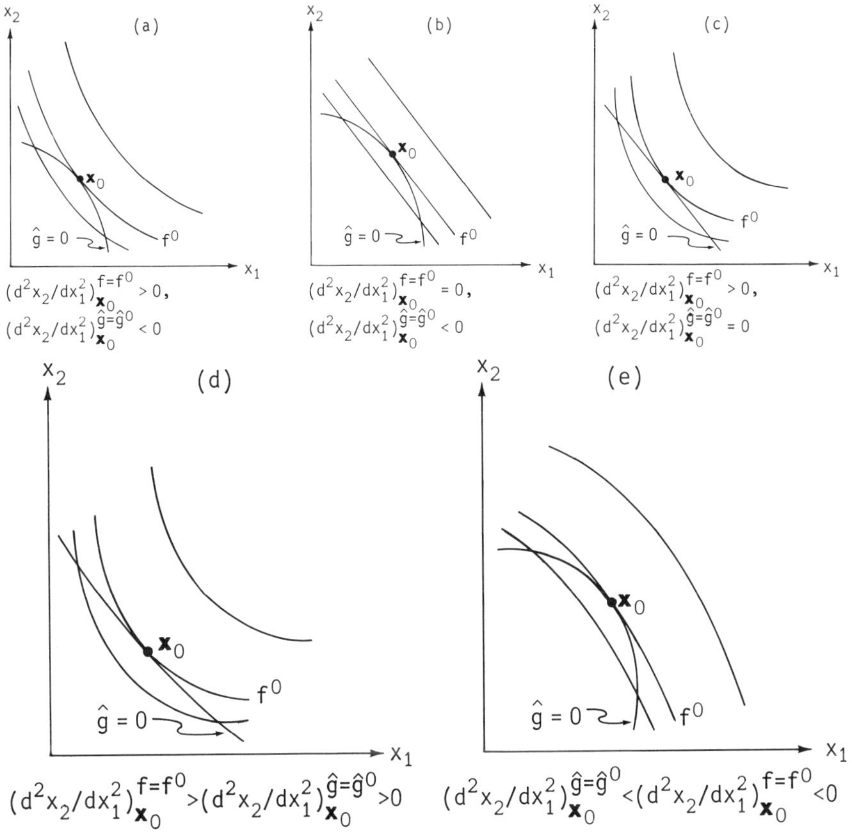

Fig. 9.5.

Note that in each instance, as we move along the constraint, we encounter successively higher level curves of f, finally reaching the maximum of f at a point of tangency between f and $\hat{g} = 0$ at $\boldsymbol{x}_0$.

9.3. The technique of Lagrange

In this section we shall develop an alternative and somewhat more flexible procedure for determining the extremes of a real-valued function whose arguments are connected by an equality constraint. We noted previously that if the real-valued function $y = f(\boldsymbol{x})$, $\boldsymbol{x} \in \mathscr{E}^n$, assumes a local extremum subject to $\hat{g}(\boldsymbol{x}) = 0$ at a point $\boldsymbol{x}_0$ interior to an open region $\mathscr{K} \subseteq \mathscr{E}^n$, then, from eq. (9.4),

$$f_i^0/\hat{g}_i^0 = f_n^0/\hat{g}_n^0, \quad i = 1, \ldots, n-1. \tag{9.4.2}$$

What this equality implies is that, at $\boldsymbol{x}_0$, f_i^0 is proportioned to $\hat{g}_i^0$, $i = 1, \ldots, n-1$, while f_n^0 is proportioned to $\hat{g}_n^0$. In this regard we state

THEOREM 9.7 (a necessary condition). *Let the real-valued functions* $y = f(\boldsymbol{x})$, $\hat{g}(\boldsymbol{x}) = 0$, $\boldsymbol{x} \in \mathscr{E}^n$, *be defined over an open region* $\mathscr{K} \subseteq \mathscr{E}^n$ *and differentiable throughout some spherical* δ*-neighborhood of the point* $\boldsymbol{x}_0 \in \mathscr{K}$. *If* f *has a local extremum subject to* $\hat{g} = 0$ *at* $\boldsymbol{x}_0$, *then there exists a scalar* λ^0 *such that* $\nabla f^0 + \lambda^0 \nabla \hat{g}^0 = \boldsymbol{0}$ *or*

$$f_i^0 + \lambda^0 \hat{g}_i^0 = 0, \quad i = 1, \ldots, n. \tag{9.13}$$

Proof. To determine the common factor of proportionality (λ^0) implied by eq. (9.4.2) and indicated in eq. (9.13), let us employ eqs. (9.2) and (9.3) to obtain

$$f_i^0 = -f_n^0 \zeta_i^0 = -f_n^0(-\hat{g}_i^0/\hat{g}_n^0) = -\hat{g}_i^0(-f_n^0/\hat{g}_n^0),$$
$$\hat{g}_n^0 \neq 0, \quad i = 1, \ldots, n-1.$$

If we now set $\lambda^0 = -f_n^0/\hat{g}_n^0$, the above expression becomes $f_i^0 + \lambda^0 \hat{g}_i^0 = 0$, $i = 1, \ldots, n-1$. Alternatively, for $\lambda^0 = -f_i^0/\hat{g}_i^0$, $\hat{g}_i^0 \neq 0$, $f_n^0 + \lambda^0 \hat{g}_n^0 = 0$. Q.E.D.

It must be noted that in defining λ^0, either in terms of $-f_i^0/\hat{g}_i^0$ or in terms of $-f_n^0/\hat{g}_n^0$, we have tacitly been assuming that at least one of the partial derivatives of $\hat{g} = 0$ is different from zero at $\boldsymbol{x}_0$. In sum, eq. (9.4.2) may alternatively be written as system (9.13) and vice versa since theorems 9.3, and 9.7 are equivalent. Hence eq. (9.13) replaces (9.1) in system (9.4), and we have

$$\left.\begin{aligned} &f_i + \lambda \hat{g}_i = 0, \quad i = 1, \ldots, n, \\ &\hat{g} = 0. \end{aligned}\right\} \tag{9.14}$$

How might such a system of equations arise? Since the partial derivatives f_i are, respectively, proportional to $\hat{g}_i$, $i = 1, \ldots, n$, let us add to f some multiple λ of $\hat{g} = 0$. That is, we shall form the function

$$L(\boldsymbol{x}, \lambda) = f(\boldsymbol{x}) + \lambda \hat{g}(\boldsymbol{x}). \tag{9.15}$$

Note that L depends upon λ as well as $\boldsymbol{x}$. This is because λ must be 'chosen' so that eq. (9.13) holds. Then if we differentiate eq. (9.15) with respect to each of its arguments we obtain system (9.14). Here eq. (9.15) will be termed the *Lagrangian of* f while λ, the factor of proportionality, is called the *Lagrange multiplier*. The essential feature of the technique of Lagrange is that we may convert a problem involving the maximization or minimization of a function f subject to an equality constraint $\hat{g} = 0$ into one without any restraint simply by forming the Lagrangian of f, $L = f + \lambda \hat{g}$. That is, optimizing $f(\boldsymbol{x})$ subject to $\hat{g}(\boldsymbol{x}) = 0$ is equivalent to optimizing the unconstrained Lagrangian $L(\boldsymbol{x}, \lambda)$ as long as $\hat{\mathrm{g}} = 0$ is satisfied. This may be accomplished by deriving system (9.14), the simultaneous solution of which yields $\boldsymbol{x}_0, \lambda^0$. It is evident that one advantage of the technique of Lagrange over that of finding the extremes of $\mathrm{F}(\hat{\boldsymbol{x}}) = \mathrm{f}(\hat{\boldsymbol{x}}, \zeta(\hat{\boldsymbol{x}}))$ is that we do not have to solve for x_n explicitly in terms of $\hat{\boldsymbol{x}}$, $x_n = \zeta(\hat{\boldsymbol{x}})$. This discussion may be summarized as

THEOREM 9.8 (a necessary condition). *Let the real-valued functions $y = \mathrm{f}(\boldsymbol{x})$, $\hat{\mathrm{g}}(\boldsymbol{x}) = 0$, $\boldsymbol{x} \in \mathscr{E}^n$, be differentiable throughout some spherical δ-neighborhood of the point $\boldsymbol{x}_0$ contained within an open region $\mathscr{K} \subseteq \mathscr{E}^n$. If f has a local extremum subject to $\hat{\mathrm{g}} = 0$ at $\boldsymbol{x}_0$, then $L(\boldsymbol{x}, \lambda) = \mathrm{f}(\boldsymbol{x}) + \lambda \hat{\mathrm{g}}(\boldsymbol{x})$ has an unconstrained local extremum at that point and*

$$\nabla_{\boldsymbol{x}} L^0 = \nabla \mathrm{f}^0 + \lambda^0 \nabla \hat{\mathrm{g}}^0 = \mathbf{0} \quad \text{or} \quad \mathrm{f}_i^0 + \lambda^0 \hat{\mathrm{g}}_i^0 = 0, \quad i = 1, \ldots, n,$$
$$L_\lambda^0 = \hat{\mathrm{g}}^0 = 0.$$

Proof. If f attains a constrained extremum at $\boldsymbol{x}_0$, the differential of f along $\hat{\mathrm{g}} = 0$ must vanish there and thus $\mathrm{df}^0 = \nabla \mathrm{f}(\boldsymbol{x}_0)'\boldsymbol{h} = 0$. Also, since $\boldsymbol{x}$ is restricted to $\hat{\mathrm{g}}(\boldsymbol{x}) = 0$, $\mathrm{d}\hat{\mathrm{g}} = 0$ for any point $\boldsymbol{x}$ satisfying this equality and thus, at $\boldsymbol{x}_0$, $\mathrm{d}\hat{\mathrm{g}}^0 = \nabla \hat{\mathrm{g}}(\boldsymbol{x}_0)'\boldsymbol{h} = 0$. Now if $\mathrm{d}\hat{\mathrm{g}}^0$ is multiplied by some undetermined scalar λ^0 and added to df^0 we obtain

$$\mathrm{d}L^0 = \mathrm{df}^0 + \lambda^0 \mathrm{d}\hat{\mathrm{g}}^0 = (\nabla \mathrm{f}(\boldsymbol{x}_0) + \lambda^0 \nabla \hat{\mathrm{g}}(\boldsymbol{x}_0))'\boldsymbol{h}.$$

From $\mathrm{d}\hat{\mathrm{g}}^0 = 0$ we obtain

$$h_n = \sum_{i=1}^{n-1} (-\hat{\mathrm{g}}_i^0/\hat{\mathrm{g}}_n^0) h_i, \quad \hat{\mathrm{g}}_n^0 \neq 0,$$

where the h_i, $i = 1, \ldots, n-1$, may be taken to be arbitrary (by the implicit function theorem). In view of this representation of h_n the above expression for $\mathrm{d}L^0$ becomes

$$\mathrm{d}L^0 = \sum_{i=1}^{n-1} \left[(\mathrm{f}_i^0 + \lambda^0 \hat{\mathrm{g}}_i^0) + (\mathrm{f}_n^0 + \lambda^0 \hat{\mathrm{g}}_n^0)(-\hat{\mathrm{g}}_i^0/\hat{\mathrm{g}}_n^0) \right] h_i.$$

If we choose $\lambda^0 = -\mathrm{f}_n^0/\hat{\mathrm{g}}_n^0$, then

$$\mathrm{d}L^0 = \sum_{i=1}^{n-1} (\mathrm{f}_i^0 + \lambda^0 \hat{\mathrm{g}}_i^0) h_i.$$

And since the h_i, $i = 1, \ldots, n-1$, are arbitrary, $\mathrm{d}L^0 = 0$ only if $\mathrm{f}_i^0 + \lambda^0 \hat{\mathrm{g}}_i^0 = 0$, $i = 1, \ldots, n-1$. Hence a necessary condition for L to have an unconstrained local extremum at $\boldsymbol{x}_0$ is $\mathrm{f}_i^0 + \lambda^0 \hat{\mathrm{g}}_i^0 = 0$, $i = 1, \ldots, n-1$, and $\lambda^0 = -\mathrm{f}_n^0/\hat{\mathrm{g}}_n^0$(or $\mathrm{f}_n^0 + \lambda^0 \hat{\mathrm{g}}_n^0 = 0$), i.e. $\nabla \mathrm{f}^0 + \lambda^0 \nabla \hat{\mathrm{g}}^0 = \mathbf{0}$. But this is equivalent to f subject to $\hat{\mathrm{g}} = 0$ having a local extremum there also. Q.E.D.

In essence, this theorem indicates that if $\nabla \mathrm{f}'\boldsymbol{h} = 0$ for all $\boldsymbol{h}$ satisfying

$\nabla\hat{g}'\boldsymbol{h} = 0$, then ∇f must be proportional to $\nabla\hat{g}$, where the constant of proportionality is $-\lambda$. For $\boldsymbol{x}\in\mathscr{E}^2$, if f subject to $\hat{g} = 0$ has a local extremum at $\boldsymbol{x}_0\in\mathscr{K}\subseteq\mathscr{E}^2$, then

$$\left.\begin{aligned} f_1+\lambda\hat{g}_1 &= 0,\\ f_2+\lambda\hat{g}_2 &= 0,\\ \hat{g} &= 0.\end{aligned}\right\} \tag{9.14.1}$$

We next look to the development of criteria with which to distinguish a constrained maximum from that of a constrained minimum at a point where the above necessary condition holds. To this end we state

THEOREM 9.9 (a sufficient condition). *Let the real-valued functions* $y = f(\boldsymbol{x})$, $\hat{g}(\boldsymbol{x}) = 0$, $\boldsymbol{x}\in\mathscr{E}^n$, *possess continuous first- and second-order partial derivatives throughout a spherical δ-neighborhood of the point $\boldsymbol{x}_0$ contained within an open region $\mathscr{K}\subseteq\mathscr{E}^n$. Then the first- and second-order partial derivatives of* $L(\boldsymbol{x}, \lambda) = f(\boldsymbol{x})+\lambda\hat{g}(\boldsymbol{x})$ *are continuous throughout $\delta(\boldsymbol{x}_0)$ also. If* $\nabla f^0+\lambda^0\nabla\hat{g}^0 = \mathbf{0}$, $L_\lambda^0 = 0$, *and*

$$\begin{vmatrix} \boldsymbol{H}_L(\boldsymbol{x}_0, \lambda^0)_{rr} & \nabla\hat{g}(\boldsymbol{x}_0)_r \\ \nabla\hat{g}(\boldsymbol{x}_0)_r' & 0 \end{vmatrix} \neq 0, \quad r = 2, \ldots, n,$$

then L, and thus f *subject to* $\hat{g} = 0$, *has a strong local extremum at* $\boldsymbol{x}_0$. *Moreover:*

(*a*) *if*

$$\Delta_r = (-1)^r \begin{vmatrix} \boldsymbol{H}_L(\boldsymbol{x}_0, \lambda^0)_{rr} & \nabla\hat{g}(\boldsymbol{x}_0)_r \\ \nabla\hat{g}(\boldsymbol{x}_0)_r' & 0 \end{vmatrix} > 0, \quad r = 2, \ldots, n, \tag{9.16}$$

then L, and thus f *subject to* $\hat{g} = 0$, *has a strong local maximum at* $\boldsymbol{x}_0$; *but*

(*b*) *if*

$$\Delta_r = \begin{vmatrix} \boldsymbol{H}_L(\boldsymbol{x}_0, \lambda^0)_{rr} & \nabla\hat{g}(\boldsymbol{x}_0)_r \\ \nabla\hat{g}(\boldsymbol{x}_0)_r' & 0 \end{vmatrix} < 0, \quad r = 2, \ldots, n, \tag{9.16.1}$$

then L, and thus f *subject to* $\hat{g} = 0$, *has a strong local minimum at* $\boldsymbol{x}_0$.

Proof. In what follows we shall indicate the conditions under which the Lagrangian of f attains a strong local extremum at $\boldsymbol{x}_0$. From eq. (5.15.4) we may write the second-order Taylor expansion of $L(\boldsymbol{x}, \lambda)$ about $\boldsymbol{x}_0$, keeping λ^0 fixed, as

$$\begin{aligned} L(\boldsymbol{x}_0+\boldsymbol{h}, \lambda^0) = {} & L(\boldsymbol{x}_0, \lambda^0)+\nabla L(\boldsymbol{x}_0,\lambda^0)'\boldsymbol{h} \\ & +\tfrac{1}{2!}\boldsymbol{h}'\boldsymbol{H}_L(\boldsymbol{x}_0+\theta\boldsymbol{h}, \lambda^0)\boldsymbol{h}, \quad 0<\theta<1. \end{aligned} \tag{9.17}$$

By hypothesis $\nabla \mathrm{f}^0 + \lambda^0 \nabla \hat{\mathrm{g}}^0 = \mathbf{0}$. Hence eq. (9.17) may be rewritten as

$$L(\boldsymbol{x}_0+\boldsymbol{h}, \lambda^0)-L(\boldsymbol{x}_0, \lambda^0) = \tfrac{1}{2!}\, \boldsymbol{h}' \boldsymbol{H}_L(\boldsymbol{x}_0+\theta \boldsymbol{h}, \lambda^0)\boldsymbol{h}, \quad 0<\theta<1. \tag{9.17.1}$$

With the second-order partial derivatives of L continuous at $\boldsymbol{x}_0$, the right-hand side of eq. (9.17.1) approaches $\frac{1}{2!}\boldsymbol{h}'\boldsymbol{H}_L(\boldsymbol{x}_0, \lambda^0)\boldsymbol{h}$ when $\theta \to 0$ and $\| \boldsymbol{h} \| < \delta$. Hence we ultimately obtain

$$L(\boldsymbol{x}_0+\boldsymbol{h}, \lambda^0)-L(\boldsymbol{x}_0, \lambda^0) \sim \tfrac{1}{2!}\boldsymbol{h}'\boldsymbol{H}_L(\boldsymbol{x}_0, \lambda^0)\boldsymbol{h}. \tag{9.17.2}$$

Now the sign of $L(\boldsymbol{x}_0+\boldsymbol{h}, \lambda^0)-L(\boldsymbol{x}_0, \lambda^0)$ will ultimately depend upon the sign of $\boldsymbol{h}'\boldsymbol{H}_L(\boldsymbol{x}_0, \lambda^0)\boldsymbol{h}$ provided that the L^0_{ij}, $i, j = 1, \ldots, n$, are not all zero. However, the arguments of this quadratic form are not independent, i.e. we must determine the sign definiteness of $\boldsymbol{h}'\boldsymbol{H}_L(\boldsymbol{x}_0, \lambda^0)\boldsymbol{h}$ for those $\boldsymbol{h}$ satisfying $\hat{\mathrm{g}}(\boldsymbol{x}_0+\boldsymbol{h}) = 0$. But this is equivalent to determining the sign of $\boldsymbol{h}'\boldsymbol{H}_L(\boldsymbol{x}_0, \lambda^0)\boldsymbol{h}$ subject to $\nabla \hat{\mathrm{g}}(\boldsymbol{x}_0)'\boldsymbol{h} = 0$. In this light, theorem 9.5 (9.4) informs us that if eq. (9.16) ((9.16.1)) holds,

$$L(\boldsymbol{x}_0+\boldsymbol{h}, \lambda^0)-L(\boldsymbol{x}_0, \lambda^0)<0(>0)$$

so that L, and thus f subject to $\hat{\mathrm{g}} = 0$, has a strong local maximum (minimum) at $\boldsymbol{x}_0$. Q.E.D.

Here eqs. (9.16) and (9.16.1) both represent a sequence of signed, bordered, principal minors of the $(n+1)$st-order bordered Hessian matrix of the Lagrangian

$$\boldsymbol{H}_L^{\hat{\mathrm{g}}}(\boldsymbol{x}_0, \lambda^0) = \begin{bmatrix} L_{11} & L_{12} & \cdots & L_{1n} & \hat{\mathrm{g}}_1 \\ L_{21} & L_{22} & \cdots & L_{2n} & \hat{\mathrm{g}}_2 \\ \vdots & \vdots & & \vdots & \vdots \\ L_{n1} & L_{n2} & \cdots & L_{nn} & \hat{\mathrm{g}}_n \\ \hat{\mathrm{g}}_1 & \hat{\mathrm{g}}_2 & \cdots & \hat{\mathrm{g}}_n & 0 \end{bmatrix}$$

(where all partial derivatives within $\boldsymbol{H}_L^{\hat{\mathrm{g}}}$ are evaluated at $\boldsymbol{x}_0, \lambda^0$). Note that since

$$L_{ij} = \mathrm{f}_{ij}+\lambda\hat{\mathrm{g}}_{ij}, \quad i,j = 1, \ldots, n, \qquad \boldsymbol{H}^{\hat{\mathrm{g}}}_{\mathrm{f}+\lambda\hat{\mathrm{g}}} = \boldsymbol{H}_L^{\hat{\mathrm{g}}}$$

so that the results obtained here are the same as those developed above in theorem 9.6. In particular, eqs. (9.6.4)–(9.6.7) also apply for the technique of Lagrange.

Given that $\boldsymbol{x} \in \mathscr{E}^2$, a sufficient condition for f subject to $\hat{\mathrm{g}} = 0$ to possess a strong local maximum at an interior point of $\mathscr{K} \subseteq \mathscr{E}^2$ is

$$\left.\begin{aligned} \mathrm{f}_1+\lambda\hat{\mathrm{g}}_1 &= 0 \\ \mathrm{f}_2+\lambda\hat{\mathrm{g}}_2 &= 0 \\ \hat{\mathrm{g}} &= 0 \end{aligned}\right\} \quad \text{and} \quad |\boldsymbol{H}_L^{\hat{\mathrm{g}}}| = \begin{vmatrix} L_{11} & L_{12} & \hat{\mathrm{g}}_1 \\ L_{21} & L_{22} & \hat{\mathrm{g}}_2 \\ \hat{\mathrm{g}}_1 & \hat{\mathrm{g}}_2 & 0 \end{vmatrix} > 0. \tag{9.16.2}$$

For a strong local minimum of f subject to $\hat{g} = 0$ at such a point it is sufficient that

$$\left.\begin{aligned} f_1+\lambda\hat{g}_1 &= 0 \\ f_2+\lambda\hat{g}_2 &= 0 \\ \hat{g} &= 0 \end{aligned}\right\} \quad \text{and} \quad |\boldsymbol{H}_L^{\hat{g}}| = \begin{vmatrix} L_{11} & L_{12} & \hat{g}_1 \\ L_{21} & L_{22} & \hat{g}_2 \\ \hat{g}_1 & \hat{g}_2 & 0 \end{vmatrix} < 0. \tag{9.16.3}$$

We mention briefly that if $\nabla f^0+\lambda^0\nabla\hat{g}^0 = \mathbf{0}$, $\hat{g}^0 = 0$, and $\boldsymbol{h}'\boldsymbol{H}_L(\boldsymbol{x}_0, \lambda^0)\boldsymbol{h} \leqslant 0\ (\geqslant 0)$ for all $\boldsymbol{h}$ satisfying $\nabla\hat{g}(\boldsymbol{x}_0)'\boldsymbol{h} = 0$, then we have a weakened sufficient or strengthened necessary condition for f subject to $\hat{g} = 0$ to attain a local maximum (minimum) at $\boldsymbol{x}_0 \in \mathscr{K} \subseteq \mathscr{E}^n$.

Example 9.7. Let the real-valued function $y = f(\boldsymbol{x}) = 3x_1^2+x_1x_2+4x_2^2$ be defined over the entirety of $\mathscr{E}^2$. Using the technique of Lagrange, determine whether or not f has an extremum over its domain when x_1, x_2 are connected by $3x_1+x_2 = 6$. We first find

$$L(\boldsymbol{x}, \lambda) = f(\boldsymbol{x})+\lambda\hat{g}(\boldsymbol{x}) = 3x_1^2+x_1x_2+4x_2^2+\lambda(6-3x_1-x_2).$$

Then

$$\begin{aligned} L_1 &= 6x_1+x_2-3\lambda = 0, \qquad L_2 = x_1+8x_2-\lambda = 0, \\ L_\lambda &= 6-3x_1-x_2 = 0. \end{aligned}$$

Solving this system simultaneously for x_1, x_2, and λ yields $\boldsymbol{x}_0' = (1.92, 0.24)$, $\lambda^0 = 3.92$. Also, since the constraint is linear,

$$|\boldsymbol{H}_L^{\hat{g}}(\boldsymbol{x}_0, \lambda^0)| = |\boldsymbol{H}_f^{\hat{g}}(\boldsymbol{x}_0, \lambda^0)| = \begin{vmatrix} 6 & 1 & -3 \\ 1 & 8 & -1 \\ -3 & -1 & 0 \end{vmatrix} = -72 < 0,$$

and thus f has a strong local minimum subject to $\hat{g} = 0$ at $\boldsymbol{x}_0$.

Example 9.8. Using the Lagrange multiplier technique, determine whether or not the real-valued function $y = f(\boldsymbol{x}) = 2x_1+x_2+6$ subject to $x_1+2x_2^2 = 3$ attains an extremum over $\mathscr{E}^2$. From

$$L(\boldsymbol{x}, \lambda) = 2x_1+x_2+6+\lambda(3-x_1-2x_2^2)$$

we find

$$L_1 = 2-\lambda = 0, \quad L_2 = 1-4\lambda x_2 = 0, \quad L_\lambda = 3-x_1-2x_2^2 = 0,$$

which yields $\boldsymbol{x}_0' = (2.97, 0.13)$, $\lambda^0 = 2$. Since f is linear,

$$|\boldsymbol{H}_L^{\hat{g}}(\boldsymbol{x}_0, \lambda^0)| = |\boldsymbol{H}_{\lambda\hat{g}}^{\hat{g}}(\boldsymbol{x}_0, \lambda^0)| = \begin{vmatrix} 0 & 0 & -1 \\ 0 & -4\lambda & -4x_2 \\ -1 & -4x_2 & 0 \end{vmatrix} = 4\lambda = 8 > 0,$$

so that f has a strong local constrained maximum at $\boldsymbol{x}_0$.

Example 9.9. Does the real-valued function $y = \mathrm{f}(\boldsymbol{x}) = 3x_1 + 4x_3 - x_1^2 - x_2^2$ subject to $x_1 + x_2 + x_3 = 6$ attain an extremum throughout $\mathscr{E}^3$? From

$$L(\boldsymbol{x}, \lambda) = 3x_1 + 4x_3 - x_1^2 - x_2^2 + \lambda(6 - x_1 - x_2 - x_3)$$

we obtain

$$L_1 = 3 - 2x_1 - \lambda = 0, \quad L_2 = -2x_2 - \lambda = 0, \quad L_3 = 4 - \lambda = 0,$$
$$L_\lambda = 6 - x_1 - x_2 - x_3 = 0,$$

and thus $\boldsymbol{x}_0' = (-\frac{1}{2}, -2, \frac{17}{2})$, $\lambda^0 = 4$. Additionally,

$$\begin{vmatrix} \boldsymbol{H}_L(\boldsymbol{x}_0, \lambda^0)_{22} & \nabla\hat{\mathrm{g}}(\boldsymbol{x}_0)_2 \\ \nabla\hat{\mathrm{g}}(\boldsymbol{x}_0)_2' & 0 \end{vmatrix} = \begin{vmatrix} -2 & 0 & -1 \\ 0 & -2 & -1 \\ -1 & -1 & 0 \end{vmatrix} = 4 > 0,$$

$$\begin{vmatrix} \boldsymbol{H}_L(\boldsymbol{x}_0, \lambda^0)_{33} & \nabla\hat{\mathrm{g}}(\boldsymbol{x}_0)_3 \\ \nabla\hat{\mathrm{g}}(\boldsymbol{x}_0)_3' & 0 \end{vmatrix} = \begin{vmatrix} -2 & 0 & 0 & -1 \\ 0 & -2 & 0 & -1 \\ 0 & 0 & 0 & -1 \\ -1 & -1 & -1 & 0 \end{vmatrix} = -4 < 0.$$

Since the indicated bordered principal minors of the bordered Hessian of the Lagrangian alternate in sign, the first being positive, we conclude that f has a strong local constrained maximum at $\boldsymbol{x}_0$.

9.4. Interpretation of the Lagrange multiplier

As indicated above, a necessary condition for f to attain an extremum subject to $\hat{\mathrm{g}} = 0$ is that $\mathrm{f}_i + \lambda\hat{\mathrm{g}}_i = 0$, $i = 1, \ldots, n$, $\hat{\mathrm{g}} = 0$. Furthermore, if this system of equations is solved simultaneously, we obtain $\boldsymbol{x}_0$, λ^0, and thus $\mathrm{f}(\boldsymbol{x}_0) = \mathrm{f}^0$. The problem which we shall now look to is as follows. What is the effect on the optimum value of f, f^0, of a small relaxation in or tightening of the constraint? To answer this question we must find and interpret λ^0. Since $\hat{\mathrm{g}} = b - \mathrm{g} = 0$, $\mathrm{d}b - \mathrm{dg} = 0$ or

$$\mathrm{d}b = \mathrm{dg} = \nabla\hat{\mathrm{g}}'\boldsymbol{h}. \tag{9.18}$$

Since we wish to find the effect of a change in b upon f^0, this last expression must be evaluated subject to the above necessary condition (theorem 9.8) holding. To accomplish this let us rewrite the equations $\mathrm{f}_i + \lambda\hat{\mathrm{g}}_i = \mathrm{f}_i - \lambda\mathrm{g}_i = 0$ as $\mathrm{g}_i = \mathrm{f}_i/\lambda$, $i = 1, \ldots, n$. A substitution of these expressions into eq. (9.18) yields

$$\mathrm{d}b = \sum_{i=1}^{n} (\mathrm{f}_i/\lambda)h_i = \frac{1}{\lambda}\nabla\mathrm{f}'\boldsymbol{h} = \frac{\mathrm{df}}{\lambda}. \tag{9.18.1}$$

Hence, $\lambda^0 = \mathrm{df}^0/\mathrm{d}b$, the total derivative of f^0 with respect to b, i.e. λ^0 is the marginal or incremental change in f^0 with respect to b. Also, λ^0 may be positive, negative, or zero (a point to which we shall turn shortly).

In a sense, we may think of λ^0 as a relative measure of the 'force' of the constraint, i.e. it indicates how tightly the constraint is binding. For instance, if f^0 represents the strong local maximum value of f subject to $\hat{g} = 0$ (the reader is asked to trace through the symmetric argument involving the minimization of f subject to $\hat{g} = 0$) and:

(a) if $\lambda^0 > 0$, a unit increase in b is positively valued since one obtains a higher maximum value of the objective function f. In fact, the increment in f^0 is exactly equal to λ^0 since $df = \lambda^0(1) > 0$. Here λ^0 may be interpreted as the marginal gain in f^0 due to a one-unit relaxation in the constraint. If b is decreased by one unit, then f must concomitantly decrease to a new optimum level, with the amount of the decrease in f^0 being determined by the magnitude of λ^0 since $df = \lambda^0(-1) < 0$. Thus λ^0 may be conceived of as the marginal cost, in terms of f^0, of a tightening of the constraint.

(b) if $\lambda^0 < 0$, a unit decrease in b is now positively valued, i.e. it increases the optimal value of the objective function. In this instance the marginal gain in f^0 due to a tightening of the constraint by one unit is determined by the value of λ^0 as $df^0 = \lambda^0(-1) > 0$. If b is increased by one unit, the marginal cost, in terms of f^0, of a loosening of the constraint is $df^0 = \lambda^0(1) < 0$ since, in this case, the maximum value of the objective function decreases.

(c) if $\lambda^0 = 0$, any incremental change in b has absolutely no effect upon the optimal value of f, f^0, and thus the constraint is not binding. That is, optimizing f subject to $\hat{g} = 0$ leads to the same critical point $\boldsymbol{x}_0$ as optimizing f alone. In this regard we state

DEFINITION 9.5. *The constraint $\hat{g} = 0$ is said to be degenerate if the maximum or minimum of* f *subject to $\hat{g} = 0$ is the same as the maximum or minimum of* f *subject to no restraint.*

In the special case where $\lambda^0 \neq 0$ and $db = \pm 1$, λ^0 will be termed the *marginal imputed value* of the constraint. That is, given that f^0 depicts a strong local maximum of f subject to $\hat{g} = 0$,

DEFINITION 9.6. *The marginal imputed value of the constraint, λ^0, is: (a) for $\lambda^0 > 0$, the minimum reduction (maximum increase) in f^0 precipitated by a one-unit decrease (increase) in b; (b) for $\lambda^0 < 0$, the maximum increase (minimum reduction) in f^0 resulting from a one-unit decrease (increase) in b.*

Alternatively, λ^0 may be referred to as a *shadow price* since, for $\lambda^0 > 0$, an extra unit of b is worth, at most, λ^0 units of f; while for $\lambda^0 < 0$, one would be willing to pay up to λ^0 units of f for the withdrawal of a unit of b. In sum, λ^0 is a measure of the infinitesimal change in f^0 with respect to a small relaxation in or tightening of the constraint $\hat{g} = 0$.

Example 9.10. In example 9.8 we found that f assumes a strong local constrained maximum at $\boldsymbol{x}_0' = (2.97, 0.13)$ with $\lambda^0 = 2$ and $f(\boldsymbol{x}_0) = f^0 = 12.07$. If we tighten the indicated constraint by one unit ($db = -1$) so that we now seek to find the strong local maximum of f subject to $x_1 + 2x_2^2 = 2$, what is the effect of this action upon f^0? One approach in answering this question would be to form the Lagrangian of f using this new constraint and then, from the above necessary condition, solve for the implied values of x_1, x_2, and λ. Then our new constrained maximum could readily be computed from f. However, our previous discussion allows us to circumvent this procedure. That is, since $df^0 = \lambda^0\, db = 2(-1) = -2$, the maximum value of f subject to $x_1 + 2x_2^2 = 2$ is $f^0 + df^0 = 10.07$. If the original constraint is changed to $x_1 + 2x_2^2 = 6$ (here we are relaxing $\hat{g} = b - g = 0$ by three units), $df^0 = \lambda^0 db = 2(3) = 6$, and thus the new constrained maximum of f is $f^0 + df^0 = 18.07$.

9.5. The Lagrangian transpose

In the previous sections we endeavored to locate an extreme value of the real-valued function $y = f(\boldsymbol{x})$ when its arguments were not free or independent variables but connected by a side relation of the form $\hat{g}(\boldsymbol{x}) = 0$. We shall refer to this undertaking as the solution of the *primal* problem. Let us now reverse the role of f and $\hat{g} = 0$, i.e. we shall attempt to solve the *transposed* problem, namely, that of finding an extremum of $g(\boldsymbol{x})$ subject to $y - f(\boldsymbol{x}) = 0$ or simply $\hat{f} = 0$. In this regard, each of the functions f, g has a dual role—each can serve as the function to be optimized or as the constraint. (Note that the transpose of the transposed problem is the primal problem itself.) For instance, if $y = f(\boldsymbol{x})$, $\boldsymbol{x} \in \mathscr{E}^2$, has a strong local maximum subject to $\hat{g} = 0$, then this extremum occurs where $\hat{g} = 0$ is tangent to a level curve of f (point A of fig. 9.6a). Here $\hat{g} = 0$ represents a fixed curve in some region $\mathscr{K} \subseteq \mathscr{E}^2$ while a whole family of contours of f is indicated since, as we move along $\hat{g} = 0$, we seek to reach the highest attainable level curve of f. If we now consider the transpose of this problem, $\hat{f} = 0$ is taken to be fixed in $\mathscr{K}$ (i.e. it now acts as a constraint on the behavior of x_1, x_2), wherein a whole family of level curves of g appears since we must now move along $\hat{f} = 0$ so as to reach a point of tangency between a level curve of g and $\hat{f} = 0$ (see point B of fig. 9.6b). In this case g is minimized subject to $\hat{f} = 0$. In sum, maximizing (minimizing) f subject to $\hat{g} = 0$ is the transpose of minimizing (maximizing) g subject to $\hat{f} = 0$. These observations may be summarized as

THEOREM 9.10 (a necessary condition). *Let the real-valued functions $y = f(\boldsymbol{x})$, $g(\boldsymbol{x}) = b$, $\boldsymbol{x} \in \mathscr{E}^n$, be defined over an open region $\mathscr{K} \subseteq \mathscr{E}^n$ and differentiable*

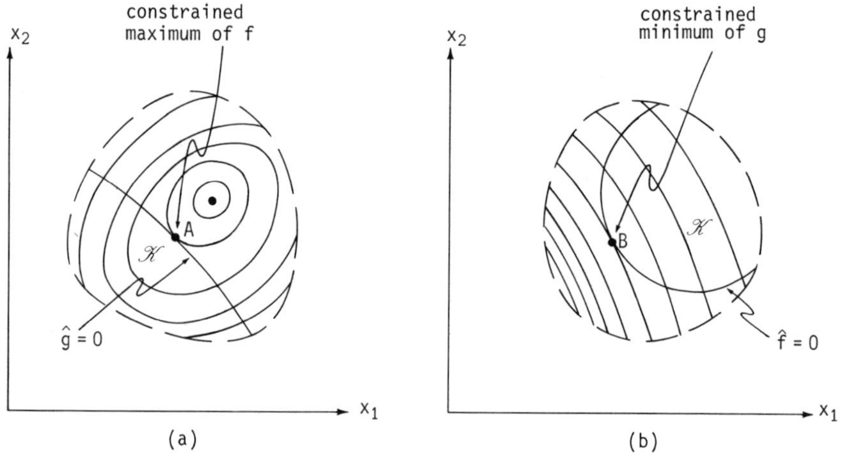

Fig. 9.6.

throughout some spherical δ-neighborhood of the point $\boldsymbol{x}_0 \in \mathscr{K}$. *If* f *has an extremum subject to* $\hat{g} = 0$ *or* g *has an extremum subject to* $\hat{f} = 0$ *at* $\boldsymbol{x}_0$, *then*

$$\left| \frac{\partial(\hat{f}, \hat{g})}{\partial(x_i, x_n)} \right|_{\boldsymbol{x}_0} = \begin{vmatrix} \hat{f}_i^0 & \hat{f}_n^0 \\ \hat{g}_i^0 & \hat{g}_n^0 \end{vmatrix} = 0 \text{ or } \frac{\hat{f}_i^0}{\hat{f}_n^0} = \frac{\hat{g}_i^0}{\hat{g}_n^0}, \quad i = 1, \ldots, n-1.$$

Proof. If from either $\hat{f} = 0$ or $\hat{g} = 0$ we solve for x_n in terms of

$$\hat{\boldsymbol{x}}' = (x_1, \ldots, x_{n-1}), \qquad x_n = \zeta(\hat{\boldsymbol{x}})$$

(the implicit function theorem above provides the conditions under which ζ exists), then, at $\boldsymbol{x}_0$,

$$\left. \begin{aligned} \hat{f}_i^0 + \hat{f}_n^0 \zeta_i(\hat{\boldsymbol{x}}_0) &= 0 \\ \hat{g}_i^0 + \hat{g}_n^0 \zeta_i(\hat{\boldsymbol{x}}_0) &= 0 \end{aligned} \right\} \quad i = 1, \ldots, n-1.$$

Now, whether f assumes an extremum subject to $\hat{g} = 0$ or g attains an extremum subject to $\hat{f} = 0$, these two implicit constraint equations must hold simultaneously. Upon multiplying the first equation by $\hat{g}_n^0$ and the second by $\hat{f}_n^0$ and equating we obtain

$$\hat{g}_n^0[\hat{f}_i^0 + \hat{f}_n^0 \zeta_i(\hat{\boldsymbol{x}}_0)] = \hat{f}_n^0[\hat{g}_i^0 + \hat{g}_n^0 \zeta_i(\hat{\boldsymbol{x}}_0)]$$

or

$$\hat{g}_n^0 \hat{f}_i^0 = \hat{f}_n^0 \hat{g}_i^0, \quad i = 1, \ldots, n-1.$$

A rearrangement of this last expression yields

$$\hat{f}_i^0 / \hat{f}_n^0 = \hat{g}_i^0 / \hat{g}_n^0, \quad i = 1, \ldots, n-1,$$

where it is assumed that not all of the partial derivatives of $\hat{f}$, $\hat{g}$ are simultaneously zero at $\boldsymbol{x}_0$. As noted above, $\hat{f}_i^0/\hat{f}_n^0 = \hat{g}_i^0/\hat{g}_n^0$, $i = 1, \ldots, n-1$, depicts a point of tangency between a contour of $\hat{f} = 0$ and a contour of $\hat{g} = 0$ at (x_i^0, x_n^0) in x_i, x_n-space. Q.E.D.

While this theorem demonstrates that the necessary conditions for an extremum in the primal and transposed problems are equivalent, it involves our being able to find ζ from either $\hat{f} = 0$ or $\hat{g} = 0$. To avoid this potentially difficult problem, we shall incorporate the Lagrangian of f subject to $\hat{g} = 0$ and the Lagrangian of g subject to $\hat{f} = 0$ into our analysis. That is, we shall construct the functions $L = \mathrm{f} + \lambda\hat{g}$ and $M = \mathrm{g} + \mu\hat{f}$ so as to demonstrate the following:

LAGRANGIAN TRANSPOSITION PRINCIPLE. *Maximizing (minimizing)* $L(\boldsymbol{x}, \lambda) = \mathrm{f}(\boldsymbol{x}) + \lambda\hat{g}(\boldsymbol{x})$ *is equivalent to minimizing (maximizing)* $M(\boldsymbol{x}, \mu) = \mathrm{g}(\boldsymbol{x}) + \mu\hat{f}(\boldsymbol{x})$.

While a formal proof of this proposition will be given below, a few preliminary remarks concerning its nature are in order. To see that this relationship holds, let us obtain, from L, the necessary condition

$$\left.\begin{aligned} L_i &= \mathrm{f}_i + \lambda\hat{g}_i = \mathrm{f}_i - \lambda \mathrm{g}_i = 0, \quad i = 1, \ldots, n, \\ L_\lambda &= \hat{g} = 0, \end{aligned}\right\} \tag{9.14.1}$$

while from M we have a similar necessary condition for a constrained extremum, namely

$$\left.\begin{aligned} M_i &= \mathrm{g}_i + \mu\hat{f}_i = \mathrm{g}_i - \mu \mathrm{f}_i = 0, \quad i = 1, \ldots, n, \\ M_\mu &= \hat{f} = 0. \end{aligned}\right\} \tag{9.19}$$

Eliminating λ between any $L_i = 0$, $i = 1, \ldots, n-1$, and $\mathrm{f}_n - \lambda \mathrm{g}_n = 0$ of system (9.14.1) and μ between any $M_i = 0$, $i = 1, \ldots, n-1$, and $\mathrm{g}_n - \mu \mathrm{f}_n = 0$ in eq. (9.19) yields, in each case, $\mathrm{f}_i/\mathrm{f}_n = \mathrm{g}_i/\mathrm{g}_n$ or $\hat{f}_i/\hat{f}_n = \hat{g}_i/\hat{g}_n$, $i = 1, \ldots, n-1$. So when we obtain a necessary condition depicting the attainment of an extremum of f subject to $\hat{g} = 0$, we are simultaneously provided with a necessary condition for an extremum of g subject to $\hat{f} = 0$. In either case, a point of tangency between a level curve of $\hat{f} = 0$ and a level curve of $\hat{g} = 0$ occurs. Note that we have introduced an additional Lagrange multiplier μ. Let us refer to μ as the *transpose Lagrange multiplier*. How shall we interpret μ? Also, what is its connection with the *primal Lagrange multiplier* λ? From $\hat{f} = y - \mathrm{f} = 0$, $dy - d\mathrm{f} = 0$ or

$$dy = d\mathrm{f} = \nabla \mathrm{f}'\boldsymbol{h}. \tag{9.20}$$

Since the role of μ^0 is to determine the effect of changes in y upon g^0, the optimum level of g, eq. (9.20) must be evaluated subject to eq. (9.19). Then, from $M_i = 0, i = 1, \ldots, n$, $\mathrm{f}_i = \mathrm{g}_i/\mu$. A substitution of these expressions into eq. (9.20) yields

$$\mathrm{d}y = \sum_{i=1}^{n} (\mathrm{g}_i/\mu)h_i = \frac{1}{\mu}\nabla \mathrm{g}'\boldsymbol{h} = \frac{\mathrm{dg}}{\mu}.$$

Hence, $\mu^0 = \mathrm{dg}^0/\mathrm{d}y$, the total derivative of g^0 with respect to y or the incremental change in g^0 with respect to y. But since $\mathrm{d}b - \mathrm{dg} = 0$, $\mathrm{d}y - \mathrm{df} = 0$, it follows that $\mu = \mathrm{d}b/\mathrm{df} = 1/\lambda$, i.e. the transpose Lagrange multiplier is the inverse of the primal Lagrange multiplier and conversely.

We noted previously that if f^0 represents the maximum value of f subject to $\hat{\mathrm{g}} = 0$, then $\lambda^0 > 0$ may be thought of as the marginal cost, in terms of f^0, of a tightening of the constraint $\hat{\mathrm{g}} = 0$. But, from the point of view of the transpose, $\mu^0 = 1/\lambda^0 > 0$ represents the marginal gain, in terms of g^0, of a relaxation in the constraint $\hat{\mathrm{f}} = 0$.

These observations on the transpose Lagrange multiplier μ provide the basis for two additional transposition theorems, the first of which is a formalization of the aforementioned Lagrangian transposition principle. In this regard:

THEOREM 9.11 (a necessary condition). *Let the real-valued functions $y = \mathrm{f}(\boldsymbol{x})$, $\mathrm{g}(\boldsymbol{x}) = b$, $\boldsymbol{x} \in \mathscr{E}^n$, be defined over an open region $\mathscr{K} \subseteq \mathscr{E}^n$ and differentiable throughout some spherical δ-neighborhood of the point $\boldsymbol{x}_0 \in \mathscr{K}$. If $L = \mathrm{f} + \lambda\hat{\mathrm{g}}$, and thus* f *subject to $\hat{\mathrm{g}} = 0$, has an extremum at $\boldsymbol{x}_0$, then $M = \mathrm{g} + \mu\hat{\mathrm{f}}$, and thus* g *subject to $\hat{\mathrm{f}} = 0$, has an extremum there also.*

Proof. If L has an extremum at $\boldsymbol{x}_0$, then

$$L_i^0 = \mathrm{f}_i^0 + \lambda^0\hat{\mathrm{g}}_i^0 = \mathrm{f}_i^0 - \lambda^0\mathrm{g}_i^0 = 0, \quad i = 1, \ldots, n,$$
$$L_\lambda^0 = \hat{\mathrm{g}}^0 = 0.$$

Since $\lambda^0 = 1/\mu^0$, $\mu^0 \neq 0$, $\mathrm{f}_i^0 - \mathrm{g}_i^0/\mu^0 = 0$ or $\mathrm{g}_i^0 - \mu^0\mathrm{f}_i^0 = \mathrm{g}_i^0 + \mu^0\hat{\mathrm{f}}_i^0 = 0$, $i = 1, \ldots, n$. Then $M_i^0 = 0$, $i = 1, \ldots, n$. And since the constraint $\hat{\mathrm{f}} = 0$ is binding at $\boldsymbol{x}_0$, $M_\mu^0 = 0$ also. Hence, eq. (9.19) is satisfied and we obtain a necessary condition for M to have an extremum at $\boldsymbol{x}_0$. Q.E.D.

We next state

THEOREM 9.12 (a sufficient condition). *Let the real-valued functions $y = \mathrm{f}(\boldsymbol{x})$, $\mathrm{g}(\boldsymbol{x}) = b$, $\boldsymbol{x} \in \mathscr{E}^n$, be defined over an open region $\mathscr{K} \subseteq \mathscr{E}^n$ and twice differentiable throughout some spherical δ-neighborhood of the point $\boldsymbol{x}_0 \in \mathscr{K}$. Furthermore, let $L = \mathrm{f} + \lambda\hat{\mathrm{g}}$, $M = \mathrm{g} + \mu\hat{\mathrm{f}}$. If*

$$\nabla\mathrm{f}^0 + \lambda^0\nabla\hat{\mathrm{g}}^0 = \mathbf{0},\ L_\lambda^0 = \hat{\mathrm{g}}^0 = 0; \qquad \nabla\mathrm{g}^0 + \mu^0\nabla\hat{\mathrm{f}}^0 = \mathbf{0},\ M_\mu^0 = 0;$$

and

$$\begin{vmatrix} H_L(x_0, \lambda^0)_{rr} & \nabla\hat{g}(x_0)_r \\ \nabla\hat{g}(x_0)'_r & 0 \end{vmatrix}, \quad \begin{vmatrix} H_M(x_0, \mu^0)_{rr} & \nabla\hat{f}(x_0)_r \\ \nabla\hat{f}(x_0)'_r & 0 \end{vmatrix} \neq 0,$$

$$r = 2, \ldots, n,$$

then both L, M (and thus f *subject to* $\hat{g} = 0$ *and* g *subject to* $\hat{f} = 0$*) each have a strong local extremum at* x_0. *Moreover,*

(*a*) *M has a strong local maximum at* x_0 *if L has a strong local minimum there; and*

(*b*) *M has a strong local minimum at* x_0 *if L attains a strong local maximum at that point.*

Proof. The rth-order bordered principal minor of the bordered Hessian determinant of L may be written as

$$\begin{vmatrix} H_L(x_0, \lambda^0)_{rr} & \nabla\hat{g}(x_0)_r \\ \nabla\hat{g}(x_0)'_r & 0 \end{vmatrix} = \begin{vmatrix} L_{11} \ldots L_{1r} & \hat{g}_1 \\ \vdots \quad\; \vdots & \vdots \\ L_{r1} \ldots L_{rr} & \hat{g}_r \\ \hat{g}_1 \ldots \hat{g}_r & 0 \end{vmatrix}$$

$$= \begin{vmatrix} f_{11} - \lambda g_{11} \ldots f_{1r} - \lambda g_{1r} & -g_1 \\ \vdots \qquad\qquad \vdots & \vdots \\ f_{r1} - \lambda g_{r1} \ldots f_{rr} - \lambda g_{rr} & -g_r \\ -g_1 \quad \ldots \quad -g_r & 0 \end{vmatrix}$$

$$= (-1)^r \begin{vmatrix} g_{11} - \mu f_{11} \ldots g_{1r} - \mu f_{1r} & \mu f_1 \\ \vdots \qquad\qquad \vdots & \vdots \\ g_{r1} - \mu f_{r1} \ldots g_{rr} - \mu f_{rr} & \mu f_r \\ -\mu f_1 \quad \ldots \quad -\mu f_r & 0 \end{vmatrix}$$

$$= (-1)^{r+1}\mu^2 \begin{vmatrix} H_M(x_0, \mu^0)_{rr} & \nabla\hat{f}(x_0)_r \\ \nabla\hat{f}(x_0)'_r & 0 \end{vmatrix}$$

(where it is understood that all the partial derivatives in the preceding expression are evaluated at x_0). So when the bordered principal minors of the bordered Hessian determinant of L alternate in sign, the first being positive (are all negative), the bordered principal minors of the Hessian of M are all negative (alternate in sign, starting positive). Hence, M has a strong local maximum (minimum) at x_0 whenever L has a strong local minimum (maximum) there. Q.E.D.

Chapter 10

A GENERALIZATION OF THE TECHNIQUE OF LAGRANGE TO m EQUALITY CONSTRAINTS

In this chapter we shall generalize the Lagrange multiplier technique to handle the case where a real-valued function of n variables $x_1, \ldots, x_n$ is optimized subject to m equality constraints in those variables. That is, we seek to maximize or minimize the real-valued function $y = \mathrm{f}(\boldsymbol{x})$, $\boldsymbol{x} \in \mathscr{E}^n$, subject to $b_j = \mathrm{g}^j(\boldsymbol{x})$ or $\hat{\mathrm{g}}^j(\boldsymbol{x}) = b_j - \mathrm{g}^j(\boldsymbol{x}) = 0$, $j = 1, \ldots, m$, where it is stipulated that $m < n$.[1]

Before proceeding to determine a necessary condition for an extremum of f subject to $\hat{\mathrm{g}}^j = 0$, $j = 1, \ldots, m$, let us pose the following problem. Given a set of m equations $\hat{\mathrm{g}}^j(\boldsymbol{x}) = 0$, $\boldsymbol{x} \in \mathscr{E}^n$, $j = 1, \ldots, m$, with $m < n$, under what conditions can we use these equations to express m of the n variables as functions of the remaining $n - m$ variables? That is, we seek to determine the existence of m functions ζ^j, $j = 1, \ldots, m$, such that we can solve for (eliminate) the variables x_j, $j = 1, \ldots, m$, in terms of $x_{m+1}, \ldots, x_n$ as

$$x_j = \zeta^j(x_{m+1}, \ldots, x_n), \quad j = 1, \ldots, m.$$

To answer this question we shall state a necessary and sufficient condition for the existence of the functions ζ^j, $j = 1, \ldots, m$, namely, the generalized existence or implicit function theorem.

THEOREM 10.1 (implicit function theorem).[2] *Let the real-valued functions $\hat{\mathrm{g}}^j(\boldsymbol{x}) = 0$, $\boldsymbol{x} \in \mathscr{E}^n$, $j = 1, \ldots, m$, $m < n$ be defined over a region $\mathscr{K} \subseteq \mathscr{E}^n$ and let $\boldsymbol{x}_0' = (x_1^0, \ldots, x_n^0)$ be a point interior to $\mathscr{K}$. If:*

(1) the functions $\hat{\mathrm{g}}^j(\boldsymbol{x}) = 0$, $j = 1, \ldots, m$, are continuous throughout some spherical δ-neighborhood of $\boldsymbol{x}_0$, $\delta(\boldsymbol{x}_0)$;

(2) $\hat{\mathrm{g}}^j(\boldsymbol{x}_0) = 0$, $j = 1, \ldots, m$, and

(3) the rank of the $(n \times m)$ matrix

$$\boldsymbol{\nabla G}(\boldsymbol{x}_0) = [\boldsymbol{\nabla} \hat{\mathrm{g}}^1(\boldsymbol{x}_0), \ldots, \boldsymbol{\nabla} \hat{\mathrm{g}}^m(\boldsymbol{x}_0)]$$

---

[1] Let us first assume that $m = n$. Since each function $\hat{\mathrm{g}}^j$ defines a surface in $\mathscr{E}^n$ and the intersection of n surfaces in $\mathscr{E}^n$ specifies a point $\{\boldsymbol{x}_*\} = \bigcap_{j=1}^n \{\boldsymbol{x} | \hat{\mathrm{g}}^j(\boldsymbol{x}) = 0\}$ it becomes trivial to optimize f subject to n constraints. But if $m < n$, m surfaces in $\mathscr{E}^n$ intersect to specify a region or surface (not just a point) of dimensionality $n - m$, all of whose points are boundary points (see Saaty and Bram, 1964, pp. 146–148).

[2] The statement of this theorem is a slight modification of the one given by Hadley (1964), pp. 47–49, and proved by Apostol (1964), pp. 146–148.

equals m, where $\boldsymbol{G}(\boldsymbol{x})$ *is an* $(m \times 1)$ *vector of implicit constraint functions* $\hat{g}^j(\boldsymbol{x}) = 0$, $j = 1, \ldots, m$, *then there exists an* ε*-neighborhood of* $\hat{\boldsymbol{x}}'_0 = (x^0_{k_1}, \ldots, x^0_{k_{n-m}}) \in \mathscr{E}^{n-m}$ $(k_1, \ldots, k_{n-m}$ *is the set of indices from* $1, \ldots, n$ *on the* $n-m$ *variables not associated with the m linearly independent rows of* $\nabla \boldsymbol{G}(\boldsymbol{x}_0))$ *such that for every* $\hat{\boldsymbol{x}}' = (x_{k_1}, \ldots, x_{k_{n-m}}) \in \varepsilon(\hat{\boldsymbol{x}}_0)$, *there exists a set of functions*

$$x_{k_j} = \zeta^j(x_{k_1}, \ldots, x_{k_{n-m}}), \quad j = 1, \ldots, m,$$

(here k_j, $j = 1, \ldots, m$, *is the set of indices from* $1, \ldots, n$ *on the m variables associated with the m linearly independent rows of* $\nabla \boldsymbol{G}(\boldsymbol{x}_0))$ *which are single-valued and continuous functions of* $\hat{\boldsymbol{x}}$ *and which possess the properties:*

(*a*) $x^0_{k_j} = \zeta^j(\hat{\boldsymbol{x}}_0), j = 1, \ldots, m,$

(*b*) *for any* $\hat{\boldsymbol{x}} \in \varepsilon(\hat{\boldsymbol{x}}_0)$, *the values of* x_{k_j}, $j = 1, \ldots, m$, *computed from* $x_{k_j} = \zeta^j(\hat{\boldsymbol{x}})$, *along with* $\hat{\boldsymbol{x}}$, *yield an* $\boldsymbol{x}$ *which satisfies* $\hat{g}^j(\boldsymbol{x}) = 0, j = 1, \ldots, m,$ *and*

(*c*) $\zeta^j(\hat{\boldsymbol{x}})$ *are differentiable throughout* $\varepsilon(\hat{\boldsymbol{x}}_0)$.

The implication of the condition $\rho(\nabla \boldsymbol{G}(\boldsymbol{x}_0)) = m$ is that the equations $\hat{g}^j(\boldsymbol{x}) = 0$, $j = 1, \ldots, m$, are not functionally dependent,[3] i.e. none of them can be expressed in terms of any (or all) of the others, a point which will be of paramount importance in what follows.

Example 10.1 Given the real-valued functions

$$\hat{g}^1 = 5 - 2x_1 x_2^{-1} + x_3 = 0, \qquad \hat{g}^2 = 3 - x_1^2 x_2^2 + x_3 = 0,$$

can we solve for two of the variables x_1, x_2, or x_3 in terms of the third? From $\boldsymbol{G}' = (\hat{g}^1, \hat{g}^2)$,

$$\nabla \boldsymbol{G} = [\nabla \hat{g}^1, \nabla \hat{g}^2] = \begin{bmatrix} -2x_2^{-1} & -2x_1 x_2^2 \\ 2x_1 x_2^{-2} & -2x_1^2 x_2 \\ 1 & 1 \end{bmatrix}$$

We may, for instance, compute

$$\begin{vmatrix} -2x_2^{-1} & -2x_1 x_2^2 \\ 2x_1 x_2^{-2} & -2x_1^2 x_2 \end{vmatrix} = 8x_1^2,$$

which is not identically zero, thus implying that $\rho(\nabla \boldsymbol{G}) = 2$. Hence, both

[3] Under what conditions will functional dependence hold? To answer this question we cite

THEOREM 10.2. *A necessary and sufficient condition for m functions of n variables,* $m \leqslant n$, *to be functionally dependent in a region* $\mathscr{K} \subseteq \mathscr{E}^n$ *is that every mth-order Jacobian determinant of these m functions with respect to m of the n variables vanishes identically in* $\mathscr{K}$.

(For a proof see Olmsted (1961), pp. 305–306, 331–333.) Clearly the requirement that $\rho(\nabla \boldsymbol{G}(\boldsymbol{x}_0)) = m$ implies that the functions $\hat{g}^j(\boldsymbol{x}) = 0, j = 1, \ldots, m$, are functionally independent since, with $\rho(\nabla \boldsymbol{G}(\boldsymbol{x}_0)) = \rho(\nabla \boldsymbol{G}(\boldsymbol{x}_0)') = m$, the existence of at least one non-vanishing mth-order Jacobian determinant of $\nabla \boldsymbol{G}(\boldsymbol{x}_0)'$ is established.

x_1, x_2 may be eliminated (since they are the variables associated with the first two (linearly independent) rows of ∇G) or

$$x_1 = \zeta^1(x_3) = \tfrac{1}{2}[4(3+x_3)]^{\frac{1}{4}}(5-x_3)^{\frac{1}{2}},$$
$$x_2 = \zeta^2(x_3) = [4(3+x_3)]^{\frac{1}{4}}/(5-x_3)^{\frac{1}{2}},$$

as the reader may verify. Can any other combination of two variables be expressed in terms of the third?

Once the existence of the functions ζ^j, $j = 1, \ldots, m$, has been verified, we can represent the variables $x_1, \ldots, x_m$ (we may assume, without loss of generality, that the first m variables have been eliminated) as

$$x_j = \zeta^j(\hat{\boldsymbol{x}}), \quad \hat{\boldsymbol{x}} \in \varepsilon(\hat{\boldsymbol{x}}_0), \quad j = 1, \ldots, m.$$

Then the function

$$\mathrm{F}(\hat{\boldsymbol{x}}) = \mathrm{f}[\zeta^1(\hat{\boldsymbol{x}}), \ldots, \zeta^m(\hat{\boldsymbol{x}}), \hat{\boldsymbol{x}}]$$

has an unconstrained local extremum at $\hat{\boldsymbol{x}}_0$ and thus at $\boldsymbol{x}_0$. Alternatively, instead of working with $\mathrm{F}(\hat{\boldsymbol{x}})$ directly, we may employ the implicit function theorem to generalize the technique of Lagrange.

10.1. Constrained local extrema of real-valued functions of *n* independent variables

In what follows we shall exclusively search for constrained extrema of the local variety. In this regard, let

$$y = \mathrm{f}(\boldsymbol{x}), \qquad \hat{\mathrm{g}}^j(\boldsymbol{x}) = 0, \quad \boldsymbol{x} \in \mathscr{E}^n, \quad j = 1, \ldots, m, \, m<n,$$

be real-valued functions defined on an open region $\mathscr{K} \subseteq \mathscr{E}^n$ with

$$\mathscr{G} = \{\boldsymbol{x} \,|\, \hat{\mathrm{g}}^j(\boldsymbol{x}) = 0, \quad \boldsymbol{x} \in \mathscr{E}^n, j = 1, \ldots, m, \, m<n\}.$$

Then we may state

Definition 10.1. *The real-valued function* $y = \mathrm{f}(\boldsymbol{x})$ *(subject to* $\hat{\mathrm{g}}^j(\boldsymbol{x}) = 0$, $\boldsymbol{x} \in \mathscr{E}^n$, $j = 1, \ldots, m$, $m<n$*) has a constrained local maximum (minimum) at* $\boldsymbol{x}_0 \in \mathscr{G} \cap \mathscr{K}$ *if there is some spherical δ-neighborhood* $\delta(\boldsymbol{x}_0) \subset \mathscr{K}$ *about* $\boldsymbol{x}_0$ *such that* $\mathrm{f}(\boldsymbol{x}_0) \geqslant \mathrm{f}(\boldsymbol{x})$ $(\leqslant \mathrm{f}(\boldsymbol{x}))$ *for all points* $\boldsymbol{x} \in \delta(\boldsymbol{x}_0) \cap \mathscr{G} \cap \mathscr{K}$.

As always, if $\mathrm{f}(\boldsymbol{x}_0) \geqslant \mathrm{f}(\boldsymbol{x})$ $(\leqslant \mathrm{f}(\boldsymbol{x}))$ and $\mathrm{f}(\boldsymbol{x}_0) = \mathrm{f}(\boldsymbol{x})$ for at least one point $\boldsymbol{x}(\neq \boldsymbol{x}_0) \in \delta(\boldsymbol{x}_0) \cap \mathscr{G} \cap \mathscr{K}$, then f has a *constrained weak local maximum (minimum)* at $\boldsymbol{x}_0$ while if $\mathrm{f}(\boldsymbol{x}_0) > \mathrm{f}(\boldsymbol{x})$ $(< \mathrm{f}(\boldsymbol{x}))$ for all $\boldsymbol{x}(\neq \boldsymbol{x}_0) \in \delta(\boldsymbol{x}_0) \cap \mathscr{G} \cap \mathscr{K}$, then f is said to have a *constrained strong local maximum (minimum) at* $\boldsymbol{x}_0$.

The Lagrangian associated with this problem is the real-valued function

$$L(\boldsymbol{x}, \boldsymbol{\lambda}) = \mathrm{f}(\boldsymbol{x}) + \sum_{j=1}^{m} \lambda_j \hat{\mathrm{g}}^j(\boldsymbol{x}) = \mathrm{f}(\boldsymbol{x}) + \boldsymbol{\lambda}' \boldsymbol{G}(\boldsymbol{x}), \tag{10.1}$$

where $\boldsymbol{x}$ is a $(n \times 1)$ vector, $\boldsymbol{\lambda}$ is a $(m \times 1)$ vector of Lagrange multipliers λ_j, $j = 1, \ldots, m$, and, as indicated above, $\boldsymbol{G}(\boldsymbol{x})$ is a $(m \times 1)$ vector of implicit constraint functions $\hat{\mathrm{g}}^j(\boldsymbol{x}) = 0, j = 1, \ldots, m$.

Our first theorem involving the location of a constrained local extremum is

THEOREM 10.2 (a necessary condition). *Let the real-valued functions* $y = \mathrm{f}(\boldsymbol{x})$, $\hat{\mathrm{g}}^j(\boldsymbol{x}) = 0, \boldsymbol{x} \in \mathscr{E}^n, j = 1, \ldots, m, m < n$, *be differentiable throughout some spherical* δ-*neighborhood of the point* $\boldsymbol{x}_0' = (x_1^0, \ldots, x_n^0)$ *contained within an open region* $\mathscr{K} \subseteq \mathscr{E}^n$. *If* f *has a local extremum subject to* $\hat{\mathrm{g}}^j(\boldsymbol{x}) = 0, j = 1, \ldots, m$, *at* $\boldsymbol{x}_0$, *then* $L(\boldsymbol{x}, \boldsymbol{\lambda}) = \mathrm{f}(\boldsymbol{x}) + \boldsymbol{\lambda}'\boldsymbol{G}(\boldsymbol{x})$ *has an unconstrained local extremum at that point and*

$$\left.\begin{aligned} \nabla_{\boldsymbol{x}} L^0 &= \nabla \mathrm{f}(\boldsymbol{x}_0) + \nabla \boldsymbol{G}(\boldsymbol{x}_0)\boldsymbol{\lambda}_0 = \mathbf{0}, \\ \nabla_{\boldsymbol{\lambda}} L^0 &= \boldsymbol{G}(\boldsymbol{x}_0) = \mathbf{0}, \end{aligned}\right\}$$

or

$$\left\{\begin{aligned} &\nabla \mathrm{f}(\boldsymbol{x}_0) + \sum_{j=1}^{m} \lambda_j^0 \nabla \hat{\mathrm{g}}^j(\boldsymbol{x}_0) = \mathbf{0}, \\ &L_{\lambda_j}^0 = 0, \quad j = 1, \ldots, m. \end{aligned}\right\} \tag{10.2}$$

In terms of the partial derivatives of f *and* $\hat{\mathrm{g}}^j = 0, j = 1, \ldots, m$, *eq. (10.2) becomes*

$$\left.\begin{aligned} L_1^0 &= \mathrm{f}_1^0 + \sum_{j=1}^{m} \lambda_j^0 \hat{\mathrm{g}}_1^j(\boldsymbol{x}_0) = 0, \\ L_2^0 &= \mathrm{f}_2^0 + \sum_{j=1}^{m} \lambda_j^0 \hat{\mathrm{g}}_2^j(\boldsymbol{x}_0) = 0, \\ &\cdots\cdots\cdots\cdots\cdots\cdots \\ L_n^0 &= \mathrm{f}_n^0 + \sum_{j=1}^{m} \lambda_j^0 \hat{\mathrm{g}}_n^j(\boldsymbol{x}_0) = 0, \\ L_{\lambda_1}^0 &= \hat{\mathrm{g}}^1(\boldsymbol{x}_0) = 0, \\ L_{\lambda_2}^0 &= \hat{\mathrm{g}}^2(\boldsymbol{x}_0) = 0, \\ &\cdots\cdots\cdots\cdots \\ L_{\lambda_m}^0 &= \hat{\mathrm{g}}^m(\boldsymbol{x}_0) = 0. \end{aligned}\right\} \tag{10.2.1}$$

Here $\nabla \mathrm{f}(\boldsymbol{x}_0)$ *is an* $(n \times 1)$ *vector of partial derivatives* f_i^0, $i = 1, \ldots, n$, *while* $\nabla \hat{\mathrm{g}}^j(\boldsymbol{x}_0)$, $j = 1, \ldots, m$, *denote* $(m \times 1)$ *vectors with elements* $\hat{\mathrm{g}}_i^j$. *In fact, these latter vectors are themselves elements of the* $(n \times m)$ *matrix*

$$\nabla \boldsymbol{G} = [\nabla \hat{\mathrm{g}}^1, \ldots, \nabla \hat{\mathrm{g}}^m].$$

Proof. If f attains a constrained extremum at $\boldsymbol{x}_0$, the differential of f along the $n-m$ dimensional constraint surface must vanish there and thus

$\nabla f(\boldsymbol{x}_0)'\boldsymbol{h} = 0$ for all $\boldsymbol{h} \in \mathscr{E}^n$ satisfying $\nabla \hat{g}^j(\boldsymbol{x}_0)'\boldsymbol{h} = 0, j = 1, \ldots, m$. If we multiply each differential $\nabla \hat{g}^j(\boldsymbol{x}_0)'\boldsymbol{h} = 0$ by some constant λ_j^0 and form the sum

$$\nabla f(\boldsymbol{x}_0)'\boldsymbol{h} + \sum_{j=1}^{m} \lambda_j^0 \nabla \hat{g}^j(\boldsymbol{x}_0)'\boldsymbol{h} = 0,$$

we obtain[4]

$$\left(\nabla f(\boldsymbol{x}_0) + \sum_{j=1}^{m} \lambda_j^0 \nabla \hat{g}^j(\boldsymbol{x}_0)\right)' \boldsymbol{h} = 0.$$

Let us assume, without loss of generality, that the Jacobian determinant associated with the first m columns of $\nabla \boldsymbol{G}(\boldsymbol{x}_0)'$, $|\boldsymbol{J_G}(x_1^0, \ldots, x_m^0)|$, does not vanish identically, so that the first m variables $x_1, \ldots, x_m$ can be expressed in terms of the last $n-m$ (independent) variables (by the implicit function theorem). Then $\boldsymbol{h}$ may be partitioned as

$$\boldsymbol{h} = \begin{bmatrix} \boldsymbol{h}_1 \\ \boldsymbol{h}_2 \end{bmatrix}, \quad \text{where } \boldsymbol{h}_1 = \begin{bmatrix} h_1 \\ \vdots \\ h_m \end{bmatrix}, \quad \boldsymbol{h}_2 = \begin{bmatrix} h_{m+1} \\ \vdots \\ h_n \end{bmatrix},$$

with the components of $\boldsymbol{h}_1$ being uniquely determined in terms of those in $\boldsymbol{h}_2$, i.e. $h_j = \zeta^j(\boldsymbol{h}_2), j = 1, \ldots, m$. Now, each component of $\boldsymbol{h}_2$ may be assumed non-zero (since the variables $x_{m+1}, \ldots, x_n$, and thus their differentials h_k, $k = m+1, \ldots, n$, are all independent) so that the components in $\boldsymbol{h}_1$, and thus in $\boldsymbol{h}$, are all non-zero. Hence

$$\left(\nabla f(\boldsymbol{x}_0) + \sum_{j=1}^{m} \lambda_j^0 \nabla \hat{g}^j(\boldsymbol{x}_0)\right)' \boldsymbol{h} = 0$$

only if

$$\nabla f(\boldsymbol{x}_0) + \sum_{j=1}^{m} \lambda_j^0 \nabla \hat{g}^j(\boldsymbol{x}_0) = \boldsymbol{0}.$$

In addition, $L_{\lambda_j}^0 = 0, j = 1, \ldots, m$. Hence the solution vector to the above constrained optimization problem may be found by solving system (10.2) or eq. (10.2.1) simultaneously. Q.E.D.

What this proof implies is that if $\nabla f(\boldsymbol{x}_0)'\boldsymbol{h} = 0$ (a homogeneous linear equation in the h_i's) and $\nabla \hat{g}^j(\boldsymbol{x}_0)'\boldsymbol{h} = 0$ (a homogeneous system of m linear equations in the h_i's), $j = 1, \ldots, m$, are to hold simultaneously, the vector $\nabla f(\boldsymbol{x}_0)$ must be linearly dependent upon the vectors $\nabla \hat{g}^j(\boldsymbol{x}_0), j = 1, \ldots, m$, i.e. $\nabla f(\boldsymbol{x}_0)$ can be written as a linear combination of the vectors $\nabla \hat{g}^j(\boldsymbol{x}_0)$. But if this is true, then there must exist scalars $\lambda_j^0, j = 1, \ldots, m$, not all zero

[4] Note that $(\alpha \boldsymbol{A} + \beta \boldsymbol{B})' = \alpha \boldsymbol{A}' + \beta \boldsymbol{B}'$ for α, β scalars.

such that

$$\nabla f(\boldsymbol{x}_0)+\sum_{j=1}^{m}\lambda_j^0\nabla \hat{g}^j(\boldsymbol{x}_0) = \mathbf{0}.$$

That the constants λ_j^0, $j = 1, \ldots, m$, are uniquely determined follows from the requirement that $\rho(\nabla \boldsymbol{G}(\boldsymbol{x}_0)) = m$. To see this we need only note that

$$\nabla \boldsymbol{G}(\boldsymbol{x}_0)\boldsymbol{\lambda}_0 = -\nabla f(\boldsymbol{x}_0)$$

implies

$$\boldsymbol{J}_{\boldsymbol{G}}(x_1^0, \ldots, x_m^0)'\boldsymbol{\lambda}_0 = -\nabla f(x_1^0, \ldots, x_m^0)$$

or

$$\boldsymbol{\lambda}_0 = [\boldsymbol{J}_{\boldsymbol{G}}(x_1^0, \ldots, x_m^0)']^{-1}(-\nabla f(x_1^0, \ldots, x_m^0)),$$

since the indicated Jacobian

$$\boldsymbol{J}_{\boldsymbol{G}} = [\partial(\hat{g}^1, \ldots, \hat{g}^m)/\partial(x_1, \ldots, x_m)]$$

was assumed to be non-singular.[5]

Before proceeding to define a sufficient condition for a strong local extremum of f subject to $\hat{g}^j = 0$, $j = 1, \ldots, m$, let us consider a couple of important theorems concerning constrained quadratic forms (Debreu, 1952). In what follows we shall consider conditions which are simultaneously necessary and sufficient for the positive or negative definiteness of a quadratic form $Q(\boldsymbol{x})$, $\boldsymbol{x} \in \mathscr{E}^n$, subject to $m<n$ linear constraints in $\boldsymbol{x}$.

First, given that the symmetric matrix $\boldsymbol{A}$ is of order $(n \times n)$, $\boldsymbol{B}$ is of order $(n \times m)$ with $\rho(\boldsymbol{B}) = m$, $\boldsymbol{x}$ is an $(n \times 1)$ vector, and $\boldsymbol{B}'\boldsymbol{x} = \mathbf{0}$ represents a homogeneous system of m linear equations in n unknowns, we have

THEOREM 10.3. *The quadratic form* $\boldsymbol{x}'\boldsymbol{A}\boldsymbol{x}$ *subject to* $\boldsymbol{B}'\boldsymbol{x} = \mathbf{0}$ *is positive definite* (>0) *for every* $\boldsymbol{x} \neq \mathbf{0}$ *if and only if*

$$\Delta_r = (-1)^m \begin{vmatrix} \boldsymbol{A}_{rr} & \vdots & \boldsymbol{B}_{rm} \\ \cdots & \vdots & \cdots \\ \boldsymbol{B}'_{rm} & \vdots & \mathbf{0} \end{vmatrix} > 0, \quad r = m+1, \ldots, n. \qquad (10.3)^6$$

Also, we have

---

[5] For a discussion on a more general necessary condition which allows for the possibility that $\rho(\nabla \boldsymbol{G}(\boldsymbol{x}_0)) \neq m$, see Hadley (1964), pp. 66–68, or Gue and Thomas (1970), pp. 43–46.

[6] Here the double subscripts on the elements of the partitioned determinant indicate the number of rows and columns which are retained as $r = m+1, \ldots, n$, e.g. $\boldsymbol{M}_{st}$ is obtained from $\boldsymbol{M}$ by keeping only the elements in the first s rows and first t columns of $\boldsymbol{M}$.

THEOREM 10.4. *The quadratic form* $x'Ax$ *subject to* $B'x = 0$ *is negative definite* (<0) *for every* $x \neq 0$ *if and only if*

$$\Delta_r = (-1)^r \begin{vmatrix} A_{rr} & \vdots & B_{rm} \\ \cdots & \vdots & \cdots \\ B'_{rm} & \vdots & 0 \end{vmatrix} > 0, \quad r = m+1, \ldots, n. \tag{10.3.1}$$

Example 10.2. Determine the sign definiteness of $x'Ax$ subject to $B'x = 0$ when

$$A = \begin{bmatrix} 2 & 1 & 0 \\ 1 & 3 & 1 \\ 0 & 1 & 2 \end{bmatrix}, \qquad B = \begin{bmatrix} 1 & 0 \\ 2 & 1 \\ 1 & 3 \end{bmatrix}.$$

Since $m+1 = 3 = n$, eq. (10.3) informs us that $x'Ax > 0$ if

$$\Delta_3 = (-1)^2 \begin{vmatrix} A_{33} & \vdots & B_{32} \\ \cdots & \vdots & \cdots \\ B'_{32} & \vdots & 0 \end{vmatrix} > 0$$

while, from eq. (10.3.1), $x'Ax < 0$ if

$$\Delta_3 = (-1)^3 \begin{vmatrix} A_{33} & \vdots & B_{32} \\ \cdots & \vdots & \cdots \\ B'_{32} & \vdots & 0 \end{vmatrix} > 0.$$

With

$$\begin{vmatrix} A_{33} & \vdots & B_{32} \\ \cdots & \vdots & \cdots \\ B'_{32} & \vdots & 0 \end{vmatrix} = \begin{vmatrix} 2 & 1 & 0 & 1 & 0 \\ 1 & 3 & 1 & 2 & 1 \\ 0 & 1 & 2 & 1 & 3 \\ 1 & 2 & 1 & 0 & 0 \\ 0 & 1 & 3 & 0 & 0 \end{vmatrix} = 24 > 0,$$

$\Delta_3 = (-1)^2 24 > 0$ and thus $x'Ax$ subject to $B'x = 0$ is positive definite.

We noted above that $\nabla \hat{g}^j(x_0)'h = 0$, $j = 1, \ldots, m$, represents a homogeneous system of m linear equations in the n unknowns h_i, $i = 1, \ldots, n$. That is, $\nabla \hat{g}^j(x_0)'h = 0$ depicts the system

$$\left.\begin{aligned} \hat{g}_1^1 h_1 + \hat{g}_2^1 h_2 + \cdots + \hat{g}_n^1 h_n &= 0 \\ \hat{g}_1^2 h_1 + \hat{g}_2^2 h_2 + \cdots + \hat{g}_n^2 h_n &= 0 \\ \cdots\cdots\cdots\cdots\cdots\cdots\cdots\cdots \\ \hat{g}_1^m h_1 + \hat{g}_2^m h_2 + \cdots + \hat{g}_n^m h_n &= 0 \end{aligned}\right\} \quad \text{or} \quad J_G h = \nabla G' h = 0,$$

where

$$J_G = [\partial(\hat{g}^1, \ldots, \hat{g}^m)/\partial(x_1, \ldots, x_n)].$$

In the following sufficient condition for a strong local constrained extremum use will be made of the coefficient matrix $\nabla G'$ of this homogeneous system and the Hessian of the Lagrangian of f. To this end we now state

THEOREM 10.5 (a sufficient condition). *Let the real-valued functions* $y = \mathrm{f}(\boldsymbol{x})$, $\hat{\mathrm{g}}^j(\boldsymbol{x}) = 0$, $\boldsymbol{x} \in \mathscr{E}^n$, $j = 1, \ldots, m$, $m < n$, *possess continuous first- and second-order partial derivatives throughout a spherical* δ*-neighborhood of the point* $\boldsymbol{x}_0$ *contained within an open region* $\mathscr{K} \subseteq \mathscr{E}^n$. *Then the first- and second-order partial derivatives of* $L(\boldsymbol{x}, \boldsymbol{\lambda}) = \mathrm{f}(\boldsymbol{x}) + \boldsymbol{\lambda}' \boldsymbol{G}(\boldsymbol{x})$ *are continuous throughout* $\delta(\boldsymbol{x}_0)$ *also. If*

$$\nabla_{\boldsymbol{x}} L^0 = \nabla \mathrm{f}(\boldsymbol{x}_0) + \nabla \boldsymbol{G}(\boldsymbol{x}_0)\boldsymbol{\lambda}_0 = \mathbf{0}, \qquad \nabla_{\boldsymbol{\lambda}} L^0 = \boldsymbol{G}(\boldsymbol{x}_0) = \mathbf{0},$$

and

$$\begin{vmatrix} \boldsymbol{H}_L(\boldsymbol{x}_0, \boldsymbol{\lambda}_0)_{rr} & \vdots & \nabla \boldsymbol{G}(\boldsymbol{x}_0)_{rm} \\ \cdots\cdots & & \cdots\cdots \\ \nabla \boldsymbol{G}(\boldsymbol{x}_0)'_{rm} & \vdots & \mathbf{0} \end{vmatrix} \neq 0, \quad r = m+1, \ldots, n,$$

then L, and thus f *subject to* $\hat{\mathrm{g}}^j = 0, j = 1, \ldots, m$, *has a strong local extremum at* $\boldsymbol{x}_0$. *Moreover:*

(*a*) *if*

$$\Delta_r = (-1)^r \begin{vmatrix} \boldsymbol{H}_L(\boldsymbol{x}_0, \boldsymbol{\lambda}_0)_{rr} & \vdots & \nabla \boldsymbol{G}(\boldsymbol{x}_0)_{rm} \\ \cdots\cdots & \vdots & \cdots\cdots \\ \nabla \boldsymbol{G}(\boldsymbol{x}_0)'_{rm} & \vdots & \mathbf{0} \end{vmatrix} > 0, \quad r = m+1, \ldots, n, \tag{10.4}$$

then L, and thus f *subject to* $\hat{\mathrm{g}}^j = 0$, $j = 1, \ldots, m$, *has a strong local maximum at* $\boldsymbol{x}_0$; *but*

(*b*) *if*

$$\Delta_r = (-1)^m \begin{vmatrix} \boldsymbol{H}_L(\boldsymbol{x}_0, \boldsymbol{\lambda}_0)_{rr} & \vdots & \nabla \boldsymbol{G}(\boldsymbol{x}_0)_{rm} \\ \cdots\cdots & \vdots & \cdots\cdots \\ \nabla \boldsymbol{G}(\boldsymbol{x}_0)'_{rm} & \vdots & \mathbf{0} \end{vmatrix} > 0, \quad r = m+1, \ldots, n, \tag{10.4.1}$$

then L, and thus f *subject to* $\hat{\mathrm{g}}^j = 0$, $j = 1, \ldots, m$, *has a strong local minimum at* $\boldsymbol{x}_0$. *Here* $\boldsymbol{H}_L(\boldsymbol{x}_0, \boldsymbol{\lambda}_0)_{rr}$ *is obtained from* $\boldsymbol{H}_L(\boldsymbol{x}_0, \boldsymbol{\lambda}_0)$ *by retaining only the elements in its first r rows and columns while* $\nabla \boldsymbol{G}(\boldsymbol{x}_0)_{rm}$ *is obtained from* $\nabla \boldsymbol{G}$ *by keeping only the elements in its first r rows.*

Proof. From eq. (5.15.4) we obtain, for $\boldsymbol{\lambda}_0$ fixed,

$$L(\boldsymbol{x}_0 + \boldsymbol{h}, \boldsymbol{\lambda}_0) - L(\boldsymbol{x}_0, \boldsymbol{\lambda}_0) = \tfrac{1}{2!} \boldsymbol{h}' \boldsymbol{H}_L(\boldsymbol{x}_0 + \theta \boldsymbol{h}, \boldsymbol{\lambda}_0)\boldsymbol{h}, \quad 0 < \theta < 1, \tag{10.5}$$

since, by hypothesis, $\nabla_{\boldsymbol{x}} L(\boldsymbol{x}_0, \boldsymbol{\lambda}_0) = \mathbf{0}$. With the second-order partial derivatives of L continuous at $\boldsymbol{x}_0$, the right-hand side of eq. (10.5) approaches

$\frac{1}{2!}\,\boldsymbol{h}'\boldsymbol{H}_L(\boldsymbol{x}_0, \boldsymbol{\lambda}_0)\boldsymbol{h}$ when $\theta \to 0$ and $\|\boldsymbol{h}\| < \delta$. Hence $L(\boldsymbol{x}_0+\boldsymbol{h}, \boldsymbol{\lambda}_0) - L(\boldsymbol{x}_0, \boldsymbol{\lambda}_0)$ has the same sign as

$$Q(\boldsymbol{h}) = \boldsymbol{h}'\boldsymbol{H}_L(\boldsymbol{x}_0, \boldsymbol{\lambda}_0)\boldsymbol{h} = \boldsymbol{h}'\begin{bmatrix} L_{11}^0 & L_{12}^0 & \dots & L_{1n}^0 \\ L_{21}^0 & L_{22}^0 & \dots & L_{2n}^0 \\ \vdots & \vdots & & \vdots \\ L_{n1}^0 & L_{n2}^0 & \dots & L_{nn}^0 \end{bmatrix}\boldsymbol{h},$$

provided that the partial derivatives L_{ij}^0, $i, j = 1, \dots, n$, are not all zero. However, the arguments of Q are not independent, i.e. we must determine the sign definiteness of $Q(\boldsymbol{h})$ for those vectors $\boldsymbol{h}$ which satisfy $\hat{g}^j(\boldsymbol{x}_0+\boldsymbol{h}) = 0$, $j = 1, \dots, m$. But this is equivalent to determining the sign of $Q(\boldsymbol{h}) = \boldsymbol{h}'\boldsymbol{H}_L(\boldsymbol{x}_0, \boldsymbol{\lambda}_0)\boldsymbol{h}$ subject to $\boldsymbol{\nabla G}(\boldsymbol{x}_0)'\boldsymbol{h} = \boldsymbol{0}$ with $\rho(\boldsymbol{\nabla G}(\boldsymbol{x}_0)) = m$. Now if

$$\Delta_r = (-1)^r \begin{vmatrix} \boldsymbol{H}_L(\boldsymbol{x}_0, \boldsymbol{\lambda}_0)_{rr} & \boldsymbol{\nabla G}(\boldsymbol{x}_0)_{rm} \\ \boldsymbol{\nabla G}(\boldsymbol{x}_0)'_{rm} & \boldsymbol{0} \end{vmatrix} > 0, \quad r = m+1, \dots, n,$$

theorem (10.5) informs us that $L(\boldsymbol{x}_0+\boldsymbol{h}, \boldsymbol{\lambda}_0) - L(\boldsymbol{x}_0, \boldsymbol{\lambda}_0) < 0$ and L, and thus f subject to $\hat{g}^j = 0$, $j = 1, \dots, m$, has a strong local maximum at $\boldsymbol{x}_0$, while if

$$\Delta_r = (-1)^m \begin{vmatrix} \boldsymbol{H}_L(\boldsymbol{x}_0, \boldsymbol{\lambda}_0)_{rr} & \boldsymbol{\nabla G}(\boldsymbol{x}_0)_{rm} \\ \boldsymbol{\nabla G}(\boldsymbol{x}_0)'_{rm} & \boldsymbol{0} \end{vmatrix} > 0, \quad r = m+1, \dots, n,$$

theorem (10.4) depicts L, and thus f subject to $\hat{g}^j = 0$, $j = 1, \dots, m$, as attaining a strong local minimum at $\boldsymbol{x}_0$ since, in this instance, $L(\boldsymbol{x}_0+\boldsymbol{h}, \boldsymbol{\lambda}_0) - L(\boldsymbol{x}_0, \boldsymbol{\lambda}_0) > 0$. Q.E.D.

Note that since $\boldsymbol{\nabla G}' = \boldsymbol{J_G}$, the indicated determinants in eqs. (10.4) and (10.4.1) often appear as

$$\begin{vmatrix} \boldsymbol{H}_L(\boldsymbol{x}_0, \boldsymbol{\lambda}_0)_{rr} & \boldsymbol{J_G}(\boldsymbol{x}_0)'_{rm} \\ \boldsymbol{J_G}(\boldsymbol{x}_0)_{rm} & \boldsymbol{0} \end{vmatrix}.$$

Let us elaborate on these determinental conditions. It should be obvious that eqs. (10.4) and (10.4.1) depict a sequence of signed, bordered, principal minors of the $(n+m \times n+m)$ bordered Hessian matrix

$$\boldsymbol{H}_L^{\boldsymbol{G}}(\boldsymbol{x}_0, \boldsymbol{\lambda}_0) = \begin{bmatrix} L_{11} & L_{12} & \dots & L_{1n} & \hat{g}_1^1 & \hat{g}_1^2 & \dots & \hat{g}_1^m \\ L_{21} & L_{22} & \dots & L_{2n} & \hat{g}_2^1 & \hat{g}_2^2 & \dots & \hat{g}_2^m \\ \vdots & \vdots & & \vdots & \vdots & \vdots & & \vdots \\ L_{n1} & L_{n2} & \dots & L_{nn} & \hat{g}_n^1 & \hat{g}_n^2 & \dots & \hat{g}_n^m \\ \hat{g}_1^1 & \hat{g}_2^1 & \dots & \hat{g}_n^1 & 0 & 0 & \dots & 0 \\ \hat{g}_1^2 & \hat{g}_2^2 & \dots & \hat{g}_n^2 & 0 & 0 & \dots & 0 \\ \vdots & & & & & & & \vdots \\ \hat{g}_1^m & \hat{g}_2^m & \dots & \hat{g}_n^m & 0 & 0 & \dots & 0 \end{bmatrix}$$

(where all the partial derivatives in $H_L^G(\boldsymbol{x}_0, \boldsymbol{\lambda}_0)$ are to be evaluated at $\boldsymbol{x}_0$). For a strong local minimum, we require that the determinants

$$\hat{\Delta}_r = \begin{vmatrix} \boldsymbol{H}_L(\boldsymbol{x}_0, \boldsymbol{\lambda}_0)_{rr} & \nabla \boldsymbol{G}(\boldsymbol{x}_0)_{rm} \\ \nabla \boldsymbol{G}(\boldsymbol{x}_0)'_{rm} & \boldsymbol{0} \end{vmatrix}, \quad r = m+1, \ldots, n,$$

each have the same sign as $(-1)^m$, where m is the number of constraints. For example, given that $n = 5$, $m = 2$, we require

$$\Delta_r = (-1)^2 \begin{vmatrix} \boldsymbol{H}_L(\boldsymbol{x}_0, \boldsymbol{\lambda}_0)_{rr} & \nabla \boldsymbol{G}(\boldsymbol{x}_0)_{r2} \\ \nabla \boldsymbol{G}(\boldsymbol{x}_0)'_{r2} & \boldsymbol{0} \end{vmatrix} > 0, \quad r = 3, 4, 5$$

or

$$\begin{vmatrix} L_{11} & L_{12} & L_{13} & \hat{g}_1^1 & \hat{g}_1^2 \\ L_{21} & L_{22} & L_{23} & \hat{g}_2^1 & \hat{g}_2^2 \\ L_{31} & L_{32} & L_{33} & \hat{g}_3^1 & \hat{g}_3^2 \\ \hat{g}_1^1 & \hat{g}_2^1 & \hat{g}_3^1 & 0 & 0 \\ \hat{g}_1^2 & \hat{g}_2^2 & \hat{g}_3^2 & 0 & 0 \end{vmatrix} > 0, \quad \begin{vmatrix} L_{11} & L_{12} & L_{13} & L_{14} & \hat{g}_1^1 & \hat{g}_1^2 \\ L_{21} & L_{22} & L_{23} & L_{24} & \hat{g}_2^1 & \hat{g}_2^2 \\ L_{31} & L_{32} & L_{33} & L_{34} & \hat{g}_3^1 & \hat{g}_3^2 \\ L_{41} & L_{42} & L_{43} & L_{44} & \hat{g}_4^1 & \hat{g}_4^2 \\ \hat{g}_1^1 & \hat{g}_2^1 & \hat{g}_3^1 & \hat{g}_4^1 & 0 & 0 \\ \hat{g}_1^2 & \hat{g}_2^2 & \hat{g}_3^2 & \hat{g}_4^2 & 0 & 0 \end{vmatrix} > 0,$$

$$\begin{vmatrix} L_{11} & L_{12} & L_{13} & L_{14} & L_{15} & \hat{g}_1^1 & \hat{g}_1^2 \\ L_{21} & L_{22} & L_{23} & L_{24} & L_{25} & \hat{g}_2^1 & \hat{g}_2^2 \\ L_{31} & L_{32} & L_{33} & L_{34} & L_{35} & \hat{g}_3^1 & \hat{g}_3^2 \\ L_{41} & L_{42} & L_{43} & L_{44} & L_{45} & \hat{g}_4^1 & \hat{g}_4^2 \\ L_{51} & L_{52} & L_{53} & L_{54} & L_{55} & \hat{g}_5^1 & \hat{g}_5^2 \\ \hat{g}_1^1 & \hat{g}_2^1 & \hat{g}_3^1 & \hat{g}_4^1 & \hat{g}_5^1 & 0 & 0 \\ \hat{g}_1^2 & \hat{g}_2^2 & \hat{g}_3^2 & \hat{g}_4^2 & \hat{g}_5^2 & 0 & 0 \end{vmatrix} > 0.$$

For a strong local maximum, the $\hat{\Delta}_r$ should alternate in sign, the first having the sign of $(-1)^{m+1}$. In this instance, given that $n = 5$, $m = 2$, we require

$$\Delta_r = (-1)^r \begin{vmatrix} \boldsymbol{H}_L(\boldsymbol{x}_0, \boldsymbol{\lambda}_0)_{rr} & \nabla \boldsymbol{G}(\boldsymbol{x}_0)_{r2} \\ \nabla \boldsymbol{G}(\boldsymbol{x}_0)'_{r2} & \boldsymbol{0} \end{vmatrix} > 0, \quad r = 3, 4, 5$$

or

$$\begin{vmatrix} L_{11} & L_{12} & L_{13} & \hat{g}_1^1 & \hat{g}_1^2 \\ L_{21} & L_{22} & L_{23} & \hat{g}_2^1 & \hat{g}_2^2 \\ L_{31} & L_{32} & L_{33} & \hat{g}_3^1 & \hat{g}_3^2 \\ \hat{g}_1^1 & \hat{g}_2^1 & \hat{g}_3^1 & 0 & 0 \\ \hat{g}_1^2 & \hat{g}_2^2 & \hat{g}_3^2 & 0 & 0 \end{vmatrix} < 0, \quad \begin{vmatrix} L_{11} & L_{12} & L_{13} & L_{14} & \hat{g}_1^1 & \hat{g}_1^2 \\ L_{21} & L_{22} & L_{23} & L_{24} & \hat{g}_2^1 & \hat{g}_2^2 \\ L_{31} & L_{32} & L_{33} & L_{34} & \hat{g}_3^1 & \hat{g}_3^2 \\ L_{41} & L_{42} & L_{43} & L_{44} & \hat{g}_4^1 & \hat{g}_4^2 \\ \hat{g}_1^1 & \hat{g}_2^1 & \hat{g}_3^1 & \hat{g}_4^1 & 0 & 0 \\ \hat{g}_1^2 & \hat{g}_2^2 & \hat{g}_3^2 & \hat{g}_4^2 & 0 & 0 \end{vmatrix} > 0,$$

$$\begin{vmatrix} L_{11} & L_{12} & L_{13} & L_{14} & L_{15} & \hat{g}_1^1 & \hat{g}_1^2 \\ L_{21} & L_{22} & L_{23} & L_{24} & L_{25} & \hat{g}_2^1 & \hat{g}_2^2 \\ L_{31} & L_{32} & L_{33} & L_{34} & L_{35} & \hat{g}_3^1 & \hat{g}_3^2 \\ L_{41} & L_{42} & L_{43} & L_{44} & L_{45} & \hat{g}_4^1 & \hat{g}_4^2 \\ L_{51} & L_{52} & L_{53} & L_{54} & L_{55} & \hat{g}_5^1 & \hat{g}_5^2 \\ \hat{g}_1^1 & \hat{g}_2^1 & \hat{g}_3^1 & \hat{g}_4^1 & \hat{g}_5^1 & 0 & 0 \\ \hat{g}_1^2 & \hat{g}_2^2 & \hat{g}_3^2 & \hat{g}_4^2 & \hat{g}_5^2 & 0 & 0 \end{vmatrix} < 0.$$

It must be noted that, since the above conditions are only sufficient and not simultaneously necessary and sufficient for a strong local constrained extremum, f subject to $\hat{g}^j = 0, j = 1, \ldots, m$, may still possess a strong local maximum or minimum even if some of the determinants $\hat{\Delta}_r$ vanish.

If

$$\nabla_{\boldsymbol{x}} L^0 = \nabla \mathrm{f}(\boldsymbol{x}_0) + \nabla \boldsymbol{G}(\boldsymbol{x}_0)\boldsymbol{\lambda}_0 = \boldsymbol{0}, \qquad \nabla_{\boldsymbol{\lambda}} L^0 = \boldsymbol{G}(\boldsymbol{x}_0) = \boldsymbol{0},$$

and $\boldsymbol{h}'\boldsymbol{H}_L(\boldsymbol{x}_0, \boldsymbol{\lambda}_0)\boldsymbol{h} \leqslant 0 (\geqslant 0)$ for all $\boldsymbol{h}$ satisfying $\nabla \boldsymbol{G}(\boldsymbol{x}_0)'\boldsymbol{h} = \boldsymbol{0}$, then we have a weakened sufficient or strengthened necessary condition for a local maximum (minimum) of f subject to $\hat{g}^j = 0, j = 1, \ldots, m$, at $\boldsymbol{x}_0$.

Example 10.3. Does the real-valued function $y = \mathrm{f}(\boldsymbol{x}) = x_1^2 + x_2^2 + x_3^2 + x_4^2$, $\boldsymbol{x} \in \mathscr{E}^4$, subject to

$$\hat{g}^1(\boldsymbol{x}) = 1 - x_1 - x_2 - x_3 - x_4 = 0, \qquad \hat{g}^2(\boldsymbol{x}) = 2 - x_1 + 2x_3 = 0$$

attain a local extremum throughout $\mathscr{E}^4$? We may answer this question in two ways. The first way is as follows. We first find

$$\nabla \boldsymbol{G} = [\nabla \hat{g}^1, \nabla \hat{g}^2] = \begin{bmatrix} -1 & -1 \\ -1 & 0 \\ -1 & 2 \\ -1 & 0 \end{bmatrix}.$$

Since $\rho(\nabla \boldsymbol{G}) = 2$, two of the variables may be eliminated or expressed in terms of the others. For example,

$$\begin{vmatrix} -1 & 2 \\ -1 & 0 \end{vmatrix} = 2 \neq 0$$

implies that x_3, x_4 may be expressed in terms of x_1, x_2 as

$$x_3 = \zeta^1(x_1, x_2) = \tfrac{1}{2}x_1 - 1, \qquad x_4 = \zeta^2(x_1, x_2) = -\tfrac{3}{2}x_1 - x_2 + 2.$$

Then we may find an extremum of

$$\begin{aligned} y &= \mathrm{f}(x_1, x_2, \zeta^1(x_1, x_2), \zeta^2(x_1, x_2)) \\ &= \mathrm{F}(x_1, x_2) = \tfrac{7}{2}x_1^2 + 2x_2^2 + 3x_1x_2 - 7x_1 - 4x_2 + 5 \end{aligned}$$

by calculating

$$\left.\begin{aligned} F_1 &= 7x_1+3x_2-7 = 0 \\ F_2 &= 4x_2+3x_1-4 = 0 \end{aligned}\right\} \text{ or } \left\{\begin{aligned} 7x_1+3x_2 &= 7 \\ 3x_1+4x_2 &= 4. \end{aligned}\right.$$

Solving this system simultaneously yields $\hat{\boldsymbol{x}}_0' = (\frac{16}{19}, \frac{7}{19})$. From ζ^1, ζ^2 we find $x_3 = -\frac{11}{19}$, $x_4 = \frac{7}{19}$, and thus $\boldsymbol{x}_0' = (\frac{16}{19}, \frac{7}{19}, -\frac{11}{19}, \frac{7}{19})$. In addition

$$F_{11}^0 = 7>0, \qquad |\boldsymbol{H}_F(\boldsymbol{x}_0)| = \begin{vmatrix} F_{11}^0 & F_{12}^0 \\ F_{21}^0 & F_{22}^0 \end{vmatrix} = \begin{vmatrix} 7 & 3 \\ 3 & 4 \end{vmatrix} = 19>0.$$

Thus F has a strong local minimum at $\hat{\boldsymbol{x}}_0$ or, equivalently, f subject to $\hat{g}^j = 0$, $j = 1, 2$, has a strong local minimum at $\boldsymbol{x}_0$.

The second way of answering the above question is as follows. From eq. (10.1) we have

$$\begin{aligned} L(\boldsymbol{x}, \boldsymbol{\lambda}) &= f(\boldsymbol{x})+\boldsymbol{\lambda}'\boldsymbol{G}(\boldsymbol{x}) \\ &= x_1^2+x_2^2+x_3^2+x_4^2+\lambda_1(1-x_1-x_2-x_3-x_4) \\ &\quad +\lambda_2(2-x_1+2x_3) \end{aligned}$$

while from eq. (10.2) we obtain

$$\begin{bmatrix} \nabla_x L \\ \nabla_\lambda L \end{bmatrix} = \boldsymbol{0} \quad \text{or} \quad \left\{\begin{aligned} L_1 &= 2x_1-\lambda_1-\lambda_2 = 0, \\ L_2 &= 2x_2-\lambda_1 = 0, \\ L_3 &= 2x_3-\lambda_1+2\lambda_2 = 0, \\ L_4 &= 2x_4-\lambda_1 = 0, \\ L_{\lambda_1} &= 1-x_1-x_2-x_3-x_4 = 0, \\ L_{\lambda_2} &= 2-x_1+2x_3 = 0 \end{aligned}\right.$$

of which the simultaneous solution is $\boldsymbol{x}_0' = (\frac{16}{19}, \frac{7}{19}, -\frac{11}{19}, \frac{7}{19})$, $\boldsymbol{\lambda}_0' = (\frac{14}{19}, \frac{18}{19})$. Also,

$$\begin{vmatrix} \boldsymbol{H}_L(\boldsymbol{x}_0, \boldsymbol{\lambda}_0)_{33} & \nabla\boldsymbol{G}(\boldsymbol{x}_0)_{32} \\ \nabla\boldsymbol{G}(\boldsymbol{x}_0)'_{32} & \boldsymbol{0} \end{vmatrix} = \begin{vmatrix} 2 & 0 & 0 & 1 & 1 \\ 0 & 2 & 0 & 1 & 0 \\ 0 & 0 & 2 & 1 & -2 \\ 1 & 1 & 1 & 0 & 0 \\ 1 & 0 & -2 & 0 & 0 \end{vmatrix} = 28>0,$$

$$\begin{vmatrix} \boldsymbol{H}_L(\boldsymbol{x}_0, \boldsymbol{\lambda}_0)_{44} & \nabla\boldsymbol{G}(\boldsymbol{x}_0)_{42} \\ \nabla\boldsymbol{G}(\boldsymbol{x}_0)'_{42} & \boldsymbol{0} \end{vmatrix} = \begin{vmatrix} 2 & 0 & 0 & 0 & 1 & 1 \\ 0 & 2 & 0 & 0 & 1 & 0 \\ 0 & 0 & 2 & 0 & 1 & -2 \\ 0 & 0 & 0 & 2 & 1 & 0 \\ 1 & 1 & 1 & 1 & 0 & 0 \\ 1 & 0 & -2 & 0 & 0 & 0 \end{vmatrix} = 76>0,$$

thus implying that f subject to $\hat{g}^j = 0$, $j = 1, 2$, attains a strong local minimum at $\boldsymbol{x}_0$ since, from eq. (10.4.1),

$$\Delta_r = (-1)^2 \begin{vmatrix} \boldsymbol{H}_L(\boldsymbol{x}_0, \boldsymbol{\lambda}_0)_{rr} & \nabla \boldsymbol{G}(\boldsymbol{x}_0)_{r2} \\ \nabla \boldsymbol{G}(\boldsymbol{x}_0)'_{r2} & \boldsymbol{0} \end{vmatrix} > 0, \quad r = 3, 4.$$

10.2. Interpretation of the Lagrange multipliers λ_j

We noted in the previous chapter that $\lambda^0 = \mathrm{df}^0/\mathrm{d}b$. A similar interpretation holds for λ_j^0; that is, λ_j^0 is a measure of the infinitesimal change in f^0 with respect to a small relaxation in or tightening of the jth constraint $\hat{\mathrm{g}}^j = b_j - \mathrm{g}^j = 0$, the other constraints remaining unchanged. Hence $\lambda_j^0 = \mathrm{df}^0/\mathrm{d}b_j$. To see this let us first indicate the effect of a change in b_j upon the optimal value of the objective function f^0 as

$$\frac{\partial \mathrm{f}^0}{\partial b_j} = \sum_{i=1}^{n} \frac{\partial \mathrm{f}(\boldsymbol{x}_0)}{\partial x_i} \frac{\mathrm{d}x_i}{\mathrm{d}b_j} = \nabla \mathrm{f}(\boldsymbol{x}_0)' \begin{bmatrix} \mathrm{d}x_1/\mathrm{d}b_j \\ \vdots \\ \mathrm{d}x_n/\mathrm{d}b_j \end{bmatrix} = \nabla \mathrm{f}(\boldsymbol{x}_0)' \left(\frac{\mathrm{d}\boldsymbol{x}}{\mathrm{d}b_j} \right).$$

Since the necessary condition for a constrained extremum (eq. (10.2)) must hold, $\nabla \mathrm{f}(\boldsymbol{x}_0) = -\nabla \boldsymbol{G}(\boldsymbol{x}_0)\boldsymbol{\lambda}_0$ and thus

$$\frac{\partial \mathrm{f}^0}{\partial b_j} = -\boldsymbol{\lambda}_0' \nabla \boldsymbol{G}(\boldsymbol{x}_0)' \left(\frac{\mathrm{d}\boldsymbol{x}}{\mathrm{d}b_j} \right) = \sum_{j=1}^{m} \lambda_j^0 \nabla \mathrm{g}^j(\boldsymbol{x}_0)' \left(\frac{\mathrm{d}\boldsymbol{x}}{\mathrm{d}b_j} \right). \tag{10.6}$$[7]

From the jth constraint $b_j - \mathrm{g}^j(\boldsymbol{x}) = 0, j = 1, \ldots, m,$

$$\frac{\mathrm{d}(b_j - \mathrm{g}^j(\boldsymbol{x}_0))}{\mathrm{d}b_k} = \frac{\mathrm{d}b_j}{\mathrm{d}b_k} - \sum_{i=1}^{n} \frac{\partial \mathrm{g}^j(\boldsymbol{x}_0)}{\partial x_i} \frac{\mathrm{d}x_i}{\mathrm{d}b_k} = 0$$

or

$$\nabla \mathrm{g}^j(\boldsymbol{x}_0)' \left(\frac{\mathrm{d}\boldsymbol{x}}{\mathrm{d}b_k} \right) = \begin{cases} 1, & k = j, \\ 0, & k \neq j. \end{cases}$$

Multiplying this last expression by λ_j^0 yields

$$\lambda_j^0 \nabla \mathrm{g}^j(\boldsymbol{x}_0)' \left(\frac{\mathrm{d}\boldsymbol{x}}{\mathrm{d}b_k} \right) = \begin{cases} \lambda_j^0, & k = j, \\ 0, & k \neq j. \end{cases} \tag{10.7}$$

If $k = j$, eq. (10.7) corresponds to the jth term (the only non-zero term) in eq. (10.6) and thus $\mathrm{df}^0/\mathrm{d}b_j = \lambda_j^0$.

---

[7] If the product $\boldsymbol{AB}$ exists, $(\boldsymbol{AB})' = \boldsymbol{B}'\boldsymbol{A}'$.

Chapter 11

KUHN–TUCKER THEORY: AN INTRODUCTION[1]

11.1. A single inequality side relation and non-negativity conditions

Perhaps the most straightforward modification of the Lagrange multiplier technique is its extension to the case where, for $\boldsymbol{x} \in \mathscr{E}^n$, either: (1) $g(\boldsymbol{x}) \leqslant b$ with $\boldsymbol{x}$ unrestricted; or (2) $g(\boldsymbol{x}) = b$ and $\boldsymbol{x} \geqslant \boldsymbol{0}$; or (3) $g(\boldsymbol{x}) \leqslant b$ with $\boldsymbol{x} \geqslant \boldsymbol{0}$. For example, assume that we desire to maximize the real-valued function $y = f(\boldsymbol{x})$ subject to $\hat{g}(\boldsymbol{x}) = b - g(\boldsymbol{x}) = 0$, $\boldsymbol{x} \in \mathscr{E}^2$, when both f, $\hat{g} = 0$ are defined over an open region $\mathscr{K} \subseteq \mathscr{E}^2$. In this instance the set of admissible points which are candidates for a constrained maximum lie along the curve AB (fig. 11.1).

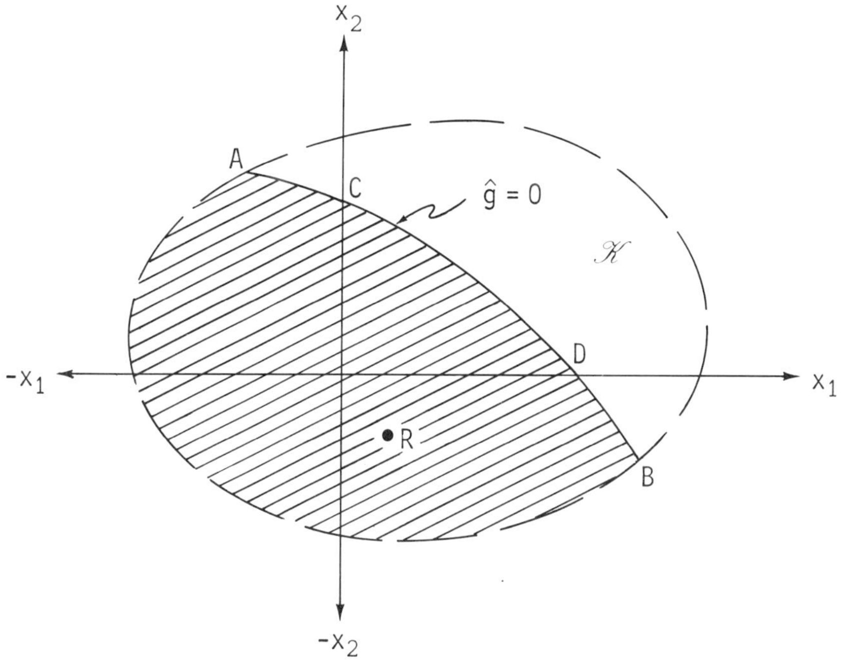

Fig. 11.1.

[1] See Neyman (1951), pp. 481–492; Graves and Wolfe (1963), pp. 67–85; Dorn (1963); and Arrow *et al.* (1958), pp. 32–37.

Let us now impose the restriction that $\mathrm{g}(\boldsymbol{x}) \leqslant b$ or $\hat{\mathrm{g}}(\boldsymbol{x}) \geqslant 0$. Here we no longer have as possible candidates for an optimum a set of points along the 'curve' $\hat{\mathrm{g}} = 0$. Rather, we have a 'region' of feasible solutions (hereafter termed the *feasible region*), namely, the shaded portion of fig. 11.1 which encompasses all points on AB and below it. To handle problems of this sort we state the following sequence of Kuhn–Tucker–Lagrange (KTL) theorems. First,

THEOREM 11.1 (a necessary condition). *Let the real-valued functions* $y = \mathrm{f}(\boldsymbol{x})$, $\hat{\mathrm{g}}(\boldsymbol{x}) \geqslant 0$, $\boldsymbol{x} \in \mathscr{E}^n$, *be defined over an open region* $\mathscr{X} \subseteq \mathscr{E}^n$ *and differentiable throughout some spherical* δ*-neighborhood of the point* $\boldsymbol{x}_0 \in \mathscr{X}$. *If* f *subject to* $\hat{\mathrm{g}} \geqslant 0$ *has a local maximum at* $\boldsymbol{x}_0$, *then*

$$\left.\begin{aligned} &\nabla \mathrm{f}^0 + \lambda^0 \nabla \hat{\mathrm{g}}^0 = \mathbf{0} \quad \textit{or} \quad \mathrm{f}_i^0 + \lambda^0 \hat{\mathrm{g}}_i^0 = 0, \quad i = 1, \ldots, n, \\ &\lambda^0 \hat{\mathrm{g}}^0 = 0, \\ &\hat{\mathrm{g}}^0 \geqslant 0, \\ &\lambda^0 \geqslant 0, \\ &x_i^0 \; \textit{unrestricted}, \quad i = 1, \ldots, n. \end{aligned}\right\} \tag{11.1}$$

Proof. (The basic guiding principle that the KTL conditions are predicated upon, indeed, the fundamental notion that will be employed in this and subsequent proofs, is that no suitably restricted permissible change (i.e. one that does not violate any constraint) in any of the variables x_i, $i = 1, \ldots, n$, can improve the optimal value of the objective function.) In order to employ the technique of Lagrange we must first transform the constraint inequality $\hat{\mathrm{g}} \geqslant 0$ into an equality by subtracting from its left-hand side the non-negative *slack variable s*. (Actually, since we require that $s \geqslant 0$, we shall subtract s^2 from the left-hand side of $\hat{\mathrm{g}} \geqslant 0$ so as to insure that it is non-negative.) Hence our *augmented constraint* becomes $\hat{\mathrm{g}} - s^2 = 0$. We may now form the *augmented Lagrangian*

$$L(\boldsymbol{x}, \lambda, s) = \mathrm{f}(\boldsymbol{x}) + \lambda(\hat{\mathrm{g}}(\boldsymbol{x}) - s^2).$$

Upon partially differentiating L with respect to each of its arguments and equating them to zero,

$$\left.\begin{aligned} L_i &= \mathrm{f}_i + \lambda \hat{\mathrm{g}}_i = 0, \quad i = 1, \ldots, n, \\ L_\lambda &= \hat{\mathrm{g}} - s^2 = 0, \\ L_s &= -2s\lambda = 0. \end{aligned}\right\} \tag{11.2}$$

From $L_\lambda = 0$ we have $s^2 = \hat{\mathrm{g}}$. If we multiply both sides of L_s by $-s/2$ we obtain $\lambda s^2 = 0$. A substitution of $s^2 = \hat{\mathrm{g}}$ into this latter expression yields, at $\boldsymbol{x}_0$, $\lambda^0 \hat{\mathrm{g}}^0 = 0$, i.e. either $\hat{\mathrm{g}}^0 = 0$ (the constraint is binding and thus $s = 0$), in which case $\lambda^0 \geqslant 0$, or $\lambda^0 = 0$, thus admitting the possibility that $\hat{\mathrm{g}}^0 > 0$ (the constraint is satisfied with excess capacity and thus $s > 0$).

If $\lambda^0 = 0$ (the constraint is not binding), then $\boldsymbol{x}_0$ is an interior point of the set of permissible solutions (such as $R \in \mathscr{E}^2$ of fig. 11.1) and $\mathrm{f}_i^0 = 0$, $i = 1, \ldots, n$, a necessary condition for an unconstrained local maximum of f.

If $\hat{g}^0 = 0$ (the constraint is binding), it must be the case that, at $\boldsymbol{x}_0$, $df^0 = (\nabla f^0)'\boldsymbol{h} = 0$ for all $\boldsymbol{h}$ which satisfy $dg^0 = (\nabla g^0)'\boldsymbol{h} = 0$ or $\nabla f^0 + \lambda^0 \nabla \hat{g}^0 = \mathbf{0}$ (as verified by theorems 9.7 and 9.8 in chapter 9).

We noted that eq. (11.1) requires $\lambda^0 \geqslant 0$. Why is this a valid restriction? From our previous analysis (chapter 9) we found that $\lambda^0 = df^0/db$. Now if f subject to $\hat{g} = b - g \geqslant 0$ has a local maximum at $\boldsymbol{x}_0$, then as b increases and the region of permissible solutions expands, f^0 cannot decrease and thus $df^0/db = \lambda^0 \geqslant 0$. In this regard, if $b > g^0$, then increasing b cannot affect $\boldsymbol{x}_0$ or f^0 so that $df^0/db = \lambda^0 = 0$. And if $b = g^0$, $df^0/db = \lambda^0 \geqslant 0$. Q.E.D.

If we desire to minimize f subject to $\hat{g} \geqslant 0$, $\boldsymbol{x} \in \mathscr{E}^n$, eq. (11.1) becomes

$$\left.\begin{array}{l} \nabla f^0 - \lambda^0 \nabla \hat{g}^0 = \mathbf{0} \quad \text{or} \quad f_i^0 - \lambda^0 \hat{g}_i^0 = 0, \quad i = 1, \ldots, n, \\ \lambda^0 \hat{g}^0 = 0, \\ \hat{g}^0 \geqslant 0, \\ \lambda^0 \geqslant 0, \\ x_i^0 \text{ unrestricted}, \quad i = 1, \ldots, n. \end{array}\right\} \tag{11.1.1}$$

To see this we need only remember that the constrained minimum of f occurs at the same point as the constrained maximum of $-f$. Then, in terms of eq. (11.1), we have

$$\left.\begin{array}{l} -\nabla f^0 + \lambda^0 \nabla \hat{g}^0 = \mathbf{0}, \\ \lambda^0 \hat{g}^0 = 0, \\ \hat{g}^0 \geqslant 0, \\ \lambda^0 \geqslant 0, \\ x_i \text{ unrestricted}, \quad i = 1, \ldots, n \end{array}\right\} \text{ or eq. (11.1.1).}$$

Example 11.1. Find the local minimum of the real-valued function

$$y = f(\boldsymbol{x}) = x_1^2 - x_1 x_2 + x_2^2 + 3x_1 + 3x_2$$

when x_1, x_2 are connected by the side relation $3x_1 + 4x_2 \geqslant 12$. To employ eq. (11.1.1) we must write the indicated inequality constraint in the general form $\hat{g} \geqslant 0$. Then $-3x_1 - 4x_2 \leqslant -12$ or $\hat{g} = -12 + 3x_1 + 4x_2 \geqslant 0$. Hence eq. (11.1.1) becomes

$$\begin{aligned} 2x_1 - x_2 + 3 - 3\lambda &= 0, \\ -x_1 + 2x_2 + 3 - 4\lambda &= 0, \\ \lambda(-12 + 3x_1 + 4x_2) &= 0, \\ -12 + 3x_1 + 4x_2 &\geqslant 0, \\ \lambda &\geqslant 0. \end{aligned}$$

Then: (a) if the constraint is not binding ($\lambda = 0$), we may solve the system

$$\begin{aligned} 2x_1 - x_2 + 3 &= 0, \\ -x_1 + 2x_2 + 3 &= 0 \end{aligned}$$

simultaneously to obtain $\boldsymbol{x}_0' = (-3, -3)$; since this critical point is not feasible (it violates the requirement that $3x_1+4x_2 \geqslant 12$) (fig. 11.2), it will be ignored; and (b) if the constraint is binding, the above system becomes

$$\begin{aligned} 2x_1 - x_2 - 3\lambda + 3 &= 0, \\ -x_1 + 2x_2 - 4\lambda + 3 &= 0, \\ 3x_1 + 4x_2 \qquad - 12 &= 0, \end{aligned}$$

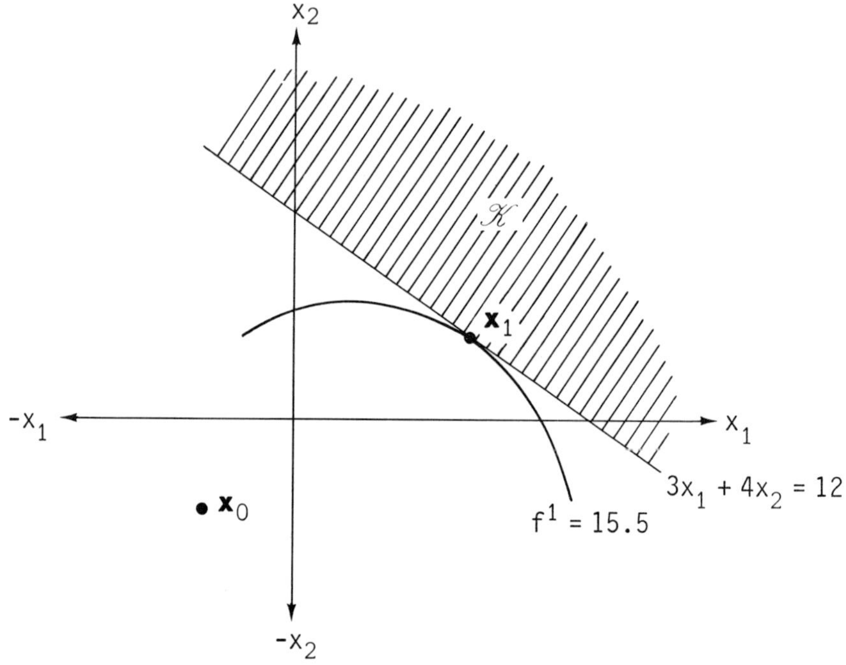

Fig. 11.2.

the simultaneous solution of which is $\boldsymbol{x}_1' = (2.5, 1.1)$ and $\lambda^1 = 1.3$. Since

$$|\boldsymbol{H}_{\mathrm{f}}^{\hat{\mathrm{g}}}(\boldsymbol{x}_1, \lambda^1)| = \begin{vmatrix} 2 & -1 & -3 \\ -1 & 2 & -4 \\ -3 & -4 & 0 \end{vmatrix} = -74 < 0,$$

f has a strong local constrained minimum at $\boldsymbol{x}_1$ with $\mathrm{f}^1 = 15.5$.

Example 11.2. Maximize the real-valued function $y = \mathrm{f}(\boldsymbol{x}) = -3x_1^2 - x_2^2$ subject to

$$2x_1 + x_2 \leqslant -2 \quad \text{or} \quad \hat{\mathrm{g}} = -2 - 2x_1 - x_2 \geqslant 0.$$

From eq. (11.1) we have

$$\begin{aligned} -6x_1-2\lambda &= 0, \\ -2x_2-\ \lambda &= 0, \\ \lambda(-2-2x_1-x_2) &= 0, \\ -2-2x_1-x_2 &\geqslant 0, \\ \lambda &\geqslant 0. \end{aligned}$$

If the constraint is not binding ($\lambda = 0$), then the above system becomes

$$\left.\begin{aligned} -6x_1 &= 0, \\ -2x_2 &= 0 \end{aligned}\right\} \quad \text{or} \quad \left\{\begin{aligned} x_1 &= 0, \\ x_2 &= 0. \end{aligned}\right.$$

However, $\boldsymbol{x}_0' = (0, 0)$ is not feasible since $\hat{g} \geqslant 0$ is violated (fig. 11.3). If the constraint is binding, then

$$\begin{aligned} -6x_1-2\lambda &= 0, \\ -2x_2-\ \lambda &= 0, \\ -2-2x_1-x_2 &= 0 \end{aligned}$$

with solution $\boldsymbol{x}_1' = (-\frac{4}{7}, -\frac{6}{7})$ and $\lambda^1 = \frac{12}{7}$. Also,

$$|\boldsymbol{H}_{\mathrm{f}}^{\hat{g}}(\boldsymbol{x}_1, \lambda^1)| = \begin{vmatrix} -6 & 0 & 2 \\ 0 & -2 & 1 \\ 2 & 1 & 0 \end{vmatrix} = 14 > 0.$$

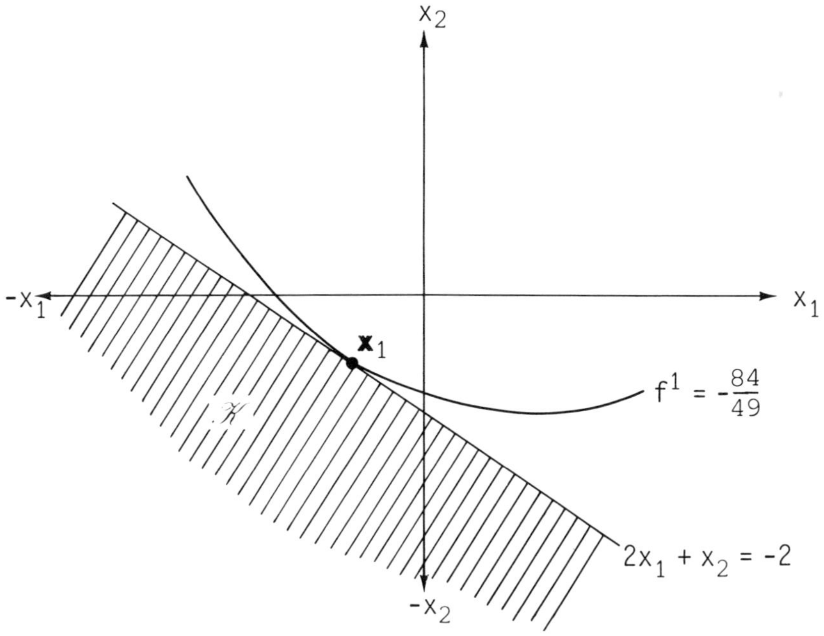

Fig. 11.3.

Thus f subject to $2x_1+x_2 \leqslant -2$ has a strong local maximum at $\boldsymbol{x}_1$ with $f(\boldsymbol{x}_1) = -\frac{84}{49}$.

These two examples have hinted at a general procedure for implementing eqs. (11.1) and (11.1.1): (1) we first determine all solutions for the case where the constraint $\hat{g} \geqslant 0$ is not binding, and we compute f^0 at those feasible points where eq. (11.1) or (11.1.1) holds with $\lambda = 0$; (2) we then repeat the procedure with the inequality constraint binding and compare the f^0 values obtained in part (1) with those obtained with $\lambda > 0$ in eqs. (11.1) and (11.1.1). The desired extremum will then be found among the solutions generated in parts (1) and (2).

We next look to the case where $\hat{g} = 0$ and $\boldsymbol{x} \geqslant \boldsymbol{0}$, $\boldsymbol{x} \in \mathscr{E}^n$. In this instance the optimal solution must be found, for example, somewhere along a curve such as that extending from C to D in fig. 11.1. The appropriate KTL necessary condition for a constrained local extremum under this set of circumstances is provided by

THEOREM 11.2 (a necessary condition). *Let the real-valued functions* $y = f(\boldsymbol{x})$, $\hat{g}(\boldsymbol{x}) = 0$, $\boldsymbol{x} \in \mathscr{E}^n$, *be defined over an open region* $\mathscr{K} \subseteq \mathscr{E}^n$ *and differentiable throughout some spherical* δ*-neighborhood of the point* $\boldsymbol{x}_0 \in \mathscr{K}$. *If* f *subject to* $\hat{g} = 0$ *and* $\boldsymbol{x} \geqslant \boldsymbol{0}$ *has a local maximum at* $\boldsymbol{x}_0$, *then*

$$\left.\begin{aligned} &\nabla f^0 + \lambda^0 \nabla \hat{g}^0 \leqslant \mathbf{0} \quad \textit{or} \quad f_i^0 + \lambda^0 \hat{g}_i^0 \leqslant 0, \quad i = 1, \ldots, n, \\ &\boldsymbol{x}_0'(\nabla f^0 + \lambda^0 \nabla \hat{g}^0) = 0 \quad \textit{or} \quad \sum_{i=1}^{n} x_i^0 (f_i^0 + \lambda^0 \hat{g}_i^0) = 0, \\ &\hat{g}^0 = 0, \\ &\lambda^0 \textit{ unrestricted}, \\ &\boldsymbol{x}_0 \geqslant \mathbf{0} \quad \textit{or} \quad x_i^0 \geqslant 0, \quad i = 1, \ldots, n. \end{aligned}\right\} \tag{11.3}$$

Proof. We shall again rely on the technique of Lagrange to carry out our proof. In this instance there are really $2+n$ inequality constraints: one equality constraint $\hat{g} = 0$ which may be written as the two inequality constraints $\hat{g} \geqslant 0$, $-\hat{g} \geqslant 0$; and the n non-negativity conditions $x_i \geqslant 0$, $i = 1, \ldots, n$ (here all inequality constraints have been written in the general form $\phi \geqslant 0$). We saw above that if an inequality constraint was of the general form $\phi \geqslant 0$, then we could transform it to an equality constraint by subtracting a non-negative slack variable from its left-hand side. In this regard, the above constraints may be transformed to $\hat{g} - s_1^2 = 0$, $-\hat{g} - s_2^2 = 0$, and $x_i - s_{2+i}^2 = 0$, $i = 1, \ldots, n$, where the slack variables $s_1, s_2, s_{2+i} \geqslant 0$, $i = 1, \ldots, n$, have been squared to insure their non-negativity. Then the augmented Lagrangian may be formed as

$$\begin{aligned} L(\boldsymbol{x}, \lambda_1, \ldots, \lambda_{2+n}, s_1, \ldots, s_{2+n}) = {} & f(\boldsymbol{x}) + \lambda_1(\hat{g}(\boldsymbol{x}) - s_1^2) + \lambda_2(-\hat{g}(\boldsymbol{x}) - s_2^2) \\ & + \sum_{i=1}^{n} \lambda_{2+i}(x_i - s_{2+i}^2) \end{aligned}$$

with

$$\left.\begin{aligned} L_i &= \mathrm{f}_i+(\lambda_1-\lambda_2)\hat{\mathrm{g}}_i+\lambda_{2+i} = 0, \quad i = 1, \ldots, n \\ L_{\lambda_1} &= \hat{\mathrm{g}}-s_1^2 = 0, \\ L_{\lambda_2} &= -\hat{\mathrm{g}}-s_2^2 = 0, \\ L_{\lambda_{2+i}} &= x_i-s_{2+i}^2 = 0, \quad i = 1, \ldots, n, \\ L_{s_1} &= -2\lambda_1 s_1 = 0, \\ L_{s_2} &= -2\lambda_2 s_2 = 0, \\ L_{s_{2+i}} &= -2\lambda_{2+i}s_{2+i} = 0, \quad i = 1, \ldots, n. \end{aligned}\right\} \tag{11.4}$$

From $L_{\lambda_{2+i}} = 0$ we obtain $s_{2+i}^2 = x_i$, while $L_{s_{2+i}} = 0$ may be written as $\lambda_{2+i}s_{2+i}^2 = 0, i = 1, \ldots, n$. Then

$$\lambda_{2+i}s_{2+i}^2 = \lambda_{2+i}x_i = 0, \quad i = 1, \ldots, n.$$

From $L_i = 0$ we have

$$\lambda_{2+i} = -(\mathrm{f}_i+(\lambda_1-\lambda_2)\hat{\mathrm{g}}_i), \quad i = 1, \ldots, n.$$

Hence

$$\lambda_{2+i}x_i = x_i(\mathrm{f}_i+(\lambda_1-\lambda_2)\hat{\mathrm{g}}_i) = 0, \quad i = 1, \ldots, n. \tag{11.5}$$

With $L_{\lambda_1}, L_{\lambda_2} = 0, s_1^2 = \hat{\mathrm{g}}, s_2^2 = -\hat{\mathrm{g}}$, while $L_{s_1}, L_{s_2} = 0$ implies that $\lambda_1 s_1^2 = 0$, $\lambda_2 s_2^2 = 0$. Combining these last two sets of equalities yields $(\lambda_1-\lambda_2)\hat{\mathrm{g}} = 0$, or, upon setting $\lambda = \lambda_1-\lambda_2$, $\lambda\hat{\mathrm{g}} = 0$. Since the constraint $\hat{\mathrm{g}} = 0$ is binding, $\lambda\hat{\mathrm{g}} = 0$ when $\hat{\mathrm{g}} = 0$ (or when $\hat{\mathrm{g}} = 0$ and $\lambda_1 = \lambda_2$, $\lambda_1 \geqslant 0$, $\lambda_2 \geqslant 0$). At $\boldsymbol{x}_0$, eq. (11.5) becomes

$$x_i^0(\mathrm{f}_i^0+\lambda^0\hat{\mathrm{g}}_i^0) = 0, \quad i = 1, \ldots, n, \quad \text{or} \quad \sum_{i=1}^{n} x_i^0(\mathrm{f}_i^0+\lambda^0\hat{\mathrm{g}}_i^0) = 0. \tag{11.5.1}$$

So, for $i = 1, \ldots, n$, either $x_i^0 = 0$, in which case f_i^0 may be less than $\lambda^0\hat{\mathrm{g}}_i^0$, or $\mathrm{f}_i^0+\lambda^0\hat{\mathrm{g}}_i^0 = 0$, whereupon x_i^0 can assume a positive value.

If $\boldsymbol{x}_0$ is a local maximum of f subject to $\hat{\mathrm{g}} = 0$ and $\boldsymbol{x} \geqslant \mathbf{0}$, then

$$\mathrm{df}^0 = (\nabla \mathrm{f}^0)'\boldsymbol{h} \leqslant 0 \tag{11.6}$$

for those vectors $\boldsymbol{h}$ which do not violate $\hat{\mathrm{g}}(\boldsymbol{x}_0+\boldsymbol{h}) = 0$ and the non-negativity conditions. Since $\mathrm{d}\hat{\mathrm{g}}^0 = (\nabla\hat{\mathrm{g}}^0)'\boldsymbol{h} = 0$, eq. (11.6) becomes

$$\mathrm{df}^0 = \sum_{i=1}^{n-1} \mathrm{f}_i^0 h_i+\mathrm{f}_n h_n = \sum_{i=1}^{n-1} \mathrm{f}_i^0 h_i+\mathrm{f}_n \sum_{i=1}^{n-2} (-\hat{\mathrm{g}}_i^0/\hat{\mathrm{g}}_n^0)h_i \leqslant 0, \quad \hat{\mathrm{g}}_n^0 \neq 0. \tag{11.6.1}$$

For $\lambda^0 = -\mathrm{f}_n^0/\hat{\mathrm{g}}_n^0$ (here we are tacitly assuming that $x_n^0 > 0$),

$$\mathrm{df}^0 = \sum_{i=1}^{n-1} (\mathrm{f}_i^0+\lambda^0\hat{\mathrm{g}}_i^0)h_i \leqslant 0. \tag{11.6.2}$$

Let us now assume that at least one other component of $\boldsymbol{x}_0$, say x_k^0, is strictly positive (and thus $\lambda_{2+k} = 0$, $s_{2+k} > 0$). Then there exists a set of sufficiently small positive and negative deviations $h_k = \delta, -\delta$ such that, for $h_k = \delta > 0$, eq. (11.6.2) becomes

$$\mathrm{f}_k^0 + \lambda^0 \hat{\mathrm{g}}_k^0 \leqslant 0,$$

while for $h_k = -\delta < 0$, eq. (11.6.2) may be written as

$$\mathrm{f}_k^0 + \lambda^0 \hat{\mathrm{g}}_k^0 \geqslant 0,$$

whence

$$\mathrm{f}_k^0 + \lambda^0 \hat{\mathrm{g}}_k^0 = 0.$$

If $x_k^0 = 0$ (so that $\lambda_{2+k} > 0$, $s_{2+k} = 0$), h_k can only be positive. Hence $h_k = \delta > 0$ in eq. (11.6.2) yields

$$\mathrm{f}_k^0 + \lambda^0 \hat{\mathrm{g}}_k^0 \leqslant 0.$$

What about the sign of λ^0? Since λ^0 is the difference between the two non-negative variables λ_1, λ_2, obviously this difference may be positive, negative, or zero. Hence λ^0 is unrestricted in sign. Q.E.D.

If we wish to minimize f subject to $\hat{\mathrm{g}} = 0$ and $\boldsymbol{x} \geqslant \mathbf{0}$, $\boldsymbol{x} \in \mathscr{E}^n$, eq. (11.3) becomes

$$\left.\begin{array}{l}
\nabla \mathrm{f}^0 - \lambda^0 \nabla \hat{\mathrm{g}}^0 \geqslant \mathbf{0} \quad \text{or} \quad \mathrm{f}_i^0 - \lambda^0 \hat{\mathrm{g}}_i^0 \geqslant 0, \quad i = 1, \ldots, n, \\
\boldsymbol{x}_0'(\nabla \mathrm{f}^0 - \lambda^0 \nabla \hat{\mathrm{g}}^0) = 0 \quad \text{or} \quad \sum_{i=1}^{n} x_i^0(\mathrm{f}_i^0 - \lambda^0 \hat{\mathrm{g}}_i^0) = 0, \\
\hat{\mathrm{g}}^0 = 0, \\
\lambda^0 \text{ unrestricted}, \\
\boldsymbol{x}_0 \geqslant \mathbf{0} \quad \text{or} \quad x_i^0 \geqslant 0, \quad i = 1, \ldots, n.
\end{array}\right\} \qquad (11.3.1)$$

by virtue of the discussion underlying eq. (11.1.1).

In actual practice how may we obtain a constrained local extremum of f under eqs. (11.3) and (11.3.1)? It is obvious that if such an extremum occurs at a point $\boldsymbol{x}_0 \in \mathscr{E}^n$, $\boldsymbol{x}_0$ must be either an interior point of the non-negative orthant, wherein each of its components is strictly positive, or a boundary point of the same, in which case one or more of its components is zero. Hence two cases emerge: (1) if $\boldsymbol{x}_0$ is a point interior to the non-negative orthant, it represents the simultaneous solution of $\nabla \mathrm{f} \pm \lambda \nabla \hat{\mathrm{g}} = \mathbf{0}$, $\hat{\mathrm{g}} = 0$; or (2) if $\boldsymbol{x}_0$ is a boundary point of the non-negative orthant, we first set each of the n variables in turn equal to zero, and thus solve n separate problems involving $n-1$ non-zero variables. For each of these problems the value of f is computed. Next, two variables are set equal to zero, with the result that we must solve $n!/2!(n-2)!$ (the total number of combinations of two variables whose values are zero) separate problems in $n-2$ non-zero variables. Again the f value for each problem is obtained. This process is continued until we finally set $n-1$ variables equal to zero, with f determined in each of these n cases. The constrained local maximum (minimum) of f is then taken to be the largest (smallest) of all of the f values determined parts in (1) and (2).

Example 11.3. Minimize the real-valued function $y = \mathrm{f}(\boldsymbol{x}) = 5x_1^2+10(x_2-3)^2$ subject to

$$x_1 - x_2^2 = 1 \quad \text{or} \quad \hat{\mathrm{g}} = 1-x_2+x_1^2 = 0, \quad \boldsymbol{x} \geqslant \boldsymbol{0}.$$

From eq. (11.2.1) we have

$$\begin{aligned} 10x_1-2\lambda x_1 &\geqslant 0,\\ 20(x_2-3)+\lambda &\geqslant 0,\\ x_1(10x_1-2\lambda x_1) &= 0,\\ x_2(20(x_2-3)+\lambda) &= 0,\\ 1-x_2+x_1^2 &= 0,\\ x_1, x_2 &\geqslant 0. \end{aligned}$$

First, if $\boldsymbol{x}_0$ is an interior point of the non-negative orthant, it must be found among the simultaneous solution of

$$\begin{aligned} 10x_1-2\lambda x_1 &= 0,\\ 20(x_2-3)+\lambda &= 0,\\ 1-x_2+x_1^2 &= 0. \end{aligned}$$

In this regard, $\boldsymbol{x}_0' = (\sqrt{\tfrac{70}{40}}, \tfrac{110}{40})$, $\lambda^0 = 5$ (fig. 11.4). Also, $\mathrm{f}(\boldsymbol{x}_0) = 9.4$. Second, since $x_1, x_2 = 0$ is not feasible, this case will be ignored. Next, since $x_2 = 0$, $x_1 > 0$ violates $\hat{\mathrm{g}} = 0$, this case will also be dismissed. Finally, for $x_1 = 0$, $x_2 > 0$, we obtain $\boldsymbol{x}_1' = (0, 1)$ as a solution to the above system with $\mathrm{f}(\boldsymbol{x}_1) = 40$. Since we are looking for the constrained minimum of f, it is obvious that it occurs at $\boldsymbol{x}_0$ and is of the strong local variety since $|\boldsymbol{H}_L^{\hat{\mathrm{g}}}(\boldsymbol{x}_0, \lambda^0)| = -140 < 0$ are required.

The time has now come to combine the necessary conditions incorporated in theorems 11.1 and 11.2 to form the generalized KTL necessary condition for a constrained local maximum. Before doing so, however, let us visualize the implied set of permissible solutions. In this instance we seek to determine a local extremum of the real-valued function $y = \mathrm{f}(\boldsymbol{x})$ when $\boldsymbol{x}$ must satisfy $\mathrm{g}(\boldsymbol{x}) \leqslant b$ or $\hat{\mathrm{g}}(\boldsymbol{x}) \geqslant 0$ and $\boldsymbol{x} \geqslant \boldsymbol{0}$, $\boldsymbol{x} \in \mathscr{E}^n$. Hence we obtain, for instance, the region of feasible solutions COD of fig. 11.1. We now turn to the proper KTL formulation of this optimization problem. To this end we state

THEOREM 11.3 (a generalized necessary condition). *Let the real-valued functions $y = \mathrm{f}(\boldsymbol{x})$, $\hat{\mathrm{g}}(\boldsymbol{x}) \geqslant 0$, $\boldsymbol{x} \in \mathscr{E}^n$, be defined over an open region $\mathscr{K} \subseteq \mathscr{E}^n$ and differentiable throughout some spherical δ-neighborhood of the point $\boldsymbol{x}_0 \in \mathscr{K}$.*

If f *subject to* $\hat{g} \geqslant 0$ *and* $\boldsymbol{x} \geqslant \mathbf{0}$ *has a local maximum at* $\boldsymbol{x}_0$, *then*

$$\left.\begin{aligned} &\nabla f^0 + \lambda^0 \nabla \hat{g}^0 \leqslant \mathbf{0} \quad \text{or} \quad f_i^0 + \lambda^0 \hat{g}_i^0 \leqslant 0, \quad i = 1, \ldots, n, \\ &\boldsymbol{x}_0'(\nabla f^0 + \lambda^0 \nabla \hat{g}^0) = 0 \quad \text{or} \quad \sum_{i=1}^{n} x_i^0 (f_i^0 + \lambda^0 \hat{g}_i^0) = 0, \\ &\lambda^0 \hat{g}^0 = 0, \\ &\hat{g}^0 \geqslant 0, \\ &\lambda^0 \geqslant 0, \\ &\boldsymbol{x}_0 \geqslant \mathbf{0} \quad \text{or} \quad x_i^0 \geqslant 0, \quad i = 1, \ldots, n. \end{aligned}\right\} \quad (11.7)^2$$

Proof. Our goal is to maximize f subject to $\hat{g} \geqslant 0$, $\boldsymbol{x} \geqslant \mathbf{0}$. To employ the technique of Lagrange these inequalities will be transformed to $\hat{g} - s_1^2 = 0$ and $x_i - s_{1+i}^2 = 0$, $i = 1, \ldots, n$, where s_1, s_{1+i}, $i = 1, \ldots, n$, are non-negative slack variables. Upon forming the augmented Lagrangian

$$L(\boldsymbol{x}, \lambda_1, \ldots, \lambda_{1+n}, s_1, \ldots, s_{1+n}) = f(\boldsymbol{x}) + \lambda_1(\hat{g}(\boldsymbol{x}) - s_1^2) + \sum_{i=1}^{n} \lambda_{1+i}(x_i - s_{1+i}^2)$$

---

[2] We have seen that eq. (11.3) is a special case of this theorem if $\hat{g} = 0$ is rewritten as $\hat{g} \geqslant 0$, $-\hat{g} \geqslant 0$ and $\lambda = \lambda_1 - \lambda_2$. That eq. (11.1) is also a special case may be verified by expressing each variable x_i as the difference between two non-negative variables x_i', x_i'', $i = 1, \ldots, n$. That is to say, $x_i = x_i' - x_i''$, $x_i', x_i'' \geqslant 0$. To see this, let us first form the augmented Lagrangian

$$L(\boldsymbol{x}_1, \boldsymbol{x}_2, \lambda_1, \ldots, \lambda_{1+2n}, s_1, \ldots, s_{1+2n}) = f(\boldsymbol{x}) + \lambda_1 (\hat{g}(\boldsymbol{x}) - s_1^2) + \sum_{i=1}^{n} \lambda_{1+i} (x_i' - s_{1+i}^2) + \sum_{i=1}^{n} \lambda_{1+n+i} (x_i'' - s_{1+n+i}^2),$$

where

$$\boldsymbol{x} = \boldsymbol{x}_1 - \boldsymbol{x}_2, \qquad \boldsymbol{x}_1' = (x_1', \ldots, x_n'), \boldsymbol{x}_2' = (x_1'', \ldots, x_n''),$$

and $s_1, \ldots, s_{1+n+i}$, $i = 1, \ldots, n$, are non-negative slack variables. In addition,

$$\left.\begin{aligned} f_{\hat{x}_i'} &= f_i & \hat{g}_{\hat{x}_i'} &= \hat{g}_i \\ f_{\hat{x}_i''} &= -f_i & \hat{g}_{\hat{x}_i''} &= -\hat{g}_i \end{aligned}\right\} \; i = 1, \ldots, n.$$

From

$$L_{\hat{x}_i'} = L_{\hat{x}_i''} = L_{\lambda j} = L_{sj} = 0, \quad i = 1, \ldots, n; \quad j = 1, \ldots, 1+2n,$$

it is easily shown that

$$\lambda_{1+i} x_i' + \lambda_{1+i+n} x_i'' = (x_i' - x_i'')(f_i + \lambda_1 \hat{g}_i) = 0, \quad i = 1, \ldots, n.$$

At $\boldsymbol{x}_0$ this system becomes, for $\lambda_1 = \lambda^0$,

$$x_i^0 (f_i^0 + \lambda^0 \hat{g}_i^0) = 0, \quad i = 1, \ldots, n.$$

With $f_i^0 + \lambda^0 \hat{g}_i^0 = 0$, x_i^0, $i = 1, \ldots, n$, may be positive, negative, or zero since it is the difference between two non-negative variables. Thus the x_i, $i = 1, \ldots, n$, are unrestricted in sign.

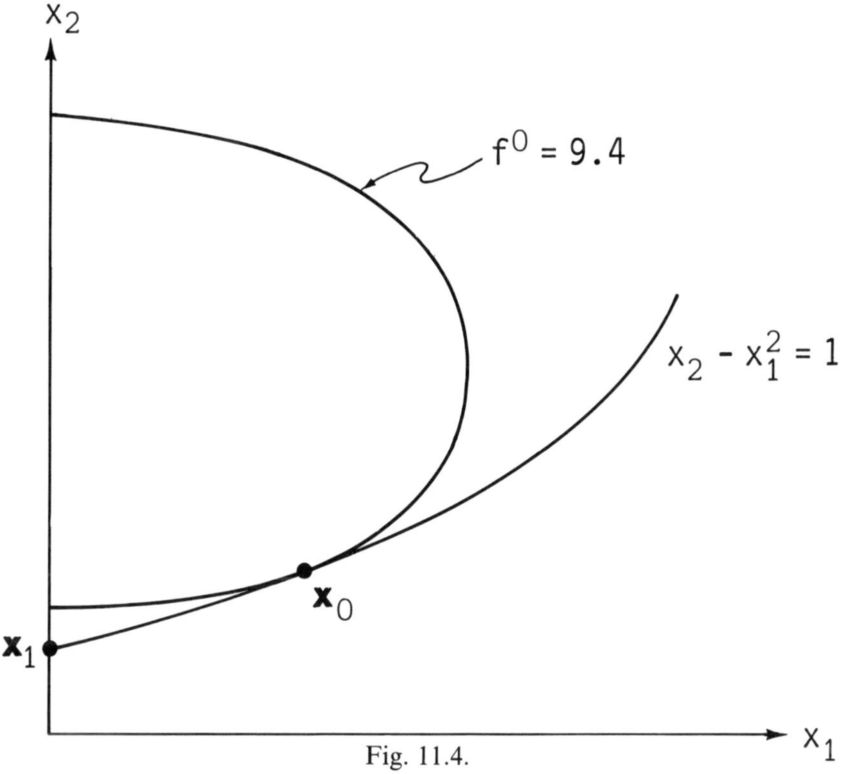

Fig. 11.4.

we obtain

$$\left.\begin{aligned} L_i &= \mathrm{f}_i + \lambda_1 \hat{\mathrm{g}}_i - \lambda_{1+i} = 0, \quad i = 1, \ldots, n \\ L_\lambda &= \hat{\mathrm{g}} - s_1^2 = 0 \\ L_{\lambda_{1+i}} &= x_i - s_{1+i}^2 = 0, \quad i = 1, \ldots, n \\ L_{s_1} &= -2\lambda_1 s_1 = 0 \\ L_{s_{1+i}} &= -2\lambda_{1+i} s_{1+i} = 0, \quad i = 1, \ldots, n. \end{aligned}\right\} \tag{11.8}$$

From L_{λ_1}, $L_{s_1} = 0$ we obtain, at $\boldsymbol{x}_0$, $\lambda^0 \hat{\mathrm{g}}^0 = 0$. That is, if the constraint $\hat{\mathrm{g}} \geqslant 0$ is not binding at $\boldsymbol{x}_0$, then $\lambda^0 = 0$, while if it is binding, $\lambda^0 \geqslant 0$ there. Combining $L_{\lambda_{1+i}} = 0$ with $L_{s_{1+i}} = 0$ yields $\lambda_{1+i} x_i = 0$, $i = 1, \ldots, n$. From $L_i = 0$ we have $\lambda_{1+i} = \mathrm{f}_i + \lambda_1 \hat{\mathrm{g}}_i$. Then, at $\boldsymbol{x}_0$, these expressions taken together imply, for $\lambda_1 = \lambda^0$,

$$x_i^0(\mathrm{f}_i^0 + \lambda^0 \hat{\mathrm{g}}_i^0) = 0, \quad i = 1, \ldots, n \quad \text{or} \quad \sum_{i=1}^{n} x_i^0(\mathrm{f}_i^0 + \lambda^0 \hat{\mathrm{g}}_i^0) = 0.$$

In this regard, for $i = 1, \ldots, n$, either $x_i^0 = 0$, allowing f_i^0 to be less than $\lambda^0 \hat{\mathrm{g}}_i^0$, or $\mathrm{f}_i^0 + \lambda^0 \hat{\mathrm{g}}_i^0 = 0$, in which case x_i^0 may be positive.

If f subject to $\hat{\mathrm{g}} \geqslant 0$ and $\boldsymbol{x} \geqslant \mathbf{0}$ attains a local maximum at $\boldsymbol{x}_0$ then, from eq. (11.6),

$$df^0 = (\nabla f^0)' \boldsymbol{h} \leqslant 0$$

for those vectors $\boldsymbol{h}$ which satisfy $d\hat{g}^0 \geqslant 0$ and the non-negativity conditions.

For $\hat{g}^0 > 0 (\lambda^0 = 0, s_1 > 0)$, the first equation of (11.7) states that $f_i^0 \leqslant 0$, $i = 1, \ldots, n$. This may be demonstrated with the aid of eq. (11.6), i.e. given $\Sigma_{i=1}^n f_i^0 h_i \leqslant 0$, let $h_i = 0$, $i \neq k$. Then, if $x_k^0 > 0 (\lambda_{1+k} = 0, s_{1+k} > 0)$, there exists a set of sufficiently small positive and negative deviations $h_k = \delta, -\delta$ such that, for $h_k = \delta > 0$, $f_k^0 \leqslant 0$ while for $h_k = -\delta < 0$, $f_k^0 \geqslant 0$ or $f_k^0 = 0$. With $x_k^0 = 0$ $(\lambda_{1+k} > 0, s_{1+k} = 0)$, $f_k^0 \leqslant 0$ since negative deviations in x_k are not permissible.

If $\hat{g}^0 = 0$ $(\lambda^0 > 0, s_1 = 0)$, the discussion proceeds in the same fashion as that supporting the proof of (11.3). Here, too, $\lambda^0 \geqslant 0$ as evidenced by the discussion presented at the end of the proof of (11.1). Q.E.D.

To minimize f subject to $\hat{g} \geqslant 0$ and $\boldsymbol{x} \geqslant \boldsymbol{0}$, $\boldsymbol{x} \in \mathscr{E}^n$, we require that

$$\left.\begin{aligned}
&\nabla f^0 - \lambda^0 \nabla \hat{g}^0 \geqslant 0 \quad \text{or} \quad f_i^0 - \lambda^0 \hat{g}_i^0 \geqslant 0, \quad i = 1, \ldots, n,\\
&\boldsymbol{x}_0'(\nabla f^0 - \lambda^0 \nabla \hat{g}^0) = 0 \quad \text{or} \quad \sum_{i=1}^{n} x_i^0 (f_i^0 - \lambda^0 \hat{g}_i^0) = 0,\\
&\lambda^0 \hat{g}^0 = 0,\\
&\hat{g}^0 \geqslant 0,\\
&\lambda^0 \geqslant 0,\\
&\boldsymbol{x}_0 \geqslant \boldsymbol{0} \quad \text{or} \quad x_i^0 \geqslant 0, \quad i = 1, \ldots, n.
\end{aligned}\right\} \qquad (11.7.1)$$

Example 11.4. Maximize the real-valued function $y = f(\boldsymbol{x}) = (2x_1 + 1)(x_2 + 1)$ subject to $x_1^2 + x_2 \leqslant 1$ or $\hat{g} = 1 - x_1^2 - x_2 \geqslant 0$ with $\boldsymbol{x} \geqslant \boldsymbol{0}$ (fig. 11.5). From eq. (11.7) we obtain

$$\begin{aligned}
2(x_2+1) - 2\lambda x_1 &\leqslant 0,\\
2x_1 + 1 - \lambda &\leqslant 0,\\
x_1(2(x_2+1) - 2\lambda x_1) &= 0,\\
x_2(2x_1 + 1 - \lambda) &= 0,\\
\lambda(1 - x_1^2 - x_2) &= 0,\\
1 - x_1^2 - x_2 &\geqslant 0,\\
\lambda &\geqslant 0,\\
x_1, x_2 &\geqslant 0.
\end{aligned}$$

We may begin our search for the constrained maximum of f by considering the following cases:

(a) If $\lambda = 0$ (the constraint is not binding) and if $x_1, x_2 \neq 0$, the above system yields

$$\begin{aligned}
2(x_2+1) &= 0,\\
2x_1 + 1 &= 0
\end{aligned}$$

with solution $x_1 = -\frac{1}{2}$, $x_2 = -1$. Obviously, this solution is inadmissible.

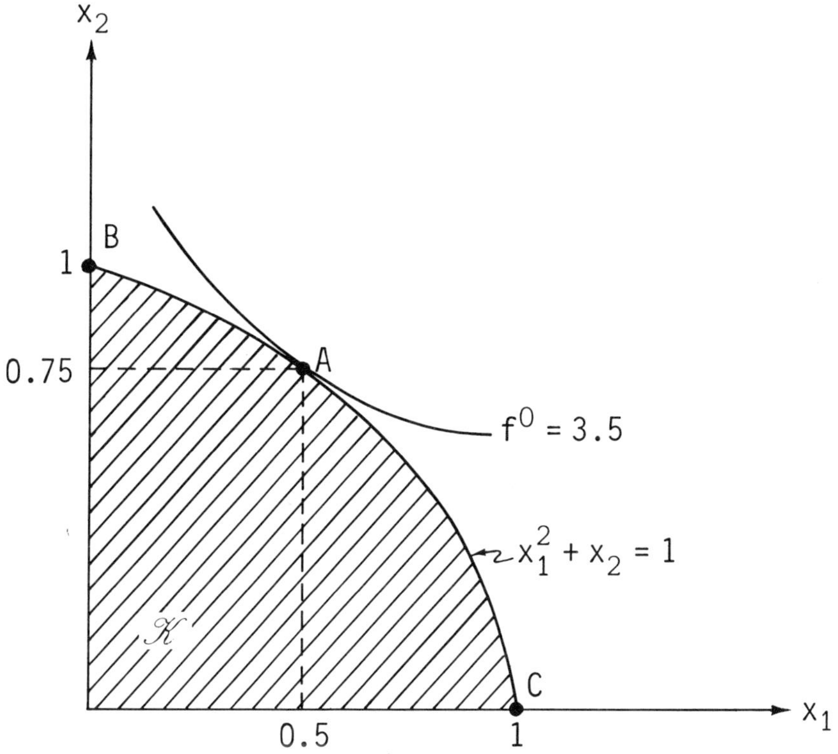

Fig. 11.5.

(b) Also, for $\lambda = 0$, the instances where $x_1 = 0$ and/or $x_2 = 0$ yield inconsistent results.

(c) If $\lambda > 0$ (the constraint is binding) and $x_1, x_2 \neq 0$, eq. (11.6) becomes

$$\begin{aligned} 2(x_2+1)-2\lambda x_1 &= 0, \\ 2x_1+1-\lambda &= 0, \\ 1-x_1^2-x_2 &= 0, \end{aligned}$$

implying that $\boldsymbol{x}_0' = (0.5, 0.75)$ and $\lambda^0 = 2$. In addition, $\mathrm{f}(\boldsymbol{x}_0) = 3.5$ (point A of fig. 11.5).

(d) If $\lambda > 0$ and $x_1 = 0$, we obtain

$$\begin{aligned} 2(x_2+1) &\leqslant 0, \\ 1-\lambda &= 0, \\ 1-x_2 &= 0 \end{aligned}$$

with $\boldsymbol{x}_1' = (0, 1)$, $\lambda^1 = 1$, and $\mathrm{f}(\boldsymbol{x}_1) = 2$ (point B of fig. 11.5).

(e) If $\lambda > 0$ and $x_2 = 0$, the above system becomes

$$\begin{aligned} 2-2\lambda x_1 &= 0, \\ 2x_1+1-\lambda &\leqslant 0, \\ 1-x_1^2 &= 0, \end{aligned}$$

implying that $\boldsymbol{x}_2' = (1, 0)$, $\lambda^2 = 1$, and $f(\boldsymbol{x}_2) = 3$ (point C of fig. 11.5). Hence the strong local constrained maximum of f occurs at $\boldsymbol{x}_0' = (0.5, 0.75)$ with $f(\boldsymbol{x}_0) = 3.5$, since $|\boldsymbol{H}_L^g(\boldsymbol{x}_0, \lambda^0)| = 8 > 0$ as required.

This example has indicated that to execute eqs. (11.7) and (11.7.1) we should: (1) first determine all solutions for the case where the constraint $\hat{g} \geqslant 0$ is not binding ($\lambda = 0$) with $x_i^0 \neq 0$, $i = 1, \ldots, n$ (so as to isolate a solution interior to the set of feasible points), and then with each variable, all pairs of variables, etc., in turn, set equal to zero (thus determining any boundary extrema); (2) then repeat this procedure with $\lambda > 0$ (the constraint is binding) and compare the f values obtained in (1) with those obtained in (2). The desired extremum will then be found among the solutions generated in parts (1) and (2).

One additional point regarding the structure of the KTL necessary conditions for a constrained extremum must be mentioned. Often, a structural constraint of the form $\hat{g} \geqslant 0$ is absent but we still require $\boldsymbol{x} \geqslant \boldsymbol{0}$, $\boldsymbol{x} \in \mathscr{E}^n$. In this instance the appropriate KTL necessary condition for a constrained local maximum of f at $\boldsymbol{x}_0$ is

$$\left.\begin{array}{lll} \nabla f^0 \leqslant \boldsymbol{0} & \text{or} & f_i^0 \leqslant 0, \\ \boldsymbol{x}_0' \nabla f^0 = 0 & \text{or} & x_i^0 f_i^0 = 0, \\ \boldsymbol{x}_0 \geqslant \boldsymbol{0} & \text{or} & x_i^0 \geqslant 0, \end{array}\right\} \quad i = 1, \ldots, n. \tag{11.8}$$

That is, either $x_i^0 = 0$, in which case $f_i^0 \leqslant 0$ or $x_i^0 > 0$, thus implying that $f_i^0 = 0$. For a constrained local minimum at $\boldsymbol{x}_0$,

$$\left.\begin{array}{lll} \nabla f^0 \geqslant \boldsymbol{0} & \text{or} & f_i^0 \geqslant 0, \\ \boldsymbol{x}_0' \nabla f^0 = 0 & \text{or} & x_i^0 f_i^0 = 0, \\ \boldsymbol{x}_0 \geqslant \boldsymbol{0} & \text{or} & x_i^0 \geqslant 0, \end{array}\right\} \quad i = 1, \ldots, n. \tag{11.8.1}$$

The proof of eqs. (11.8) and (11.8.1) is left as an exercise to the reader.

It must be emphasized that the above KTL conditions for identifying optimal points are only necessary and not sufficient conditions, e.g. the fact that a feasible solution satisfies the KTL conditions does not mean that it is optimal, but if it fails to satisfy them, it is definitely not optimal. In short, since the KTL conditions are a prerequisite for an optimal solution, they must be satisfied at any constrained extremum and thus provide a means of checking any admissible solution for optimality.

The sole purpose of this chapter has been to introduce the reader to the type of reasoning involved in generalizing the technique of Lagrange. The content was not intended to be exhaustive since only the bare essentials of Kuhn–Tucker theory were meant to be conveyed. Indeed such notions as a constraint qualification, convex and concave Lagrangians, a saddle point of the Lagrangian, complementary slackness, and duality, have been purposely ignored and will be considered in the next chapter.

Chapter 12

KUHN–TUCKER THEORY: A GENERALIZATION TO m INEQUALITY CONSTRAINTS

12.1. A generalized necessary condition for a constrained local extremum

The problem which we shall now consider is as follows. We desire to maximize the real-valued function $y = \mathrm{f}(\boldsymbol{x})$ subject to m inequality constraints $b_j - \mathrm{g}^j(\boldsymbol{x}) \geqslant 0$, $j = 1, \ldots, m$, and n non-negativity conditions $\boldsymbol{x} \geqslant \mathbf{0}$, $\boldsymbol{x}' = (x_1, \ldots, x_n) \in \mathscr{E}^n$.[1] If we form the $(m \times 1)$ vector-valued function

$$\boldsymbol{G}(\boldsymbol{x}) = \begin{bmatrix} b_1 - \mathrm{g}^1(\boldsymbol{x}) \\ \vdots \\ b_m - \mathrm{g}^m(\boldsymbol{x}) \end{bmatrix} = \begin{bmatrix} \hat{\mathrm{g}}^1(\boldsymbol{x}) \\ \vdots \\ \hat{\mathrm{g}}^m(\boldsymbol{x}) \end{bmatrix} \geqslant \mathbf{0},$$

then our problem may be rewritten as maximizing the real-valued function $y = \mathrm{f}(\boldsymbol{x})$ subject to $\boldsymbol{G}(\boldsymbol{x}) \geqslant \mathbf{0}$, $\boldsymbol{x} \geqslant \mathbf{0}$, $\boldsymbol{x} \in \mathscr{E}^n$. Here $\boldsymbol{G}(\boldsymbol{x}) \geqslant \mathbf{0}$, $\boldsymbol{x} \geqslant \mathbf{0}$ define a region of feasible or admissible solutions in $\mathscr{E}^n$. That is to say,

DEFINITION 12.1. *The feasible region $\mathscr{K} \subseteq \mathscr{E}^n$ is the set of points (vectors) $\boldsymbol{x}$ which simultaneously satisfy all the inequality constraints and non-negativity conditions, i.e.*

$$\mathscr{K} = \{\boldsymbol{x} \mid \boldsymbol{G}(\boldsymbol{x}) \geqslant \mathbf{0}, \boldsymbol{x} \geqslant \mathbf{0}, \boldsymbol{x} \in \mathscr{E}^n\}.$$

Thus the above problem simply becomes: maximize the real-valued function $y = \mathrm{f}(\boldsymbol{x})$ subject to $\boldsymbol{x} \in \mathscr{K}$. Further,

DEFINITION 12.2. *A point $\boldsymbol{x}$ is called a feasible point if $\boldsymbol{x} \in \mathscr{K}$.*

For convenience, the restrictions $x_i \geqslant 0$, $i = 1, \ldots, n$, will be rewritten as $\hat{\mathrm{g}}^{m+i}(\boldsymbol{x}) \geqslant 0$, $i = 1, \ldots, n$. Hence, we ultimately maximize the real-valued

[1] Here we do not require that $m < n$ as was the case when we optimized f subject to m equality constraints. In this instance the inequalities $b_j - g^j(\boldsymbol{x}) \geqslant 0$, $j = 1, \ldots, m$, merely define a region the size of which varies inversely with the number of constraints m.

function $y = \mathrm{f}(\boldsymbol{x})$ subject to $\boldsymbol{x} \in \mathscr{K} = \{\boldsymbol{x} | \bar{\boldsymbol{G}}(\boldsymbol{x}) \geqslant \boldsymbol{0},\ \boldsymbol{x} \in \mathscr{E}^n\}$, where

$$\bar{\boldsymbol{G}}(\boldsymbol{x}) = \begin{bmatrix} \hat{\mathrm{g}}^1(\boldsymbol{x}) \\ \vdots \\ \hat{\mathrm{g}}^m(\boldsymbol{x}) \\ \hat{\mathrm{g}}^{m+1}(\boldsymbol{x}) \\ \vdots \\ \hat{\mathrm{g}}^{m+n}(\boldsymbol{x}) \end{bmatrix} \geqslant \boldsymbol{0}$$

is an $(m+n \times 1)$ vector-valued function whose jth component is $\hat{\mathrm{g}}^j(\boldsymbol{x}) \geqslant 0$, $j = 1, \ldots, m+n$. In this formulation $\boldsymbol{x}$ is unrestricted.

We noted in the previous chapter that the general guiding principle upon which the Kuhn–Tucker–Lagrange (KTL) (necessary) conditions are predicated is that no permissible change in $\boldsymbol{x}$ can improve the optimal value of the objective function. How are we to characterize such admissible changes? Additionally, it was noted in chapter 2 that any vector $\boldsymbol{x} \in \mathscr{E}^n$ may serve to specify a direction. In this regard, a feasible direction may be taken to be a vector such that a small movement along it violates no constraint. So if $\boldsymbol{x}$ is feasible, a feasible direction at $\boldsymbol{x}$ is a vector $\boldsymbol{h}$ such that $\boldsymbol{x}+t\boldsymbol{h}$ is feasible for t sufficiently small, i.e. if $\boldsymbol{x}+t\boldsymbol{h}$ is feasible whenever $\boldsymbol{x}$ is, $\boldsymbol{h}$ specifies a feasible direction. Hence, we can always move a short distance from $\boldsymbol{x}$ in the $\boldsymbol{h}$-direction and still remain in the feasible region $\mathscr{K}$. More specifically,

DEFINITION 12.3. *Let $\delta(\boldsymbol{x}_0)$ be a suitably restricted spherical δ-neighborhood about the feasible point $\boldsymbol{x}_0 \in \mathscr{E}^n$. Then the $(n+1)$ vector $\boldsymbol{h}$ is a feasible direction at $\boldsymbol{x}_0$ if there exists a scalar $t \geqslant 0$, $0 \leqslant t < \delta$, such that $\boldsymbol{x}_0 + t\boldsymbol{h}$ is feasible.*

In this regard,

DEFINITION 12.4. *For $\delta(\boldsymbol{x}_0)$ a suitably restricted spherical δ-neighborhood about the feasible point $\boldsymbol{x}_0 \in \mathscr{E}^n$, the set of feasible directions at $\boldsymbol{x}_0$, $\mathscr{D}(\boldsymbol{x}_0)$, is the collection of all $(n \times 1)$ vectors $\boldsymbol{h}$ such that $\boldsymbol{x}_0 + t\boldsymbol{h}$ is feasible for t sufficiently small, i.e.*

$$\mathscr{D}(\boldsymbol{x}_0) = \{\boldsymbol{h} | \textit{if } \boldsymbol{x}_0 \in \mathscr{K}, \textit{ then } \boldsymbol{x}_0 + t\boldsymbol{h} \in \mathscr{K}, 0 \leqslant t < \delta\}.$$

Geometrically, $\mathscr{D}(\boldsymbol{x}_0)$ is a *tangent support cone* approximating $\mathscr{K}$ in the neighborhood of $\boldsymbol{x}_0$, i.e. it is the finite cone containing all feasible directions at $\boldsymbol{x}_0$ and is generated by the tangent or supporting hyperplanes to $\mathscr{K}$ at $\boldsymbol{x}_0$ (fig. 12.1). To see this we need only remember that since each supporting hyperplane to $\mathscr{K}$ at $\boldsymbol{x}_0$, $\nabla\hat{\mathrm{g}}^j(\boldsymbol{x}_0)'(\boldsymbol{x}-\boldsymbol{x}_0) = 0$, specifies a closed half-space $\nabla\hat{\mathrm{g}}^j(\boldsymbol{x}_0)'(\boldsymbol{x}-\boldsymbol{x}_0) \geqslant 0$, the tangent support cone $\mathscr{D}(\boldsymbol{x}_0)$ represents that portion of the intersection of these closed half-spaces in the immediate vicinity of $\boldsymbol{x}_0$.

What is the relationship between the set $\mathscr{D}(\boldsymbol{x}_0)$, where $\boldsymbol{x}_0$ is now assumed to be an optimal (local maximal) point, and: (a) $\mathrm{f}(\boldsymbol{x}_0)$; (b) $\bar{\boldsymbol{G}}(\boldsymbol{x}_0) \geqslant \boldsymbol{0}$? To

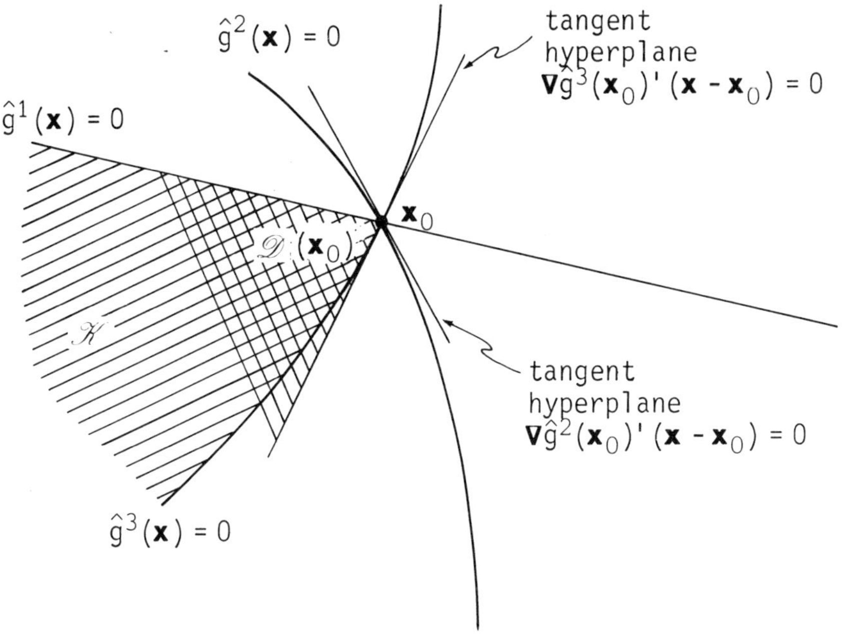

Fig. 12.1.

answer part (a) we state

THEOREM 12.1. *If the real-valued function* $y = \mathrm{f}(\boldsymbol{x})$, $\boldsymbol{x} \in \mathscr{K}$, *attains a local maximum at* $\boldsymbol{x}_0$, *than any movement from* $\boldsymbol{x}_0$ *along a feasible direction* $\boldsymbol{h}$ *cannot increase the value of* f, *i.e.*

$$\mathrm{df}^0 = \nabla \mathrm{f}(\boldsymbol{x}_0)'\boldsymbol{h} \leqslant 0, \quad \boldsymbol{h} \in \mathscr{D}(\boldsymbol{x}_0).$$

Proof. If $\mathrm{f}(\boldsymbol{x}_0)$ is a local maximum of $\mathrm{f}(\boldsymbol{x})$, $\boldsymbol{x} \in \mathscr{K}$, then

$$\mathrm{f}(\boldsymbol{x}_0 + t\boldsymbol{h}) - \mathrm{f}(\boldsymbol{x}_0) \leqslant 0, \quad \boldsymbol{h} \in \mathscr{D}(\boldsymbol{x}_0).$$

Hence,

$$\{\mathrm{f}(\boldsymbol{x}_0 + t\boldsymbol{h}) - \mathrm{f}(\boldsymbol{x}_0)\}/t \leqslant 0$$

and

$$\lim_{t \to 0} \{\mathrm{f}(\boldsymbol{x}_0 + t\boldsymbol{h}) - \mathrm{f}(\boldsymbol{x}_0)\}/t = \nabla \mathrm{f}(\boldsymbol{x}_0)'\boldsymbol{h} \leqslant 0. \quad \text{Q.E.D.}$$

That is, the directional derivative of f at $\boldsymbol{x}_0$, $\nabla \mathrm{f}(\boldsymbol{x}_0)'\boldsymbol{h}$, exhibits a decrease in any feasible direction. Since ∇f indicates the direction of maximum increase in f, a small movement $\boldsymbol{h}$ in any direction such that $\nabla \mathrm{f}(\boldsymbol{x}_0)'\boldsymbol{h} > 0$ (the angle between $\nabla \mathrm{f}(\boldsymbol{x}_0)$ and $\boldsymbol{h}$ is acute $(< \pi/2)$) increases f. So if the local maximum of f is at $\boldsymbol{x}_0$, $\nabla f(\boldsymbol{x}_0)'\boldsymbol{h} \leqslant 0$ for all $\boldsymbol{h} \in \mathscr{D}(\boldsymbol{x}_0)$. Hence, no feasible direction may form an acute angle between itself and $\nabla f(\boldsymbol{x}_0)$.

Next, for any optimal $\boldsymbol{x} \in \mathscr{K}$, it is usually the case that not all (if any) of the inequality constraints are binding or hold as an equality. To incorporate this observation in our analysis let us divide the components of $\bar{G}(\boldsymbol{x}) \geqslant \boldsymbol{0}$ into two mutually exclusive classes: those constraints which are binding at $\boldsymbol{x}$, $\hat{g}^j(\boldsymbol{x}) = 0$, and those which are not, $\hat{g}^j(\boldsymbol{x}) > 0, j = 1, \ldots, m, m+1, \ldots, m+n$. If we let $\mathscr{J} = \{j \mid \hat{g}^j(\boldsymbol{x}) = 0, \boldsymbol{x} \in \mathscr{E}^n\}$ depict the index set of binding constraints, then $\hat{g}^j(\boldsymbol{x}) > 0$ if $j \notin \mathscr{J}$. In what follows we shall ignore those constraints $\hat{g}^j(\boldsymbol{x}) \geqslant 0$ for which $j \notin \mathscr{J}$ since if $j \notin \mathscr{J}$ and $\hat{g}^j(\boldsymbol{x}) > 0$, then $\hat{g}^j(\boldsymbol{x} + t\boldsymbol{h}) > 0$ for t sufficiently small. So, to determine the connection between $\mathscr{D}(\boldsymbol{x}_0)$ ($\boldsymbol{x}_0$ optimal) and $\bar{G}(\boldsymbol{x}_0) \geqslant \boldsymbol{0}$ we need only consider those constraints with indices $j \in \mathscr{J}$, since if any constraint is inactive at $\boldsymbol{x}_0$, then for all $\boldsymbol{x} = \boldsymbol{x}_0 + t\boldsymbol{h} \in \delta(\boldsymbol{x}_0)$, the constraint remains inactive. To this end,

THEOREM 12.2. *If* $\boldsymbol{h} \in \mathscr{D}(\boldsymbol{x}_0)$ *(*$\boldsymbol{x}_0$ *optimal), then* $\nabla \hat{g}^j(\boldsymbol{x}_0)'\boldsymbol{h} \geqslant 0$, $j \in \mathscr{J}$.

Proof. For $\boldsymbol{h} \in \mathscr{D}(\boldsymbol{x}_0)$, $\hat{g}^j(\boldsymbol{x}_0 + \boldsymbol{h}) \geqslant 0$ for $\boldsymbol{h}$ small, $j \in \mathscr{J}$. By Taylor's formula,

$$\hat{g}^j(\boldsymbol{x}_0 + \boldsymbol{h}) \sim \hat{g}^j(\boldsymbol{x}_0) + \nabla \hat{g}^j(\boldsymbol{x}_0)'\boldsymbol{h}, \quad j \in \mathscr{J}.$$

With $\hat{g}^j(\boldsymbol{x}_0) = 0$, $\hat{g}^j(\boldsymbol{x}_0 + \boldsymbol{h}) \geqslant 0$ implies $\nabla \hat{g}^j(\boldsymbol{x}_0)'\boldsymbol{h} \geqslant 0$ (or $-\nabla \hat{g}^j(\boldsymbol{x}_0)'\boldsymbol{h} \leqslant 0$), $j \in \mathscr{J}$. Q.E.D.

To interpret this theorem we note that $\nabla \hat{g}^j(\boldsymbol{x}_0)$ is normal to $\hat{g}^j(\boldsymbol{x}) = 0$ at $\boldsymbol{x}_0$ and points in the direction of maximum increase of $\hat{g}^j(\boldsymbol{x}) = 0, j \in \mathscr{J}$. It may be described as an inward pointing or interior normal to the boundary of $\mathscr{K}$ at $\boldsymbol{x}_0$. So if $\boldsymbol{h}$ is a feasible direction, it makes a non-obtuse angle ($\leqslant \pi/2$) with all the interior normals to the boundary of $\mathscr{K}$ at $\boldsymbol{x}_0$. Geometrically, the interior normals or gradients of the binding constraints form a finite cone containing all feasible directions making non-obtuse angles with the supports to $\mathscr{K}$ at $\boldsymbol{x}_0$. Such a cone is polar to the tangent support cone $\mathscr{D}(\boldsymbol{x}_0)$ and will be termed the *polar support cone*, $\mathscr{D}(\boldsymbol{x}_0)^+$ (fig. 12.2a). Hence, given the tangent support cone $\mathscr{D}(\boldsymbol{x}_0)$ of feasible directions $\boldsymbol{h}$, the polar support cone $\mathscr{D}(\boldsymbol{x}_0)^+$ is the cone spanned by the gradients $\nabla \hat{g}^j(\boldsymbol{x}_0)$ such that for $\boldsymbol{h} \in \mathscr{D}(\boldsymbol{x}_0)$, $\nabla \hat{g}^j(\boldsymbol{x}_0)'\boldsymbol{h} \geqslant 0, j \in \mathscr{J}$. Alternatively, $-\nabla \hat{g}^j(\boldsymbol{x}_0)$ indicates the direction of maximum decrease of $\hat{g}^j(\boldsymbol{x}) = 0, j \in \mathscr{J}$, and represents an outward-pointing or exterior normal to the boundary of $\mathscr{K}$ at $\boldsymbol{x}_0$. If $\boldsymbol{h}$ is a feasible direction, it must now make a non-acute angle ($\geqslant \pi/2$) with all the outward-pointing normals to the boundary of $\mathscr{K}$ at $\boldsymbol{x}_0$. Again relying upon geometry, the exterior normals or negative gradients of the binding constraints form a finite cone containing all feasible directions making non-acute angles with the supports to $\mathscr{K}$ at $\boldsymbol{x}_0$. This cone is the dual of the tangent support cone $\mathscr{D}(\boldsymbol{x}_0)$ and is called the *dual support cone*, $\mathscr{D}(\boldsymbol{x}_0)^*$ (fig. 12.2b.). Hence, the dual

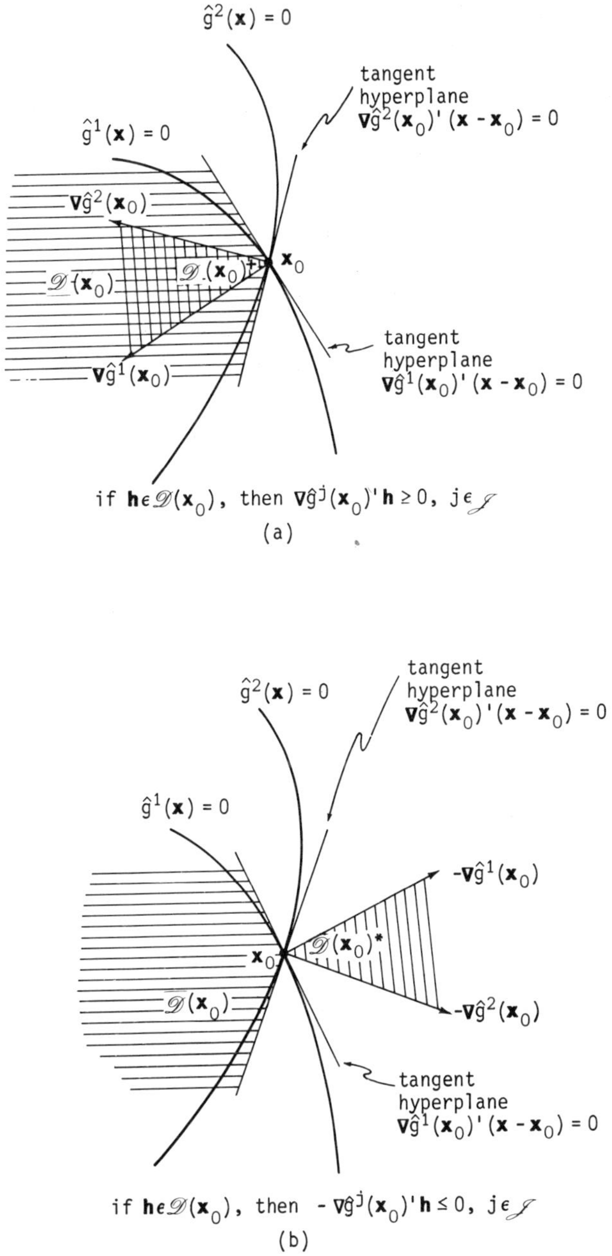

$\hat{g}^2(\mathbf{x}) = 0$
tangent hyperplane $\nabla\hat{g}^2(\mathbf{x}_0)'(\mathbf{x} - \mathbf{x}_0) = 0$
$\hat{g}^1(\mathbf{x}) = 0$
$\nabla\hat{g}^2(\mathbf{x}_0)$
$\mathbf{x}_0$
$\mathscr{D}(\mathbf{x}_0)$
$\mathscr{D}(\mathbf{x}_0)^+$
tangent hyperplane $\nabla\hat{g}^1(\mathbf{x}_0)'(\mathbf{x} - \mathbf{x}_0) = 0$
$\nabla\hat{g}^1(\mathbf{x}_0)$
if $\mathbf{h} \in \mathscr{D}(\mathbf{x}_0)$, then $\nabla\hat{g}^j(\mathbf{x}_0)'\mathbf{h} \geq 0$, $j \in \mathscr{J}$
(a)
$\hat{g}^2(\mathbf{x}) = 0$
tangent hyperplane $\nabla\hat{g}^2(\mathbf{x}_0)'(\mathbf{x} - \mathbf{x}_0) = 0$
$\hat{g}^1(\mathbf{x}) = 0$
$-\nabla\hat{g}^1(\mathbf{x}_0)$
$\mathbf{x}_0$
$\mathscr{D}(\mathbf{x}_0)^*$
$\overline{\mathscr{D}}(\mathbf{x}_0)$
$-\nabla\hat{g}^2(\mathbf{x}_0)$
tangent hyperplane $\nabla\hat{g}^1(\mathbf{x}_0)'(\mathbf{x} - \mathbf{x}_0) = 0$
if $\mathbf{h} \in \mathscr{D}(\mathbf{x}_0)$, then $-\nabla\hat{g}^j(\mathbf{x}_0)'\mathbf{h} \leq 0$, $j \in \mathscr{J}$
(b)

Fig. 12.2.

support cone $\mathscr{D}(\boldsymbol{x}_0)^*$ is the cone spanned by the negative gradients $-\nabla \hat{g}^j(\boldsymbol{x}_0)$ such that for each $\boldsymbol{h} \in \mathscr{D}(\boldsymbol{x}_0)$, $-\nabla \hat{g}^j(\boldsymbol{x}_0)'\boldsymbol{h} \leqslant 0, j \in \mathscr{J}$.

At this point let us collect together our major results. We found that if f subject to $\hat{g}^j(\boldsymbol{x}) = 0, j \in \mathscr{J}$, assumes its local maximum at $\boldsymbol{x}_0$, then

$$\nabla f(\boldsymbol{x}_0)'\boldsymbol{h} \leqslant 0 \quad \text{for all } \boldsymbol{h} \text{ satisfying} \quad \nabla \hat{g}^j(\boldsymbol{x}_0)'\boldsymbol{h} \geqslant 0, \quad j \in \mathscr{J}, \quad \boldsymbol{h} \in \mathscr{D}(\boldsymbol{x}_0). \tag{12.1}$$

How may we interpret this necessary condition? Given any $\boldsymbol{h} \in \mathscr{D}(\boldsymbol{x}_0)$, eq. (12.1) will hold if $\nabla f(\boldsymbol{x}_0)$ lies within the finite cone spanned by the exterior normals $-\nabla \hat{g}^j(\boldsymbol{x}_0), j \in \mathscr{J}$, i.e. $\nabla f(\boldsymbol{x}_0) \in \mathscr{D}(\boldsymbol{x}_0)^*$ (or if $-\nabla f(\boldsymbol{x}_0)$ is contained within the finite cone generated by the interior normals $\nabla \hat{g}^j(\boldsymbol{x}_0), j \in \mathscr{J}$, i.e. $-\nabla f(\boldsymbol{x}_0) \in \mathscr{D}(\boldsymbol{x}_0)^+$). Hence, eq. (12.1) requires that the gradient of f be a non-negative linear combination of the negative gradients of the binding constraints at $\boldsymbol{x}_0$ (fig. 12.3). In this regard, there must exist real numbers $\lambda_j^0 \geqslant 0$ such that

$$\nabla f(\boldsymbol{x}_0) = \sum_j \lambda_j^0(-\nabla \hat{g}^j(\boldsymbol{x}_0)), \quad j \in \mathscr{J}. \tag{12.2}$$

Under what conditions will the numbers $\lambda_j^0 \geqslant 0, j \in \mathscr{J}$, exist? Before answering this question let us look to a potential source of difficulty which we have, up to now, conveniently ignored. Theorem 12.2 demonstrated that if $\boldsymbol{h} \in \mathscr{D}(\boldsymbol{x}_0)$, then $\nabla \hat{g}^j(\boldsymbol{x}_0)'\boldsymbol{h} \geqslant 0$, $j \in \mathscr{J}$. Unfortunately, if $\nabla \hat{g}^j(\boldsymbol{x}_0)'\boldsymbol{h} \geqslant 0$, $j \in \mathscr{J}$, we may not legitimately conclude that $\boldsymbol{h} \in \mathscr{D}(\boldsymbol{x}_0)$, i.e. there may exist directions $\boldsymbol{h}$ which satisfy $\nabla \hat{g}^j(\boldsymbol{x}_0)'\boldsymbol{h} \geqslant 0$, $j \in \mathscr{J}$, but which are not feasible. Hence, it need not be true that $\nabla f(\boldsymbol{x}_0)'\boldsymbol{h} \leqslant 0$ for all $\boldsymbol{h}$ satisfying $\nabla \hat{g}^j(\boldsymbol{x}_0)'\boldsymbol{h} \geqslant 0, j \in \mathscr{J}$. To avoid such occurrences, Kuhn and Tucker, among others, have imposed a regularity condition on the constraints called a *constraint qualification.*[2] The purpose of this constraint qualification is simply to preclude the existence of directions $\boldsymbol{h}$ such that $\nabla f(\boldsymbol{x}_0)'\boldsymbol{h} > 0$ for $\nabla \hat{g}^j(\boldsymbol{x}_0)'\boldsymbol{h} \geqslant 0, j \in \mathscr{J}$. Since most instances in which the converse of theorem 12.2 does not hold are mathematical fabrications, we may assume, without loss of generality, that if $\boldsymbol{h} \in \mathscr{D}(\boldsymbol{x}_0)$, then $\nabla \hat{g}^j(\boldsymbol{x}_0)'\boldsymbol{h} \geqslant 0$, $j \in \mathscr{J}$, and conversely, i.e.

$$\{\boldsymbol{h} \mid \nabla f(\boldsymbol{x}_0)'\boldsymbol{h} > 0, \nabla \hat{g}^j(\boldsymbol{x}_0)'\boldsymbol{h} \geqslant 0, j \in \mathscr{J}\} = \phi.$$

In what follows, then, our attention will be restricted to those feasible regions $\mathscr{K}$ which satisfy the regularity condition, namely, that at an optimal point $\boldsymbol{x}_0$, $\nabla \hat{g}^j(\boldsymbol{x}_0)'\boldsymbol{h} \geqslant 0$, $j \in \mathscr{J}$, implies $\boldsymbol{h} \in \mathscr{D}(\boldsymbol{x}_0)$ (or $-\nabla \hat{g}^j(\boldsymbol{x}_0)'\boldsymbol{h} \leqslant 0$, $j \in \mathscr{J}$, implies $\boldsymbol{h} \in \mathscr{D}(\boldsymbol{x}_0)$). We now return to our initial question concerning the existence of non-negative λ_j^0's, $j \in \mathscr{J}$.

---

[2] For a discussion of the Kuhn–Tucker constraint qualification, as well as a description of some additional regularity requirements, see Appendix A to this chapter.

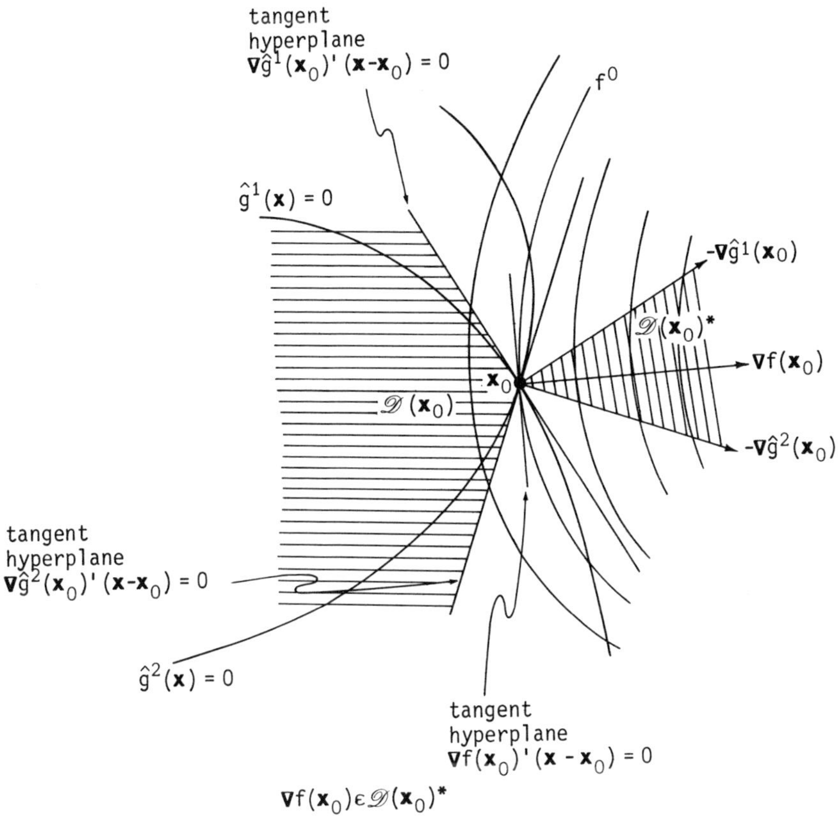

Fig. 12.3.

The verification procedure which we shall employ hinges upon the application of the Minkowski–Farkas theorem presented in chapter 1. In terms of the notation used there, if: $\boldsymbol{b} = \nabla \mathrm{f}(\boldsymbol{x}_0)$; the vectors $-\nabla \hat{\mathrm{g}}^j(\boldsymbol{x}_0)$, $j \in \mathscr{J}$, are taken to be the columns of $\boldsymbol{A}$; and the λ_j^0's, $j \in \mathscr{J}$, are the elements of $\boldsymbol{\lambda} \geqslant \boldsymbol{0}$, then, given that the regularity requirement holds, i.e. that

$$\{\boldsymbol{h} \mid \nabla \mathrm{f}(\boldsymbol{x}_0)'\boldsymbol{h} > 0,\ \nabla \hat{\mathrm{g}}^j(\boldsymbol{x}_0)'\boldsymbol{h} \geqslant 0,\ j \in \mathscr{J}\} = \phi$$

(here system (II) of the theorem of the separating hyperplane has no solution), a necessary and sufficient condition for $\nabla \mathrm{f}(\boldsymbol{x}_0)$ to lie within the finite cone spanned by the vectors $-\nabla \hat{\mathrm{g}}^j(\boldsymbol{x}_0)$ is that $\nabla \mathrm{f}(\boldsymbol{x}_0)'\boldsymbol{h} \leqslant 0$ for all $\boldsymbol{h}$ satisfying $-\nabla \hat{\mathrm{g}}^j(\boldsymbol{x}_0)'\boldsymbol{h} \leqslant 0$, $j \in \mathscr{J}$. Hence, there exist real numbers $\lambda_j^0 \geqslant 0$ such that

$$\nabla \mathrm{f}(\boldsymbol{x}_0) = \sum_j \lambda_j^0(-\nabla \hat{\mathrm{g}}^j(\boldsymbol{x}_0)), \quad j \in \mathscr{J}.$$

We may incorporate all the constraints (active or otherwise) $\hat{g}^j(\boldsymbol{x}) \geqslant 0$, $j = 1, \ldots, m+n$, into our discussion by defining the scalar λ_j^0 as zero whenever $\hat{g}^j(\boldsymbol{x}_0) > 0$ or $j \notin \mathscr{J}$. Then eq. (12.2) is equivalent to the system

$$\left.\begin{array}{l} \nabla f(\boldsymbol{x}_0) = \sum_{j=1}^{m+n} \lambda_j^0(-\nabla \hat{g}^j(\boldsymbol{x}_0)), \\ \left.\begin{array}{l} \lambda_j^0 \hat{g}^j(\boldsymbol{x}_0) = 0, \\ \hat{g}^j(\boldsymbol{x}_0) \geqslant 0, \\ \lambda_j^0 \geqslant 0, \end{array}\right\} \quad j = 1, \ldots, m+n, \\ \boldsymbol{x}_0 \text{ unrestricted.} \end{array}\right\} \tag{12.3}$$

Note that $\lambda_j^0 \hat{g}^j(\boldsymbol{x}_0) = 0$ for all values of j since if $\hat{g}^j(\boldsymbol{x}_0) > 0$, then $\lambda_j^0 = 0$, while if $\hat{g}^j(\boldsymbol{x}_0) = 0$, then $\lambda_j^0 \geqslant 0$. How might a system such as this arise? To formalize the answer we shall look to

THEOREM 12.3 (a generalized necessary condition). *Let the real-valued function $y = f(\boldsymbol{x})$ and the vector-valued function $\bar{\boldsymbol{G}}(\boldsymbol{x}) \geqslant \mathbf{0}$, $\boldsymbol{x} \in \mathscr{E}^n$, be defined over an open region $\mathscr{K}$ and differentiable throughout some spherical δ-neighborhood of the point $\boldsymbol{x}_0 \in \mathscr{K}$. If f subject to $\boldsymbol{x} \in \mathscr{K} = \{\boldsymbol{x} | \bar{\boldsymbol{G}}(\boldsymbol{x}) \geqslant 0, \boldsymbol{x} \in \mathscr{E}^n\}$ has a local maximum at $\boldsymbol{x}_0$, then, subject to the regularity condition*

$$\{\boldsymbol{h} | \nabla f(\boldsymbol{x}_0)'\boldsymbol{h} > 0, \nabla \hat{g}^j(\boldsymbol{x}_0)'\boldsymbol{h} \geqslant 0, j \in \mathscr{J}\} = \phi,$$

$$\left.\begin{array}{l} \nabla f(\boldsymbol{x}_0) + \nabla \bar{\boldsymbol{G}}(\boldsymbol{x}_0)\boldsymbol{\lambda}_0 = \mathbf{0}, \\ \boldsymbol{\lambda}_0' \bar{\boldsymbol{G}}(\boldsymbol{x}_0) = 0, \\ \bar{\boldsymbol{G}}(\boldsymbol{x}_0) = \mathbf{0}, \\ \boldsymbol{\lambda}_0 \geqslant \mathbf{0}, \\ \boldsymbol{x}_0 \textit{ unrestricted}, \end{array}\right\} \textit{ or } \left\{\begin{array}{l} \nabla f(\boldsymbol{x}_0) + \sum_{j=1}^{m+n} \lambda_j^0 \nabla \hat{g}^j(\boldsymbol{x}_0) = \mathbf{0}, \\ \sum_{j=1}^{m+n} \lambda_j^0 \hat{g}^j(\boldsymbol{x}_0) = 0, \\ \left.\begin{array}{l} \hat{g}^j(\boldsymbol{x}_0) \geqslant 0, \\ \lambda_j^0 \geqslant 0, \end{array}\right\} \quad j = 1, \ldots, m+n, \\ x_i^0 \textit{ unrestricted}, \quad i = 1, \ldots, n. \end{array}\right. \tag{12.4}$$

Here $\nabla \bar{\boldsymbol{G}}(\boldsymbol{x}_0)$ is an $(n \times m+n)$ matrix whose jth column is the vector $\nabla \hat{g}^j(\boldsymbol{x}_0)$, $j = 1, \ldots, m+n$, i.e.

$$\nabla \bar{\boldsymbol{G}}(\boldsymbol{x}_0) = [\nabla \hat{g}^1(\boldsymbol{x}_0), \ldots, \nabla \hat{g}^{m+n}(\boldsymbol{x}_0)].$$

Proof. The augmented Lagrangian associated with this problem is

$$L(\boldsymbol{x}, \boldsymbol{\lambda}, \boldsymbol{s}) = f(\boldsymbol{x}) + \boldsymbol{\lambda}'(\bar{\boldsymbol{G}}(\boldsymbol{x}) - \boldsymbol{s}),$$

where the inequality constraint $\bar{\boldsymbol{G}}(\boldsymbol{x}) \geqslant \mathbf{0}$ has been converted to an equality constraint $\bar{\boldsymbol{G}}(\boldsymbol{x}) - \boldsymbol{s} = \mathbf{0}$ by subtracting an $(m+n \times 1)$ vector of non-negative slack variables from the left-hand side of the former. Here

$$\boldsymbol{s} = \begin{bmatrix} s_1^2 \\ \vdots \\ s_{m+n}^2 \end{bmatrix} \geqslant \mathbf{0} \quad \text{with} \quad s_j^2 = \hat{g}^j(\boldsymbol{x}), \quad j = 1, \ldots, m+n.$$

Then

$$\begin{aligned} \nabla_{\boldsymbol{x}} L &= \nabla f(\boldsymbol{x}) + \nabla \bar{G}(\boldsymbol{x})\boldsymbol{\lambda} = \mathbf{0}, \\ \nabla_{\boldsymbol{\lambda}} L &= \bar{G}(\boldsymbol{x}) - \boldsymbol{s} = \mathbf{0}, \\ \nabla_{\boldsymbol{s}} L &= \boldsymbol{\lambda} = \mathbf{0}. \end{aligned}$$

Given that the regularity requirement holds at $\boldsymbol{x}_0$, the Minkowski–Farkas theorem implies the existence of a $\boldsymbol{\lambda}_0 \geqslant \mathbf{0}$ such that $\nabla f(\boldsymbol{x}_0) + \nabla \bar{G}(\boldsymbol{x}_0)\boldsymbol{\lambda}_0 = \mathbf{0}$ if and only if $\nabla f(\boldsymbol{x}_0)'\boldsymbol{h} \leqslant 0$ for all $\boldsymbol{h}$ satisfying $\nabla \hat{g}^j(\boldsymbol{x}_0)'\boldsymbol{h} \geqslant 0$, $j \in \mathscr{J}$. Next, from $\nabla_{\boldsymbol{\lambda}} L = \mathbf{0}$ we obtain $\boldsymbol{s} = \bar{G}(\boldsymbol{x})$ while $\boldsymbol{\lambda} = \mathbf{0}$ may be transformed to $\boldsymbol{\lambda}'\boldsymbol{s} = 0$. Combining these last two equalities yields, at $\boldsymbol{x}_0$, $\boldsymbol{\lambda}_0'\bar{G}(\boldsymbol{x}_0) = 0$. In this regard, if the jth constraint $\hat{g}^j(\boldsymbol{x}_0) \geqslant 0$, $j = 1, \ldots, m+n$, is not binding at $\boldsymbol{x}_0$ ($j \notin \mathscr{J}$), then $s_j > 0$, $\lambda_j^0 = 0$ while if $j \in \mathscr{J}$, $s_j = 0$, $\lambda_j^0 \geqslant 0$. Hence, at least one of each pair $(\lambda_j^0, \hat{g}^j(\boldsymbol{x}_0))$ vanishes, thus guaranteeing that $\boldsymbol{\lambda}_0'\bar{G}(\boldsymbol{x}_0) = 0$. Q.E.D.

When we formed the $(m+n \times 1)$ matrix $\bar{G}(\boldsymbol{x}) \geqslant \mathbf{0}$ the n non-negativity conditions $\boldsymbol{x} \geqslant \mathbf{0}$ were treated in a fashion similar to the other constraints. That is, $x_i \geqslant 0$ was converted to $\hat{g}^{m+i}(\boldsymbol{x}) \geqslant 0$, $i = 1, \ldots, n$. However, if the non-negativity conditions are not written in this fashion but appear explicitly as $\boldsymbol{x} \geqslant \mathbf{0}$, as is often the case, eq. (12.4) may be rewritten in the equivalent form

$$\left.\begin{aligned} &\nabla f(\boldsymbol{x}_0) + \nabla G(\boldsymbol{x}_0)\boldsymbol{\lambda}_0 \leqslant \mathbf{0}, \\ &\boldsymbol{x}_0'(\nabla f(\boldsymbol{x}_0) + \nabla G(\boldsymbol{x}_0)\boldsymbol{\lambda}_0) = 0, \\ &\boldsymbol{\lambda}_0' G(\boldsymbol{x}_0) = 0, \\ &G(\boldsymbol{x}_0) \geqslant \mathbf{0}, \\ &\boldsymbol{\lambda}_0 \geqslant \mathbf{0}, \\ &\boldsymbol{x}_0 \geqslant \mathbf{0}, \end{aligned}\right\} \text{ or } \left\{\begin{aligned} &\nabla f(\boldsymbol{x}_0) + \sum_{j=1}^{m} \lambda_j^0 \nabla \hat{g}^j(\boldsymbol{x}_0) \leqslant \mathbf{0}, \text{ or} \\ &f_i^0 + \sum_{j=1}^{m} \lambda_j^0 \hat{g}_i^j(\boldsymbol{x}_0) \leqslant 0, \quad i = 1, \ldots, n, \\ &\sum_{i=1}^{n} x_i^0 \Big(f_i^0 + \sum_{j=1}^{m} \lambda_j^0 \hat{g}_i^j(\boldsymbol{x}_0)\Big) = 0, \\ &\sum_{j=1}^{m} \lambda_j^0 \hat{g}^j(\boldsymbol{x}_0) = 0, \\ &\left.\begin{aligned} &\hat{g}^j(\boldsymbol{x}_0) \geqslant 0, \\ &\lambda_j^0 \geqslant 0, \end{aligned}\right\} \quad j = 1, \ldots, m, \\ &x_i^0 \geqslant 0, \quad i = 1, \ldots, n, \end{aligned}\right\} \tag{12.5}$$

where it is now to be understood that

$$G(\boldsymbol{x}_0) = \begin{bmatrix} \hat{g}^1(\boldsymbol{x}_0) \\ \vdots \\ \hat{g}^m(\boldsymbol{x}_0) \end{bmatrix} \geqslant \mathbf{0}$$

is of order $(m \times 1)$; $\nabla G(\boldsymbol{x}_0) = [\nabla \hat{g}^1(\boldsymbol{x}_0), \ldots, \nabla \hat{g}^m(\boldsymbol{x}_0)]$ is of order $(n \times m)$; and

$\boldsymbol{\lambda}_0$ is an $(m\times 1)$ vector of Lagrange multipliers λ_j^0. In this regard, for $i = 1, \ldots, n$, either $x_i^0 = 0$, allowing f_i^0 to be less than $-\Sigma_{j=1}^m \lambda_j^0 \hat{g}^j(\boldsymbol{x}_0)$, or $f_i^0 = \Sigma_{j=1}^m \lambda_j^0 \hat{g}^j(\boldsymbol{x}_0)$, in which case x_i^0 may be positive. Since at least one of these alternatives must hold, it follows that

$$\sum_{i=1}^{n} x_i^0 \left(f_i^0 + \sum_{j=1}^{m} \lambda_j^0 \hat{g}^j(\boldsymbol{x}_0) \right) = 0.$$

Additionally, if the jth constraint $\hat{g}^j(\boldsymbol{x}) \geqslant 0$, $j = 1, \ldots, m$, is inactive at $\boldsymbol{x}_0$, then $s_j > 0$, $\lambda_j^0 = 0$, while if it is binding there, $s_j = 0$, $\lambda_j^0 \geqslant 0$. Here, too, at least one of these alternatives holds, implying that $\Sigma_{j=1}^m \lambda_j^0 \hat{g}^j(\boldsymbol{x}_0) = 0$.

If the real-valued function $y = f(\boldsymbol{x})$ is to be minimized subject to $\boldsymbol{x} \in \mathscr{K} = \{\boldsymbol{x} \mid \bar{\boldsymbol{G}}(\boldsymbol{x}) \geqslant \boldsymbol{0}, \boldsymbol{x} \in \mathscr{E}^n\}$, eq. (12.4) becomes, at $\boldsymbol{x}_0$,

$$\left.\begin{aligned} &\nabla f(\boldsymbol{x}_0) - \nabla \bar{\boldsymbol{G}}(\boldsymbol{x}_0)\boldsymbol{\lambda}_0 = \boldsymbol{0},\\ &\boldsymbol{\lambda}_0' \bar{\boldsymbol{G}}(\boldsymbol{x}_0) = 0,\\ &\bar{\boldsymbol{G}}(\boldsymbol{x}_0) \geqslant \boldsymbol{0},\\ &\boldsymbol{\lambda}_0 \geqslant \boldsymbol{0},\\ &\boldsymbol{x}_0 \text{ unrestricted,} \end{aligned}\right\} \text{ or } \left\{\begin{aligned} &\nabla f(\boldsymbol{x}_0) - \sum_{j=1}^{m+n} \lambda_j^0 \nabla \hat{g}^j(\boldsymbol{x}_0) = \boldsymbol{0},\\ &\sum_{j=1}^{m+n} \lambda_j^0 \hat{g}^j(\boldsymbol{x}_0) = 0,\\ &\left.\begin{aligned}&\hat{g}^j(\boldsymbol{x}_0) \geqslant 0,\\ &\lambda_j^0 \geqslant 0,\end{aligned}\right\} \quad j = 1, \ldots, m+n\\ &x_i^0 \text{ unrestricted,} \quad i = 1, \ldots, n, \end{aligned}\right\} \tag{12.4.1}$$

since $\min f = -\max\{-f\}$. Additionally, under this same transformation, eq. (12.5) becomes

$$\left.\begin{aligned} &\nabla f(\boldsymbol{x}_0) - \nabla \boldsymbol{G}(\boldsymbol{x}_0)\boldsymbol{\lambda}_0 \geqslant \boldsymbol{0},\\ &\boldsymbol{x}_0'(\nabla f(\boldsymbol{x}_0) - \nabla \boldsymbol{G}(\boldsymbol{x}_0)\boldsymbol{\lambda}_0) = 0,\\ &\boldsymbol{\lambda}_0' \boldsymbol{G}(\boldsymbol{x}_0) = 0,\\ &\boldsymbol{G}(\boldsymbol{x}_0) \geqslant \boldsymbol{0},\\ &\boldsymbol{\lambda}_0 \geqslant \boldsymbol{0},\\ &\boldsymbol{x}_0 \geqslant \boldsymbol{0}, \end{aligned}\right\} \text{ or } \left\{\begin{aligned} &\nabla f(\boldsymbol{x}_0) - \sum_{j=1}^{m} \lambda_j^0 \nabla \hat{g}^j(\boldsymbol{x}_0) \geqslant \boldsymbol{0}, \text{ or}\\ &f_i^0 - \sum_{j=1}^{m} \lambda_j^0 \hat{g}_i^j(\boldsymbol{x}_0) \geqslant 0, \; i = 1, \ldots, n,\\ &\sum_{i=1}^{n} x_i^0 (f_i^0 - \sum_{j=1}^{m} \lambda_j^0 \hat{g}_i^j(\boldsymbol{x}_0)) = 0,\\ &\sum_{j=1}^{m} \lambda_j^0 \hat{g}^j(\boldsymbol{x}_0) = 0,\\ &\left.\begin{aligned}&\hat{g}^j(\boldsymbol{x}_0) \geqslant 0,\\ &\lambda_j^0 \geqslant 0,\end{aligned}\right\} \quad j = 1, \ldots, m\\ &x_i^0 \geqslant 0, \quad i = 1, \ldots, n. \end{aligned}\right\} \tag{12.5.1}$$

Example 12.1. Maximize the real-valued function

$$y = f(x_1, x_2) = -2x_1^2 - 3x_2^2 + 4x_1x_2 + 4x_1 + 2x_2$$

subject to

$$x_1 + 3x_2 \leqslant 6, \qquad 4x_1^2 + x_2^2 \leqslant 16, \qquad x_1, x_2 \geqslant 0.$$

To employ eq. (12.4) let us set

$$\bar{\boldsymbol{G}}(\boldsymbol{x}) = \begin{bmatrix} \hat{g}^1(x_1, x_2) \\ \hat{g}^2(x_1, x_2) \\ \hat{g}^3(x_1, x_2) \\ \hat{g}^4(x_1, x_2) \end{bmatrix} = \begin{bmatrix} 6 - x_1 - 3x_2 \\ 16 - 4x_1^2 - x_2^2 \\ x_1 \\ x_2 \end{bmatrix} \geqslant \boldsymbol{0}.$$

Then $\mathscr{K} = \{\boldsymbol{x} | \bar{\boldsymbol{G}}(\boldsymbol{x}) \geqslant \boldsymbol{0}, \boldsymbol{x} \in \mathscr{E}^2\}$ (fig. 12.4). From eq. (12.4)

$$\left.\begin{aligned} \nabla \mathrm{f}(\boldsymbol{x}) + \nabla \bar{\boldsymbol{G}}(\boldsymbol{x})\boldsymbol{\lambda} &= \begin{bmatrix} -4x_1 + 4x_2 + 4 - \lambda_1 - 8\lambda_2 x_1 + \lambda_3 \\ -6x_2 + 4x_1 + 2 - 3\lambda_1 - 2\lambda_2 x_2 + \lambda_4 \end{bmatrix} = \boldsymbol{0}, \\ \boldsymbol{\lambda}'\bar{\boldsymbol{G}}(\boldsymbol{x}) &= \lambda_1(6 - x_1 - 3x_2) + \lambda_2(16 - 4x_1^2 - x_2^2) \\ &\quad + \lambda_3 x_1 + \lambda_4 x_2 = 0, \\ \bar{\boldsymbol{G}}(\boldsymbol{x}) &= \begin{bmatrix} 6 - x_1 - 3x_2 \\ 16 - 4x_1^2 - x_2^2 \\ x_1 \\ x_2 \end{bmatrix} \geqslant \boldsymbol{0}, \quad \boldsymbol{\lambda} = \begin{bmatrix} \lambda_1 \\ \lambda_2 \\ \lambda_3 \\ \lambda_4 \end{bmatrix} \geqslant \boldsymbol{0}. \end{aligned}\right\} \quad (12.6)$$

We noted above that eq. (12.4) is only a necessary condition for a constrained local maximum. That is to say, if eq. (12.4) is satisfied at a point $\boldsymbol{x}_0 \in \mathscr{K}$, f may or may not attain a maximum there; but if eq. (12.4) does not hold at $\boldsymbol{x}_0$, f definitely does not attain any such extremum at that point. Our procedure then will be to test various points of $\mathscr{K}$ for optimality. A likely candidate is point A of fig. 12.4. Hence, for $j = 1, 2 \in \mathscr{J}$, eq. (12.6) becomes

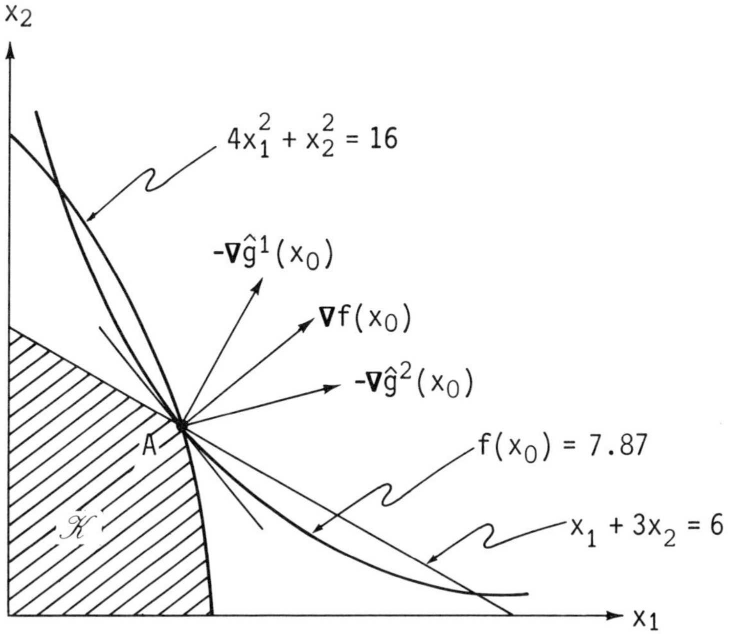

Fig. 12.4.

$$\left.\begin{aligned}
&\text{(a) } -4x_1+4x_2+4-\lambda_1-8\lambda_2 x_1 = 0;\\
&\text{(b) } -6x_2+4x_1+2-3\lambda_1-2\lambda_2 x_2 = 0;\\
&\quad \lambda_1(0)+\lambda_2(0)+0(x_1)+0(x_2) = 0;\\
&\text{(c) } 6-x_1-3x_2 = 0, \quad \lambda_1 \geqslant 0;\\
&\text{(d) } 16-4x_1^2-x_2^2 = 0, \quad \lambda_2 \geqslant 0;\\
&\quad x_1>0, \quad \lambda_3 = 0;\\
&\quad x_2>0, \quad \lambda_4 = 0.
\end{aligned}\right\} \tag{12.6.1}$$

From eq. (12.6.1(c), (d)) we obtain $(x_1^0, x_2^0) = (1.88, 1.37)$. A substitution of these values into eq. (12.6.1(a), (b)) yields $\lambda_1^0 = 0.31$, $\lambda_2^0 = 0.11$. In addition, f(1.88, 1.37) = 7.87. Hence f has a strong local constrained maximum at point A of fig. 12.4. (Note that at this point ∇f is a member of the cone spanned by the negative gradients of the binding constraints at $\boldsymbol{x}_0$.) In fact, point A is the only point which satisfies eq. (12.4).

Example 12.2. Minimize the real-valued function $y = \mathrm{f}(x_1, x_2) = (x_1-2)^2 + (x_2-1)^2$, where $-1 \leqslant x_1 \leqslant 1$, $0 \leqslant x_2 \leqslant \frac{1}{2}$. From the first restriction we obtain $\hat{g}^1(x_1, x_2) = 1-x_1 \geqslant 0$, $\hat{g}^2(x_1, x_2) = 1+x_1 \geqslant 0$; from the second $\hat{g}^3(x_1, x_2) = \frac{1}{2}-x_2 \geqslant 0$, $\hat{g}^4(x_1, x_2) = x_2 \geqslant 0$. Then

$$\bar{\boldsymbol{G}}(\boldsymbol{x}) = \begin{bmatrix}\hat{g}^1(x_1, x_2)\\ \hat{g}^2(x_1, x_2)\\ \hat{g}^3(x_1, x_2)\\ \hat{g}^4(x_1, x_2)\end{bmatrix} = \begin{bmatrix}1-x_1\\ 1+x_1\\ \frac{1}{2}-x_2\\ x_2\end{bmatrix} \geqslant \mathbf{0}.$$

From eq. (12.4.1)

$$\left.\begin{aligned}
&\nabla \mathrm{f}(\boldsymbol{x}) - \nabla\bar{\boldsymbol{G}}(\boldsymbol{x})\boldsymbol{\lambda} = \begin{bmatrix}2(x_1-2)+\lambda_1-\lambda_2\\ 2(x_2-1)+\lambda_3-\lambda_4\end{bmatrix} = \mathbf{0},\\
&\boldsymbol{\lambda}'\bar{\boldsymbol{G}}(\boldsymbol{x}) = \lambda_1(1-x_1)+\lambda_2(1+x_1)+\lambda_3(\tfrac{1}{2}-x_2)+\lambda_4 x_2 = 0,\\
&\bar{\boldsymbol{G}}(\boldsymbol{x}) = \begin{bmatrix}1-x_1\\ 1+x_1\\ \frac{1}{2}-x_2\\ x_2\end{bmatrix} \geqslant \mathbf{0}, \qquad \boldsymbol{\lambda} = \begin{bmatrix}\lambda_1\\ \lambda_2\\ \lambda_3\\ \lambda_4\end{bmatrix} \geqslant \mathbf{0}.
\end{aligned}\right\} \tag{12.7}$$

For $j = 1, 3 \in \mathscr{J}$, eq. (12.7) becomes

$$\left.\begin{aligned}
&\text{(a) } 2(x_1-2)+\lambda_1 = 0;\\
&\text{(b) } 2(x_2-1)+\lambda_3 = 0;\\
&\quad \lambda_1(0)+0(x_1+1)+\lambda_3(0)+0(x_2) = 0;\\
&\text{(c) } 1-x_1 = 0, \quad \lambda_1 \geqslant 0;\\
&\quad x_1+1>0, \quad \lambda_2 = 0;\\
&\text{(d) } \tfrac{1}{2}-x_2 = 0, \quad \lambda_3 \geqslant 0;\\
&\quad x_2>0, \quad \lambda_4 = 0.
\end{aligned}\right\} \tag{12.7.1}$$

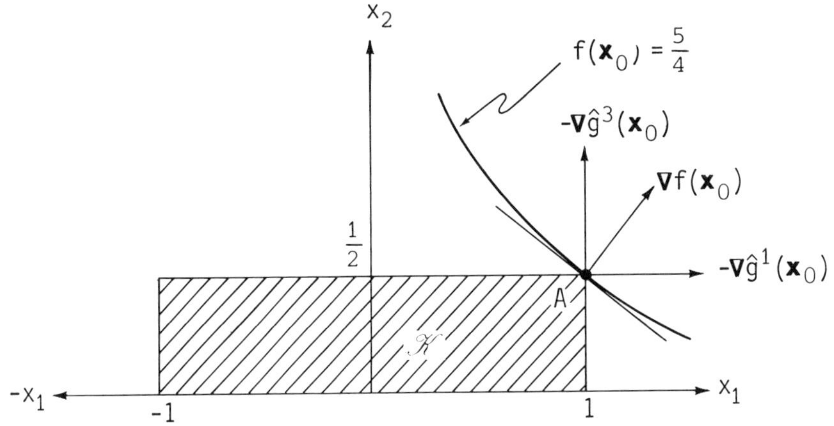

Fig. 12.5.

Employing eq. (12.7.1(c), (d)) yields $x_0' = (1, \frac{1}{2})$. Evaluating eq. (12.7.1(a), (b)) at this point (point A of fig. 12.5) gives $\lambda_1^0 = 2$, $\lambda_3^0 = 1$ with $\mathrm{f}(x_0) = \frac{5}{4}$ representing the strong local constrained minimum of f over $\mathscr{K}$.

12.2. Convex and concave Lagrangians

In this section we shall busy ourselves with analyzing the circumstances under which the KTL conditions are both necessary and sufficient to insure not only a constrained local extremum but a constrained global extremum as well. In our analysis of the KTL optionality conditions we have not as yet assumed any specific functional forms for the real-valued functions $y = \mathrm{f}(x)$, $\hat{\mathrm{g}}^j(x) \geq 0$, $j = 1, \ldots, m$, $x \in \mathscr{E}^n$. In this section such an assumption will be made. We shall first undertake a demonstration of the conditions under which the set of all points satisfying $\hat{\mathrm{g}}^j(x) \geq 0$, $j = 1, \ldots, m$, is a convex set.

THEOREM 12.4. *If the real-valued function* $\hat{\mathrm{g}}^j(x) \geq 0$, $x \in \mathscr{E}^n$, *is concave, then the set* $\mathscr{K}_j = \{x \,|\, \hat{\mathrm{g}}^j(x) \geq 0, x \in \mathscr{E}^n\}$ *is convex,*[3] $j = 1, \ldots, m$.

Proof. For $x_1, x_2 \in \mathscr{K}_j \subseteq \mathscr{E}^n$, $\hat{\mathrm{g}}^j(x_1) \geq 0$, $\hat{\mathrm{g}}^j(x_2) \geq 0$. In addition, let $\hat{\mathrm{g}}^j(x_1) \geq \hat{\mathrm{g}}^j(x_2)$. With $\hat{\mathrm{g}}^j$ concave,

$$\hat{\mathrm{g}}^j(x_c) \geq \theta \hat{\mathrm{g}}^j(x_2) + (1-\theta)\hat{\mathrm{g}}^j(x_1), \quad 0 \leq \theta \leq 1,$$

where $x_c = \theta x_2 + (1-\theta)x_1$. With $\hat{\mathrm{g}}^j(x_1) \geq \hat{\mathrm{g}}^j(x_2)$,

$$\theta \hat{\mathrm{g}}^j(x_2) + (1-\theta)\hat{\mathrm{g}}^j(x_1) \geq \theta \hat{\mathrm{g}}^j(x_2) + (1-\theta)\hat{\mathrm{g}}(x_2) = \hat{\mathrm{g}}(x_2) \geq 0.$$

Hence, $\hat{\mathrm{g}}^j(x_c) \geq \hat{\mathrm{g}}^j(x_2) \geq 0$ so that $x_c \in \mathscr{K}^j$, and thus $\mathscr{K}_j$ is convex. Q.E.D.

[3] Note that for $\hat{\mathrm{g}}^j = b - \mathrm{g}^j \geq 0$, $j = 1, \ldots, m$, to be concave over a convex set, g^j must be convex since if g^j is convex, $-\mathrm{g}^j$ is concave and conversely.

So if $\hat{g}^j \geqslant 0, j = 1, \ldots, m$, is concave, the set of points satisfying this inequality is a convex set. Before employing this theorem in our search for constrained extrema we state

THEOREM 12.5. *Let the real-valued functions $h^i(\boldsymbol{x})$, $\boldsymbol{x} \in \mathscr{E}^n$, $i = 1, \ldots, k$, be concave over the convex region $\mathscr{K} \subseteq \mathscr{E}^n$. Then any non-negative linear combination of the h^i is concave over $\mathscr{K}$, i.e. if $h^1, \ldots, h^k$ are all concave on $\mathscr{K}$, then so is*

$$h(\boldsymbol{x}) = \sum_{i=1}^{k} \alpha_i h^i(\boldsymbol{x}), \quad \alpha_i \geqslant 0, \quad i = 1, \ldots, k.$$

Proof. For $\boldsymbol{x}_1, \boldsymbol{x}_2 \in \mathscr{K}$, let $\boldsymbol{x}_c = \theta \boldsymbol{x}_2 + (1-\theta)\boldsymbol{x}_1 \in \mathscr{K}, 0 \leqslant \theta \leqslant 1$. If the functions h^i, $i = 1, \ldots, k$, are all concave over $\mathscr{K}$, then

$$\theta h^i(\boldsymbol{x}_2) + (1-\theta)h^i(\boldsymbol{x}_1) \leqslant h^i(\boldsymbol{x}_c), \quad 0 \leqslant \theta \leqslant 1,$$

and thus, for $\alpha_i \geqslant 0$, $i = 1, \ldots, k$,

$$\theta \alpha_i h^i(\boldsymbol{x}_2) + (1-\theta)\alpha_i h^i(\boldsymbol{x}_i) \leqslant \alpha_i h^i(\boldsymbol{x}_c).$$

Upon summing over all i we obtain

$$\theta \sum_{i=1}^{k} \alpha_i h^i(\boldsymbol{x}_2) + (1-\theta) \sum_{i=1}^{k} \alpha_i h^i(\boldsymbol{x}_1) \leqslant \sum_{i=1}^{k} \alpha_i h^i(\boldsymbol{x}_c). \tag{12.8}$$

If we define $h(\boldsymbol{x}) = \Sigma_{i=1}^{k} \alpha_i h^i(\boldsymbol{x})$, then eq. (12.8) may be written as

$$\theta h(\boldsymbol{x}_2) + (1-\theta)h(\boldsymbol{x}_1) \leqslant h(\boldsymbol{x}_c).$$

Hence, $h(\boldsymbol{x})$ is concave whenever the h^i are, and $\alpha_i \geqslant 0$, $i = 1, \ldots, k$. Q.E.D. Also,

THEOREM 12.6. *The intersection of a finite number of convex sets is convex, i.e. if the sets $\mathscr{S}_i$, $i = 1, \ldots, k$, are all convex, then $\mathscr{S} = \bigcap_{i=1}^{k} \mathscr{S}_i$ is convex.*

Proof. If $\boldsymbol{x}_1, \boldsymbol{x}_2 \in \mathscr{S}$, then $\boldsymbol{x}_1, \boldsymbol{x}_2 \in \mathscr{S}_i$, $i = 1, \ldots, k$. With each $\mathscr{S}_i$ convex,

$$\boldsymbol{x}_c = \theta \boldsymbol{x}_2 + (1-\theta)\boldsymbol{x}_1 \in \mathscr{S}_i, \quad i = 1, \ldots, k, \quad 0 \leqslant \theta \leqslant 1.$$

Hence, $\boldsymbol{x}_c \in \bigcap_{i=1}^{k} \mathscr{S}_i = \mathscr{S}$. Q.E.D.

Now the feasible region $\mathscr{K} = \{\boldsymbol{x} | \hat{g}^j(\boldsymbol{x}) \geqslant 0, \boldsymbol{x} \in \mathscr{E}^n, j = 1, \ldots, m+n\}$. If each g^j is convex, then $\hat{g}^j \geqslant 0, j = 1, \ldots, m$, is concave. Obviously each $\hat{g}^{m+i} \geqslant 0$, $i = 1, \ldots, n$, is concave. By theorem 12.4, $\mathscr{K}_j = \{\boldsymbol{x} | \hat{g}^j(\boldsymbol{x}) \geqslant 0, \boldsymbol{x} \in \mathscr{E}^n\}$, $j = 1, \ldots, m+n$, is convex. With $\mathscr{K} = \bigcap_{j=1}^{m+n} \mathscr{K}_j$, $\mathscr{K}$ must also be a convex set by the preceding theorem.

In light of these remarks, if the real-valued functions $y = f(\boldsymbol{x})$, $\hat{g}^j(\boldsymbol{x}) \geqslant 0$, $j = 1, \ldots, m$, are strictly concave over the convex region

$$\mathscr{K} = \{\boldsymbol{x} | \bar{\boldsymbol{G}}(\boldsymbol{x}) \geqslant \boldsymbol{0}, \boldsymbol{x} \in \mathscr{E}^n\},$$

then eq. (12.4) becomes a necessary and sufficient condition for a strong local (and thus strong global) constrained maximum of f. More specifically,

THEOREM 12.7 (a generalized necessary and sufficient condition). *Let the real-valued function* $y = \mathrm{f}(\boldsymbol{x})$ *and the vector-valued function* $\bar{\boldsymbol{G}}(\boldsymbol{x}) \geqslant \boldsymbol{0}$, $\boldsymbol{x} \in \mathscr{E}^n$, *be strictly concave over the convex region* $\mathscr{K} = \{\boldsymbol{x} | \bar{\boldsymbol{G}}(\boldsymbol{x}) \geqslant \boldsymbol{0},\ \boldsymbol{x} \in \mathscr{E}^n\}$ *and differentiable at* $\boldsymbol{x}_0 \in \mathscr{K}$ *with*

$$\{\boldsymbol{h} | \nabla \mathrm{f}(\boldsymbol{x}_0)'\boldsymbol{h} > 0,\ \nabla \hat{\mathrm{g}}^j(\boldsymbol{x}_0)'\boldsymbol{h} \geqslant 0, j \in \mathscr{I}\} = \phi.$$

Then f *subject to* $\bar{\boldsymbol{G}}(\boldsymbol{x}) \geqslant \boldsymbol{0}$ *has a strong global maximum at* $\boldsymbol{x}_0$ *if and only if eq. (12.4) holds.*

Proof. We shall treat the strictly concave case only. A similar proof holds for f, $\bar{\boldsymbol{G}}$ strictly convex on $\mathscr{K}$, in which case f attains a strong global constrained minimum at $\boldsymbol{x}_0$. (Necessity.) If eq. (12.4) is not satisfied, then $\boldsymbol{x}_0$ cannot be a constrained extremum of f. (Sufficiency.) For $\boldsymbol{x} \in \mathscr{K}$,

$$\mathrm{f}(\boldsymbol{x}) \leqslant \mathrm{f}(\boldsymbol{x}) + \boldsymbol{\lambda}_0'\bar{\boldsymbol{G}}(\boldsymbol{x}) = L(\boldsymbol{x}, \boldsymbol{\lambda}_0).$$

With $L(\boldsymbol{x}, \boldsymbol{\lambda}_0)$ strictly concave in $\boldsymbol{x}$ over $\mathscr{K}$,

$$\begin{aligned} L(\boldsymbol{x}, \boldsymbol{\lambda}_0) &< L(\boldsymbol{x}_0, \boldsymbol{\lambda}_0) + \nabla_{\boldsymbol{x}} L(\boldsymbol{x}_0, \boldsymbol{\lambda}_0)'(\boldsymbol{x} - \boldsymbol{x}_0) \\ &= \mathrm{f}(\boldsymbol{x}_0) + \boldsymbol{\lambda}_0'\bar{\boldsymbol{G}}(\boldsymbol{x}_0) + (\nabla \mathrm{f}(\boldsymbol{x}_0) + \nabla \bar{\boldsymbol{G}}(\boldsymbol{x}_0)\boldsymbol{\lambda}_0)'(\boldsymbol{x} - \boldsymbol{x}_0) = \mathrm{f}(\boldsymbol{x}_0). \end{aligned}$$

Hence $\mathrm{f}(\boldsymbol{x}_0) > L(\boldsymbol{x}, \boldsymbol{\lambda}_0) \geqslant \mathrm{f}(\boldsymbol{x})$, $\boldsymbol{x} \in \mathscr{K}$, and thus f has a strong global constrained maximum at $\boldsymbol{x}_0$. Q.E.D.

12.3. Lagrangian saddle points

Throughout this section we shall assume that $\boldsymbol{x} \in \mathscr{E}^n$ and $\boldsymbol{\lambda} \in \mathscr{E}^m$, where $\boldsymbol{\lambda}$ is a vector of Lagrange multipliers λ_j, $j = 1, \ldots, m$. Then

DEFINITION 12.5. *A point* $(\boldsymbol{x}_0, \boldsymbol{\lambda}_0) \in \mathscr{E}^{n+m}$ *is termed a local saddle point of the Lagrangian* $L(\boldsymbol{x}, \boldsymbol{\lambda}) = \mathrm{f}(\boldsymbol{x}) + \boldsymbol{\lambda}'\boldsymbol{G}(\boldsymbol{x})$ *if there exists an open spherical δ-neighborhood about* $(\boldsymbol{x}_0, \boldsymbol{\lambda}_0)$, $\delta(\boldsymbol{x}_0, \boldsymbol{\lambda}_0)$, *such that*

$$L(\boldsymbol{x}, \boldsymbol{\lambda}_0) \leqslant L(\boldsymbol{x}_0, \boldsymbol{\lambda}_0) \leqslant L(\boldsymbol{x}_0, \boldsymbol{\lambda}) \tag{12.9}$$

for all $(\boldsymbol{x}, \boldsymbol{\lambda}) \in \delta(\boldsymbol{x}_0, \boldsymbol{\lambda}_0)$, $\boldsymbol{x} \geqslant \boldsymbol{0}$, $\boldsymbol{\lambda} \geqslant \boldsymbol{0}$.

Similarly,

DEFINITION 12.6. *A point* $(\boldsymbol{x}_0, \boldsymbol{\lambda}_0) \in \mathscr{E}^{n+m}$ *is termed a global saddle point of the Lagrangian* $L(\boldsymbol{x}, \boldsymbol{\lambda}) = \mathrm{f}(\boldsymbol{x}) + \boldsymbol{\lambda}'\boldsymbol{G}(\boldsymbol{x})$ *if*

$$L(\boldsymbol{x}, \boldsymbol{\lambda}_0) \leqslant L(\boldsymbol{x}_0, \boldsymbol{\lambda}_0) \leqslant L(\boldsymbol{x}_0, \boldsymbol{\lambda}) \tag{12.10}$$

for all $(\boldsymbol{x}, \boldsymbol{\lambda}) \in \mathscr{E}^{n+m}$, $\boldsymbol{x} \geqslant \boldsymbol{0}$, $\boldsymbol{\lambda} \geqslant \boldsymbol{0}$.

What these definitions imply is that $L(\boldsymbol{x}, \boldsymbol{\lambda})$ simultaneously attains, either locally or globally, a maximum with respect to $\boldsymbol{x}$, and a minimum with respect to $\boldsymbol{\lambda}$. Hence, eqs. (12.9) and (12.10) may be rewritten as

$$L(\boldsymbol{x}_0, \boldsymbol{\lambda}_0) = \max_{x \geq 0} \{\min_{\lambda \geq 0} L(\boldsymbol{x}, \boldsymbol{\lambda})\} = \min_{\lambda \geq 0} \{\max_{x \geq 0} L(\boldsymbol{x}, \boldsymbol{\lambda})\}, \tag{12.11}$$

and interpreted in either a local or global sense.

Under what conditions will there exist a local (global) saddle point at $(\boldsymbol{x}_0, \boldsymbol{\lambda}_0)$? More specifically, we look to the solution of what may be called the

SADDLE-POINT PROBLEM. *To find a point* $(\boldsymbol{x}_0, \boldsymbol{\lambda}_0)$ *such that eq. (12.9) holds for all* $(\boldsymbol{x}, \boldsymbol{\lambda}) \in \delta(\boldsymbol{x}_0, \boldsymbol{\lambda}_0)$ *or eq. (12.10) holds for all* $(\boldsymbol{x}, \boldsymbol{\lambda}) \in \mathscr{E}^{n+m}$, $\boldsymbol{x} \geq \boldsymbol{0}$, $\boldsymbol{\lambda} \geq \boldsymbol{0}$.

According to eq. (12.11) we shall now see that determining a saddle point of the Lagrangian corresponds to maximinimizing or minimaximizing it. To this end we state first

THEOREM 12.8 (a necessary condition).[4] *Let* $\nabla_{\boldsymbol{x}} L$, $\nabla_{\boldsymbol{\lambda}} L$ *be respectively defined for all* $\boldsymbol{x} \in \delta(\boldsymbol{x}_0)$, $\boldsymbol{\lambda} \in \delta(\boldsymbol{\lambda}_0)$. *If* $L(\boldsymbol{x}, \boldsymbol{\lambda})$ *has a local saddle point at* $(\boldsymbol{x}_0, \boldsymbol{\lambda}_0)$, *then*

$$\left.\begin{aligned} &(a)\ \nabla_{\boldsymbol{x}} L^0 \leq \boldsymbol{0},\ (\nabla_{\boldsymbol{x}} L^0)' \boldsymbol{x}_0 = 0,\ \boldsymbol{x}_0 \geq \boldsymbol{0}; \\ &(b)\ \nabla_{\boldsymbol{\lambda}} L^0 \geq \boldsymbol{0},\ (\nabla_{\boldsymbol{\lambda}} L^0)' \boldsymbol{\lambda}_0 = 0,\ \boldsymbol{\lambda}_0 \geq \boldsymbol{0}. \end{aligned}\right\} \tag{12.12}$$

Proof. If $L(\boldsymbol{x}, \boldsymbol{\lambda}_0)$ has a local maximum in the $\boldsymbol{x}$-direction at $\boldsymbol{x}_0 \geq \boldsymbol{0}$, then eq. (11.8) and thus eq. (12.12(a)) holds. That is, either $x_i^0 = 0$, in which case $L_{x_i}^0 \leq 0$, or $x_i^0 > 0$, implying that $L_{x_i}^0 = 0$. If $L(\boldsymbol{x}_0, \boldsymbol{\lambda})$ has a local minimum in the $\boldsymbol{\lambda}$-direction at $\boldsymbol{\lambda}_0 \geq \boldsymbol{0}$, eq. (12.12(b)) holds because eq. (11.8.1) does. In this instance, either $\lambda_j^0 = 0$, in which case $L_{\lambda_j}^0 \geq 0$, or $\lambda_j^0 > 0$, implying that $L_{\lambda_j}^0 = 0$. Q.E.D.

We next consider

THEOREM 12.9 (a sufficient condition).[5] *Let* $\nabla_{\boldsymbol{x}} L$, $\nabla_{\boldsymbol{\lambda}} L$ *be respectively defined for all* $\boldsymbol{x} \in \delta(\boldsymbol{x}_0)$, $\boldsymbol{\lambda} \in \delta(\boldsymbol{\lambda}_0)$, $\boldsymbol{x} \geq \boldsymbol{0}$, $\boldsymbol{\lambda} \geq \boldsymbol{0}$. *If eq. (12.12) holds, then* $L(\boldsymbol{x}, \boldsymbol{\lambda})$ *has a local saddle point at* $(\boldsymbol{x}_0, \boldsymbol{\lambda}_0)$ *if*

$$\left.\begin{aligned} &(a)\ L(\boldsymbol{x}, \boldsymbol{\lambda}_0) \leq L(\boldsymbol{x}_0, \boldsymbol{\lambda}_0) + (\nabla_{\boldsymbol{x}} L^0)'(\boldsymbol{x} - \boldsymbol{x}_0); \\ &(b)\ L(\boldsymbol{x}_0, \boldsymbol{\lambda}) \geq L(\boldsymbol{x}_0, \boldsymbol{\lambda}_0) + (\nabla_{\boldsymbol{\lambda}} L^0)'(\boldsymbol{\lambda} - \boldsymbol{\lambda}_0). \end{aligned}\right\} \tag{12.13}$$

[4] See Kuhn and Tucker (1951), pp. 482–483.
[5] See Kuhn and Tucker (1951), p. 483.

Proof. Eqs. (12.13(a), (b)) may be rewritten as

$$L(\boldsymbol{x}, \boldsymbol{\lambda}_0) \leqslant L(\boldsymbol{x}_0, \boldsymbol{\lambda}_0) + (\nabla_x L^0)'\boldsymbol{x} - (\nabla_x L^0)'\boldsymbol{x}_0,$$
$$L(\boldsymbol{x}_0, \boldsymbol{\lambda}) \geqslant L(\boldsymbol{x}_0, \boldsymbol{\lambda}_0) + (\nabla_\lambda L^0)'\boldsymbol{\lambda} - (\nabla_\lambda L^0)'\boldsymbol{\lambda}_0.$$

From eq. (12.12(a)),

$$L(\boldsymbol{x}, \boldsymbol{\lambda}_0) \leqslant L(\boldsymbol{x}_0, \boldsymbol{\lambda}_0) + (\nabla_x L^0)'\boldsymbol{x} \leqslant L(\boldsymbol{x}_0, \boldsymbol{\lambda}_0),$$

while from eq. (12.12(b)),

$$L(\boldsymbol{x}_0, \boldsymbol{\lambda}) \geqslant L(\boldsymbol{x}_0, \boldsymbol{\lambda}_0) + (\nabla_\lambda L^0)'\boldsymbol{\lambda} \geqslant L(\boldsymbol{x}_0, \boldsymbol{\lambda}_0).$$

Combining these latter two sets of inequalities yields $L(\boldsymbol{x}, \boldsymbol{\lambda}_0) \leqslant L(\boldsymbol{x}_0, \boldsymbol{\lambda}_0) \leqslant L(\boldsymbol{x}_0, \boldsymbol{\lambda})$. Q.E.D.

Finally, we state

THEOREM 12.10 (a necessary and sufficient condition).[6] *Let* $L(\boldsymbol{x}, \boldsymbol{\lambda})$ *be defined for all* $(\boldsymbol{x}, \boldsymbol{\lambda}) \in \delta(\boldsymbol{x}_0, \boldsymbol{\lambda}_0)$, *where* $\boldsymbol{x}$ *is unrestricted and* $\boldsymbol{\lambda} \geqslant \mathbf{0}$. *Then* $L(\boldsymbol{x}, \boldsymbol{\lambda})$ *has a local saddle point at* $(\boldsymbol{x}_0, \boldsymbol{\lambda}_0)$ *if and only if*

$$\left.\begin{array}{ll} (a) & L(\boldsymbol{x}, \boldsymbol{\lambda}_0) \text{ attains a local maximum at } \boldsymbol{x}_0, \ \boldsymbol{x} \in \delta(\boldsymbol{x}_0); \\ (b) & \bar{\boldsymbol{G}}(\boldsymbol{x}_0) \geqslant \mathbf{0}; \\ (c) & \boldsymbol{\lambda}_0' \bar{\boldsymbol{G}}(\boldsymbol{x}_0) = 0. \end{array}\right\} \qquad (12.14)$$

Proof. (Necessity.) The left-hand inequality of eq. (12.9) is equivalent to eq. (12.14(a)). The right-hand inequality in eq. (12.9) implies that $\mathrm{f}(\boldsymbol{x}_0) + \boldsymbol{\lambda}'\bar{\boldsymbol{G}}(\boldsymbol{x}_0) \geqslant \mathrm{f}(\boldsymbol{x}_0) + \boldsymbol{\lambda}_0'\bar{\boldsymbol{G}}(\boldsymbol{x}_0)$ or $(\boldsymbol{\lambda} - \boldsymbol{\lambda}_0)'\bar{\boldsymbol{G}}(\boldsymbol{x}_0) \geqslant 0$. If $\bar{\boldsymbol{G}}(\boldsymbol{x}_0) \leqslant \mathbf{0}$, $\boldsymbol{\lambda} \in \delta(\boldsymbol{\lambda}_0)$ may be chosen sufficiently large so that $\boldsymbol{\lambda} - \boldsymbol{\lambda}_0 \geqslant \mathbf{0}$ or $(\boldsymbol{\lambda} - \boldsymbol{\lambda}_0)'\bar{\boldsymbol{G}}(\boldsymbol{x}_0) \leqslant 0$ whence $L(\boldsymbol{x}_0, \boldsymbol{\lambda}) \geqslant L(\boldsymbol{x}_0, \boldsymbol{\lambda}_0)$ is violated. Hence, eq. (12.14(b)) must hold. If $\boldsymbol{\lambda} = \mathbf{0}$, $(\boldsymbol{\lambda} - \boldsymbol{\lambda}_0)'\bar{\boldsymbol{G}}(\boldsymbol{x}_0) = \boldsymbol{\lambda}_0'\bar{\boldsymbol{G}}(\boldsymbol{x}_0) \leqslant 0$. But since $\boldsymbol{\lambda}_0 \geqslant \mathbf{0}$, $\bar{\boldsymbol{G}}(\boldsymbol{x}_0) \geqslant \mathbf{0}$ together imply $\boldsymbol{\lambda}_0'\bar{\boldsymbol{G}}(\boldsymbol{x}_0) \geqslant 0$, we see that eq. (12.14(c)) holds as well. So if $L(\boldsymbol{x}, \boldsymbol{\lambda})$ assumes a local saddle point at $(\boldsymbol{x}_0, \boldsymbol{\lambda}_0)$, eq. (12.14) holds.

(Sufficiency.) If $\boldsymbol{x}_0$ maximizes $L(\boldsymbol{x}, \boldsymbol{\lambda}_0)$, $\boldsymbol{x} \in \delta(\boldsymbol{x}_0)$, then $L(\boldsymbol{x}_0, \boldsymbol{\lambda}_0) \geqslant L(\boldsymbol{x}, \boldsymbol{\lambda}_0)$. If $\boldsymbol{\lambda}_0'\bar{\boldsymbol{G}}(\boldsymbol{x}_0) = 0$, then $L(\boldsymbol{x}_0, \boldsymbol{\lambda}_0) = \mathrm{f}(\boldsymbol{x}_0)$. Hence, $L(\boldsymbol{x}_0, \boldsymbol{\lambda}) = \mathrm{f}(\boldsymbol{x}_0) + \boldsymbol{\lambda}'\bar{\boldsymbol{G}}(\boldsymbol{x}_0) = L(\boldsymbol{x}_0, \boldsymbol{\lambda}_0) + \boldsymbol{\lambda}'\bar{\boldsymbol{G}}(\boldsymbol{x}_0)$ or $L(\boldsymbol{x}_0, \boldsymbol{\lambda}) \geqslant L(\boldsymbol{x}_0, \boldsymbol{\lambda}_0)$ since $\boldsymbol{\lambda}'\bar{\boldsymbol{G}}(\boldsymbol{x}_0) \geqslant 0$ if $\bar{\boldsymbol{G}}(\boldsymbol{x}_0) \geqslant \mathbf{0}$. So if eq. (12.14) holds, $L(\boldsymbol{x}, \boldsymbol{\lambda})$ has a local saddle point at $(\boldsymbol{x}_0, \boldsymbol{\lambda}_0)$. Q.E.D.

Up to this point we have not made any assumption about the form of $L(\boldsymbol{x}, \boldsymbol{\lambda}_0)$, $L(\boldsymbol{x}_0, \boldsymbol{\lambda})$. Let us now assume that $L(\boldsymbol{x}, \boldsymbol{\lambda}_0)$ is a concave function of $\boldsymbol{x}$

---

[6] Lasdon (1970), pp. 84–85.

and $L(\boldsymbol{x}_0, \boldsymbol{\lambda})$ is a convex function of $\boldsymbol{\lambda}$. In this regard, for $L(\boldsymbol{x}, \boldsymbol{\lambda}_0)$ concave, $L(\boldsymbol{x}, \boldsymbol{\lambda}_0) \leqslant L(\boldsymbol{x}_0, \boldsymbol{\lambda}_0) + (\nabla_{\boldsymbol{x}} L^0)'(\boldsymbol{x} - \boldsymbol{x}_0)$, while for $L(\boldsymbol{x}_0, \boldsymbol{\lambda})$ convex, $L(\boldsymbol{x}_0, \boldsymbol{\lambda}) \geqslant L(\boldsymbol{x}_0, \boldsymbol{\lambda}_0) + (\nabla_{\boldsymbol{\lambda}} L^0)'(\boldsymbol{\lambda} - \boldsymbol{\lambda}_0)$. Here the former (latter) expression depicts the equation of a hyperplane in $\mathscr{E}^{n+m}$ which is tangent to the surface $L(\boldsymbol{x}, \boldsymbol{\lambda})$ at $(\boldsymbol{x}_0, \boldsymbol{\lambda}_0)$ and lies above (below) it for all $\boldsymbol{x} \neq \boldsymbol{x}_0 (\boldsymbol{\lambda} \neq \boldsymbol{\lambda}_0)$. But these expressions are just eqs. (12.13(a), (b)). Hence, eqs. (12.13(a), (b)) are always satisfied at $(\boldsymbol{x}_0, \boldsymbol{\lambda}_0)$ if $L(\boldsymbol{x}, \boldsymbol{\lambda})$ is concave in $\boldsymbol{x} (\boldsymbol{\lambda} = \boldsymbol{\lambda}_0)$ and convex in $\boldsymbol{\lambda} (\boldsymbol{x} = \boldsymbol{x}_0)$.[7] These observations are incorporated in

THEOREM 12.11 (a necessary and sufficient condition). *Let $L(\boldsymbol{x}, \boldsymbol{\lambda}_0)$ be concave in $\boldsymbol{x}$ and $L(\boldsymbol{x}_0, \boldsymbol{\lambda})$ convex in $\boldsymbol{\lambda}$ with $\nabla_{\boldsymbol{x}} L$, $\nabla_{\boldsymbol{\lambda}} L$ respectively defined for all $\boldsymbol{x} \in \delta(\boldsymbol{x}_0)$, $\boldsymbol{\lambda} \in \delta(\boldsymbol{\lambda}_0)$, $\boldsymbol{x} \geqslant \boldsymbol{0}$, $\boldsymbol{\lambda} \geqslant \boldsymbol{0}$. Then $(\boldsymbol{x}_0, \boldsymbol{\lambda}_0)$ is a local saddle point of $L(\boldsymbol{x}, \boldsymbol{\lambda})$ if and only if eq. (12.12) holds.*

Proof. (Necessity.) Theorem 12.8. (Sufficiency.) Theorem 12.9. Q.E.D.

It is important to note three essential differences between these two necessary and sufficient conditions (theorems 12.10 and 12.11): (1) the first does not require differentiability of the Lagrangian whereas the second does; (2) theorem 12.11 hypothesizes that $L(\boldsymbol{x}, \boldsymbol{\lambda}_0)$ is concave in $\boldsymbol{x}$ and $L(\boldsymbol{x}_0, \boldsymbol{\lambda})$ is convex in $\boldsymbol{\lambda}$ (hence the local saddle point obtained at $(\boldsymbol{x}_0, \boldsymbol{\lambda}_0)$ is also of the global variety under the concavity-convexity assumption); and (3) in theorem 12.10, $\boldsymbol{x}$ is unrestricted whereas in theorem 12.11 we specifically require that $\boldsymbol{x} \geqslant \boldsymbol{0}$.

In the previous section we determined a set of necessary conditions for the solution to a problem of the form: maximize the real-valued function $y = \mathrm{f}(\boldsymbol{x})$ subject to a set of (m) inequality constraints and (n) non-negativity conditions. This problem will be referred to as the (local)

MAXIMUM PROBLEM. *To find a point $\boldsymbol{x}_0 \in \mathscr{E}^n$ which maximizes $\mathrm{f}(\boldsymbol{x})$ subject to $\bar{\boldsymbol{G}}(\boldsymbol{x}) \geqslant \boldsymbol{0}$ with $\boldsymbol{x}$ unrestricted or $\boldsymbol{G}(\boldsymbol{x}) \geqslant \boldsymbol{0}$, $\boldsymbol{x} \geqslant \boldsymbol{0}$.*

What is the connection between the solution of the local maximum problem and the solution of the local saddle-point problem? In what follows

[7] To see this let f, $\boldsymbol{G}$ be concave. (Note that $\boldsymbol{G} = \boldsymbol{b} - \boldsymbol{g}$ will be concave if $\boldsymbol{g}$ is convex.) Then

$$\left.\begin{aligned} \mathrm{f}(\boldsymbol{x}) &\leqslant \mathrm{f}(\boldsymbol{x}_0) + \nabla \mathrm{f}(\boldsymbol{x}_0)'(\boldsymbol{x} - \boldsymbol{x}_0) \\ \boldsymbol{G}(\boldsymbol{x}) &\leqslant \boldsymbol{G}(\boldsymbol{x}_0) + \nabla \boldsymbol{G}(\boldsymbol{x}_0)'(\boldsymbol{x} - \boldsymbol{x}_0) \end{aligned}\right\} \boldsymbol{x} \geqslant \boldsymbol{0}.$$

In this regard, for $\boldsymbol{\lambda}_0 \geqslant \boldsymbol{0}$, $\boldsymbol{\lambda}_0' \boldsymbol{G}(\boldsymbol{x}) \leqslant \boldsymbol{\lambda}_0' \boldsymbol{G}(\boldsymbol{x}_0) + \boldsymbol{\lambda}_0' \nabla \boldsymbol{G}(\boldsymbol{x}_0)'(\boldsymbol{x} - \boldsymbol{x}_0)$, and thus

$$\begin{aligned} L(\boldsymbol{x}, \boldsymbol{\lambda}_0) &= \mathrm{f}(\boldsymbol{x}) + \boldsymbol{\lambda}_0' \boldsymbol{G}(\boldsymbol{x}) \leqslant \mathrm{f}(\boldsymbol{x}_0) + \boldsymbol{\lambda}_0' \boldsymbol{G}(\boldsymbol{x}_0) + \nabla \mathrm{f}(\boldsymbol{x}_0)'(\boldsymbol{x} - \boldsymbol{x}_0) + \boldsymbol{\lambda}_0' \nabla \boldsymbol{G}(\boldsymbol{x}_0)'(\boldsymbol{x} - \boldsymbol{x}_0) \\ &= L(\boldsymbol{x}_0, \boldsymbol{\lambda}_0) + (\nabla \mathrm{f}(\boldsymbol{x}_0) + \nabla \boldsymbol{G}(\boldsymbol{x}_0) \boldsymbol{\lambda}_0)'(\boldsymbol{x} - \boldsymbol{x}_0) \\ &= L(\boldsymbol{x}_0, \boldsymbol{\lambda}_0) + (\nabla_{\boldsymbol{x}} L^0)'(\boldsymbol{x} - \boldsymbol{x}_0). \end{aligned}$$

Hence eq. (12.13(a)) holds. Since $L = \mathrm{f} + \boldsymbol{\lambda}' \boldsymbol{G}$ is a linear function of $\boldsymbol{\lambda}$, $L(\boldsymbol{x}_0, \boldsymbol{\lambda}) = L(\boldsymbol{x}_0, \boldsymbol{\lambda}_0) + (\nabla_{\boldsymbol{\lambda}} L^0)'(\boldsymbol{\lambda} - \boldsymbol{\lambda}_0)$, and thus eq. (12.13(b)) holds as well.

we shall consider a battery of important theorems which serve to establish a bond between them. First

THEOREM 12.12 (a sufficient condition).[8] *Let* $L(\boldsymbol{x}, \boldsymbol{\lambda})$ be *defined for all* $(\boldsymbol{x}, \boldsymbol{\lambda}) \in \delta(\boldsymbol{x}_0, \boldsymbol{\lambda}_0)$, *where* $\boldsymbol{x}$ *is unrestricted and* $\boldsymbol{\lambda} \geqslant \mathbf{0}$. *If* $(\boldsymbol{x}_0, \boldsymbol{\lambda}_0)$ *is a local saddle point for* $L(\boldsymbol{x}, \boldsymbol{\lambda})$, *then* $\boldsymbol{x}_0$ *solves the local maximum problem.*

Proof. Let $(\boldsymbol{x}_0, \boldsymbol{\lambda}_0)$ be a local saddle point for $L(\boldsymbol{x}, \boldsymbol{\lambda})$. Then eq. (12.14) holds. In this regard, $L(\boldsymbol{x}_0, \boldsymbol{\lambda}_0) \geqslant L(\boldsymbol{x}, \boldsymbol{\lambda}_0)$ or $\mathrm{f}(\boldsymbol{x}_0) + \boldsymbol{\lambda}_0' \boldsymbol{G}(\boldsymbol{x}_0) = \mathrm{f}(\boldsymbol{x}_0) \geqslant \mathrm{f}(\boldsymbol{x}) + \boldsymbol{\lambda}_0' \boldsymbol{G}(\boldsymbol{x})$. Since $\boldsymbol{\lambda}_0' \boldsymbol{G}(\boldsymbol{x}) \geqslant 0$, $\mathrm{f}(\boldsymbol{x}_0) \geqslant \mathrm{f}(\boldsymbol{x})$ for all $\boldsymbol{x} \in \delta(\boldsymbol{x}_0)$. Q.E.D.

Theorem 12.12 did not require that the Lagrangian be differentiable or that $\boldsymbol{x} \geqslant \mathbf{0}$. An alternative sufficient condition which does require these conditions is

THEOREM 12.13 (a sufficient condition).[9] *Let* $L(\boldsymbol{x}, \boldsymbol{\lambda})$ *be defined for all* $(\boldsymbol{x}, \boldsymbol{\lambda}) \in \delta(\boldsymbol{x}_0, \boldsymbol{\lambda}_0)$, $\boldsymbol{x} \geqslant \mathbf{0}$, $\boldsymbol{\lambda} \geqslant \mathbf{0}$, *with* $\nabla_{\boldsymbol{x}} L$ *defined for all* $\boldsymbol{x} \in \delta(\boldsymbol{x}_0)$. *If eqs. (12.12) and (12.3(a)) hold for* $\boldsymbol{x}_0$ *and some* $\boldsymbol{\lambda}_0$, *then* $\boldsymbol{x}_0$ *solves the local maximum problem.*

Proof. Since

$$\begin{aligned} L(\boldsymbol{x}, \boldsymbol{\lambda}_0) &= \mathrm{f}(\boldsymbol{x}) + \boldsymbol{\lambda}_0' \boldsymbol{G}(\boldsymbol{x}) \leqslant L(\boldsymbol{x}_0, \boldsymbol{\lambda}_0) + (\nabla_{\boldsymbol{x}} L^0)'(\boldsymbol{x} - \boldsymbol{x}_0) \\ &= L(\boldsymbol{x}_0, \boldsymbol{\lambda}_0) + (\nabla_{\boldsymbol{x}} L^0)' \boldsymbol{x} \leqslant L(\boldsymbol{x}_0, \boldsymbol{\lambda}_0) = \mathrm{f}(\boldsymbol{\lambda}_0), \end{aligned}$$

and $\boldsymbol{\lambda}_0' \boldsymbol{G}(\boldsymbol{x}) \geqslant 0$ because $\boldsymbol{G}(\boldsymbol{x}) \geqslant \mathbf{0}$, it follows that $\mathrm{f}(\boldsymbol{x}) + \boldsymbol{\lambda}_0' \boldsymbol{G}(\boldsymbol{x}) \leqslant \mathrm{f}(\boldsymbol{x}_0)$ or $\mathrm{f}(\boldsymbol{x}_0) \geqslant \mathrm{f}(\boldsymbol{x})$ for all $\boldsymbol{x} \in \delta(\boldsymbol{x}_0)$. Q.E.D.

The importance of the developments in this section is that they set the stage for a discussion of the famous Kuhn–Tucker equivalence theorem. This theorem (given below) establishes the notion that the existence of an optimal solution to the local maximum problem is equivalent (under certain restrictions) to the existence of a local saddle point of the associated Lagrangian of f. Hence, maximization subject to inequality constraints is equivalent to maximinimizing (minimaximizing) the Lagrangian subject to no restraint. We saw above (theorem 12.12) that if $(\boldsymbol{x}_0, \boldsymbol{\lambda}_0)$ solves the local saddle-point problem, then $\boldsymbol{x}_0$ solves the local maximum problem. Moreover, theorem 12.12 holds without any restrictions whatever on the Lagrangian (e.g. concavity) or on the constraint set (i.e. a constraint qualification). What about the converse statement? That is, given that $\boldsymbol{x}_0$ solves the local maximum problem, is it possible to find a $\boldsymbol{\lambda}_0$ for which $(\boldsymbol{x}_0, \boldsymbol{\lambda}_0)$ solves the local saddle-point problem? In general, the answer is no. If we assume only that the Lagrangian is concave, the answer is still no. But if the Lagrangian is deemed concave *and* a constraint qualification is imposed on the constraint set, the answer is in the affirmative. Moreover, the local constrained maximum of f and the local saddle point of L are necessarily global in character by virtue

[8] See Lasdon (1970), pp. 85–86; Arrow *et al.* (1958), pp. 33–34.
[9] See Kuhn and Tucker (1951), p. 485.

of the concavity assumption. In this regard we look to the

KUHN–TUCKER EQUIVALENCE THEOREM I (a necessary and sufficient condition).[10] *Let the real-valued function* $y = \mathrm{f}(\boldsymbol{x})$ *and the vector-valued function* $\bar{\boldsymbol{G}}(\boldsymbol{x}) \geqslant \mathbf{0}$, $\boldsymbol{x} \in \mathscr{E}^n$, *be concave over the convex region* $\mathscr{K} = \{\boldsymbol{x} \mid \bar{\boldsymbol{G}}(\boldsymbol{x}) \geqslant \mathbf{0},\ \boldsymbol{x} \in \mathscr{E}^n\}$ *with the property that for some* $\boldsymbol{x}_* \in \mathscr{K}$, $\bar{\boldsymbol{G}}(\boldsymbol{x}_*) > \mathbf{0}$ *(the constraint qualification). Then* $\boldsymbol{x}_0$ *solves the global maximum problem if and only if there exists a* $\boldsymbol{\lambda}_0 \geqslant \mathbf{0}$ *such that* $(\boldsymbol{x}_0, \boldsymbol{\lambda}_0)$ *solves the global saddle-point problem.*

Proof. (Necessity.) Let $\boldsymbol{x}_0$ solve the global maximum problem. Then we must demonstrate the existence of a $\boldsymbol{\lambda}_0 \geqslant \mathbf{0}$ such that $(\boldsymbol{x}_0, \boldsymbol{\lambda}_0)$ solves the global saddle-point problem. Our initial step will be to construct two disjoint convex sets and separate them by a hyperplane. To this end let us define point sets $\mathscr{A}, \mathscr{B} \in \mathscr{E}^{m+n+1}$ with $(m+n+1 \times 1)$ elements $\begin{bmatrix} y \\ \boldsymbol{Y} \end{bmatrix}$ such that

$$\mathscr{A} = \left\{ \begin{bmatrix} y \\ \boldsymbol{Y} \end{bmatrix} \middle| \begin{bmatrix} y \\ \boldsymbol{Y} \end{bmatrix} \leqslant \begin{bmatrix} \mathrm{f}(\boldsymbol{x}) \\ \bar{\boldsymbol{G}}(\boldsymbol{x}) \end{bmatrix} \text{ for some } \boldsymbol{x} \right\},$$

$$\mathscr{B} = \left\{ \begin{bmatrix} y \\ \boldsymbol{Y} \end{bmatrix} \middle| \begin{bmatrix} y \\ \boldsymbol{Y} \end{bmatrix} > \begin{bmatrix} \mathrm{f}(\boldsymbol{x}_0) \\ \mathbf{0} \end{bmatrix} \right\},$$

where y is a scalar and $\boldsymbol{Y} \in \mathscr{E}^{m+n}$. By theorem 12.4, $\mathscr{A}$ is a convex set. $\mathscr{B}$ is also convex since, by definition, it is bounded by hyperplanes parallel to the coordinate axes of $\mathscr{E}^{m+n+1}$, and thus represents an open subset interior to an orthant of $\mathscr{E}^{m+n+1}$ with vertex (corner point) at $\begin{bmatrix} \mathrm{f}(\boldsymbol{x}_0) \\ \mathbf{0} \end{bmatrix}$ (see fig. 12.6 for hypothetical $\mathscr{A}, \mathscr{B} \subset \mathscr{E}^2$). Now $\mathscr{B}$ has been defined in terms of $\boldsymbol{x}_0$ and, since $\boldsymbol{x}_0$ solves the global maximum problem, $\mathscr{A} \cap \mathscr{B} = \phi$. By the weak separation theorem (chapter 1), there exists a separating hyperplane

$$\begin{bmatrix} \lambda \\ \boldsymbol{\lambda} \end{bmatrix}' \begin{bmatrix} y \\ \boldsymbol{Y} \end{bmatrix} = \lambda y + \boldsymbol{\lambda}' \boldsymbol{Y} = \alpha$$

with normal $\begin{bmatrix} \lambda \\ \boldsymbol{\lambda} \end{bmatrix} \neq \mathbf{0}$, λ a scalar and $\boldsymbol{\lambda} \in \mathscr{E}^{m+n}$, such that

$$\begin{bmatrix} \lambda \\ \boldsymbol{\lambda} \end{bmatrix}' \begin{bmatrix} y_{\mathscr{A}} \\ \boldsymbol{Y}_{\mathscr{A}} \end{bmatrix} \leqslant \begin{bmatrix} \lambda \\ \boldsymbol{\lambda} \end{bmatrix}' \begin{bmatrix} y_{\mathscr{B}} \\ \boldsymbol{Y}_{\mathscr{B}} \end{bmatrix}$$

or

$$\lambda y_{\mathscr{A}} + \boldsymbol{\lambda}' \boldsymbol{Y}_{\mathscr{A}} \leqslant \lambda y_{\mathscr{B}} + \boldsymbol{\lambda}' \boldsymbol{Y}_{\mathscr{B}} \quad \text{for all } \begin{bmatrix} y_{\mathscr{A}} \\ \boldsymbol{Y}_{\mathscr{A}} \end{bmatrix} \in \mathscr{A},\ \begin{bmatrix} y_{\mathscr{B}} \\ \boldsymbol{Y}_{\mathscr{B}} \end{bmatrix} \in \mathscr{B}. \tag{12.15}$$

[10] The proof here follows the version of the Kuhn–Tucker theorem presented by Uzawa (1958), pp. 34–35. For a discussion of the theorem in the context of convex programming see Künzi *et al.* (1966), pp. 63–66.

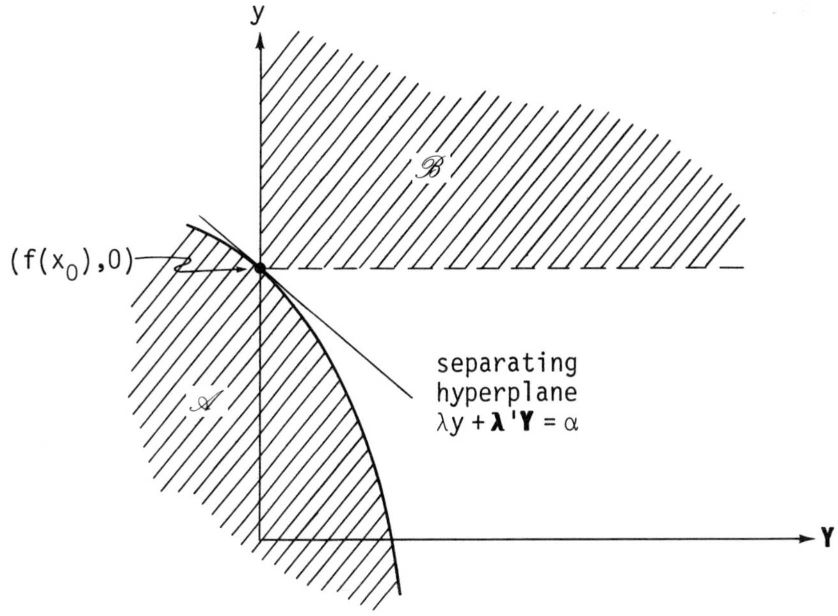

Fig. 12.6.

Again employing the definition of $\mathscr{B}$ we see that the components of $\begin{bmatrix} y_{\mathscr{B}} \\ \boldsymbol{Y}_{\mathscr{B}} \end{bmatrix}$ may be arbitrarily large. Hence, $\begin{bmatrix} \lambda \\ \boldsymbol{\lambda} \end{bmatrix} \geqslant \begin{bmatrix} 0 \\ \boldsymbol{0} \end{bmatrix}$ since if any component of this vector is negative, the corresponding component of $\begin{bmatrix} y_{\mathscr{B}} \\ \boldsymbol{Y}_{\mathscr{B}} \end{bmatrix}$ can be chosen large enough to violate eq. (12.15). Thus $\begin{bmatrix} \lambda \\ \boldsymbol{\lambda} \end{bmatrix}$ has all non-negative components (with at least one component strictly positive since otherwise the separating hyperplane is degenerate). If we set

$$\begin{bmatrix} y_{\mathscr{A}} \\ \boldsymbol{Y}_{\mathscr{A}} \end{bmatrix} = \begin{bmatrix} \mathrm{f}(\boldsymbol{x}) \\ \overline{\boldsymbol{G}}(\boldsymbol{x}) \end{bmatrix}, \qquad \begin{bmatrix} y_{\mathscr{B}} \\ \boldsymbol{Y}_{\mathscr{B}} \end{bmatrix} = \begin{bmatrix} \mathrm{f}(\boldsymbol{x}_0) \\ \boldsymbol{0} \end{bmatrix},$$

then, with $\begin{bmatrix} \mathrm{f}(\boldsymbol{x}_0) \\ \boldsymbol{0} \end{bmatrix}$ on the boundary of $\mathscr{B}$, eq. (12.15) yields

$$\lambda \mathrm{f}(\boldsymbol{x}) + \boldsymbol{\lambda}'\overline{\boldsymbol{G}}(\boldsymbol{x}) \leqslant \lambda \mathrm{f}(\boldsymbol{x}_0) \quad \text{for all } \boldsymbol{x}. \tag{12.16}$$

We noted above that $\lambda \geqslant 0$. If $\lambda = 0$, then eq. (12.16) yields $\boldsymbol{\lambda}'\overline{\boldsymbol{G}}(\boldsymbol{x}) \leqslant 0$ for all $\boldsymbol{x}$. But this violates the constraint qualification, i.e. it contradicts the hypothesis that there exists an $\boldsymbol{x}_*$ for which $\overline{\boldsymbol{G}}(\boldsymbol{x}_*) > \boldsymbol{0}$ or, since $\boldsymbol{\lambda}$ has at least one positive component, $\boldsymbol{\lambda}'\overline{\boldsymbol{G}}(\boldsymbol{x}_*) > 0$. Hence, $\lambda > 0$. Accordingly eq. (12.16) becomes

$$f(\boldsymbol{x})+\boldsymbol{\lambda}_0'\bar{\boldsymbol{G}}(\boldsymbol{x})\leqslant f(\boldsymbol{x}_0), \quad \boldsymbol{\lambda}_0' = \boldsymbol{\lambda}'/\lambda,$$

or

$$L(\boldsymbol{x}, \boldsymbol{\lambda}_0)\leqslant f(\boldsymbol{x}_0) \quad \text{for all } \boldsymbol{x}. \tag{12.16.1}$$

If $\boldsymbol{x} = \boldsymbol{x}_0$ in eq. (12.16.1), then $L(\boldsymbol{x}_0, \boldsymbol{\lambda}_0) = f(\boldsymbol{x}_0)+\boldsymbol{\lambda}_0'\bar{\boldsymbol{G}}(\boldsymbol{x}_0)\leqslant f(\boldsymbol{x}_0)$ whence $\boldsymbol{\lambda}_0'\bar{\boldsymbol{G}}(\boldsymbol{x}_0)\leqslant 0$. But $\boldsymbol{\lambda}_0\geqslant \mathbf{0}$, $\bar{\boldsymbol{G}}(\boldsymbol{x}_0)\geqslant \mathbf{0}$ implies $\boldsymbol{\lambda}_0'\bar{\boldsymbol{G}}(\boldsymbol{x}_0)\geqslant 0$. Hence, $\boldsymbol{\lambda}_0'\bar{\boldsymbol{G}}(\boldsymbol{x}_0) = 0$. Collecting our results we have:

$$\text{(a) } L(\boldsymbol{x}, \boldsymbol{\lambda}_0)\leqslant f(\boldsymbol{x}_0) = f(\boldsymbol{x}_0)+\boldsymbol{\lambda}_0'\bar{\boldsymbol{G}}(\boldsymbol{x}_0) = L(\boldsymbol{x}_0, \boldsymbol{\lambda}_0),$$

i.e. $L(\boldsymbol{x}, \boldsymbol{\lambda}_0)$ attains a global maximum at $\boldsymbol{x}_0$; (b) $\boldsymbol{\lambda}_0'\bar{\boldsymbol{G}}(\boldsymbol{x}_0) = 0$; and (c) $\bar{\boldsymbol{G}}(\boldsymbol{x}_0) \geqslant \mathbf{0}$. But these three relations are just the global version of eqs. (12.14(a), (b), (c)). Hence the saddle-point problem is solved.

(Sufficiency.) Let $(\boldsymbol{x}_0, \boldsymbol{\lambda}_0)$ solve the global saddle-point problem. Then theorem 12.10 applies in a global sense and thus the global maximum problem is solved. Q.E.D. (Note that to prove sufficiency the assumptions of a concave Lagrangian and a constraint qualification were not employed.)

In sum, $\boldsymbol{x}_0$ solves the global maximum problem if $(\boldsymbol{x}_0, \boldsymbol{\lambda}_0)$ solves the global saddle-point problem, while $\boldsymbol{x}_0$ solves the maximum problem only if $\boldsymbol{x}_0$ and some $\boldsymbol{\lambda}_0$ solve the saddle-point problem, given that $L(\boldsymbol{x}, \boldsymbol{\lambda})$ is concave and a constraint qualification is imposed on the constraint set.

The above version of the Kuhn–Tucker equivalence theorem did not require differentiability of the Lagrangian. If $L(\boldsymbol{x}, \boldsymbol{\lambda}) = f(\boldsymbol{x})+\boldsymbol{\lambda}'\bar{\boldsymbol{G}}(\boldsymbol{x})$ is differentiable as well as concave, then, subject to the above constraint qualification, the global saddle-point inequalities are equivalent to the KTL conditions (eq. (12.4)) which are now both necessary and sufficient to insure that $\boldsymbol{x}_0$ is a solution to the global maximum problem. In this instance we cite

KUHN–TUCKER EQUIVALENCE THEOREM II (a necessary and sufficient condition).[11] *Let the real-valued function* $y = f(\boldsymbol{x})$ *and the vector-valued function* $\bar{\boldsymbol{G}}(\boldsymbol{x})\geqslant \mathbf{0}$, $\boldsymbol{x}\in\mathscr{E}^n$, *be concave and differentiable over the convex region* $\mathscr{K} = \{\boldsymbol{x}|\bar{\boldsymbol{G}}(\boldsymbol{x})\geqslant \mathbf{0}, \boldsymbol{x}\in\mathscr{E}^n\}$ *with the property that for some* $\boldsymbol{x}_*\in\mathscr{K}$, $\bar{\boldsymbol{G}}(\boldsymbol{x}_*)>\mathbf{0}$. *Then* $\boldsymbol{x}_0$ *solves the global maximum problem if and only if there exists a* $\boldsymbol{\lambda}_0\geqslant\mathbf{0}$ *such that* $(\boldsymbol{x}_0, \boldsymbol{\lambda}_0)$ *solves the saddle-point problem with*

$$\nabla f(\boldsymbol{x}_0)+\nabla\bar{\boldsymbol{G}}(\boldsymbol{x}_0)\boldsymbol{\lambda}_0 = \mathbf{0}, \qquad \bar{\boldsymbol{G}}(\boldsymbol{x}_0)\geqslant\mathbf{0}, \qquad \boldsymbol{\lambda}_0'\bar{\boldsymbol{G}}(\boldsymbol{x}_0) = 0.$$

Proof. By the preceding theorem, $\boldsymbol{x}_0$ solves the maximum problem if and only if there exists a $\boldsymbol{\lambda}_0\geqslant\mathbf{0}$ such that $(\boldsymbol{x}_0, \boldsymbol{\lambda}_0)$ solves the saddle-point problem. With the Lagrangian differentiable, if $L(\boldsymbol{x}, \boldsymbol{\lambda}_0)$ attains a global maximum

[11] Lasdon (1970), pp. 90–91.

at $\boldsymbol{x}_0$, then $L(\boldsymbol{x}, \boldsymbol{\lambda}_0)$ is stationary at $(\boldsymbol{x}_0, \boldsymbol{\lambda}_0)$, and thus $\nabla_{\boldsymbol{x}} L^0 = \nabla \mathrm{f}(\boldsymbol{x}_0) + \nabla \bar{\boldsymbol{G}}(\boldsymbol{x}_0)\boldsymbol{\lambda}_0 = \mathbf{0}$ replaces eq. (12.14(a)). Hence eq. (12.14) becomes

$$\left.\begin{array}{l} \text{(a) } \nabla \mathrm{f}(\boldsymbol{x}_0) + \nabla \bar{\boldsymbol{G}}(\boldsymbol{x}_0)\boldsymbol{\lambda}_0 = \mathbf{0}, \\ \text{(b) } \bar{\boldsymbol{G}}(\boldsymbol{x}_0) \geqslant \mathbf{0}, \\ \text{(c) } \boldsymbol{\lambda}_0' \bar{\boldsymbol{G}}(\boldsymbol{x}_0) = 0, \end{array}\right\} \quad \text{or} \quad \text{eq. (12.4) since } \boldsymbol{\lambda}_0 \geqslant \mathbf{0}. \tag{12.14.1}$$

Thus the KTL conditions are necessary and sufficient for a global maximum at $\boldsymbol{x}_0$ if the Lagrangian is concave and differentiable and the constraint set or feasible region satisfies a constraint qualification. Q.E.D.

This equivalence may be expressed in an alternative fashion by employing equivalence theorem I (with $\boldsymbol{G}(\boldsymbol{x}) \geqslant \mathbf{0}$, $\boldsymbol{x} \geqslant \mathbf{0}$ replacing $\bar{\boldsymbol{G}}(\boldsymbol{x}) \geqslant \mathbf{0}$) and theorem 12.10. Then from eq. (12.12) we obtain

$$\left.\begin{array}{l} \left.\begin{array}{l} \nabla_{\boldsymbol{x}} L^0 \leqslant \mathbf{0}, \\ (\nabla_{\boldsymbol{x}} L^0)' \boldsymbol{x}_0 = 0, \\ \boldsymbol{x}_0 \geqslant \mathbf{0}, \end{array}\right\} \text{ or } \left\{\begin{array}{l} \nabla \mathrm{f}(\boldsymbol{x}_0) + \nabla \boldsymbol{G}(\boldsymbol{x}_0)\boldsymbol{\lambda}_0 \leqslant \mathbf{0}, \\ \boldsymbol{x}_0'(\nabla \mathrm{f}(\boldsymbol{x}_0) + \nabla \boldsymbol{G}(\boldsymbol{x}_0)\boldsymbol{\lambda}_0) = 0, \\ \boldsymbol{x}_0 \geqslant \mathbf{0}, \end{array}\right. \\ \\ \left.\begin{array}{l} \nabla_{\boldsymbol{\lambda}} L^0 \geqslant \mathbf{0}, \\ (\nabla_{\boldsymbol{\lambda}} L^0)' \boldsymbol{\lambda}_0 = 0, \\ \boldsymbol{\lambda}_0 \geqslant \mathbf{0}, \end{array}\right\} \text{ or } \left\{\begin{array}{l} \boldsymbol{G}(\boldsymbol{x}_0) \geqslant \mathbf{0}, \\ \boldsymbol{\lambda}_0' \boldsymbol{G}(\boldsymbol{x}_0) = 0, \\ \boldsymbol{\lambda}_0 \geqslant \mathbf{0}. \end{array}\right. \end{array}\right\} \tag{12.5}$$

That is, eq. (12.5) holds at $(\boldsymbol{x}_0, \boldsymbol{\lambda}_0)$ and is necessary and sufficient for a global maximum at $\boldsymbol{x}_0$ under the hypotheses of equivalence theorem II (with $\boldsymbol{G}(\boldsymbol{x}) \geqslant \mathbf{0}$, $\boldsymbol{x} \geqslant \mathbf{0}$ instead of $\bar{\boldsymbol{G}}(\boldsymbol{x}) \geqslant \mathbf{0}$).

A numerical technique which, under certain restrictions, insures convergence to a saddle point of $L(\boldsymbol{x}, \boldsymbol{\lambda})$, and thus to a constrained global maximum of f, is illustrated in Appendix B to this chapter. An additional numerical method which converts a problem involving the maximization of f subject to a set of inequality constraints into an unconstrained maximization problem is presented in Appendix C.

12.4. Lagrangian duality

In this section we shall analyze the attainment of a saddle point of the Lagrangian $L(\boldsymbol{x}, \boldsymbol{\lambda})$ from a slightly different point of view. We noted above that $L(\boldsymbol{x}, \boldsymbol{\lambda})$ has a saddle point at $(\boldsymbol{x}_0, \boldsymbol{\lambda}_0) \in \mathscr{E}^{n+m}$ if $L(\boldsymbol{x}, \boldsymbol{\lambda}_0) \leqslant L(\boldsymbol{x}_0, \boldsymbol{\lambda}_0) \leqslant L(\boldsymbol{x}_0, \boldsymbol{\lambda})$, i.e. $L(\boldsymbol{x}, \boldsymbol{\lambda})$ simultaneously attains a maximum at $\boldsymbol{x}_0$ and a minimum at $\boldsymbol{\lambda}_0$. In this regard,

$$L(\boldsymbol{x}_0, \boldsymbol{\lambda}_0) = \max_{\boldsymbol{x} \geqslant \mathbf{0}} \{\min_{\boldsymbol{\lambda} \geqslant \mathbf{0}} L(\boldsymbol{x}, \boldsymbol{\lambda})\} = \min_{\boldsymbol{\lambda} \geqslant \mathbf{0}} \{\max_{\boldsymbol{x} \geqslant \mathbf{0}} L(\boldsymbol{x}, \boldsymbol{\lambda})\}.$$

Under what conditions is this three-way equality valid? Also, how is $L(\boldsymbol{x}_0, \boldsymbol{\lambda}_0)$ determined in actual practice? In answering these questions we shall define two distinct yet closely allied problems, namely, the primal problem and its corresponding dual. But before we get to specifics, let us quite generally indicate the essential features of duality. Duality theory, or more properly, a duality theorem, is a statement of a particular relationship between two optimization problems, where one of them, the *primal*, is a constrained maximization (minimization) problem and the other, the *dual*, is a constrained minimization (maximization) problem. Moreover, this association is such that the existence of an optimal solution to one of these problems guarantees an optimal solution to the other with the result that their extreme values are equal.

Let us denote the *primal function* as

$$L_p(\mathbf{x}) = \min_{\boldsymbol{\lambda} \geqslant \mathbf{0}} L(\mathbf{x}, \boldsymbol{\lambda}) = \min_{\boldsymbol{\lambda} \geqslant \mathbf{0}} \{\mathrm{f}(\mathbf{x}) + \boldsymbol{\lambda}'\bar{\mathbf{G}}(\mathbf{x})\}.$$

With $\bar{\mathbf{G}}(\mathbf{x}) \geqslant \mathbf{0}$, $\boldsymbol{\lambda} \geqslant \mathbf{0}$, it follows that $L_p(\mathbf{x}) = \mathrm{f}(\mathbf{x})$. Hence, we may take the following problem to be the

PRIMAL PROBLEM. *Maximize the real-valued function* $y = \mathrm{f}(\mathbf{x})$ *subject to* $\mathbf{x} \in \mathscr{K} = \{\mathbf{x} \mid \bar{\mathbf{G}}(\mathbf{x}) \geqslant \mathbf{0}, \mathbf{x} \in \mathscr{E}^n\}$, i.e.

$$\max_{\mathbf{x} \in \mathscr{K}} \{L_p(\mathbf{x})\} = \max_{\mathbf{x} \in \mathscr{K}} \{\mathrm{f}(\mathbf{x})\}.$$

Note that the primal problem stated here is coincident with the maximum problem of the previous section(s). So when we speak of the primal problem, we are actually referring to the maximum problem. To obtain the *dual function* let us set $L_{\mathrm{md}}(\boldsymbol{\lambda}) = \max_{\mathbf{x} \in \mathscr{K}} L(\mathbf{x}, \boldsymbol{\lambda})$. In this case we may now define the

MINIMAX DUAL. *Minimize the real-valued function*

$$L_{\mathrm{md}}(\boldsymbol{\lambda}) = \max_{\mathbf{x} \in \mathscr{K}} L(\mathbf{x}, \boldsymbol{\lambda})$$

subject to $\boldsymbol{\lambda} \in \mathscr{K}_{\mathrm{md}} = \{\boldsymbol{\lambda} \mid \boldsymbol{\lambda} \geqslant \mathbf{0}, \boldsymbol{\lambda} \in \mathscr{E}^{m+n}\}$, *i.e.*

$$\min_{\boldsymbol{\lambda} \in \mathscr{K}_{\mathrm{md}}} \{L_{\mathrm{md}}(\boldsymbol{\lambda})\}.$$

In sum, our primal–minimax–dual pair of problems is represented as

Primal

$$\max_{\mathbf{x} \in \mathscr{K}} \{\min_{\boldsymbol{\lambda} \in \mathscr{K}_{\mathrm{md}}} L(\mathbf{x}, \boldsymbol{\lambda})\} = \max_{\mathbf{x} \in \mathscr{K}} \{\mathrm{f}(\mathbf{x})\},$$

Minimax Dual

$$\min_{\boldsymbol{\lambda} \in \mathscr{K}_{\mathrm{md}}} \{\max_{\mathbf{x} \in \mathscr{K}} L(\mathbf{x}, \boldsymbol{\lambda})\} = \min_{\boldsymbol{\lambda} \in \mathscr{K}_{\mathrm{md}}} \{L_{\mathrm{md}}(\boldsymbol{\lambda})\}.$$

The minimax dual is a rather general form of a duality relationship. More specifically, we now turn to the development of an alternative dual to the above primal (maximum) problem which is equivalent to the minimax dual and exhibits considerable computational efficiency. To this end let us assume that the real-valued function $y = \mathrm{f}(\boldsymbol{x})$ and the vector-valued function $\bar{\boldsymbol{G}}(\boldsymbol{x})$ are concave and differentiable for $\boldsymbol{x} \in \mathscr{E}^n$. Then a necessary and sufficient condition for $L(\boldsymbol{x}, \boldsymbol{\lambda}_0)$, $\boldsymbol{\lambda}_0 \in \mathscr{K}_{\mathrm{md}}$, to attain a local (and thus global) maximum with respect to $\boldsymbol{x}$ at $(\boldsymbol{x}_0, \boldsymbol{\lambda}_0)$ is $\nabla_{\boldsymbol{x}} L^0 = \mathbf{0}$. So if we take $L_{\mathrm{md}}(\boldsymbol{\lambda}) = L(\boldsymbol{x}, \boldsymbol{\lambda}) = \mathrm{f}(\boldsymbol{x}) + \boldsymbol{\lambda}'\bar{\boldsymbol{G}}(\boldsymbol{x})$ and minimize this new dual function, subject to $\nabla_{\boldsymbol{x}} L = \mathbf{0}$, $\boldsymbol{\lambda} \in \mathscr{K}_{\mathrm{md}}$, then we obtain what we shall simply call the

DUAL PROBLEM.[12] *Minimize the real-valued function* $L(\boldsymbol{x}, \boldsymbol{\lambda}) = \mathrm{f}(\boldsymbol{x}) + \boldsymbol{\lambda}'\bar{\boldsymbol{G}}(\boldsymbol{x})$ *subject to*

$$(\boldsymbol{x}, \boldsymbol{\lambda}) \in \mathscr{K}_{\mathrm{d}} = \{(\boldsymbol{x}, \boldsymbol{\lambda}) \mid \nabla_{\boldsymbol{x}} L = \mathbf{0}, (\boldsymbol{x}, \boldsymbol{\lambda}) \in \mathscr{E}^{m+2n}, \boldsymbol{\lambda} \geqslant \mathbf{0}\}.$$

In short, our primal–dual pair of problems now appears as

$$\begin{array}{cc} \textit{Primal} & \textit{Dual} \\ \max\limits_{\boldsymbol{x} \in \mathscr{K}} \{\mathrm{f}(\boldsymbol{x})\}, & \min\limits_{(\boldsymbol{x}, \boldsymbol{\lambda}) \in \mathscr{K}_{\mathrm{d}}} \{L(\boldsymbol{x}, \boldsymbol{\lambda})\}. \end{array}$$

Note that in the formulation of the dual problem $\boldsymbol{x}$ is unrestricted in sign.

What properties or special features does the dual problem possess and how is it related to the primal problem? We noted earlier that:

(a) if one of the problems (e.g. the primal) is a constrained maximization (minimization) problem, then the other (the dual) must be a constrained minimization (maximization) problem.

(b) the value of $\mathrm{f}(\boldsymbol{x})$, $\boldsymbol{x} \in \mathscr{K}$, in the primal problem is always less than or equal to the value of $L(\boldsymbol{x}, \boldsymbol{\lambda})$, $(\boldsymbol{x}, \boldsymbol{\lambda}) \in \mathscr{K}_{\mathrm{d}}$, in the dual problem.

To verify (b) we cite

DUALITY THEOREM 1.[13] *Let the real-valued function* $y = \mathrm{f}(\boldsymbol{x})$ *and the vector-valued function* $\bar{\boldsymbol{G}}(\boldsymbol{x})$ *be concave and differentiable for all* $\boldsymbol{x} \in \mathscr{E}^n$. *If* $\boldsymbol{x}_1 \in \mathscr{K} = \{\boldsymbol{x} \mid \bar{\boldsymbol{G}}(\boldsymbol{x}) \geqslant \mathbf{0}, \boldsymbol{x} \in \mathscr{E}^n\}$ *and*

$$(\boldsymbol{x}_2, \boldsymbol{\lambda}_2) \in \mathscr{K}_{\mathrm{d}} = \{(\boldsymbol{x}, \boldsymbol{\lambda}) \mid \nabla_{\boldsymbol{x}} L = \mathbf{0}, (\boldsymbol{x}, \boldsymbol{\lambda}) \in \mathscr{E}^{m+2n}, \boldsymbol{\lambda} \geqslant \mathbf{0}\},$$

then the dual problem always provides an upper bound for the primal problem, i.e.

$$\sup_{\boldsymbol{x} \in \mathscr{K}} \mathrm{f}(\boldsymbol{x}) = \mathrm{f}(\boldsymbol{x}_1) \leqslant \inf_{(\boldsymbol{x}, \boldsymbol{\lambda}) \in \mathscr{K}_{\mathrm{d}}} L(\boldsymbol{x}, \boldsymbol{\lambda}) = L(\boldsymbol{x}_2, \boldsymbol{\lambda}_2).$$

---

[12] See Wolfe (1961), p. 239.

[13] See Wolfe (1961), p. 240.

Proof. With f concave at $\boldsymbol{x}_2$ and $\nabla f(\boldsymbol{x}_2)+\nabla\bar{\boldsymbol{G}}(\boldsymbol{x}_2)\boldsymbol{\lambda}_2 = \mathbf{0}$,

$$f(\boldsymbol{x}_1)\leqslant f(\boldsymbol{x}_2)+\nabla f(\boldsymbol{x}_2)'(\boldsymbol{x}_1-\boldsymbol{x}_2) = f(\boldsymbol{x}_2)-\boldsymbol{\lambda}_2'\nabla\bar{\boldsymbol{G}}(\boldsymbol{x}_2)'(\boldsymbol{x}_1-\boldsymbol{x}_2).$$

Since $\bar{\boldsymbol{G}}(\boldsymbol{x})$ is concave at $\boldsymbol{x}_2$,

$$\bar{\boldsymbol{G}}(\boldsymbol{x}_1)\leqslant\bar{\boldsymbol{G}}(\boldsymbol{x}_2)+\nabla\bar{\boldsymbol{G}}(\boldsymbol{x}_2)'(\boldsymbol{x}_1-\boldsymbol{x}_2),$$

$$\boldsymbol{\lambda}_2'(\bar{\boldsymbol{G}}(\boldsymbol{x}_1)-\bar{\boldsymbol{G}}(\boldsymbol{x}_2))\leqslant\boldsymbol{\lambda}_2'\nabla\bar{\boldsymbol{G}}(\boldsymbol{x}_2)'(\boldsymbol{x}_1-\boldsymbol{x}_2),$$

and thus

$$\begin{aligned} f(\boldsymbol{x}_1)&\leqslant f(\boldsymbol{x}_2)-\boldsymbol{\lambda}_2'\nabla\bar{\boldsymbol{G}}(\boldsymbol{x}_2)'(\boldsymbol{x}_1-\boldsymbol{x}_2)\leqslant f(\boldsymbol{x}_2)+\boldsymbol{\lambda}_2'(\bar{\boldsymbol{G}}(\boldsymbol{x}_2)-\bar{\boldsymbol{G}}(\boldsymbol{x}_1))\\ &= L(\boldsymbol{x}_2, \boldsymbol{\lambda}_2)-\boldsymbol{\lambda}_2'\bar{\boldsymbol{G}}(\boldsymbol{x}_1).\end{aligned}$$

With $\boldsymbol{\lambda}_2$, $\bar{\boldsymbol{G}}(\boldsymbol{x}_1)\geqslant\mathbf{0}$, it follows that $f(\boldsymbol{x}_1)\leqslant L(\boldsymbol{x}_2, \boldsymbol{\lambda}_2)$. Q.E.D.

Next,

(c) $\boldsymbol{x}_0\in\mathscr{K}$ solves the primal problem and $(\boldsymbol{x}_0, \boldsymbol{\lambda}_0)\in\mathscr{K}_d$ solves the dual problem if and only if $f(\boldsymbol{x}_0) = L(\boldsymbol{x}_0, \boldsymbol{\lambda}_0)$.

That this equality is necessary follows from the fact that if $\boldsymbol{x}_0\in\mathscr{K}$ solves the primal problem and $f(\boldsymbol{x}_0)<L(\boldsymbol{x}_1, \boldsymbol{\lambda}_1)$, $(\boldsymbol{x}_1, \boldsymbol{\lambda}_1)\in\mathscr{K}_d$, then $(\boldsymbol{x}_1, \boldsymbol{\lambda}_1)$ cannot solve the dual problem since, by eq. (12.4), there exists an $\boldsymbol{\lambda}_0$ such that $f(\boldsymbol{x}_0) = L(\boldsymbol{x}_0, \boldsymbol{\lambda}_0)<L(\boldsymbol{x}_1, \boldsymbol{\lambda}_1)$, $(\boldsymbol{x}_0, \boldsymbol{\lambda}_0)\in\mathscr{K}_d$. It is sufficient, since if $f(\boldsymbol{x}_0) = L(\boldsymbol{x}_1, \boldsymbol{\lambda}_1)$, $\boldsymbol{x}_0\in\mathscr{K}$, $(\boldsymbol{x}_1, \boldsymbol{\lambda}_1)\in\mathscr{K}_d$, then

$$f(\boldsymbol{x}_0) = \sup_{\boldsymbol{x}\in\mathscr{K}} f(\boldsymbol{x}) \quad\text{and}\quad L(\boldsymbol{x}_1, \boldsymbol{\lambda}_1) = \inf_{(\boldsymbol{x}, \boldsymbol{\lambda})\in\mathscr{K}_d} L(\boldsymbol{x}, \boldsymbol{\lambda}).$$

Hence the value of the primal (dual) function cannot be increased (decreased) beyond $f(\boldsymbol{x}_0)$ ($L(\boldsymbol{x}_0, \boldsymbol{\lambda}_0)$). Also:

(d) there exists an optimal solution to the primal problem if and only if there exists an optimal solution to the dual problem, in which case property (c) above holds.

To see this we state

DUALITY THEOREM 2. *Let the real-valued function* $y = f(\boldsymbol{x})$ *and the vector-valued function* $\bar{\boldsymbol{G}}(\boldsymbol{x})$ *be concave and differentiable for all* $\boldsymbol{x}\in\mathscr{K} = \{\boldsymbol{x}|\bar{\boldsymbol{G}}(\boldsymbol{x})\geqslant\mathbf{0}, \boldsymbol{x}\in\mathscr{E}^n\}$ *with the property that for some* $\boldsymbol{x}_*\in\mathscr{K}$, $\bar{\boldsymbol{G}}(\boldsymbol{x}_*)>\mathbf{0}$. *If* $\boldsymbol{x}_0$ *solves the primal problem, then there exists a* $\boldsymbol{\lambda}_0\geqslant\mathbf{0}$, $\boldsymbol{\lambda}_0\in\mathscr{E}^{m+n}$, *such that* $(\boldsymbol{x}_0, \boldsymbol{\lambda}_0)$ *solves the dual problem.*[14] *Conversely, let* $f(\boldsymbol{x})$, $\bar{\boldsymbol{G}}(\boldsymbol{x})$ *be concave and differentiable with the associated Lagrangian* $L(\boldsymbol{x}, \boldsymbol{\lambda})$ *twice differentiable for all* $\boldsymbol{x}\in\mathscr{E}^n$. *If*

$$(\boldsymbol{x}_0, \boldsymbol{\lambda}_0)\in\mathscr{K}_d = \{(\boldsymbol{x}, \boldsymbol{\lambda})|\nabla_{\boldsymbol{x}}L = \mathbf{0}, (\boldsymbol{x}, \boldsymbol{\lambda})\in\mathscr{E}^{m+2n}, \boldsymbol{\lambda}\geqslant\mathbf{0}\}$$

solves the dual problem and the nth-order Hessian matrix of $L(\boldsymbol{x}, \boldsymbol{\lambda})$ *is non-*

[14] See Wolfe (1961), p. 241.

singular at $(\boldsymbol{x}_0, \boldsymbol{\lambda}_0)$ (*i.e. if* $|\nabla_{\boldsymbol{x}}^2 L^0| \neq 0$), *then, subject to the above constraint qualification,* $\boldsymbol{x}_0$ *solves the primal problem.*[15] *In each case* $\mathrm{f}(\boldsymbol{x}_0) = L(\boldsymbol{x}_0, \boldsymbol{\lambda}_0)$.

Proof. If $\boldsymbol{x}_0$ solves the primal problem, then eq. (12.4) holds, i.e. $(\boldsymbol{x}_0, \boldsymbol{\lambda}_0) \in \mathscr{K}_{\mathrm{d}}$. For $(\boldsymbol{x}, \boldsymbol{\lambda}) \in \mathscr{K}_{\mathrm{d}}$,

$$L(\boldsymbol{x}_0, \boldsymbol{\lambda}_0) - L(\boldsymbol{x}, \boldsymbol{\lambda}) = \mathrm{f}(\boldsymbol{x}_0) - \mathrm{f}(\boldsymbol{x}) - \boldsymbol{\lambda}'\bar{\boldsymbol{G}}(\boldsymbol{x}).$$

With f, $\bar{\boldsymbol{G}}$ concave at each $\boldsymbol{x} \in \mathscr{E}^n$, it follows that

$$\begin{aligned} \mathrm{f}(\boldsymbol{x}_0) &\leqslant \mathrm{f}(\boldsymbol{x}) + \nabla \mathrm{f}(\boldsymbol{x})'(\boldsymbol{x}_0 - \boldsymbol{x}), \\ \bar{\boldsymbol{G}}(\boldsymbol{x}_0) &\leqslant \bar{\boldsymbol{G}}(\boldsymbol{x}) + \nabla \bar{\boldsymbol{G}}(\boldsymbol{x})'(\boldsymbol{x}_0 - \boldsymbol{x}). \end{aligned}$$

Then

$$\begin{aligned} L(\boldsymbol{x}_0, \boldsymbol{\lambda}_0) - L(\boldsymbol{x}, \boldsymbol{\lambda}) &\leqslant \nabla \mathrm{f}(\boldsymbol{x})'(\boldsymbol{x}_0 - \boldsymbol{x}) - \boldsymbol{\lambda}'\bar{\boldsymbol{G}}(\boldsymbol{x}) \\ &\leqslant \nabla \mathrm{f}(\boldsymbol{x})'(\boldsymbol{x}_0 - \boldsymbol{x}) - \boldsymbol{\lambda}'\bar{\boldsymbol{G}}(\boldsymbol{x}_0) + \boldsymbol{\lambda}'\nabla \bar{\boldsymbol{G}}(\boldsymbol{x})'(\boldsymbol{x}_0 - \boldsymbol{x}) \\ &= (\nabla \mathrm{f}(\boldsymbol{x}) + \nabla \bar{\boldsymbol{G}}(\boldsymbol{x})\boldsymbol{\lambda})'(\boldsymbol{x}_0 - \boldsymbol{x}) - \boldsymbol{\lambda}'\bar{\boldsymbol{G}}(\boldsymbol{x}_0). \end{aligned}$$

Since $\nabla \mathrm{f}(\boldsymbol{x}) + \nabla \bar{\boldsymbol{G}}(\boldsymbol{x})\boldsymbol{\lambda} = \boldsymbol{0}$ and $\bar{\boldsymbol{G}}(\boldsymbol{x}_0) \geqslant \boldsymbol{0}$, $\boldsymbol{\lambda} \geqslant \boldsymbol{0}$,

$$L(\boldsymbol{x}_0, \boldsymbol{\lambda}_0) - L(\boldsymbol{x}, \boldsymbol{\lambda}) \leqslant -\boldsymbol{\lambda}'\bar{\boldsymbol{G}}(\boldsymbol{x}_0) \leqslant 0 \quad \text{or} \quad L(\boldsymbol{x}_0, \boldsymbol{\lambda}_0) \leqslant L(\boldsymbol{x}, \boldsymbol{\lambda}).$$

Thus $(\boldsymbol{x}_0, \boldsymbol{\lambda}_0)$ minimizes $L(\boldsymbol{x}, \boldsymbol{\lambda})$ for all $(\boldsymbol{x}, \boldsymbol{\lambda}) \in \mathscr{K}_{\mathrm{d}}$. In addition, from eq. (12.4), $L(\boldsymbol{x}_0, \boldsymbol{\lambda}_0) = \mathrm{f}(\boldsymbol{x}_0) + \boldsymbol{\lambda}_0'\bar{\boldsymbol{G}}(\boldsymbol{x}_0) = \mathrm{f}(\boldsymbol{x}_0)$.

(Conversely.) The Lagrangian associated with the dual problem is

$$\begin{aligned} L_{\mathrm{d}}(\boldsymbol{x}, \boldsymbol{\lambda}, \boldsymbol{v}) &= -L(\boldsymbol{x}, \boldsymbol{\lambda}) - \boldsymbol{v}'\nabla_{\boldsymbol{x}} L \\ &= -\mathrm{f}(\boldsymbol{x}) - \boldsymbol{\lambda}'\bar{\boldsymbol{G}}(\boldsymbol{x}) - \boldsymbol{v}'(\nabla \mathrm{f}(\boldsymbol{x}) + \nabla \bar{\boldsymbol{G}}(\boldsymbol{x})\boldsymbol{\lambda}) \end{aligned}$$

(we seek the constrained maximum of $-L(\boldsymbol{x}, \boldsymbol{\lambda})$), where $\boldsymbol{v}$ is an $(n \times 1)$ vector of Lagrange multipliers v_i, $i = 1, \ldots, n$. Since the constraint $\nabla_{\boldsymbol{x}} L = \boldsymbol{0}$ is satisfied as an equality, the v_i, $i = 1, \ldots, n$, are unrestricted in sign, as is $\boldsymbol{x}$. Our only sign restriction involves $\boldsymbol{\lambda} \geqslant \boldsymbol{0}$. For $(\boldsymbol{x}_0, \boldsymbol{\lambda}_0)$ to solve the dual problem it is necessary that a $\boldsymbol{v}_0$ exists such that

$$\left.\begin{aligned} \nabla_{\boldsymbol{x}} L_{\mathrm{d}}^0 &= -\nabla \mathrm{f}(\boldsymbol{x}_0) - \nabla \bar{\boldsymbol{G}}(\boldsymbol{x}_0)\boldsymbol{\lambda}_0 - \nabla_{\boldsymbol{x}}^2 L^0 \boldsymbol{v}_0 = \boldsymbol{0} \quad \text{or} \\ &\qquad \nabla \mathrm{f}(\boldsymbol{x}_0) + \nabla \bar{\boldsymbol{G}}(\boldsymbol{x}_0)\boldsymbol{\lambda}_0 + \nabla_{\boldsymbol{x}}^2 L^0 \boldsymbol{v}_0 = \boldsymbol{0}, \\ \nabla_{\boldsymbol{\lambda}} L_{\mathrm{d}}^0 &= -\bar{\boldsymbol{G}}(\boldsymbol{x}_0) - \nabla \bar{\boldsymbol{G}}(\boldsymbol{x}_0)'\boldsymbol{v}_0 \leqslant \boldsymbol{0}, \\ \boldsymbol{\lambda}_0'(&-\bar{\boldsymbol{G}}(\boldsymbol{x}_0) - \nabla \bar{\boldsymbol{G}}(\boldsymbol{x}_0)'\boldsymbol{v}_0) = 0, \\ \nabla_{\boldsymbol{v}} L_{\mathrm{d}}^0 &= -\nabla \mathrm{f}(\boldsymbol{x}_0) - \nabla \bar{\boldsymbol{G}}(\boldsymbol{x}_0)\boldsymbol{\lambda}_0 = \boldsymbol{0}, \text{ or} \\ &\qquad \nabla \mathrm{f}(\boldsymbol{x}_0) + \nabla \bar{\boldsymbol{G}}(\boldsymbol{x}_0)\boldsymbol{\lambda}_0 = \boldsymbol{0}, \\ &\boldsymbol{x}_0 \text{ unrestricted}, \\ &\boldsymbol{\lambda}_0 \geqslant \boldsymbol{0}, \\ &\boldsymbol{v}_0 \text{ unrestricted}. \end{aligned}\right\} \tag{12.17}$$

[15] See Mangasarian (1962), pp. 301–302; Graves and Wolfe (1963), pp. 58–60.

Substituting $\nabla_{\boldsymbol{v}} L^0_{\mathrm{d}} = \mathbf{0}$ into $\nabla_{\boldsymbol{x}} L^0_{\mathrm{d}} = \mathbf{0}$ yields

$$\begin{aligned}\nabla^2_{\boldsymbol{x}} L^0 \boldsymbol{v}_0 &= \nabla(\nabla \mathrm{f}(\boldsymbol{x}) + \nabla \bar{\boldsymbol{G}}(\boldsymbol{x})\boldsymbol{\lambda}_0)_0 \boldsymbol{v}_0 \\ &= \left(\nabla^2 \mathrm{f}(\boldsymbol{x}_0) + \nabla \left(\sum_{j=1}^{m+n} \lambda_j^0 \nabla \hat{\mathrm{g}}^j(\boldsymbol{x}) \right)_0 \right) \boldsymbol{v}_0 \\ &= \left(\nabla^2 \mathrm{f}(\boldsymbol{x}_0) + \sum_{j=1}^{m+n} \lambda_j^0 \nabla^2 \hat{\mathrm{g}}^j(\boldsymbol{x}_0) \right) \boldsymbol{v}_0 \\ &= \left(\boldsymbol{H}_{\mathrm{f}}(\boldsymbol{x}_0) + \sum_{j=1}^{m+n} \lambda_j^0 \boldsymbol{H}_{\hat{\mathrm{g}}^j}(\boldsymbol{x}_0) \right) \boldsymbol{v}_0 = \mathbf{0},\end{aligned}$$

where $\boldsymbol{H}_{\mathrm{f}}(\boldsymbol{x}_0)$, $\boldsymbol{H}_{\hat{\mathrm{g}}^j}(\boldsymbol{x}_0)$ are, respectively, the nth-order Hessian matrices of f and $\hat{\mathrm{g}}^j$, $j = 1, \ldots, m+n$. If

$$|\nabla^2_{\boldsymbol{x}} L^0| = \left| \boldsymbol{H}_{\mathrm{f}}(\boldsymbol{x}_0) + \sum_{j=1}^{m+n} \lambda_j^0 \boldsymbol{H}_{\hat{\mathrm{g}}^j}(\boldsymbol{x}_0) \right| \neq 0,^{16}$$

then $\boldsymbol{v}_0 = [\nabla^2_{\boldsymbol{x}} L^0]^{-1}\mathbf{0} = \mathbf{0}$ and thus eq. (12.17) becomes

$$\left.\begin{aligned}&\nabla \mathrm{f}(\boldsymbol{x}_0) + \nabla \bar{\boldsymbol{G}}(\boldsymbol{x}_0)\boldsymbol{\lambda}_0 = \mathbf{0}, \\ &\bar{\boldsymbol{G}}(\boldsymbol{x}_0) \geqslant \mathbf{0} \quad (\text{i.e. } \boldsymbol{x}_0 \in \mathscr{K}), \\ &\boldsymbol{\lambda}_0' \bar{\boldsymbol{G}}(\boldsymbol{x}_0) = 0, \\ &\boldsymbol{\lambda}_0 \geqslant \mathbf{0},\end{aligned}\right\} \quad \text{or eq. (12.4).}$$

Since the Lagrangian is concave and differentiable, eq. (12.4) provides us with a necessary and sufficient condition for a saddle point of $L(\boldsymbol{x}, \boldsymbol{\lambda})$ at $(\boldsymbol{x}_0, \boldsymbol{\lambda}_0)$. And by the Kuhn–Tucker equivalence theorem II, eq. (12.4) is necessary and sufficient for a solution to the primal problem. With $\boldsymbol{\lambda}_0' \bar{\boldsymbol{G}}(\boldsymbol{x}_0) = 0$ it is also true that $\mathrm{f}(\boldsymbol{x}_0) = L(\boldsymbol{x}_0, \boldsymbol{\lambda}_0)$. Q.E.D.

It is important to note that since f, $\boldsymbol{G}$ are concave, the solutions to the primal and dual problems are global in character.

Our final primal–dual relationship involves the complementary slackness or orthogonality conditions $\boldsymbol{\lambda}_0' \boldsymbol{s} = 0$, $\boldsymbol{x}_0' \boldsymbol{t} = 0$. Let us first consider how this set of equalities arises. The primal–dual pair of problems may be rewritten as

Primal

$$\max_{\boldsymbol{x} \in \mathscr{K}} \{\mathrm{f}(\boldsymbol{x})\},$$

---

[16] A condition which is sufficient to insure that $|\nabla^2_{\boldsymbol{x}} L^0| \neq 0$ is that $L(\boldsymbol{x}, \boldsymbol{\lambda}_0)$ be strictly concave at $\boldsymbol{x}_0$ (i.e. either $\mathrm{f}(\boldsymbol{x})$ is strictly concave at $\boldsymbol{x}_0$ or for some $j \in \mathscr{J}$, $\lambda_j^0 > 0$, $\hat{\mathrm{g}}^j(\boldsymbol{x})$ is strictly concave at $\boldsymbol{x}_0$). In this instance $\nabla^2_{\boldsymbol{x}} L^0$ is negative definite and thus non-singular. Hence $\rho[\nabla^2_{\boldsymbol{x}} L^0] = n$, and we are assured that the homogeneous system $\nabla^2_{\boldsymbol{x}} L^0 \boldsymbol{v}_0 = \mathbf{0}$ has a unique solution $\boldsymbol{v}_0 = \mathbf{0}$.

where

$$\mathscr{K} = \{\boldsymbol{x} | \boldsymbol{G}(\boldsymbol{x}) \geqslant \mathbf{0}, \boldsymbol{x} \geqslant \mathbf{0}, \boldsymbol{x} \in \mathscr{E}^n\}.$$

Dual

$$\min_{(\boldsymbol{x}, \boldsymbol{\lambda}) \in \mathscr{K}_d} \{L(\boldsymbol{x}, \boldsymbol{\lambda}) - \boldsymbol{x}' \nabla_{\boldsymbol{x}} L\},$$

where

$$\mathscr{K}_{\mathrm{d}} = \{(\boldsymbol{x}, \boldsymbol{\lambda}) | \nabla_{\boldsymbol{x}} L \leqslant \mathbf{0}, (\boldsymbol{x}, \boldsymbol{\lambda}) \in \mathscr{E}^{n+m}, \boldsymbol{\lambda} \geqslant \mathbf{0}\},$$

where $\boldsymbol{x}$ is unrestricted in the dual, and it is assumed that the real-valued function $y = \mathrm{f}(\boldsymbol{x})$ and the vector-valued function $\boldsymbol{G}(\boldsymbol{x}) \geqslant \mathbf{0}$ are concave and differentiable and $L(\boldsymbol{x}, \boldsymbol{\lambda})$ is twice differentiable for all $\boldsymbol{x} \in \mathscr{E}^n$. The Lagrangian associated with the dual problem is

$$\begin{aligned} L_{\mathrm{d}}(\boldsymbol{x}, \boldsymbol{\lambda}, \boldsymbol{v}, \boldsymbol{t}) &= -L(\boldsymbol{x}, \boldsymbol{\lambda}) + \boldsymbol{x}' \nabla_{\boldsymbol{x}} L - \boldsymbol{v}'(\nabla_{\boldsymbol{x}} L + \boldsymbol{t}) \\ &= -\mathrm{f}(\boldsymbol{x}) - \boldsymbol{\lambda}' \boldsymbol{G}(\boldsymbol{x}) + \boldsymbol{x}'(\nabla \mathrm{f}(\boldsymbol{x}) + \nabla \boldsymbol{G}(\boldsymbol{x}) \boldsymbol{\lambda}) \\ &\quad - \boldsymbol{v}'(\nabla \mathrm{f}(\boldsymbol{x}) + \nabla \boldsymbol{G}(\boldsymbol{x}) \boldsymbol{\lambda} + \boldsymbol{t}), \end{aligned}$$

where $\boldsymbol{v}$ is an $(n \times 1)$ vector of Lagrange multipliers v_i, $i = 1, \ldots, n$, and the inequality constraint $\nabla_{\boldsymbol{x}} L \leqslant \mathbf{0}$ has been converted to an equality constraint by introducing the $(n \times 1)$ vector of dual slack variables

$$\boldsymbol{t} = \begin{bmatrix} t_1^2 \\ \vdots \\ t_n^2 \end{bmatrix} \geqslant \mathbf{0}$$

with

$$t_i^2 = -\mathrm{f}_i(\boldsymbol{x}) - \sum_{j=1}^{m} \lambda_j \hat{g}_i^j(\boldsymbol{x}) \geqslant 0, \quad i = 1, \ldots, n.$$

Given that the above constraint qualification holds, a necessary condition for $(\boldsymbol{x}_0, \boldsymbol{\lambda}_0)$ to solve the dual problem is the existence of a $\boldsymbol{v}_0 \geqslant \mathbf{0}$ such that

$$\left.\begin{aligned} &\nabla_{\boldsymbol{x}}^2 L_{\mathrm{d}}^0 = \nabla_{\boldsymbol{x}}^2 L^0(\boldsymbol{x}_0 - \boldsymbol{v}_0) = \mathbf{0}, \\ &\nabla_{\boldsymbol{\lambda}} L_{\mathrm{d}}^0 = -\boldsymbol{G}(\boldsymbol{x}_0) + \nabla \boldsymbol{G}(\boldsymbol{x}_0)'(\boldsymbol{x}_0 - \boldsymbol{v}_0) \leqslant \mathbf{0}, \\ &\boldsymbol{\lambda}_0'(-\boldsymbol{G}(\boldsymbol{x}_0) + \nabla \boldsymbol{G}(\boldsymbol{x}_0)'(\boldsymbol{x}_0 - \boldsymbol{v}_0)) = 0, \\ &\nabla_{\boldsymbol{v}} L_{\mathrm{d}}^0 = \nabla \mathrm{f}(\boldsymbol{x}_0) + \nabla \boldsymbol{G}(\boldsymbol{x}_0) \boldsymbol{\lambda}_0 + \boldsymbol{t} = \mathbf{0} \quad \text{or} \\ &\qquad \nabla \mathrm{f}(\boldsymbol{x}_0) + \nabla \boldsymbol{G}(\boldsymbol{x}_0) \boldsymbol{\lambda}_0 \leqslant \mathbf{0}, \\ &\boldsymbol{v}_0'(\nabla \mathrm{f}(\boldsymbol{x}_0) + \nabla \boldsymbol{G}(\boldsymbol{x}_0) \boldsymbol{\lambda}_0) = 0, \\ &\boldsymbol{x}_0 \text{ unrestricted}, \\ &\boldsymbol{\lambda}_0 \geqslant \mathbf{0}, \\ &\boldsymbol{v}_0 \geqslant \mathbf{0}. \end{aligned}\right\} \tag{12.18}$$

If $\nabla_x^2 L^0$ is non-singular, then $x_0 - v_0 = \mathbf{0}$.[17] Hence,

$$v_0'(\nabla f(x_0) + \nabla G(x_0)\lambda_0) = x_0'\nabla_x L^0 = x_0' t = 0.$$

In addition, since the primal Lagrangian may be written as $L(x, \lambda, s) = f(x) + \lambda'(G(x) - s)$, where

$$s = \begin{bmatrix} s_1^2 \\ \vdots \\ s_m^2 \end{bmatrix} \geqslant \mathbf{0}, \qquad s_j^2 = \hat{g}^j(x) \geqslant 0, \quad j = 1, \ldots, m,$$

is an $(m \times 1)$ vector of primal slack variables, then $\lambda_0' G(x_0) = 0$ may be rewritten as $\lambda_0' s = 0$, since $G(x) - s = \mathbf{0}$. Collecting these results we have the *complementary slackness or orthogonality conditions* $\lambda_0' s = 0$, $x_0' t = 0$. That is to say, given $\lambda_0' s = \Sigma_{j=1}^m \lambda_j^0 s_j^2 = 0$, if $s_j^2 > 0$ (implying that $\hat{g}^j(x_0) > 0$), then $\lambda_j^0 = 0$; and if $\lambda_j^0 > 0$ (so that $\hat{g}^j(x_0) = 0$), then $s_j^2 = 0$. Additionally, given $x_0' t = \Sigma_{i=1}^n x_i^0 t_i^2 = 0$, if $t_i^2 > 0$ (implying $f_i(x_0) + \Sigma_{j=1}^m \lambda_j^0 \hat{g}^j(x_0) < 0$), then $x_i^0 = 0$; and if $x_i^0 > 0$ (in which case $f_i(x_0) + \Sigma_{j=1}^m \lambda_j^0 \hat{g}^j(x_0) = 0$), then $t_i^2 = 0$. Hence, at least one of each pair (λ_j^0, s_j^2) for the primal and (x_i^0, t_i^2) for the dual must vanish at $x_0 \in \mathscr{K}$, $(x_0, \lambda_0) \in \mathscr{K}_d$. In short, if the jth dual variable λ_j is different from zero in the optimal dual solution, then the jth primal slack variable equals zero in the optimal primal solution; and if the variable x_i appears in the optimal primal solution, then the ith dual slack variable is equal to zero in the optimal dual solution. In light of these remarks we have:

(e) $x_0 \in \mathscr{K}$ solves the primal problem and $(x_0, \lambda_0) \in \mathscr{K}_d$ solves the dual problem if and only if x_0, (x_0, λ_0) satisfy the complementary slackness conditions $\lambda_0' s = 0$, $x_0' t = 0$.

That these orthogonality conditions are necessary may be demonstrated by noting that if $x_0 \in \mathscr{K}$, $(x_0, \lambda_0) \in \mathscr{K}_d$ solve the primal and dual problems respectively, then from (c) above, $f(x_0) = L(x_0, \lambda_0)$ and thus

$$\begin{aligned} f(x_0) - L(x_0, \lambda_0) &= L(x_0, \lambda_0, s) + L_d(x_0, \lambda_0, v_0, t) \\ &= f(x_0) + \lambda_0'(G(x_0) - s) - f(x_0) - \lambda_0' G(x_0) \\ &\quad + x_0'(\nabla f(x_0) + \nabla G(x_0)\lambda_0) \\ &\quad - v_0'(\nabla f(x_0) + \nabla G(x_0)\lambda_0 + t) \\ &= -\lambda_0' s - x_0' t = 0, \end{aligned}$$

[17] Note that with $x_0 - v_0 = \mathbf{0}$, eq. (12.18) reduces to

$$\left.\begin{aligned} &\nabla f(x_0) + \nabla G(x_0)\lambda_0 \leqslant \mathbf{0}, \\ &x_0'(\nabla f(x_0) + \nabla G(x_0)\lambda_0) = 0, \\ &G(x_0) \geqslant \mathbf{0}, \\ &\lambda_0' G(x_0) = 0, \\ &x_0 \geqslant \mathbf{0}, \\ &\lambda_0 \geqslant \mathbf{0}, \end{aligned}\right\} \text{ or eq. (12.5).}$$

only if $\boldsymbol{\lambda}_0' \boldsymbol{s} = \boldsymbol{x}_0' \boldsymbol{t} = 0$. It is sufficient, since if

$$\boldsymbol{\lambda}_0' \boldsymbol{s}(=\boldsymbol{\lambda}_0' G(\boldsymbol{x}_0)) = \boldsymbol{x}_0' \boldsymbol{t}(=\boldsymbol{x}_0' \nabla_{\boldsymbol{x}} L^0) = 0,$$

then

$$L(\boldsymbol{x}_0, \boldsymbol{\lambda}_0) = \mathrm{f}(\boldsymbol{x}_0), \qquad L_{\mathrm{d}}(\boldsymbol{x}_0, \boldsymbol{\lambda}_0) = L(\boldsymbol{x}_0, \boldsymbol{\lambda}_0),$$

whence $\mathrm{f}(\boldsymbol{x}_0) = L(\boldsymbol{x}_0, \boldsymbol{\lambda}_0)$ and thus (c) holds.[18]

12.5. Appendix A: Constraint qualifications[19]

It was mentioned in the text above that in order for eq. (12.2) to hold at an optimal (maximal) point $\boldsymbol{x}_0 \in \mathscr{K}$, some form of restriction on the nature of the constraint set in the immediate vicinity of $\boldsymbol{x}_0$ is in order. What sort of anomalous behavior may occur? In general, if the constraint set has a special property at a boundary point $\bar{\boldsymbol{x}}$ which it does not have at any other of its boundary points, then $\bar{\boldsymbol{x}}$ is termed an *exceptional* (or *singular*) point of $\mathscr{K}$. Such points exist if, for instance, $\mathscr{K}$ possesses a *cusp* (e.g. a cusp occurs at $\bar{\boldsymbol{x}}$ if a variable point moving from A to $\bar{\boldsymbol{x}}$ in fig. A.1(a) stops abruptly at $\bar{\boldsymbol{x}}$ and reverses its direction towards C) or is *degenerate* (in the sense that it has but a single point $\bar{\boldsymbol{x}}$ (fig. A.1(b)). Hence the reason why a regularity condition is necessary is that it serves to rule out such exceptional behavior or singularities on the boundary of the constraint set. Let us now be more specific.

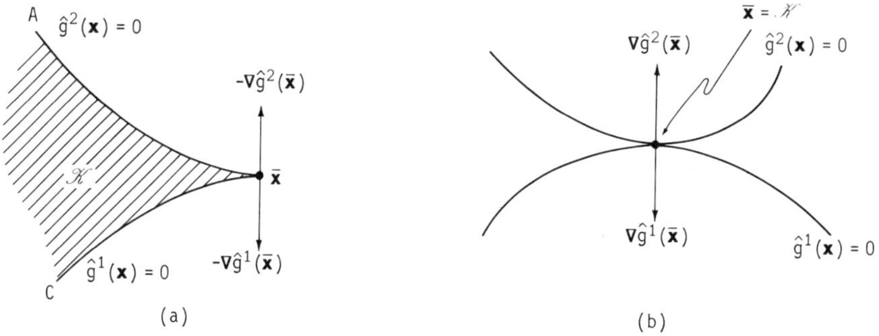

Fig. A.1.

[18] Those readers interested in pursuing the study of duality theory beyond the introductory discussion presented here should consult Geoffrion (1972), pp. 65–101; Abadie (1967), pp. 3–20, 77–98; Rockafellar (1970), pp. 95–140, 263–342.

[19] The material presented herein draws heavily from the discussions given by Graves and Wolfe (1963), pp. 483–484; Fiacco and McCormick (1968), pp. 19–24.

We noted previously that at an optimal point $\boldsymbol{x}_0$, if $\boldsymbol{h}\in\mathscr{D}(\boldsymbol{x}_0)$, then: (1) $\nabla\hat{g}^j(\boldsymbol{x}_0)'\boldsymbol{h}\geqslant 0$, $j\in\mathscr{J}$; and (2) $\nabla f(\boldsymbol{x}_0)'\boldsymbol{h}\leqslant 0$. However, if $\nabla\hat{g}^j(\boldsymbol{x}_0)'\boldsymbol{h}\geqslant 0$, $j\in\mathscr{J}$, it need not be true that $\boldsymbol{h}\in\mathscr{D}(\boldsymbol{x}_0)$. Hence, there may exist inadmissible directions $\boldsymbol{h}$ such that $\nabla f(\boldsymbol{x}_0)'\boldsymbol{h}\leqslant 0$ is violated even though $\nabla\hat{g}^j(\boldsymbol{x}_0)'\boldsymbol{h}\geqslant 0$, $j\in\mathscr{J}$. To see this let us examine

Example A.1.[20] Let us write $\mathscr{K}$ (fig. A.2) as $\mathscr{K} = \{\boldsymbol{x}\,|\,\bar{\boldsymbol{G}}(\boldsymbol{x})\geqslant\boldsymbol{0},\ \boldsymbol{x}\in\mathscr{E}^2\}$, where

$$\bar{\boldsymbol{G}}(\boldsymbol{x}) = \begin{bmatrix}\hat{g}^1(\boldsymbol{x})\\ \hat{g}^2(\boldsymbol{x})\\ \hat{g}^3(\boldsymbol{x})\end{bmatrix} = \begin{bmatrix}(1-x_1)^3-x_2\\ x_1\\ x_2\end{bmatrix}\geqslant\boldsymbol{0}.$$

For $\boldsymbol{x}_0' = (1,0)$, $\mathscr{J} = \{1,3\}$ and thus $\nabla\hat{g}^1(\boldsymbol{x}_0)' = (0,-1)$, $\nabla\hat{g}^3(\boldsymbol{x}_0)' = (0,1)$. Now we require that

$$\left.\begin{aligned}\nabla\hat{g}^1(\boldsymbol{x}_0)'\boldsymbol{h} &= (0,\,-1)\begin{bmatrix}h_1\\ h_2\end{bmatrix} = -h_2\geqslant 0,\\ \nabla\hat{g}^3(\boldsymbol{x}_0)'\boldsymbol{h} &= (0,\,1)\begin{bmatrix}h_1\\ h_2\end{bmatrix} = h_2\geqslant 0\end{aligned}\right\}\tag{A.1}$$

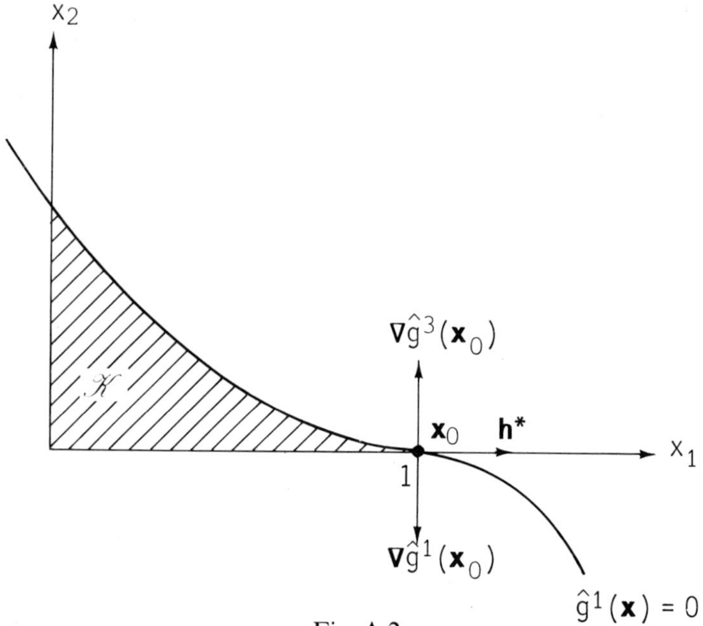

Fig. A.2.

[20] Kuhn and Tucker (1951), pp. 483–484.

for all admissible $\boldsymbol{h}$, i.e. if $\boldsymbol{h}\in\mathscr{D}(\boldsymbol{x}_0) = [0\leqslant x_1\leqslant 1]$, then $\nabla\hat{g}^j(\boldsymbol{x}_0)'\boldsymbol{h}\geqslant 0$, $j\in\mathscr{J}$. If we let $(\boldsymbol{h}^*)' = (1, 0)$, then $\boldsymbol{h}^*$ satisfies eq. (A.1) (since in eq. (A.1) h_1 is arbitrary while $h_2 = 0$) but $\boldsymbol{h}^*\notin\mathscr{D}(\boldsymbol{x}_0)$. Hence, there are directions $\boldsymbol{h}$ which satisfy $\nabla\hat{g}^j(\boldsymbol{x}_0)'\boldsymbol{h}\geqslant 0$, $j\in\mathscr{J}$, yet are inadmissible. To avoid such instances various regularity requirements on the constraint set or constraint qualifications have been advanced to enable us to determine the circumstances under which we may be assured that if a direction $\boldsymbol{h}$ satisfies $\nabla\hat{g}^j(\boldsymbol{x}_0)'\boldsymbol{h}\geqslant 0$, $j\in\mathscr{J}$, then $\boldsymbol{h}\in\mathscr{D}(\boldsymbol{x}_0)$ whence $\nabla f(\boldsymbol{x}_0)'\boldsymbol{h}\leqslant 0$ or

$$\{\boldsymbol{h}\,|\,\nabla f(\boldsymbol{x}_0)'\boldsymbol{h}>0,\ \nabla\hat{g}^j(\boldsymbol{x}_0)'\boldsymbol{h}\geqslant 0, j\in\mathscr{J}\} = \{\cdot\} = \phi.$$

Before getting to their specifics let us discuss some preliminary mathematical notions.

First,

DEFINITION A.1. *A continuous differentiable arc in* $\mathscr{E}^n$,

$$\boldsymbol{x} = \boldsymbol{\phi}(t) \quad or \quad \begin{bmatrix} x_1 \\ \vdots \\ x_n \end{bmatrix} = \begin{bmatrix} \phi_1(t) \\ \vdots \\ \phi_n(t) \end{bmatrix}, \quad t\in[0, \varepsilon]\in\mathscr{E}^1,$$

t a parameter, is a mapping or transformation from $\mathscr{E}^1$ to $\mathscr{E}^n$ such that $\mathrm{d}x_i/\mathrm{d}t = \phi_i'(t)$, *$i = 1, \ldots, n$, exists.*

It is assumed that $\boldsymbol{\phi}(t)$ does not intersect itself, has two distinct ends (i.e. $\boldsymbol{x}\in[\boldsymbol{\phi}(0), \boldsymbol{\phi}(\varepsilon)]$), and has a tangent vector

$$\boldsymbol{\phi}'(t) = \begin{bmatrix} \phi_1'(t) \\ \vdots \\ \phi_n'(t) \end{bmatrix} = \boldsymbol{h},$$

for each $t\in[0, \varepsilon]$. As far as its initial point is concerned, $\boldsymbol{\phi}(t)$ is said to emanate from $\boldsymbol{x}_0$ if $\boldsymbol{\phi}(0) = \boldsymbol{x}_0$. Next,

DEFINITION A.2. *Let $\boldsymbol{x} = \boldsymbol{\phi}(t)\in\mathscr{E}^n$, $t\in[0, \varepsilon]$, be a continuous differentiable arc such that $\boldsymbol{\phi}(0) = \boldsymbol{x}_0$. The vector $\boldsymbol{h}$ is said to be tangent to $\boldsymbol{\phi}(t)$ at $\boldsymbol{x}_0$ if $\boldsymbol{h} = \boldsymbol{\phi}'(0)$, i.e.*

$$\begin{bmatrix} h_1 \\ \vdots \\ h_n \end{bmatrix} = \begin{bmatrix} \phi_1'(0) \\ \vdots \\ \phi_n'(0) \end{bmatrix}.$$

Since t is required to be non-negative, it is to be understood that

$$\phi_i'(0) = \lim_{t\to 0+} \frac{\phi_i(t)-\phi_i(0)}{t}, \quad i = 1, \ldots, n.$$

In the light of these two definitions we may now state the

KUHN–TUCKER CONSTRAINT QUALIFICATION.[21] *Let*

$$x_0 \in \mathscr{K} = \{x | \bar{G}(x) \geq 0,\ x \in \mathscr{E}^n\}$$

with $\bar{G}(x)$ *differentiable throughout some open spherical* δ*-neighborhood of* x_0, $\delta(x_0)$. *Then the Kuhn–Tucker constraint qualification holds locally at* x_0 *if for each* $h \neq 0$ *satisfying* $\nabla \hat{g}^j(x_0)'h \geq 0$, $j \in \mathscr{J}$, *there is in* $\delta(x_0)$ *a continuous differentiable arc* $x = \phi(t)$, $\phi(0) = x_0$, *such that for each* $t \in [0, \varepsilon]$, $\bar{G}(x) = \bar{G}(\phi(t)) \geq 0$, *and* $h = \phi'(0)$.

Hence the constraint set satisfies the Kuhn–Tucker constraint qualification at x_0 if every $h \neq 0$ satisfying $\nabla \hat{g}^j(x_0)'h \geq 0$, $j \in \mathscr{J}$, is tangent to a continuous differentiable arc emanating from x_0 and contained in $\mathscr{K}$. Obviously h^* in the above example fails to meet this criterion. Looked at in another fashion, the sort of difficulty indicated in the above example emerged simply because h^* pointed in a direction away from and not into the constraint set. But if the Kuhn–Tucker constraint qualification holds at x_0, then every $h \neq 0$ satisfying $\nabla \hat{g}^j(x_0)'h \geq 0$, $j \in \mathscr{J}$, points into or enters $\mathscr{K}$ from x_0 since it is tangent to a continuous differentiable arc emanating from x_0 and contained in $\mathscr{K}$. Geometrically, if every $h \neq 0$ satisfying $\nabla \hat{g}^j(x_0)'h \geq 0$, $j \in \mathscr{J}$, enters $\mathscr{K}$ from x_0, then the polar support cone $\mathscr{D}(x_0)^+$ is a subset of the tangent support cone $\mathscr{D}(x_0)$. This is not true for the constraint set depicted in fig. A.2.

The importance of the Kuhn–Tucker constraint qualification is that it is sufficient to guarantee that $\{\cdot\} = \phi$ which in turn is necessary and sufficient (by the Minkowski–Farkas theorem) to insure the existence of a $\lambda_0 \geq 0$ such that $\nabla f(x_0) = \Sigma_j \lambda_j^0(-\nabla \hat{g}^j(x_0))$, $j \in \mathscr{J}$. To see this we state the following

KUHN–TUCKER THEOREM (a necessary condition). *Let the real-valued function* $y = f(x)$ *and the vector-valued function* $\bar{G}(x) \geq 0$, $x \in \mathscr{E}^n$, *be differentiable throughout some spherical* δ*-neighborhood of the point* x_0, $\delta(x_0)$. *If* f *subject to* $x \in \mathscr{K} = \{x | \bar{G}(x) \geq 0,\ x \in \mathscr{E}^n\}$ *has a local maximum at* x_0, *then, subject to the Kuhn–Tucker constraint qualification,* $\{\cdot\} = \phi$ *and thus there exists a vector* $\lambda_0 \geq 0$ *such that* $\nabla f(x_0) = \Sigma_j \lambda_j^0(-\nabla \hat{g}^j(x_0))$, $j \in \mathscr{J}$.

Proof.[22] Given

$$x = \phi(t) \in \delta(x_0) \subset \mathscr{K}, \quad t \in [0, \varepsilon], \quad \phi(0) = x_0,$$

if $h \neq 0$ is tangent to $\phi(t)$ at x_0, then $\phi'(0) = h$ and, since

$$\hat{g}^j(\phi(t)) \geq \hat{g}^j(\phi(0)), \quad t \in [0, \varepsilon], \quad j \in \mathscr{J},$$

it follows that

$$(d/dt)\hat{g}^j(\phi(t))\big|_{t=0} = \nabla \hat{g}^j(\phi(0))'\phi'(0) = \nabla \hat{g}^j(x_0)'h \geq 0, \quad j \in \mathscr{J}.$$

[21] See Graves and Wolfe (1963), p. 483.
[22] See Fiacco and McCormick (1968), p. 20.

(If no such $\boldsymbol{h}$ can be found, then $\{\cdot\} = \phi$ and the theorem is proved.) Next, the rate of change of $f(\boldsymbol{x})$ along $\boldsymbol{\phi}(t)$ at $\boldsymbol{x}_0$ is

$$(d/dt)f(\boldsymbol{\phi}(t))\big|_{t=0} = \nabla f(\boldsymbol{\phi}(0))'\boldsymbol{\phi}'(0) = \nabla f(\boldsymbol{x}_0)'\boldsymbol{h}.$$

Since $\boldsymbol{x}_0$ is optimal (maximal) and $\boldsymbol{\phi}(t)\in\mathscr{K}$, $t\in[0, \varepsilon]$, it follows that $f(\boldsymbol{\phi}(0)) = f(\boldsymbol{x}_0)\geqslant f(\boldsymbol{\phi}(t))$ for all $t\in[0, \varepsilon]$, i.e. f cannot increase along $\boldsymbol{\phi}(t)$ as t does, $t\in[0, \varepsilon]$. Hence, $\nabla f(\boldsymbol{x}_0)'\boldsymbol{h}\leqslant 0$ and thus $\{\cdot\} = \boldsymbol{\phi}$. An application of the Minkowski–Farkas lemma now yields a $\boldsymbol{\lambda}_0\geqslant\boldsymbol{0}$ such that

$$\nabla f(\boldsymbol{x}_0) = \sum_j \lambda_j^0(-\nabla \hat{g}^j(\boldsymbol{x}_0)), \quad j\in\mathscr{J}. \quad \text{Q.E.D.}$$

Three important facts regarding the Kuhn–Tucker constraint qualification must be mentioned. First, the condition $\{\cdot\} = \phi$ is weaker than the Kuhn–Tucker constraint qualification since the latter implies the former but not conversely. Second, the Kuhn–Tucker constraint qualification is only sufficient, and not both necessary (prerequisite) and sufficient, to guarantee that $\{\cdot\} = \phi$, i.e. if the constraint set does not satisfy the Kuhn–Tucker constraint qualification at $\boldsymbol{x}_0\in\mathscr{K}$, it is still possible that $\boldsymbol{x}_0$ yields a local maximum of f with $\{\cdot\} = \phi$. That this is so may be seen from

Example A.2. Maximize the real-valued function $y = f(\boldsymbol{x}) = x_1x_2$ subject to $\boldsymbol{x}\in\mathscr{K}$, where $\mathscr{K}$ is taken to be the constraint set defined above (fig. A.2). From eq. (12.4)

$$\nabla f(\boldsymbol{x})+\nabla\bar{\boldsymbol{G}}(\boldsymbol{x})\boldsymbol{\lambda} = \begin{bmatrix} x_2-3(1-x_1)^2\lambda_1+\lambda_2 \\ x_1 \quad -\lambda_1 \quad +\lambda_3\end{bmatrix} = \boldsymbol{0},$$

$$\boldsymbol{\lambda}'\bar{\boldsymbol{G}}(\boldsymbol{x}) = \lambda_1((1-x_1)^3-x_2)+\lambda_2x_1+\lambda_3x_2 = 0,$$

$$\bar{\boldsymbol{G}}(\boldsymbol{x}) = \begin{bmatrix}(1-x_1)^3-x_2 \\ x_1 \\ x_2\end{bmatrix}\geqslant\boldsymbol{0}, \qquad \boldsymbol{\lambda} = \begin{bmatrix}\lambda_1\\ \lambda_2\\ \lambda_3\end{bmatrix}\geqslant\boldsymbol{0}.$$

For $\mathscr{J} = \{1, 3\}$, this system becomes

$$\begin{aligned}
&(a)\ x_2-3(1-x_1)^2\lambda_1 = 0;\\
&(b)\ x_1-\lambda_1+\lambda_3 = 0;\\
&\quad\ \lambda_1(0)+0(x_1)+\lambda_3(0) = 0;\\
&(c)\ (1-x_1)^3-x_2 = 0, \lambda\geqslant 0;\\
&\quad\ x_1>0, \lambda_2 = 0;\\
&(d)\ x_2 = 0, \lambda_3\geqslant 0.
\end{aligned}$$

From (a), (b), (c), and (d) we obtain

$$\boldsymbol{x}_0' = (1, 0), \qquad \boldsymbol{\lambda}_0' = (1+\lambda_3^0, 0, \lambda_3^0)\geqslant\boldsymbol{0}'.$$

We noted above that the Kuhn–Tucker constraint qualification is violated at $\boldsymbol{x}_0' = (1, 0)$. Yet here f assumes a constrained local maximum at that point. Finally, the Kuhn–Tucker constraint qualification is *always* satisfied if the constraints $\hat{g}^j(\boldsymbol{x}) \geqslant 0$, $j = 1, \ldots, m+n$, are all linear. To verify this we need only define $\boldsymbol{x} = \boldsymbol{\phi}(t) \in \delta(\boldsymbol{x}_0) \subset \mathscr{K}$, $t \in [0, \varepsilon]$, $\boldsymbol{\phi}(0) = \boldsymbol{x}_0$, as $\boldsymbol{x} = \boldsymbol{x}_0 + t\boldsymbol{h}$, $\boldsymbol{h} \neq \boldsymbol{0}$, in the above proof of the Kuhn–Tucker theorem. The rationalization here is that if $\boldsymbol{h}$ satisfies $\nabla \hat{g}^j(\boldsymbol{x}_0)'\boldsymbol{h} \geqslant 0$, $j \in \mathscr{J}$, and $\boldsymbol{\phi}(t) = \boldsymbol{x}_0 + t\boldsymbol{h}$ emanates from $\boldsymbol{x}_0$ and lies within the constraint set, then $\boldsymbol{h} \in \mathscr{D}(\boldsymbol{x}_0)$ since $\boldsymbol{h}$ is defined as a feasible direction at $\boldsymbol{x}_0$ if $\boldsymbol{x}_0 + t\boldsymbol{h} \in \mathscr{K}$.

A second regularity condition on the constraint set which is sufficient to guarantee that $\{\cdot\} = \phi$ and the subsequent existence of a $\boldsymbol{\lambda}_0 \geqslant \boldsymbol{0}$ such that $\nabla f(\boldsymbol{x}_0) = \Sigma_j \lambda_j^0 (-\nabla \hat{g}^j(\boldsymbol{x}_0))$, $j \in \mathscr{J}$, is the linear independence of the gradients of the binding constraints at $\boldsymbol{x}_0$. As will be indicated shortly, it is actually a sufficient condition for the Kuhn–Tucker constraint qualification to hold. In this regard we state the

FIACCO–MCCORMICK REGULARITY REQUIREMENT.[23] *Let*

$$\boldsymbol{x}_0 \in \mathscr{K} = \{\boldsymbol{x} \mid \bar{\boldsymbol{G}}(\boldsymbol{x}) \geqslant \boldsymbol{0},\ \boldsymbol{x} \in \mathscr{E}^n\}$$

with $\bar{\boldsymbol{G}}(\boldsymbol{x})$ differentiable throughout some spherical δ-neighborhood of $\boldsymbol{x}_0$, $\delta(\boldsymbol{x}_0)$. If at $\boldsymbol{x}_0$ the set of vectors $\{\nabla \hat{g}^j(\boldsymbol{x}_0),\ j \in \mathscr{J}\}$ is linearly independent, then the Kuhn–Tucker constraint qualification holds there also and thus $\{\cdot\} = \phi$.

Note that $\{\cdot\} = \phi$ is a considerably weaker condition than the Fiacco–McCormick regularity requirement since the latter implies the Kuhn–Tucker constraint qualification which in turn implies $\{\cdot\} = \phi$.

Example A.3. Given that

$$\bar{\boldsymbol{G}}(\boldsymbol{x}) = \begin{bmatrix} \hat{g}^1(x_1, x_2) \\ \hat{g}^2(x_1, x_2) \\ \hat{g}^3(x_1, x_2) \\ \hat{g}^4(x_1, x_2) \end{bmatrix} = \begin{bmatrix} 10 - x_1^2 - x_2^2 \\ 3x_1 - 2 \\ x_1 \\ x_2 \end{bmatrix} \geqslant \boldsymbol{0},$$

does $\{\cdot\} = \phi$ at

$$\boldsymbol{x}_0' = (1, 3) \in \mathscr{K} = \{\boldsymbol{x} \mid \bar{\boldsymbol{G}}(\boldsymbol{x}) \geqslant \boldsymbol{0},\ \boldsymbol{x} \in \mathscr{E}^2\}?$$

For $\mathscr{J} = \{1, 2\}$, the gradients of the binding constraints at $\boldsymbol{x}_0$ are

$$\nabla \hat{g}^1(\boldsymbol{x}_0) = \begin{bmatrix} -2 \\ -6 \end{bmatrix}, \qquad \nabla \hat{g}^2(\boldsymbol{x}_0) = \begin{bmatrix} 3 \\ -1 \end{bmatrix}.$$

Since $|\nabla \hat{g}^1(\boldsymbol{x}_0), \nabla \hat{g}^2(\boldsymbol{x}_0)| = 20 \neq 0$, it follows that $\{\cdot\} = \phi$.

---

[23] See Fiacco and McCormick (1968), pp. 21–22.

The above constraint qualifications have all made use of the differentiability property of the vector-valued function $\bar{G}(x)$. A final constraint qualification which does not do so but requires that the functions defining $\mathscr{K}$ be concave is

SLATER'S CONSTRAINT QUALIFICATION. *Let the vector-valued function* $\bar{G}(x)$ *be concave with* $\mathscr{K} = \{x \mid \bar{G}(x) \geqslant 0, x \in \mathscr{E}^n\}$ *a convex subset of* $\mathscr{E}^n$. *Then* $\bar{G}(x) \geqslant 0$ *satisfies Slater's constraint qualification on* $\mathscr{K}$ *if there exists an* $x_* \in \mathscr{K}$ *such that* $\bar{G}(x_*) > 0$.

The implication here is that $\mathscr{K}$ has a non-empty interior.

12.6. Appendix B: Arrow–Hurwicz gradient techniques

We noted above that under certain conditions a given solution $\bar{x}$ of the constrained maximum problem implies the existence of a $\bar{\lambda} \geqslant 0$ such that $(\bar{x}, \bar{\lambda})$ provides a solution to the saddle-value problem and conversely. This notion was incorporated in the aforementioned Kuhn–Tucker equivalence theorem(s). In this section we shall examine a set of theorems on a differential gradient method for approximating a saddle point of the Lagrangian form $L(x, \lambda) = f(x) + \lambda' G(x)$, $x \geqslant 0$, $\lambda \geqslant 0$. Since the saddle point and constrained maximum problems are formally equivalent, we may be sure that if we find a point $(\bar{x}, \bar{\lambda})$ for which $L(x, \bar{\lambda}) \leqslant L(\bar{x}, \bar{\lambda}) \leqslant L(\bar{x}, \lambda)$, $\bar{x}, \bar{\lambda} \geqslant 0$, then also

$$f(\bar{x}) \geqslant f(x), \; x \in \mathscr{K} = \{x \mid G(x) \geqslant 0, \; x \geqslant 0, \; x \in \mathscr{E}^n\}.$$

To this end we state

THEOREM B.1.[24] *Let the real-valued function* $L(x, \lambda)$ *be strictly concave in* x, *convex in* λ, *and differentiable at* $(\bar{x}, \bar{\lambda}) \in \mathscr{E}^{n+m}$. *If L has a global saddle point at* $(\bar{x}, \bar{\lambda})$, *then, given the arbitrary non-negative initial value* $[x(0), \lambda(0)]$, *the solution* $[x(t), \lambda(t)]$ *of the (Arrow–Hurwicz*[25]*) system of differential equations,*

$$\left.\begin{aligned} \frac{dx_i}{dt} &= \begin{cases} 0 \quad \text{if } x_i = 0, \quad \dfrac{\partial L(x(t), \lambda(t))}{\partial x_i} < 0, \\ \dfrac{\partial L(x(t), \lambda(t))}{\partial x_i} \quad \text{otherwise}, \quad i = 1, \dots, n; \end{cases} \\ \frac{d\lambda_j}{dt} &= \begin{cases} 0 \quad \text{if } \lambda_j = 0, \quad \dfrac{\partial L(x(t), \lambda(t))}{\partial \lambda_j} > 0, \\ -\dfrac{\partial L(x(t), \lambda(t))}{\partial \lambda_j} \quad \text{otherwise}, \quad j = 1, \dots, m, \end{cases} \end{aligned}\right\} \tag{B.1}$$

converges to $(\bar{x}, \bar{\lambda})$ *as* $t \to \infty$.

[24] See Arrow *et al.* (1958), pp. 127–132.
[25] See Arrow *et al.* (1958), 117–126.

In this regard, a saddle point $(\bar{\boldsymbol{x}}, \bar{\boldsymbol{\lambda}})$ of L may be characterized as a singular point[26] of system (B.1) since if

$$\mathrm{d}x_i/\mathrm{d}t = 0, \quad i = 1, \ldots, n; \qquad \mathrm{d}\lambda_j/\mathrm{d}t = 0, \quad j = 1, \ldots, m,$$

then

$$\nabla_{\boldsymbol{x}} \bar{L} \leqslant \mathbf{0},\ \bar{\boldsymbol{x}}' \nabla_{\boldsymbol{x}} \bar{L} = 0,\ \bar{\boldsymbol{x}} \geqslant \mathbf{0}; \qquad \nabla_{\boldsymbol{\lambda}} \bar{L} \geqslant \mathbf{0},\ \bar{\boldsymbol{\lambda}}' \nabla_{\boldsymbol{\lambda}} \bar{L} = 0,\ \bar{\boldsymbol{\lambda}} \geqslant \mathbf{0}.$$

For $L(\boldsymbol{x}, \boldsymbol{\lambda}) = \mathrm{f}(\boldsymbol{x}) + \boldsymbol{\lambda}' \boldsymbol{G}(\boldsymbol{x}),\ \boldsymbol{x} \geqslant \mathbf{0},\ \boldsymbol{\lambda} \geqslant \mathbf{0}$, eq. (B.1) becomes

$$\left.\begin{aligned} \frac{\mathrm{d}x_i}{\mathrm{d}t} &= \begin{cases} 0 & \text{if } x_i = 0, \quad \mathrm{f}_i + \sum_{j=1}^{m} \lambda_j \hat{\mathrm{g}}_i^j < 0, \\ \mathrm{f}_i + \sum_{j=1}^{m} \lambda_j \hat{\mathrm{g}}_i^j & \text{otherwise}, \quad i = 1, \ldots, n; \end{cases} \\ \frac{\mathrm{d}\lambda_j}{\mathrm{d}t} &= \begin{cases} 0 & \text{if } \lambda_j = 0,\ \hat{\mathrm{g}}^j > 0, \\ -\hat{\mathrm{g}}^j & \text{otherwise}, \quad j = 1, \ldots, m. \end{cases} \end{aligned}\right\} \tag{B.2}$$

Now the previous theorem stated that system (B.1) converges to the global saddle point $(\bar{\boldsymbol{x}}, \bar{\boldsymbol{\lambda}})$ if L is strictly concave in $\boldsymbol{x}$. Hence eq. (B.2) converges to a constrained global maximum of f if f is strictly concave and the $\hat{\mathrm{g}}^j$, $j = 1, \ldots, m$, are concave. Note also that system (B.2) has been constructed so that λ_j increases when $\boldsymbol{x}$ violates the jth constraint. When λ_j becomes positive, its effect is to pull $\boldsymbol{x}$ back into $\mathscr{K}$; if λ_j is initially non-negative, it remains so for all t.

System (B.2) describes an iterative process wherein each iteration is identified with a unit of time. For computational convenience, the continuous model characterized by eq. (B.2) will be approximated by a finite difference scheme by relating the values of the x_i, λ_j in period t to their values in the immediately preceding period $t-1$, where $t = 1, 2, \ldots$ Hence, eq. (B.2) becomes

$$\left.\begin{aligned} x_{i,t} &= \begin{cases} 0 & \text{if } x_{i,t-1} = 0 \text{ and } \mathrm{f}_i(\boldsymbol{x}_{t-1}) + \sum_{j=1}^{m} \lambda_{j,t-1} \hat{\mathrm{g}}_i^j(\boldsymbol{x}_{t-1}) < 0, \\ x_{i,t-1} + \tau \left[\mathrm{f}_i(\boldsymbol{x}_{t-1}) + \sum_{j=1}^{m} \lambda_{j,t-1} \hat{\mathrm{g}}_i^j(\boldsymbol{x}_{t-1}) \right] & \text{otherwise}, \end{cases} \\ & \qquad i = 1, \ldots, n; \\ \lambda_{j,t} &= \begin{cases} 0 & \text{if } \lambda_{j,t-1} = 0 \text{ and } \hat{\mathrm{g}}^j(\boldsymbol{x}_{t-1}) > 0, \\ \lambda_{j,t-1} - \tau \hat{\mathrm{g}}^j(\boldsymbol{x}_{t-1}) & \text{otherwise}, \quad j = 1, \ldots, m, \end{cases} \end{aligned}\right\}$$

(B.2.1)

[26] The point $(\boldsymbol{x}, \boldsymbol{\lambda})$ is termed a *singular point* of eq. (B.1) if $\mathrm{d}x_i/\mathrm{d}t = 0$, $i = 1, \ldots, n$; $\mathrm{d}\lambda_j/\mathrm{d}t = 0$, $j = 1, \ldots, m$.

where τ, the length of each step toward $(\bar{\boldsymbol{x}}, \bar{\boldsymbol{\lambda}})$, is taken to be a sufficiently small positive constant so as to insure convergence to $(\bar{\boldsymbol{x}}, \bar{\boldsymbol{\lambda}})$. That is to say, for $t = 1$, we: (1) start at some initial value $x_{i,0}(\lambda_{j,0})$ and compute $\partial L/\partial x_i|_{t=1}$ $(\partial L/\partial \lambda_j|_{t=1})$; (2) take a step in the direction of steepest ascent (descent), $\partial L/\partial x_i|_{t=1}$ $(\partial L/\partial \lambda_j|_{t=1})$, using a step length τ to obtain a new point

$$x_{i,1} = x_{i,0} + \tau[\partial L/\partial x_i|_{t=1}] \; (\lambda_{j,1} = \lambda_{j,0} + \tau[\partial L/\partial \lambda_j|_{t=1}]).$$

The process is repeated until $|x_{i,t} - x_{i,t-1}|$ $(|\lambda_{j,t} - \lambda_{j,t-1}|)$ is as small as desired with the process described by eq. (B.2.1) converging to a strong global maximum (minimum) in the $\boldsymbol{x}(\boldsymbol{\lambda})$-direction as $t \to \infty$.

Example B.1. Maximize the strictly concave real-valued function

$$y = \mathrm{f}(x_1, x_2) = -x_1^2 - x_2^2 + 2x_1 + 3x_2$$

subject to the concave structural constraints

$$\hat{\mathrm{g}}^1(x_1, x_2) = 1 - 2x_1 - x_2 \geqslant 0, \qquad \hat{\mathrm{g}}^2(x_1, x_2) = 1 - x_1 - 2x_2 \geqslant 0$$

with $x_1, x_2 \geqslant 0$. Now $\mathrm{f}_1 = -2x_1 + 2$, $\mathrm{f}_2 = -2x_2 + 3$, $\hat{\mathrm{g}}_1^1 = -2$, $\hat{\mathrm{g}}_2^1 = -1$, $\hat{\mathrm{g}}_1^2 = -1$, and $\hat{\mathrm{g}}_2^2 = -2$. Hence eq. (B.2.1) becomes, for $\tau = 0.1$,

$$\left.\begin{aligned} x_{1,t} &= x_{1,t-1} + 0.1[-2x_{1,t-1} + 2 - 2\lambda_{1,t-1} - \lambda_{2,t-1}], \\ x_{2,t} &= x_{2,t-1} + 0.1[-2x_{2,t-1} + 3 - \lambda_{1,t-1} - 2\lambda_{2,t-1}], \\ \lambda_{1,t} &= \lambda_{1,t-1} - 0.1[1 - 2x_{1,t-1} - x_{2,t-1}], \\ \lambda_{2,t} &= \lambda_{2,t-1} - 0.1[1 - x_{1,t-1} - 2x_{2,t-1}]. \end{aligned}\right\} \tag{B.2.2}$$

(If at any time an equation on the right-hand side of eq. (B.2.2) becomes negative, eq. (B.2.1) informs us that the corresponding variable is set equal to zero for that iteration.) Given the (arbitrary) set of initial values $x_{1,0} = 1$, $x_{2,0} = 1$, $\lambda_{1,0} = 1$, and $\lambda_{2,0} = 1$, the time-paths of the variables $x_{1,t}$, $x_{2,t}$, $\lambda_{1,t}$, and $\lambda_{2,t}$ are illustrated in fig. B.1 with $x_{1,\infty} = 0.33$, $x_{2,\infty} = 0.33$, $\lambda_{1,\infty} = 0.11$, and $\lambda_{2,\infty} = 1.11$. Hence the Lagrangian of f has a global saddle point at $(\bar{\boldsymbol{x}}, \bar{\boldsymbol{\lambda}})$, where $\bar{\boldsymbol{x}}' = (0.33, 0.33)$, $\bar{\boldsymbol{\lambda}}' = (0.11, 1.11)$, and thus f attains a strong local maximum at $\bar{\boldsymbol{x}}' = (0.33, 0.33)$.

Theorem (B.1) requires that L be strictly concave in $\boldsymbol{x}$ (i.e. f is strictly concave and the $\hat{\mathrm{g}}^j$, $j = 1, \ldots, m$, are concave). This restriction may be relaxed somewhat by employing a modified gradient method which may be applied to any concave function $L(\boldsymbol{x}, \boldsymbol{\lambda})$. The *modified gradient technique* pertains to the following modified problem: if $\rho^j(Z)$ is a strictly increasing, strictly concave function of Z with $\rho^j(0) = 0$, then the constraint $\hat{\mathrm{g}}^j \geqslant 0$ is equivalent to the modified constraint $\rho^j(\hat{\mathrm{g}}^j) \geqslant 0$, and the original problem of maximizing f subject to $\hat{\mathrm{g}}^j \geqslant 0$, $\boldsymbol{x} \geqslant \mathbf{0}$, is equivalent to the modified problem

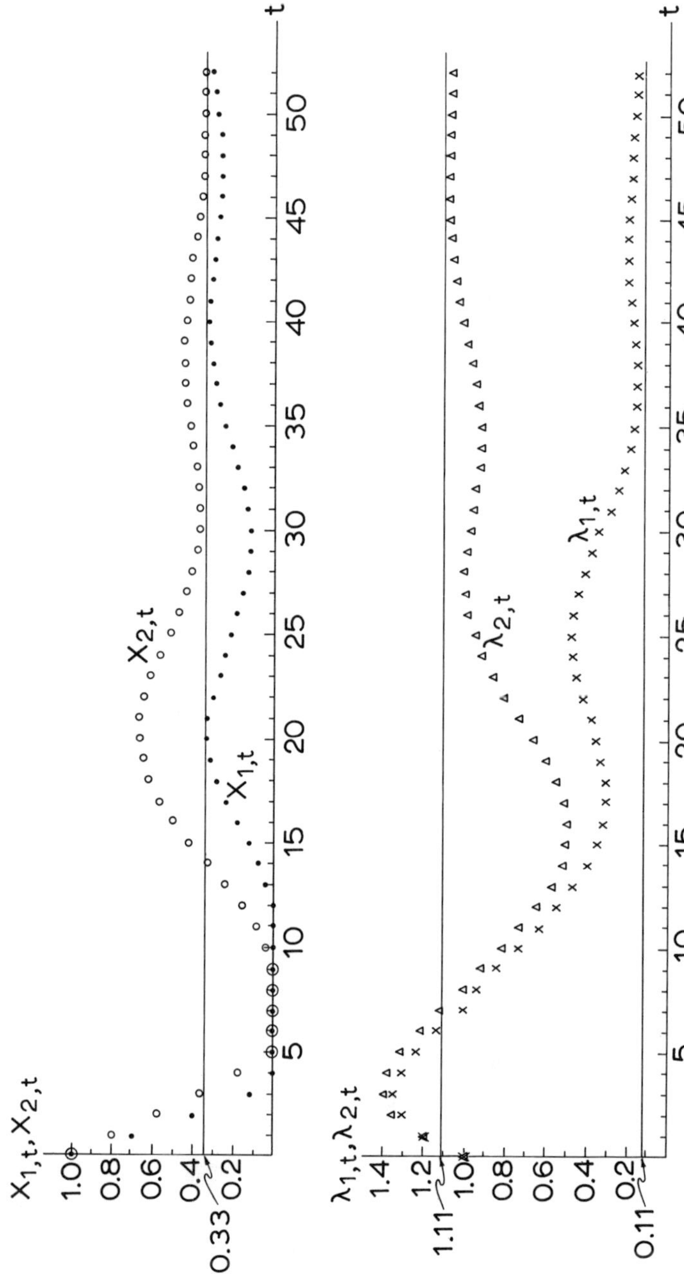

Fig. B.1.

of maximizing f subject to $\rho^j(\hat{g}^j) \geqslant 0$, $\boldsymbol{x} \geqslant \mathbf{0}$, $j = 1, \ldots, m$.[27] Thus we have

THEOREM B.2.[28] *Let the real-valued functions* $y = f(\boldsymbol{x})$, $\hat{g}^j(\boldsymbol{x})$ *be concave and* $\rho^j(Z)$ *a strictly increasing, strictly concave real-valued function with* $\rho^j(0) = 0$, $j = 1, \ldots, m$. *If* $\bar{\boldsymbol{x}}$ *maximizes* f *subject to* $\hat{g}^j \geqslant 0$, $j = 1, \ldots, m$, *then the solution* $[\boldsymbol{x}(t), \boldsymbol{\lambda}(t)]$ *of the modified Lagrangian*

$$L(\boldsymbol{x}, \boldsymbol{\lambda}) = f(\boldsymbol{x}) + \sum_{j=1}^{m} \lambda_j \rho^j(\hat{g}^j(\boldsymbol{x}))$$

converges to a global saddle point $(\bar{\boldsymbol{x}}, \bar{\boldsymbol{\lambda}})$ *for some* $\bar{\boldsymbol{\lambda}} \geqslant \mathbf{0}$.

The modified version of eq. (B.2.1) is thus

$$\left.\begin{aligned} x_{i,t} &= \begin{cases} 0 \quad \text{if } x_{i,t-1} = 0 \quad \text{and} \quad f_i(\boldsymbol{x}_{t-1}) + \sum_{j=1}^{m} \lambda_{j,t-1} \dfrac{\partial}{\partial x_i} \rho^j(\hat{g}^j_i(\boldsymbol{x}_{t-1})) < 0, \\ x_{i,t-1} + \tau \left[f_i(\boldsymbol{x}_{t-1}) + \sum_{j=1}^{m} \lambda_{j,t-1} \dfrac{\partial}{\partial x_i} \rho^j(\hat{g}^j_i(\boldsymbol{x}_{t-1})) \right] \\ \text{otherwise}, \quad i = 1, \ldots, n; \end{cases} \\ \lambda_{j,t} &= \begin{cases} 0 \quad \text{if } \lambda_{j,t-1} = 0 \quad \text{and} \quad \rho^j(\hat{g}^j(\boldsymbol{x}_{t-1})) > 0, \\ \lambda_{j,t-1} - \tau \rho^j(\hat{g}^j(\boldsymbol{x}_{t-1})) \text{ otherwise}, \quad j = 1, \ldots, m. \end{cases} \end{aligned}\right\} \quad \text{(B.3)}$$

How may the functions $\rho^j(Z)$ be chosen? One possibility is

$$\rho^j(Z) = 1 - (1 - Z)^{1+\eta_j}, \quad \eta_j > 0. \tag{B.4}$$

If $Z < 1$, then eq. (B.4) is a strictly increasing, strictly concave function so that if $\hat{g}^j(\boldsymbol{x}(t)) < 1$ for all t, then eq. (B.3) converges to a global saddle point and thus a strong global constrained maximum of f. Another function which insures convergence (without restriction) is

$$\rho^j(Z) = 1 - \exp(-\eta_j Z), \quad \eta_j > 0. \qquad \text{(B.4.1)}^{29}$$

Example B.2. Construct system (B.3) given that we desire to maximize the concave real-valued function $y = f(x_1, x_2) = (x_1 x_2)^{\frac{1}{4}}$ subject to $\hat{g}^1(x_1, x_2) = 1 - 2x_1 - x_2 \geqslant 0$, $x_1, x_2 \geqslant 0$. With $f_1 = \frac{1}{4} x_1^{-\frac{3}{4}} x_2^{\frac{1}{4}}$, $f_2 = \frac{1}{4} x_1^{\frac{1}{4}} x_2^{-\frac{3}{4}}$, $\hat{g}^1_1 = -2$, $\hat{g}^1_2 = -1$, and $\rho^1 = 1 - (1 - \hat{g}^1(x_1, x_2))^{1+\eta_1}$, eq. (B.3) becomes, for $\tau = 0.01$,

---

27 See Arrow *et al.* (1958), p. 137.
28 See Arrow *et al.* (1958), pp. 133–145.
29 See Arrow *et al.* (1958), p. 138.

$\eta = 1$,

$$\left.\begin{aligned} x_{1,t} &= x_{1,t-1}+0.01 \\ &\quad [\tfrac{1}{2}(x_{1,t-1})^{-\frac{1}{2}}(x_{2,t-1})^{\frac{1}{2}}-4\lambda_{t-1}(2x_{1,t-1}+x_{2,t-1})], \\ x_{2,t} &= x_{2,t-1}+0.01 \\ &\quad [\tfrac{1}{2}(x_{1,t-1})^{\frac{1}{2}}(x_{2,t-1})^{-\frac{1}{2}}-2\lambda_{t-1}(2x_{1,t-1}+x_{2,t-1})], \\ \lambda_t &= \lambda_{t-1}-0.01\,[1-(2x_{1,t-1}+x_{2,t-1})]. \end{aligned}\right\} \quad \text{(B.3.1)}$$

If we seek to maximize f subject to $\boldsymbol{G}(\boldsymbol{x})\geqslant \mathbf{0}$, $\boldsymbol{x}\geqslant\mathbf{0}$, $\boldsymbol{x}\in\mathscr{E}^n$, and it is not the case that f and the $\hat{g}^j$ are concave, $j = 1, \ldots, m$, we may still solve the maximum problem (although now only locally) by using the transformation $1-(1-\hat{g}^j)^{1+\eta}\geqslant 0$, where $\eta_j = \eta$, $j = 1, \ldots, m$, is a positive even integer. That is, the constraint $\hat{g}^j\geqslant 0$ is equivalent to the modified constraint $1-(1-\hat{g}^j)^{1+\eta}\geqslant 0$, and the original problem of maximizing f subject to $\hat{g}^j\geqslant 0$, $\boldsymbol{x}\geqslant\mathbf{0}$, is equivalent to the modified problem of maximizing f subject to $1-(1-\hat{g}^j)^{1+\eta}\geqslant 0$, $\boldsymbol{x}\geqslant\mathbf{0}$, $j = 1, \ldots, m$. Hence,

THEOREM B.3.[30] *Let the real-valued functions* $y = \mathrm{f}(\boldsymbol{x})$, $\hat{g}^j(\boldsymbol{x})$ $j = 1, \ldots, m$, *be defined over a region* $\mathscr{K} = \{\boldsymbol{x}\,|\,\boldsymbol{G}(\boldsymbol{x})\geqslant\mathbf{0},\ \boldsymbol{x}\geqslant\mathbf{0},\ \boldsymbol{x}\in\mathscr{E}^n\}$ *and differentiable throughout some spherical* δ*-neighborhood of the point* $\bar{\boldsymbol{x}}\in\mathscr{K}$. *If* $\bar{\boldsymbol{x}}$ *maximizes* f *subject to* $\hat{g}^j\geqslant 0$, *then the solution* $[\boldsymbol{x}(t), \boldsymbol{\lambda}(t)]$ *of the modified Lagrangian*

$$L(\boldsymbol{x}, \boldsymbol{\lambda}) = \mathrm{f}(\boldsymbol{x})+\sum_{j=1}^{m}\lambda_j\{1-[1-\hat{g}^j(\boldsymbol{x})]^{1+\eta}\}$$

converges locally to a saddle point $(\bar{\boldsymbol{x}}, \bar{\boldsymbol{\lambda}})$ *for some* $\bar{\boldsymbol{\lambda}}\geqslant\mathbf{0}$ *and* η *sufficiently large.*

Our second modification of eq. (B.2.1) is thus

$$\left.\begin{aligned} x_{i,t} &= \begin{cases} 0 \ \text{ if } x_{i,t-1} = 0 \ \text{ and } \ \mathrm{f}_i(\boldsymbol{x}_{t-1}) \\ \quad +(1+\eta)\displaystyle\sum_{j=1}^{m}\lambda_{j,t-1}[1-\hat{g}^j(\boldsymbol{x}_{t-1})]^{\eta}\hat{g}^j_i(\boldsymbol{x}_{t-1})<0, \\ x_{i,t-1}+\tau\{\mathrm{f}_i(\boldsymbol{x}_{t-1})+(1+\eta)\displaystyle\sum_{j=1}^{m}\lambda_{j,t-1}[1-\hat{g}^j(\boldsymbol{x}_{t-1})]^{\eta} \\ \quad \hat{g}^j_i(\boldsymbol{x}_{t-1})\} \ \text{otherwise}, \quad i = 1, \ldots, n; \end{cases} \\ \lambda_{j,t} &= \begin{cases} 0 \ \text{ if } \lambda_{j,t-1} = 0 \ \text{ and } \ 1-[1-\hat{g}^j(\boldsymbol{x}_{t-1})]^{1+\eta}>0, \\ \lambda_{j,t-1}-\tau\{1-[1-\hat{g}^j(\boldsymbol{x}_{t-1})]^{1+\eta}\} \ \text{otherwise}, \\ j = 1, \ldots, m. \end{cases} \end{aligned}\right\} \quad \text{(B.5)}$$

[30] See Arrow and Hurwicz (1957), pp. 258–265.

12.7. Appendix C: Sequential unconstrained techniques[31]

In this section we shall consider the development of a solution technique for the maximum problem stated earlier, namely: maximize the real-valued function $y = \mathrm{f}(\boldsymbol{x})$ subject to $\boldsymbol{x} \in \mathscr{K} = \{\boldsymbol{x} | \bar{\boldsymbol{G}}(\boldsymbol{x}) \geqslant \boldsymbol{0},\ \boldsymbol{x} \in \mathscr{E}^n\}$. In what follows we shall assume that such an extremum occurs at $\boldsymbol{x}_* \in \mathscr{K}$. We noted previously that if we are faced with finding an extremum of f subject to a set of equality constraints, we could employ the technique of Lagrange to convert the said constrained problem into one without any restriction on the variables simply by forming the associated Lagrangian of f, the reason being that f attains a constrained extremum at the same value of $\boldsymbol{x}$ as its unconstrained Lagrangian. In this section we shall proceed in a similar fashion, i.e. we shall see how to convert a maximization problem involving inequality constraints into a sequence of sub-problems involving no restraints on the variables.

Let us begin by introducing a modification of the function to be maximized, $\mathrm{f}(\boldsymbol{x})$. To incorporate the effect of the constraints on f, we form a *penalty function*

$$\mathrm{P}(\boldsymbol{x}, r) = \mathrm{f}(\boldsymbol{x}) + r\mathrm{B}(\boldsymbol{x}), \tag{C.1}$$

where $r > 0$ and

$$\mathrm{B}(\boldsymbol{x}) = \begin{cases} 0 & \text{for } \boldsymbol{x} \in \mathscr{K}, \\ -\infty & \text{for } \boldsymbol{x} \notin \mathscr{K}. \end{cases}$$

Here $\mathrm{B}(\boldsymbol{x})$ is termed a *barrier function* or *boundary repulsion term* whose role is to impose an infinite penalty for leaving the feasible region $\mathscr{K}$ while the parameter r denotes the size of the penalty incurred. In this regard, since the maximum of f must be approached along a path which lies entirely within the interior of $\mathscr{K}$, the term $\mathrm{B}(\boldsymbol{x})$ serves as a barrier which drives the maximum solution away from the boundary of $\mathscr{K}$, where $\hat{\mathrm{g}}^j(\boldsymbol{x}) = 0$, $j \in \mathscr{J}$, so that none of the constraints is violated. Since an infinite penalty for leaving the feasible region cannot be imposed directly, our next step is to approximate $\mathrm{B}(\boldsymbol{x})$ by a sequence of functions that approach $\mathrm{B}(\boldsymbol{x})$ in the limit.

We noted above that a necessary condition for $\mathrm{f}(\boldsymbol{x})$ subject to $\boldsymbol{x} \in \mathscr{K}$ to attain a local maximum at a point $\boldsymbol{x}_0$ is the existence of a set of non-negative numbers λ_j^0, $j = 1, \ldots, m+n$, such that eq. (12.4) holds, i.e.

$$\nabla \mathrm{f}(\boldsymbol{x}_0) + \sum_{j=1}^{m+n} \lambda_j^0 \nabla \hat{\mathrm{g}}^j(\boldsymbol{x}_0) = \boldsymbol{0},$$

[31] See Fiacco and McCormick (1968), pp. 39–52; Fiacco and McCormick (1964a); Fiacco and McCormick (1964b).

$$\left.\begin{aligned} &\lambda_j^0 \hat{g}^j(\boldsymbol{x}_0) = 0, \\ &\hat{g}^j(\boldsymbol{x}_0) \geqslant 0, \\ &\lambda_j^0 \geqslant 0, \end{aligned}\right\} \quad j = 1, \ldots, m+n,$$
$$\boldsymbol{x}_0 \text{ unrestricted.}$$

To insure that $\lambda_j^0 \geqslant 0$, let $\lambda_j^0 = \alpha_j^2$, $j = 1, \ldots, m+n$. Hence, the previous system becomes

$$\left.\begin{aligned} &\nabla f(\boldsymbol{x}_0) + \sum_{j=1}^{m+n} \alpha_j^2 \nabla \hat{g}^j(\boldsymbol{x}_0) = \mathbf{0}, \\ &\left.\begin{aligned} &\alpha_j \hat{g}^j(\boldsymbol{x}_0) = 0, \\ &\hat{g}^j(\boldsymbol{x}_0) \geqslant 0, \end{aligned}\right\} \quad j = 1, \ldots, m+n, \\ &\boldsymbol{x}_0 \text{ unrestricted.} \end{aligned}\right\} \tag{C.2}$$

Let us now consider a suitably restricted movement from $(\boldsymbol{x}_0, \boldsymbol{\lambda}_0)$ such that for some point depending on r, $(\boldsymbol{x}(r), \boldsymbol{\lambda}(r))$, near $(\boldsymbol{x}_0, \boldsymbol{\lambda}_0)$, eq. (C.2) becomes

$$\left.\begin{aligned} &\text{(a) } \nabla f(\boldsymbol{x}(r)) + \sum_{j=1}^{m+n} \alpha(r)_j^2 \nabla \hat{g}^j(\boldsymbol{x}(r)) = \mathbf{0}, \\ &\left.\begin{aligned} &\text{(b) } \alpha(r)_j \hat{g}^j(\boldsymbol{x}(r)) = r^{\frac{1}{2}} > 0, \\ &\text{(c) } \hat{g}^j(\boldsymbol{x}(r)) > 0, \end{aligned}\right\} \quad j = 1, \ldots, m+n, \\ &\text{(d) } \boldsymbol{x}(r) \text{ unrestricted.} \end{aligned}\right\} \tag{C.3}$$

Here eq. (C.3c) indicates that $\boldsymbol{x}(r)$ is an interior point of $\mathscr{K}$ while eq. (C.3b) implies that $\alpha(r)_j = r^{\frac{1}{2}}/\hat{g}^j(\boldsymbol{x}(r)) > 0$, $j = 1, \ldots, m+n$. A substitution of this latter expression into eq. (C.3a) yields

$$\nabla f(\boldsymbol{x}(r)) + \sum_{j=1}^{m+n} \frac{r}{\hat{g}^j(\boldsymbol{x}(r))^2} \nabla \hat{g}^j(\boldsymbol{x}(r)) = \mathbf{0},$$

i.e. the gradient of the penalty function

$$R(\boldsymbol{x}, r) = f(\boldsymbol{x}) - r \sum_{j=1}^{m+n} \frac{1}{\hat{g}^j(\boldsymbol{x})} \tag{C.1.1}$$

vanishes at $\boldsymbol{x}(r)$. If we let

$$C(\boldsymbol{x}) = -\sum_{j=1}^{m+n} \frac{1}{\hat{g}^j(\boldsymbol{x})}, \quad \hat{g}^j(\boldsymbol{x}) \geqslant 0, \quad j = 1, \ldots, m+n,$$

then clearly $C(\boldsymbol{x}) \to -\infty$ when $\hat{g}^j(\boldsymbol{x}) \to 0$ as required. (Given that eq. (12.4) holds, a suitably restricted movement from $(\boldsymbol{x}_0, \boldsymbol{\lambda}_0)$ may alternatively be written as

$$\left.\begin{array}{l} \text{(a) } \nabla \mathrm{f}(\boldsymbol{x}(r))+\sum_{j=1}^{m+n} \lambda(r)_j \nabla \hat{\mathrm{g}}^j(\boldsymbol{x}(r)) = \mathbf{0}, \\ \left.\begin{array}{l} \text{(b) } \lambda(r)_j \hat{\mathrm{g}}^j(\boldsymbol{x}(r)) = r>0, \\ \text{(c) } \hat{\mathrm{g}}^j(\boldsymbol{x}(r))>0, \\ \text{(d) } \lambda(r)_j \geqslant 0, \end{array}\right\} \quad j = 1, \ldots, m+n, \\ \text{(e) } \boldsymbol{x}(r) \text{ unrestricted.} \end{array}\right\} \qquad \text{(C.3.1)}$$

Then, from eq. (C.3.1b), $\lambda(r)_j = r/\hat{\mathrm{g}}^j(\boldsymbol{x}(r))>0$, $j = 1, \ldots, m+n$. Upon substituting this term into eq. (C.3.1a) we obtain

$$\nabla \mathrm{f}(\boldsymbol{x}(r))+\sum_{j=1}^{m+n} \frac{r}{\hat{\mathrm{g}}^j(\boldsymbol{x}(r))} \nabla \hat{\mathrm{g}}^j(\boldsymbol{x}(r)) = \mathbf{0}$$

or

$$\mathrm{S}(\boldsymbol{x}, r) = \mathrm{f}(\boldsymbol{x})+r \sum_{j=1}^{m+n} \ln \hat{\mathrm{g}}^j(\boldsymbol{x}), \qquad \text{(C.1.2)}$$

the *logarithmic penalty function*. If we set

$$\mathrm{D}(\boldsymbol{x}) = \sum_{j=1}^{m+n} \ln \hat{\mathrm{g}}^j(\boldsymbol{x}), \quad \hat{\mathrm{g}}^j(\boldsymbol{x}) \geqslant 0, \quad j = 1, \ldots, m+n,$$

then, here too, $\mathrm{D}(\boldsymbol{x}) \to -\infty$ as $\hat{\mathrm{g}}^j(\boldsymbol{x}) \to 0$ since $\ln 0 = -\infty$.

How is the unconstrained maximum of $\mathrm{R}(\boldsymbol{x}, r)$, and thus of $\mathrm{f}(\boldsymbol{x})$ subject to $\boldsymbol{x} \in \mathscr{K}$, attained? We noted above that we would solve our constrained maximization problem by transforming it into a sequence of unconstrained sub-problems. Specifically, we seek to determine an unconstrained maximum of eq. (C.1.1) over a strictly monotonic decreasing sequence of r values $\{r_i\}_{i=1}^{\infty}$ such that $r_i < r_{i-1}$ with $\lim_{i \to \infty} r_i = 0$. That is to say, if in each sub-problem we determine a feasible $\boldsymbol{x}(r_i)$ which maximizes $\mathrm{R}(\boldsymbol{x}, r_i)$ for each $r_i < r_{i-1}$, we obtain a sequence of $\boldsymbol{x}(r_i)$ values such that $\boldsymbol{x}(r_i) \to \boldsymbol{x}_*$, and hence $\mathrm{f}(\boldsymbol{x}(r_i)) \to \mathrm{f}(\boldsymbol{x}_*)$, as $r_i \to 0$, $i = 1, 2, \ldots$ So with r_i small, the unconstrained maximum of $\mathrm{R}(\boldsymbol{x}, r_i)$ becomes arbitrarily close to the constrained maximum of f. In particular, a summary of the conditions which insure convergence of the sequence $\{\mathrm{R}(\boldsymbol{x}, r_i)\}_{i=1}^{\infty}$ to $\mathrm{f}(\boldsymbol{x}_*)$ is provided by

THEOREM C.1.[32] *Let the real-valued function* $y = \mathrm{f}(\boldsymbol{x})$ *and the vector-valued function* $\overline{\boldsymbol{G}}(\boldsymbol{x}) \geqslant \mathbf{0}$, $\boldsymbol{x} \in \mathscr{E}^n$, *be twice differentiable and concave (with at least one*

[32] For a proof see Fiacco and McCormick (1964a), pp. 361–362.

of the functions $\mathrm{f}(\boldsymbol{x}), \hat{\mathrm{g}}^j(\boldsymbol{x}) \geqslant 0,\ j = 1, \ldots, m+n$, *strictly concave) over the convex region* $\mathscr{K} = \{\boldsymbol{x} | \overline{\boldsymbol{G}}(\boldsymbol{x}) \geqslant \mathbf{0},\ \boldsymbol{x} \in \mathscr{E}^n\}$. *Then*

$$\mathrm{R}(\boldsymbol{x}, r_i) = \mathrm{f}(\boldsymbol{x}) - r_i \sum_{j=1}^{m+n} \frac{1}{\hat{\mathrm{g}}^j(\boldsymbol{x})}, \quad i = 1, 2, \ldots; \quad r_i > 0,$$

is twice differentiable and strictly concave[33] *over* $\mathscr{K}$. *In addition, let* $\mathscr{K}$ *possess a non-empty interior. If* $\lim_{i \to \infty} r_i = 0$, *then the strong global constrained maximum of* f *is determined as*

$$\lim_{r_i \to 0} \{\max_{\boldsymbol{x}} \mathrm{R}(\boldsymbol{x}, r_i)\} = \mathrm{gl} \max_{\boldsymbol{x}} \mathrm{f} = \mathrm{f}(\boldsymbol{x}_*)$$

with $\mathrm{f}(\boldsymbol{x}(r_i)) \geqslant \mathrm{f}(\boldsymbol{x}(r_{i-1}))$, *i.e.* f *is monotonic*[34] *non-decreasing for each* $r_i < r_{i-1}$.

To see exactly how the process works, let us choose an initial estimate of $\boldsymbol{x}_*$, $\boldsymbol{x}_0 \in \mathscr{K}$, with $\overline{\boldsymbol{G}}(\boldsymbol{x}_0) > \mathbf{0}$ ($\boldsymbol{x}_0$ is an interior point of $\mathscr{K}$) and obtain an initial r, r_i, by minimizing the square of the length of the gradient of R at $\boldsymbol{x}_0$.[35] To this end we form, from

$$\nabla \mathrm{R}(\boldsymbol{x}_0, r) = \nabla \mathrm{f}(\boldsymbol{x}_0) - r \nabla \sum_{j=1}^{m+n} \frac{1}{\hat{\mathrm{g}}^j(\boldsymbol{x}_0)},$$

$$\mathrm{g}(r) = \|\nabla \mathrm{R}(\boldsymbol{x}_0, r)\|^2 = \|\nabla \mathrm{f}(\boldsymbol{x}_0)\|^2 - 2r \nabla \mathrm{f}(\boldsymbol{x}_0)' \nabla \sum_{j=1}^{m+n} \frac{1}{\hat{\mathrm{g}}^j(\boldsymbol{x}_0)} + r^2 \left\| \nabla \sum_{j=1}^{m+n} \frac{1}{\hat{\mathrm{g}}^j(\boldsymbol{x}_0)} \right\|^2.$$

Upon equating $\mathrm{g}'(r)$ to zero we obtain[36]

$$r_1 = \left[\nabla \mathrm{f}(\boldsymbol{x}_0)' \nabla \sum_{j=1}^{m+n} \frac{1}{\hat{\mathrm{g}}^j(\boldsymbol{x}_0)}\right] \Bigg/ \left\| \nabla \sum_{j=1}^{m+n} \frac{1}{\hat{\mathrm{g}}^j(\boldsymbol{x}_0)} \right\|^2.$$

Given r_1, we maximize $\mathrm{R}(\boldsymbol{x}, r_1)$ so as to obtain $\boldsymbol{x}(r_1)$ as the solution of $\nabla \mathrm{R}(\boldsymbol{x}, r_1) = \mathbf{0}$. It is clear that $\boldsymbol{x}(r_1)$ is an interior point of $\mathscr{K}$, i.e. $\overline{\boldsymbol{G}}(\boldsymbol{x}(r_1)) > \mathbf{0}$, since $\mathrm{R}(\boldsymbol{x}, r_1) \to -\infty$ as the boundary of $\mathscr{K}$ is approached. Next, for any

---

[33] If $\hat{\mathrm{g}}^j \geqslant 0$ is concave, then $1/\hat{\mathrm{g}}^j$ is convex and thus $-1/\hat{\mathrm{g}}^j$ is concave, $j = 1, \ldots, m+n$.

[34] For a proof regarding the monotonicity of f see Fiacco and McCormick (1964a), pp. 364–365.

[35] If an initial feasible point $\boldsymbol{x}_0$ is not readily available, repeated application of the method itself can be used to generate such a point. On all this see Fiacco and McCormick (1964a), pp. 365–366.

[36] For an alternative method of determining r_1, see Fiacco and McCormick (1964b), pp. 605–606.

$r_2 < r_1$, we maximize $\mathrm{R}(\boldsymbol{x}, r_2)$, this time determining $\boldsymbol{x}(r_2)$ as the solution of $\nabla\mathrm{R}(\boldsymbol{x}, r_2) = \mathbf{0}$. Here too $\bar{\boldsymbol{G}}(\boldsymbol{x}(r_2)) > \mathbf{0}$. By repeating this maximization process for a monotonic decreasing sequence of r values $r_1 > r_2 > \cdots > r_i > 0$, we obtain a corresponding sequence of $\boldsymbol{x}$ values $\boldsymbol{x}(r_1), \boldsymbol{x}(r_2), \ldots, \boldsymbol{x}(r_i)$ such that for each i, $\bar{\boldsymbol{G}}(\boldsymbol{x}(r_i)) > \mathbf{0}$.

We indicated above the conditions under which the sequence $\{\mathrm{R}(\boldsymbol{x}, r_i)\}_{i=1}^{\infty}$ converges to $\mathrm{f}(\boldsymbol{x}_*)$. In order to determine when this sequential unconstrained maximization process should be terminated, let us analyze the dual problem associated with the primal problem of maximizing $\mathrm{f}(\boldsymbol{x})$ subject to $\boldsymbol{x} \in \mathscr{K}$. That is, let us minimize the real-valued function $L(\boldsymbol{x}, \boldsymbol{\lambda}) = \mathrm{f}(\boldsymbol{x}) + \boldsymbol{\lambda}'\bar{\boldsymbol{G}}(\boldsymbol{x})$ subject to $(\boldsymbol{x}, \boldsymbol{\lambda}) \in \mathscr{K}_{\mathrm{d}} = \{(\boldsymbol{x}, \boldsymbol{\lambda}) | \nabla_{\boldsymbol{x}} L = \mathbf{0}, (\boldsymbol{x}, \boldsymbol{\lambda}) \in \mathscr{E}^{m+2n}, \boldsymbol{\lambda} \geqslant \mathbf{0}\}$. As we shall now see, the dual problem specifies an upper bound for $\mathrm{f}(\boldsymbol{x}_*)$. This being the case, since the dual problem generates an upper bound and the current $\mathrm{f}(\boldsymbol{x}(r_i))$ determines a lower bound for f, the process may be terminated as soon as the difference between these upper and lower limits for $\mathrm{f}(\boldsymbol{x}_*)$ is less than some prescribed value. Furthermore, when the primal problem is solved, we obtain a set of points $(\boldsymbol{x}, \boldsymbol{\lambda})$ which are dual feasible and which minimize $L(\boldsymbol{x}, \boldsymbol{\lambda})$ as $r_i \to 0$. Given that the assumptions underlying theorem C.1 hold, let us assume that $\boldsymbol{x}(r_i)$ maximizes $\mathrm{R}(\boldsymbol{x}, r_i)$, i.e.

$$\nabla\mathrm{R}(\boldsymbol{x}(r_i), r_i) = \nabla\mathrm{f}(\boldsymbol{x}(r_i)) + r_i \sum_{j=1}^{m+n} \frac{1}{\hat{\mathrm{g}}^j(\boldsymbol{x}(r_i))^2} \nabla\hat{\mathrm{g}}^j(\boldsymbol{x}(r_i)) = \mathbf{0}.$$

If we let $\lambda(r_i)_j = r_i/\hat{\mathrm{g}}^j(\boldsymbol{x}(r_i))^2 > 0$, $j = 1, \ldots, m+n$, then

$$\nabla\mathrm{R}(\boldsymbol{x}(r_i), r_i) = \nabla\mathrm{f}(\boldsymbol{x}(r_i)) + \sum_{j=1}^{m+n} \lambda(r_i)_j \nabla\hat{\mathrm{g}}^j(\boldsymbol{x}(r_i)) = \nabla_{\boldsymbol{x}} L = \mathbf{0},$$

so that $(\boldsymbol{x}(r_i), \boldsymbol{\lambda}(r_i)) \in \mathscr{K}_{\mathrm{d}}$. From the previous expression we obtain

$$L(\boldsymbol{x}(r_i), \boldsymbol{\lambda}(r_i)) = \mathrm{f}(\boldsymbol{x}(r_i)) - r_i \sum_{j=1}^{m+n} 1/\hat{\mathrm{g}}^j(\boldsymbol{x}(r_i)).$$

Furthermore, from duality theorem 1, $\mathrm{f}(\boldsymbol{x}(r_i)) \leqslant L(\boldsymbol{x}(r_i), \boldsymbol{\lambda}(r_i))$, and thus

$$\mathrm{f}(\boldsymbol{x}(r_i)) \leqslant \mathrm{f}(\boldsymbol{x}_*) \leqslant \mathrm{f}(\boldsymbol{x}(r_i)) - r_i \sum_{j=1}^{m+n} 1/\hat{\mathrm{g}}^j(\boldsymbol{x}(r_i)).$$

Thus a lower bound on $\mathrm{f}(\boldsymbol{x}_*)$ is the value of f obtained by maximizing $\mathrm{R}(\boldsymbol{x}, r_i)$, $\mathrm{f}(\boldsymbol{x}(r_i))$, while an upper bound is the current minimum value of the dual function $L(\boldsymbol{x}(r_i), \boldsymbol{\lambda}(r_i))$. Here the term $-r_i \sum_{j=1}^{m+n} 1/\hat{\mathrm{g}}^j(\boldsymbol{x}(r_i))$ may be thought of as an error bound on the difference $\mathrm{f}(\boldsymbol{x}_*) - \mathrm{f}(\boldsymbol{x}(r_i))$. And as hinted above, if the error bound is less than some preset tolerance level, the process may be terminated. To determine the circumstances under which the error bound goes to zero we state

THEOREM C.2.[37] *Given that the conditions of theorem C.1 hold, as* $\boldsymbol{x}(r_i) \to \boldsymbol{x}_*$, *and thus* $\mathrm{f}(\boldsymbol{x}(r_i)) \to \mathrm{f}(\boldsymbol{x}_*)$, *when* $r_i \to 0$, *there is generated a sequence of points* $(\boldsymbol{x}(r_i), \boldsymbol{\lambda}(r_i)) \in \mathscr{K}_{\mathrm{d}}$ *and a corresponding sequence of* $L(\boldsymbol{x}(r_i), \boldsymbol{\lambda}(r_i))$ *values such that*

$$\lim_{r_i \to 0} L(\boldsymbol{x}(r_i), \boldsymbol{\lambda}(r_i)) = \mathrm{f}(\boldsymbol{x}_*).$$

Example C.1. Maximize the real-valued function $y = \mathrm{f}(\boldsymbol{x}) = -x_1^2 - (x_2 - 2)^2$ subject to $x_1 \geqslant 0$, $x_2 \geqslant 2$. If we set $\hat{\mathrm{g}}^1 = x_1 \geqslant 0$, $\hat{\mathrm{g}}^2 = x_2 - 2 \geqslant 0$, then we may form the penalty function as

$$\mathrm{R}(\boldsymbol{x}, r) = -x_1^2 - (x_2 - 2)^2 - r/x_1 - r/(x_2 - 2).$$

Then

$$\begin{aligned} \partial \mathrm{R}/\partial x_1 &= -2x_1 + r x_1^{-2} = 0, \\ \partial \mathrm{R}/\partial x_2 &= -2(x_2 - 2) + r(x_2 - 2)^{-2} = 0. \end{aligned}$$

Solving for x_1, x_2 in terms of any general r yields

$$x_1 = (r/2)^{\frac{1}{3}}, \qquad x_2 = 2 + (r/2)^{\frac{1}{3}}$$

so that

$$\lim_{r \to 0} x_1 = 0 = x_1^*, \qquad \lim_{r \to 0} x_2 = 2 = x_2^*.$$

In addition, since

$$\mathrm{R}(r) = -2(r/2)^{\frac{2}{3}} - 2r(r/2)^{-\frac{1}{3}}, \qquad \lim_{r \to 0} \mathrm{R}(r) = 0 = \mathrm{f}(\boldsymbol{x}_*).$$

Hence f attains a strong local constrained maximum at $\boldsymbol{x}'_* = (0, 2)$ with $\mathrm{f}^* = 0$ since the naturally ordered principal minors of the Hessian of R alternate in sign (beginning negative) if none of the constraints are violated and $r > 0$.

Note that in this example we have actually obtained an analytical solution in which $\boldsymbol{x}_* = \lim_{r \to 0} \boldsymbol{x}(r)$. In more complicated problems a numerical approximation to $\boldsymbol{x}_*$ must be obtained in which we maximize $\mathrm{R}(\boldsymbol{x}, r_i)$ for each positive $r_i < r_{i-1}$. This approach is examined in

Example C.2. Maximize the real-valued function $y = \mathrm{f}(\boldsymbol{x}) = x_1 + \frac{1}{2}x_2$ subject to $x_1 \leqslant 1$, $x_2 \leqslant -x_1^2 + 4$. Upon setting $\hat{\mathrm{g}}^1 = 1 - x_1 \geqslant 0$, $\hat{\mathrm{g}}^2 = 4 - x_2 - x_1^2$, we

---

[37] See Fiacco and McCormick (1964a), p. 363.

form the penalty function

$$R(\boldsymbol{x}, r) = x_1 + \tfrac{1}{2}x_2 - r/(1-x_1) - r/(4-x_2-x_1^2).$$

Let $\boldsymbol{x}_0' = (0.5, 2)$. Clearly $\boldsymbol{G}(\boldsymbol{x}_0) > \boldsymbol{0}$ as illustrated in fig. C.1. Then

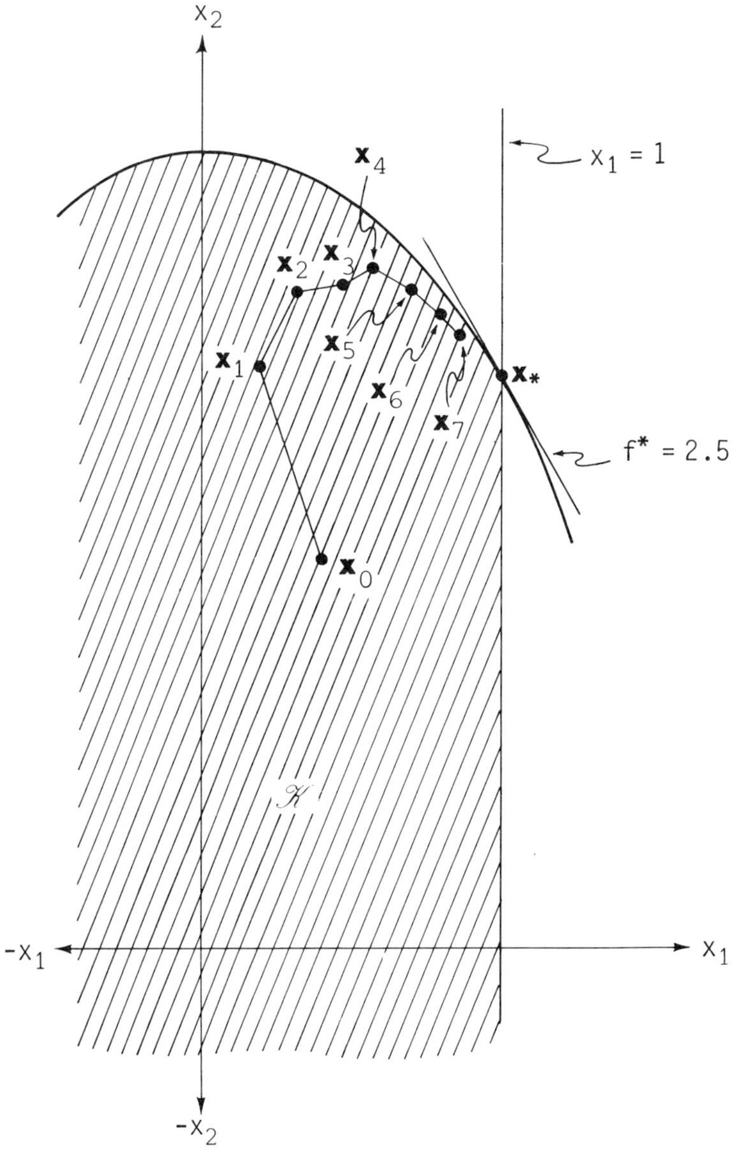

Fig. C.1.

$$r_1 = \nabla f(\boldsymbol{x}_0)'\nabla \sum_{j=1}^{2} \frac{1}{\hat{g}^j(\boldsymbol{x}_0)} \Bigg/ \left\| \nabla \sum_{j=1}^{2} \frac{1}{\hat{g}^j(\boldsymbol{x}_0)} \right\|^2 = 0.24,$$

and thus

$$R(\boldsymbol{x}, r_1) = x_1 + \tfrac{1}{2}x_2 - 0.24/(1-x_1) - 0.24/(4-x_2-x_1^2).$$

Setting $\nabla R(\boldsymbol{x}, r_1) = \mathbf{0}$ yields

$$1 - 0.24(1-x_1)^{-2} + 0.48x_1(4-x_2-x_1^2)^{-2} = 0.$$
$$\tfrac{1}{2} - 0.24(4-x_2-x_1^2)^{-2} = 0.$$

Table C.1.

r	$x_1(r)$	$x_2(r)$	$f(\boldsymbol{x}(r))$
r_1 0.24	0.34	3.06	1.87
r_2 0.12	0.47	3.29	2.12
r_3 0.06	0.59	3.30	2.24
r_4 0.03	0.65	3.34	2.32
r_5 0.015	0.73	3.30	2.38
r_6 0.0075	0.79	3.26	2.42
r_7 0.00375	0.83	3.23	2.45
⋮ ⋮	⋮	⋮	⋮

Upon combining these last two expressions and solving for x_1, we obtain $x_1 = 0.34$. Hence, $\boldsymbol{x}_1' = (0.34, 3.06)$. To generate the next approximation to $\boldsymbol{x}_*$, $\boldsymbol{x}_2$, let us choose $r_2 = 0.12 < r_1$ and maximize $R(\boldsymbol{x}, r_2)$. Here $\boldsymbol{x}_2' = (0.47, 3.29)$ is determined as the solution of $\nabla R(\boldsymbol{x}, r_2) = \mathbf{0}$. By repeating this process for a monotonic decreasing sequence of r values, the components of $\boldsymbol{x}_*$ are ultimately obtained. Table C.1. provides a summary of how the process converges to $\boldsymbol{x}_*' = (1, 3)$ with $f(\boldsymbol{x}_*) = 2.5$.

Chapter 13

KUHN–TUCKER THEORY WITH MIXED CONSTRAINTS

13.1. Equality and inequality side-relations

In this chapter we seek to solve a problem of the following form: maximize the real-valued function $y = \mathrm{f}(\boldsymbol{x})$ subject to: (1) m inequality constraints $b_j - \mathrm{g}^j(\boldsymbol{x}) \geqslant 0$, $j = 1, \ldots, m$; (2) p equality constraints $b_k - h^k(\boldsymbol{x}) = 0$, $k = 1, \ldots, p$; and (3) n non-negativity conditions $\boldsymbol{x} \geqslant \boldsymbol{0}$, $\boldsymbol{x}' = (x_1, \ldots, x_n) \in \mathscr{E}^n$. Upon forming the $(m \times 1)$ and $(p \times 1)$ vector-valued functions, respectively,

$$\boldsymbol{G}(\boldsymbol{x}) = \begin{bmatrix} b_1 - \mathrm{g}^1(\boldsymbol{x}) \\ \vdots \\ b_m - \mathrm{g}^m(\boldsymbol{x}) \end{bmatrix} = \begin{bmatrix} \hat{\mathrm{g}}^1(\boldsymbol{x}) \\ \vdots \\ \hat{\mathrm{g}}^m(\boldsymbol{x}) \end{bmatrix} \geqslant \boldsymbol{0},$$

$$\boldsymbol{H}(\boldsymbol{x}) = \begin{bmatrix} b_1 - h^1(\boldsymbol{x}) \\ \vdots \\ b_p - h^p(\boldsymbol{x}) \end{bmatrix} = \begin{bmatrix} \hat{h}^1(\boldsymbol{x}) \\ \vdots \\ \hat{h}^p(\boldsymbol{x}) \end{bmatrix} = \boldsymbol{0},$$

our problem may be rewritten as maximizing the real-valued function $y = \mathrm{f}(\boldsymbol{x})$ subject to

$$\boldsymbol{x} \in \mathscr{K} = \{\boldsymbol{x} \mid \boldsymbol{G}(\boldsymbol{x}) \geqslant \boldsymbol{0},\ \boldsymbol{H}(\boldsymbol{x}) = \boldsymbol{0},\ \boldsymbol{x} \geqslant \boldsymbol{0},\ \boldsymbol{x} \in \mathscr{E}^n\},$$

where $\mathscr{K}$ is the region of feasible or admissible solutions in $\mathscr{E}^n$. If the ith non-negativity condition is written as $\hat{\mathrm{g}}^{m+i}(\boldsymbol{x}) \geqslant 0$, $i = 1, \ldots, n$, then we ultimately maximize $y = \mathrm{f}(\boldsymbol{x})$ subject to

$$\boldsymbol{x} \in \mathscr{K} = \{\boldsymbol{x} \mid \bar{\boldsymbol{G}}(\boldsymbol{x}) \geqslant \boldsymbol{0},\ \boldsymbol{H}(\boldsymbol{x}) = \boldsymbol{0},\ \boldsymbol{x} \in \mathscr{E}^n\},$$

where

$$\bar{\boldsymbol{G}}(\boldsymbol{x}) = \begin{bmatrix} \hat{\mathrm{g}}^1(\boldsymbol{x}) \\ \vdots \\ \hat{\mathrm{g}}^m(\boldsymbol{x}) \\ \hat{\mathrm{g}}^{m+1}(\boldsymbol{x}) \\ \vdots \\ \hat{\mathrm{g}}^{m+n}(\boldsymbol{x}) \end{bmatrix} \geqslant \boldsymbol{0},$$

and $\boldsymbol{x}$ is unrestricted in sign.

If f attains a local maximum at $\boldsymbol{x}_0 \in \mathscr{K}$, then, as noted in the previous chapter, any movement from $\boldsymbol{x}_0$ along a feasible direction $\boldsymbol{h}$ cannot increase the value of f or $\nabla f(\boldsymbol{x}_0)'\boldsymbol{h} \leqslant 0$, $\boldsymbol{h} \in \mathscr{D}(\boldsymbol{x}_0)$. Moreover, given that $\boldsymbol{x}_0$ is optimal, if $\boldsymbol{h} \in \mathscr{D}(\boldsymbol{x}_0)$, then here too $\nabla \hat{g}^j(\boldsymbol{x}_0)'\boldsymbol{h} \geqslant 0$, $j \in \mathscr{J}$. Additionally, we are now admitting to our discussion the equality constraints $\hat{h}^k(\boldsymbol{x}) = 0$, $k = 1, \ldots, p$. In this regard, for $\boldsymbol{h}$ a feasible direction, $\nabla \hat{h}^k(\boldsymbol{x})'\boldsymbol{h} = 0$, $k = 1, \ldots, p$. To see this we state

THEOREM 13.1. *If* $\boldsymbol{h} \in \mathscr{D}(\boldsymbol{x}_0)$ ($\boldsymbol{x}_0$ *optimal*), *then* $\nabla \hat{h}^k(\boldsymbol{x}_0)'\boldsymbol{h} = 0$, $k = 1, \ldots, p$.

Proof. The equality constraint $\hat{h}^k(\boldsymbol{x}) = 0$ may be written as the two inequality constraints $\hat{h}^k(\boldsymbol{x}) \geqslant 0$, $-\hat{h}^k(\boldsymbol{x}) \geqslant 0$. For $\boldsymbol{h} \in \mathscr{D}(\boldsymbol{x}_0)$, it follows that $\hat{h}^k(\boldsymbol{x}_0 + \boldsymbol{h}) \geqslant 0$, $-\hat{h}^k(\boldsymbol{x}_0 + \boldsymbol{h}) \geqslant 0$ for $\boldsymbol{h}$ small and, from Taylor's formula,

$$\hat{h}^k(\boldsymbol{x}_0 + \boldsymbol{h}) \sim \hat{h}^k(\boldsymbol{x}_0) + \nabla \hat{h}^k(\boldsymbol{x}_0)'\boldsymbol{h},$$
$$-\hat{h}^k(\boldsymbol{x}_0 + \boldsymbol{h}) \sim -\hat{h}^k(\boldsymbol{x}_0) - \nabla \hat{h}^k(\boldsymbol{x}_0)'\boldsymbol{h}.$$

Given that we require $\hat{h}^k(\boldsymbol{x}_0) = 0$, $\hat{h}^k(\boldsymbol{x}_0 + \boldsymbol{h}) \geqslant 0$ implies $\nabla \hat{h}^k(\boldsymbol{x}_0)'\boldsymbol{h} \geqslant 0$ while $-\hat{h}^k(\boldsymbol{x}_0 + \boldsymbol{h}) \geqslant 0$ implies $-\nabla \hat{h}^k(\boldsymbol{x}_0)'\boldsymbol{h} \geqslant 0$ or $\nabla \hat{h}^k(\boldsymbol{x}_0)'\boldsymbol{h} \leqslant 0$. Hence, $\nabla \hat{h}^k(\boldsymbol{x}_0)'\boldsymbol{h} = 0$. Q.E.D.

In sum, if f subject to $\hat{g}^j(\boldsymbol{x}) = 0$, $j \in \mathscr{J}$, $\hat{h}^k(\boldsymbol{x}) = 0$, $k = 1, \ldots, p$, assumes its local maximum at $\boldsymbol{x}_0$, then

$$\nabla f(\boldsymbol{x}_0)'\boldsymbol{h} \leqslant 0, \quad \text{for all } \boldsymbol{h} \text{ satisfying} \quad \nabla \hat{g}^j(\boldsymbol{x}_0)'\boldsymbol{h} \leqslant 0, \quad j \in \mathscr{J},$$
$$\nabla \hat{h}^k(\boldsymbol{x}_0)'\boldsymbol{h} = 0, \quad k = 1, \ldots, p, \quad \boldsymbol{h} \in \mathscr{D}(\boldsymbol{x}_0). \tag{13.1}$$

Under what circumstances will eq. (13.1) hold? Given any $\boldsymbol{h} \in \mathscr{D}(\boldsymbol{x}_0)$, eq. (13.1) will hold if $\nabla f(\boldsymbol{x}_0)$ lies within the finite cone spanned by the exterior normals (to the boundary of $\mathscr{K}$ at $\boldsymbol{x}_0$)

$$-\nabla \hat{g}^j(\boldsymbol{x}_0), \quad j \in \mathscr{J}, \qquad -\nabla \hat{h}^k(\boldsymbol{x}_0), \qquad \nabla \hat{h}^k(\boldsymbol{x}_0), \quad k = 1, \ldots, p.$$

Hence the gradient of f is a non-negative linear combination of the negative gradients of the binding constraints $\hat{g}^j$, $j \in \mathscr{J}$, $\hat{h}^k$, and $-\hat{h}^k$ at $\boldsymbol{x}_0$. In this regard there must exist, respectively, real numbers $\lambda_j^0 \geqslant 0$, $(\mu_k^1)^0 \geqslant 0$, and $(\mu_k^2)^0 \geqslant 0$, $k = 1, \ldots, p$, such that

$$\nabla f(\boldsymbol{x}_0) = \sum_j \lambda_j^0(-\nabla \hat{g}^j(\boldsymbol{x}_0)) + \sum_{k=1}^{p} (\mu_k^1)^0 (-\nabla \hat{h}^k(\boldsymbol{x}_0))$$
$$+ \sum_{k=1}^{p} (\mu_k^2)^0 (\nabla \hat{h}^k(\boldsymbol{x}_0))$$
$$= \sum_j \lambda_j^0(-\nabla \hat{g}^j(\boldsymbol{x}_0)) - \sum_{k=1}^{p} ((\mu_k^1)^0 - (\mu_k^2)^0) \nabla \hat{h}^k(\boldsymbol{x}_0), \quad j \in \mathscr{J}. \tag{13.2}$$

What are the prerequisite conditions for the numbers $\lambda_j^0 \geqslant 0$, $j \in \mathscr{J}$, $(\mu_k^1)^0 \geqslant 0$, and $(\mu_k^2)^0 \geqslant 0$, $k = 1, \ldots, p$, to exist? If we assume that there do not exist directions $\boldsymbol{h}$ such that $\nabla f(\boldsymbol{x}_0)'\boldsymbol{h} > 0$ for

$$\nabla \hat{g}^j(\boldsymbol{x}_0)'\boldsymbol{h} \geqslant 0, \quad j \in \mathscr{J}, \qquad \nabla \hat{h}^k(\boldsymbol{x}_0)'\boldsymbol{h} = 0, \quad k = 1, \ldots, p,$$

i.e.

$$\{\boldsymbol{h}|\nabla \mathrm{f}(\boldsymbol{x}_0)'\boldsymbol{h}>0, \nabla \hat{\mathrm{g}}^j(\boldsymbol{x}_0)'\boldsymbol{h}\geqslant 0, j\in\mathscr{J}, \nabla \hat{h}^k(\boldsymbol{x}_0)'\boldsymbol{h} = 0, k = 1, \ldots, p\} = \phi,$$

then, by the Minkowski–Farkas theorem,[1] a necessary and sufficient condition for $\nabla \mathrm{f}(\boldsymbol{x}_0)$ to lie within the finite cone spanned by the vectors $-\nabla \hat{\mathrm{g}}^j(\boldsymbol{x}_0)$, $j\in\mathscr{J}$, $-\nabla \hat{h}^k(\boldsymbol{x}_0)$, $\nabla \hat{h}^k(\boldsymbol{x}_0)$, $k = 1, \ldots, p$, is that $\nabla \mathrm{f}(\boldsymbol{x}_0)'\boldsymbol{h}\leqslant 0$ for all $\boldsymbol{h}$ satisfying $-\nabla \hat{\mathrm{g}}^j(\boldsymbol{x}_0)'\boldsymbol{h}\leqslant 0$, $j\in\mathscr{J}$, $-\nabla \hat{h}^k(\boldsymbol{x}_0)'\boldsymbol{h} = 0$, $\nabla \hat{h}^k(\boldsymbol{x}_0)'\boldsymbol{h} = 0$, $k = 1, \ldots, p$. Hence, there exist real numbers $\lambda_j^0\geqslant 0$, $(\mu_k^1)^0\geqslant 0$, and $(\mu_k^2)^0\geqslant 0$ such that eq. (13.2) holds.

A regularity condition which serves to rule out the existence of directions $\boldsymbol{h}$ such that $\nabla \mathrm{f}(\boldsymbol{x}_0)'\boldsymbol{h}>0$ for $\nabla \mathrm{g}^j(\boldsymbol{x}_0)'\boldsymbol{h}\geqslant 0, j\in\mathscr{J}, \nabla \hat{h}^k(\boldsymbol{x}_0)'\boldsymbol{h} = 0, k = 1, \ldots, p$, is the

KUHN–TUCKER CONSTRAINT QUALIFICATION.[2] *Let*

$$\boldsymbol{x}_0\in\mathscr{K} = \{\boldsymbol{x}|\bar{\boldsymbol{G}}(\boldsymbol{x})\geqslant\boldsymbol{0}, \boldsymbol{H}(\boldsymbol{x}) = \boldsymbol{0}, \boldsymbol{x}\in\mathscr{E}^n\}$$

with $\bar{\boldsymbol{G}}(\boldsymbol{x})$, $\boldsymbol{H}(\boldsymbol{x})$ *differentiable throughout some spherical* δ*-neighborhood of* $\boldsymbol{x}_0$, $\delta(\boldsymbol{x}_0)$. *Then the Kuhn–Tucker constraint qualification holds locally at* $\boldsymbol{x}_0$ *if for each* $\boldsymbol{h}\neq\boldsymbol{0}$ *satisfying* $\nabla \hat{\mathrm{g}}^j(\boldsymbol{x}_0)'\boldsymbol{h}\geqslant 0, j\in\mathscr{J}, \nabla \hat{h}^k(\boldsymbol{x}_0)'\boldsymbol{h} = 0, k = 1, \ldots, p$, *there is in* $\delta(\boldsymbol{x}_0)$ *a continuous differentiable arc* $\boldsymbol{x} = \boldsymbol{\phi}(t)$, $\boldsymbol{\phi}(0) = \boldsymbol{x}_0$, *such that for each* $t\in[0, \varepsilon]$, $\bar{\boldsymbol{G}}(\boldsymbol{x}) = \bar{\boldsymbol{G}}(\boldsymbol{\phi}(t))\geqslant\boldsymbol{0}$, $\boldsymbol{H}(\boldsymbol{x}) = \boldsymbol{H}(\boldsymbol{\phi}(t)) = \boldsymbol{0}$, *and* $\boldsymbol{h} = \boldsymbol{\phi}'(0)$.

Hence the constraint set satisfies the Kuhn–Tucker constraint qualification at $\boldsymbol{x}_0$ if every $\boldsymbol{h}\neq\boldsymbol{0}$ satisfying $\nabla \hat{\mathrm{g}}^j(\boldsymbol{x}_0)'\boldsymbol{h}\geqslant 0$, $j\in\mathscr{J}$, $\nabla \hat{h}^k(\boldsymbol{x}_0)'\boldsymbol{h} = 0$, $k = 1, \ldots, p$, is tangent to a continuous differentiable arc emanating from $\boldsymbol{x}_0$ and contained in $\mathscr{K}$. In this regard, the Kuhn–Tucker constraint qualification is sufficient to guarantee that

$$\{\boldsymbol{h}|\nabla \mathrm{f}(\boldsymbol{x}_0)'\boldsymbol{h}>0, \nabla \hat{\mathrm{g}}^j(\boldsymbol{x}_0)'\boldsymbol{h}\geqslant 0, j\in\mathscr{J}, \nabla \hat{h}^k(\boldsymbol{x}_0)'\boldsymbol{h} = 0, k = 1, \ldots, p\} = \phi$$

which in turn is necessary and sufficient (by the Minkowski–Farkas theorem) to insure the existence of the non-negative multipliers λ_j^0, $(\mu_k^1)^0$, and $(\mu_k^2)^0$ so that eq. (13.2) holds. This observation is summarized by the

KUHN–TUCKER THEOREM (a necessary condition).[3] *Let the real-valued function* $y = \mathrm{f}(\boldsymbol{x})$ *and the vector-valued functions* $\bar{\boldsymbol{G}}(\boldsymbol{x})\geqslant\boldsymbol{0}$, $\boldsymbol{H}(\boldsymbol{x}) = \boldsymbol{0}$, $\boldsymbol{x}\in\mathscr{E}^n$,

---

[1] To employ the Minkowski–Farkas theorem (as stated in chapter 1), set $\boldsymbol{b} = \nabla \mathrm{f}(\boldsymbol{x}_0)$, $\boldsymbol{A} = [\boldsymbol{A}_1 \vdots \boldsymbol{A}_2 \vdots \boldsymbol{A}_3]$, and $\boldsymbol{\lambda}' = (\boldsymbol{\lambda}_1', \boldsymbol{\lambda}_2', \boldsymbol{\lambda}_3')\geqslant\boldsymbol{0}'$, where the vectors $-\nabla \hat{\mathrm{g}}^j(\boldsymbol{x}_0), j\in\mathscr{J}, -\nabla \hat{h}^k(\boldsymbol{x}_0), \nabla \hat{h}^k(\boldsymbol{x}_0)$, $k = 1, \ldots, p$, are taken to be, respectively, the columns of $\boldsymbol{A}_1$, $\boldsymbol{A}_2$, and $\boldsymbol{A}_3$; and λ_j^0, $(\mu_k^1)^0$, and $(\mu_k^2)^0$ are, respectively, the components of $\boldsymbol{\lambda}_1$, $\boldsymbol{\lambda}_2$, and $\boldsymbol{\lambda}_3$.

[2] See Kuhn and Tucker (1951), p. 483.

[3] See Fiacco and McCormick (1968), p. 20.

be differentiable throughout some spherical δ-neighborhood of the point $\mathbf{x}_0$, $\delta(\mathbf{x}_0)$. *If* f *subject to*

$$\mathbf{x}\in\mathscr{K} = \{\mathbf{x}|\bar{\mathbf{G}}(\mathbf{x})\geqslant\mathbf{0},\ \mathbf{H}(\mathbf{x}) = \mathbf{0},\ \mathbf{x}\in\mathscr{E}^n\}$$

has a local maximum at $\mathbf{x}_0$, *then, subject to the Kuhn–Tucker constraint qualification,*

$$\{\mathbf{h}|\nabla \mathrm{f}(\mathbf{x}_0)'\mathbf{h}>0,\ \nabla\hat{\mathrm{g}}^j(\mathbf{x}_0)'\mathbf{h}\geqslant 0,\ j\in\mathscr{J},\ \nabla\hat{h}^k(\mathbf{x}_0)'\mathbf{h} = 0,\ k = 1, \ldots, p\} \\ = \phi,$$

and thus there exist vectors $\boldsymbol{\lambda}_0\geqslant\mathbf{0}$, $\boldsymbol{\mu}_0^1\geqslant\mathbf{0}$, *and* $\boldsymbol{\mu}_0^2\geqslant\mathbf{0}$ *such that*

$$\nabla \mathrm{f}(\mathbf{x}_0) = \sum_j \lambda_j^0(-\nabla\hat{\mathrm{g}}^j(\mathbf{x}_0))-\sum_{k=1}^{p}((\mu_k^1)^0-(\mu_k^2)^0)\nabla\hat{h}^k(\mathbf{x}_0),\quad j\in\mathscr{J}.$$

An additional regularity requirement which is also sufficient to guarantee that $\{\mathbf{h}|\nabla \mathrm{f}(\mathbf{x}_0)'\mathbf{h}>0,\ \nabla\hat{\mathrm{g}}^j(\mathbf{x}_0)'\mathbf{h}\geqslant 0,\ j\in\mathscr{J},\ \nabla\hat{h}^k(\mathbf{x}_0)'\mathbf{h} = 0,\ k = 1, \ldots, p\} = \phi$ and the subsequent existence of vectors $\boldsymbol{\lambda}_0\geqslant\mathbf{0}$, $\boldsymbol{\mu}_0^1\geqslant\mathbf{0}$, and $\boldsymbol{\mu}_0^2\geqslant\mathbf{0}$ such that eq. (13.2) obtains, is the linear independence of the gradients of the binding constraints at $\mathbf{x}_0$. That is to say,

FIACCO–MCCORMICK REGULARITY REQUIREMENT.[4] *Let*

$$\mathbf{x}_0\in\mathscr{K} = \{\mathbf{x}|\bar{\mathbf{G}}(\mathbf{x})\geqslant\mathbf{0},\ \mathbf{H}(\mathbf{x}) = \mathbf{0},\ \mathbf{x}\in\mathscr{E}^n\}$$

with $\bar{\mathbf{G}}(\mathbf{x})$, $\mathbf{H}(\mathbf{x})$ *differentiable throughout some spherical δ-neighborhood of* $\mathbf{x}_0$, $\delta(\mathbf{x}_0)$. *If at* $\mathbf{x}_0$ *the vectors*

$$\{\nabla\hat{\mathrm{g}}^j(\mathbf{x}_0),\ j\in\mathscr{J}\},\qquad \{\nabla\hat{h}^k(\mathbf{x}_0),\ k = 1, \ldots, p\}$$

are linearly independent, then the Kuhn–Tucker constraint qualification holds there also, and thus

$$\{\mathbf{h}|\nabla \mathrm{f}(\mathbf{x}_0)'\mathbf{h}>0,\ \nabla\hat{\mathrm{g}}^j(\mathbf{x}_0)'\mathbf{h}\geqslant 0,\ j\in\mathscr{J},\ \nabla\hat{h}^k(\mathbf{x}_0)'\mathbf{h} = 0,\ k = 1, \ldots, p\} \\ = \phi.$$

We now turn to the principal theorem of this section, namely

THEOREM 13.2 (a generalized necessary condition for mixed constraints). *Let the real-valued function* $y = \mathrm{f}(\mathbf{x})$ *and the vector-valued functions* $\bar{\mathbf{G}}(\mathbf{x})\geqslant\mathbf{0}$, $\mathbf{H}(\mathbf{x}) = \mathbf{0}$, $\mathbf{x}\in\mathscr{E}^n$, *be defined over an open region* $\mathscr{K}$ *and differentiable throughout some spherical δ-neighborhood of the point* $\mathbf{x}_0\in\mathscr{K}$. *If* f *subject to*

$$\mathbf{x}\in\mathscr{K} = \{\mathbf{x}|\bar{\mathbf{G}}(\mathbf{x})\geqslant\mathbf{0},\ \mathbf{H}(\mathbf{x}) = \mathbf{0},\ \mathbf{x}\in\mathscr{E}^n\}$$

[4] See Fiacco and McCormick (1968), pp. 21–22.

has a local maximum at $\mathbf{x}_0$, *then, subject to the regularity condition*

$$\{\mathbf{h} | \nabla \mathrm{f}(\mathbf{x}_0)'\mathbf{h} > 0, \nabla \hat{\mathrm{g}}^j(\mathbf{x}_0)'\mathbf{h} \geqslant 0, j \in \mathscr{J}, \nabla \hat{h}^k(\mathbf{x}_0)'\mathbf{h} = 0, k = 1, \ldots, p\} = \phi,$$

$$\left.\begin{aligned} &\nabla \mathrm{f}(\mathbf{x}_0) + \nabla \bar{\mathbf{G}}(\mathbf{x}_0)\boldsymbol{\lambda}_0 + \nabla \mathbf{H}(\mathbf{x}_0)\boldsymbol{\mu}_0 = \mathbf{0}, \\ &\boldsymbol{\lambda}_0'\bar{\mathbf{G}}(\mathbf{x}_0) = 0, \\ &\bar{\mathbf{G}}(\mathbf{x}_0) \geqslant \mathbf{0}, \\ &\mathbf{H}(\mathbf{x}_0) = \mathbf{0}, \\ &\boldsymbol{\lambda}_0 \geqslant \mathbf{0}, \\ &\boldsymbol{\mu}_0 \text{ unrestricted}, \\ &\mathbf{x}_0 \text{ unrestricted}, \end{aligned}\right\}$$

or

$$\left.\begin{aligned} &\nabla \mathrm{f}(\mathbf{x}_0) + \sum_{j=1}^{m+n} \lambda_j^0 \nabla \hat{\mathrm{g}}^j(\mathbf{x}_0) + \sum_{k=1}^{p} \mu_k^0 \nabla \hat{h}^k(\mathbf{x}_0) = \mathbf{0}, \\ &\sum_{j=1}^{m+n} \lambda_j^0 \hat{\mathrm{g}}^j(\mathbf{x}_0) = 0, \\ &\left.\begin{aligned} &\hat{\mathrm{g}}^j(\mathbf{x}_0) \geqslant 0, \\ &\lambda_j^0 \geqslant 0, \end{aligned}\right\} \quad j = 1, \ldots, m+n, \\ &\left.\begin{aligned} &\hat{h}^k(\mathbf{x}_0) = 0, \\ &\mu_k^0 \text{ unrestricted}, \end{aligned}\right\} \quad k = 1, \ldots, p, \\ &x_i^0 \text{ unrestricted}, \quad i = 1, \ldots, n. \end{aligned}\right\} \tag{13.3}$$

Here $\nabla \bar{\mathbf{G}}(\mathbf{x}_0)$ *is an* $(n \times m+n)$ *matrix whose jth column is the vector* $\nabla \hat{\mathrm{g}}^j(\mathbf{x}_0)$, $j = 1, \ldots, m+n$, *i.e.* $\nabla \bar{\mathbf{G}}(\mathbf{x}_0) = [\nabla \hat{\mathrm{g}}^1(\mathbf{x}_0), \ldots, \nabla \hat{\mathrm{g}}^{m+n}(\mathbf{x}_0)]$; $\nabla \mathbf{H}(\mathbf{x}_0)$ *is an* $(n \times p)$ *matrix whose kth column is* $\nabla \hat{h}^k(\mathbf{x}_0)$, $k = 1, \ldots, p$, or $\nabla \mathbf{H}(\mathbf{x}_0) = [\nabla \hat{h}^1(\mathbf{x}_0), \ldots, \nabla \hat{h}^p(\mathbf{x}_0)]$; *and* $\boldsymbol{\lambda}_0$, $\boldsymbol{\mu}_0$ *are, respectively,* $(m+n \times 1)$ *and* $(p \times 1)$ *vectors of Lagrange multipliers.*

Proof. The augmented Lagrangian associated with this problem is

$$L(\mathbf{x}, \boldsymbol{\lambda}, \boldsymbol{\mu}^1, \boldsymbol{\mu}^2, \mathbf{s}_1, \mathbf{s}_2, \mathbf{s}_3) = \mathrm{f}(\mathbf{x}) + \boldsymbol{\lambda}'(\bar{\mathbf{G}}(\mathbf{x}) - \mathbf{s}_1) + (\boldsymbol{\mu}^1)'(\mathbf{H}(\mathbf{x}) - \mathbf{s}_2) + (\boldsymbol{\mu}^2)'(-\mathbf{H}(\mathbf{x}) - \mathbf{s}_3),$$

where: (1) the inequality constraint $\bar{\mathbf{G}}(\mathbf{x}) \geqslant \mathbf{0}$ has been converted to an equality constraint $\bar{\mathbf{G}}(\mathbf{x}) - \mathbf{s}_1 = \mathbf{0}$ by subtracting an $(m+n \times 1)$ vector of non-negative slack variables

$$\mathbf{s}_1 = \begin{bmatrix} (s_1^1)^2 \\ \vdots \\ (s_{m+n}^1)^2 \end{bmatrix} \geqslant \mathbf{0}, \qquad (s_j^1)^2 = \hat{\mathrm{g}}^j(\mathbf{x}), \quad j = 1, \ldots, m+n,$$

from the left-hand side of the former; and (2) the equality constraint $\mathbf{H}(\mathbf{x}) = \mathbf{0}$, or equivalently, $\mathbf{H}(\mathbf{x}) \geqslant \mathbf{0}$, $-\mathbf{H}(\mathbf{x}) \geqslant \mathbf{0}$, has been transformed to $\mathbf{H}(\mathbf{x}) - \mathbf{s}_2 = \mathbf{0}$,

$-H(x)-s_3 = \mathbf{0}$, with

$$s_2 = \begin{bmatrix}(s_1^2)^2\\ \vdots \\ (s_p^2)^2\end{bmatrix} \geqslant \mathbf{0}, \qquad (s_k^2)^2 = \hat{h}^k(x), \quad k = 1, \ldots, p,$$

$$s_3 = \begin{bmatrix}(s_1^3)^2\\ \vdots \\ (s_p^3)^2\end{bmatrix} \geqslant \mathbf{0}, \qquad (s_k^3)^2 = -\hat{h}^k(x), \quad k = 1, \ldots, p,$$

subtracted from the left-hand sides of $H(x) \geqslant \mathbf{0}$, $-H(x) \geqslant \mathbf{0}$, respectively. Then

$$\begin{aligned}
\nabla_x L &= \nabla f(x) + \nabla \bar{G}(x)\lambda + \nabla H(x)\,(\mu^1 - \mu^2) = \mathbf{0},\\
\nabla_\lambda L &= \bar{G}(x) - s_1 = \mathbf{0},\\
\nabla_{\mu^1} L &= H(x) - s_2 = \mathbf{0},\\
\nabla_{\mu^2} L &= -H(x) - s_3 = \mathbf{0},\\
\nabla_{s_1} L &= \lambda = \mathbf{0},\\
\nabla_{s_2} L &= \mu^1 = \mathbf{0},\\
\nabla_{s_3} L &= \mu^2 = \mathbf{0}.
\end{aligned}$$

Given that the regularity requirement holds at x_0, the Minkowski–Farkas theorem implies the existence of vectors $\lambda_0 \geqslant \mathbf{0}$, $\mu_0^1 \geqslant \mathbf{0}$, and $\mu_0^2 \geqslant \mathbf{0}$ such that

$$\nabla f(x_0) + \nabla \bar{G}(x_0)\lambda_0 + \nabla H(x_0)(\mu_0^1 - \mu_0^2) = \mathbf{0},$$

if and only if $\nabla f(x_0)' h \leqslant 0$ for all h satisfying

$$\nabla \hat{g}^j(x_0)' h \geqslant 0, \quad j \in \mathscr{J}, \qquad \nabla \hat{h}^k(x_0)' h = 0, \quad k = 1, \ldots, p.$$

Next, from $\nabla_\lambda L = \mathbf{0}$ we obtain $s_1 = \bar{G}(x)$ while $\nabla_{s_1} L = \lambda = \mathbf{0}$ may be transformed to $\lambda' s_1 = 0$. Combining these last two equalities yields, at x_0, $\lambda_0' \bar{G}(x_0) = 0$. In this regard, if the jth constraint $\hat{g}^j(x_0) \geqslant 0$, $j = 1, \ldots, m+n$, is not binding at x_0 ($j \notin \mathscr{J}$), then $(s_j^1)^2 > 0$, $\lambda_j^0 = 0$ while if $j \in \mathscr{J}$, $(s_j^1)^2 = 0$, $\lambda_j^0 \geqslant 0$. Hence, at least one of each pair $(\lambda_j^0, \hat{g}^j(x_0))$ vanishes, thus guaranteeing that $\lambda_0' \bar{G}(x_0) = 0$. With $\nabla_{\mu^1} L$, $\nabla_{\mu^2} L = \mathbf{0}$, $s_2 = H(x)$, $s_3 = -H(x)$ while $\nabla_{s_2} L$, $\nabla_{s_3} L = \mathbf{0}$ imply, respectively, that $(\mu^1)' s_2 = 0$, $(\mu^2)' s_3 = 0$. Combining these last two sets of equalities yields, at x_0, $(\mu_0^1 - \mu_0^2)' H(x_0) = 0$, or, upon setting $\mu_0 = \mu_0^1 - \mu_0^2$, $\mu_0' H(x_0) = 0$. Since $H(x_0)$ is binding, $(\mu_0^1 - \mu_0^2)' H(x_0) = 0$ when $H(x_0) = \mathbf{0}$ (or when $H(x_0) = \mathbf{0}$ and $\mu_0^1 = \mu_0^2$, $\mu_0^1, \mu_0^2 \geqslant \mathbf{0}$). With μ_0 the difference between two non-negative vectors μ_0^1, μ_0^2, it is obviously unrestricted in sign. So for $\mu_0 = \mu_0^1 - \mu_0^2$, we obtain

$$\nabla f(x_0) + \nabla G(x_0)\lambda_0 + \nabla H(x_0)\mu_0 = \mathbf{0}. \quad \text{Q.E.D.}$$

If the n non-negativity conditions are not treated as structural constraints (i.e. not incorporated in $G(x)$) but appear explicitly as $x \geqslant \mathbf{0}$, then eq. (13.3) appears as

$$\left.\begin{array}{l}
\nabla f(\boldsymbol{x}_0)+\nabla \boldsymbol{G}(\boldsymbol{x}_0)\boldsymbol{\lambda}_0+\nabla \boldsymbol{H}(\boldsymbol{x}_0)\boldsymbol{\mu}_0 \leqslant \mathbf{0}, \\
\boldsymbol{x}_0'(\nabla f(\boldsymbol{x}_0)+\nabla \boldsymbol{G}(\boldsymbol{x}_0)\boldsymbol{\lambda}_0+\nabla \boldsymbol{H}(\boldsymbol{x}_0)\boldsymbol{\mu}_0) = 0, \\
\boldsymbol{\lambda}_0'\boldsymbol{G}(\boldsymbol{x}_0) = 0, \\
\boldsymbol{G}(\boldsymbol{x}_0) \geqslant \mathbf{0}, \\
\boldsymbol{H}(\boldsymbol{x}_0) = \mathbf{0}, \\
\boldsymbol{\lambda}_0 \geqslant \mathbf{0}, \\
\boldsymbol{\mu}_0 \text{ unrestricted}, \\
\boldsymbol{x}_0 \geqslant \mathbf{0},
\end{array}\right\}$$

or

$$\left.\begin{array}{l}
\nabla f(\boldsymbol{x}_0)+\sum_{j=1}^{m} \lambda_j^0 \nabla \hat{g}^j(\boldsymbol{x}_0)+\sum_{k=1}^{p} \mu_k^0 \nabla \hat{h}^k(\boldsymbol{x}_0) \leqslant 0, \text{ or} \\
f_i^0+\sum_{j=1}^{m} \lambda_j^0 \hat{g}_i^j(\boldsymbol{x}_0)+\sum_{k=1}^{p} \mu_k^0 \hat{h}_i^k(\boldsymbol{x}_0) \leqslant 0, \quad i = 1, \ldots, n, \\
\sum_{i=1}^{n} x_i^0 \left(f_i^0+\sum_{j=1}^{m} \lambda_j^0 \hat{g}_i^j(\boldsymbol{x}_0)+\sum_{k=1}^{p} \mu_k^0 \hat{h}_i^k(\boldsymbol{x}_0)\right) = 0, \\
\sum_{j=1}^{m} \lambda_j^0 \hat{g}^j(\boldsymbol{x}_0) = 0, \\
\left.\begin{array}{l} \hat{g}^j(\boldsymbol{x}_0) \geqslant 0, \\ \lambda_j^0 \geqslant 0, \end{array}\right\} \quad j = 1, \ldots, m, \\
\left.\begin{array}{l} \hat{h}^k(\boldsymbol{x}_0) = 0, \\ \mu_k^0 \text{ unrestricted}, \end{array}\right\} \quad k = 1, \ldots, p, \\
x_i^0 \geqslant 0, \quad i = 1, \ldots, n,
\end{array}\right\} \tag{13.4}$$

where

$$\boldsymbol{G}(\boldsymbol{x}_0) = \begin{bmatrix} \hat{g}^1(\boldsymbol{x}_0) \\ \vdots \\ \hat{g}^m(\boldsymbol{x}_0) \end{bmatrix} \geqslant \mathbf{0}$$

is of order $(m \times 1)$; $\nabla \boldsymbol{G}(\boldsymbol{x}_0) = [\nabla \hat{g}^1(\boldsymbol{x}_0), \ldots, \nabla \hat{g}^m(\boldsymbol{x}_0)]$ is of order $(n \times m)$; and $\boldsymbol{\lambda}_0$ is an $(m \times 1)$ vector of Lagrange multipliers. In this regard, for $i = 1, \ldots, n$, either $x_i^0 = 0$, thus allowing f_i^0 to be less than

$$-\sum_{j=1}^{m} \lambda_j^0 \hat{g}_i^j(\boldsymbol{x}_0)-\sum_{k=1}^{p} \mu_k^0 \hat{h}_i^k(\boldsymbol{x}_0)$$

or

$$f_i^0 = -\sum_{j=1}^{m} \lambda_j^0 \hat{g}_i^j(\boldsymbol{x}_0)-\sum_{k=1}^{p} \mu_k^0 \hat{h}_i^k(\boldsymbol{x}_0),$$

in which case x_i^0 may be positive. Since at least one of these alternatives must hold, it follows that

$$\sum_{i=1}^{n} x_i^0 \left(f_i^0 + \sum_{j=1}^{m} \lambda_j^0 \hat{g}_i^j(\boldsymbol{x}_0) + \sum_{k=1}^{p} \mu_k^0 \hat{h}_i^k(\boldsymbol{x}_0) \right) = 0.$$

In addition, if the jth constraint $\hat{g}^j(\boldsymbol{x}_0) \geqslant 0$, $j = 1, \ldots, m$, is inactive at $\boldsymbol{x}_0$, then $s_j > 0$, $\lambda_j^0 = 0$; while if it is binding there, $s_j = 0$, $\lambda_j^0 \geqslant 0$. Here, too, at least one of these alternatives holds, implying that $\Sigma_{j=1}^m \lambda_j^0 \hat{g}^j(\boldsymbol{x}_0) = 0$.

If the real-valued function $y = f(\boldsymbol{x})$ is minimized subject to

$$\boldsymbol{x} \in \mathscr{K} = \{\boldsymbol{x} \mid \bar{\boldsymbol{G}}(\boldsymbol{x}) \geqslant \boldsymbol{0}, \boldsymbol{H}(\boldsymbol{x}) = \boldsymbol{0}, \boldsymbol{x} \in \mathscr{E}^n\},$$

eq. (13.3) becomes, at $\boldsymbol{x}_0$,

$$\left.\begin{array}{l} \nabla f(\underline{\boldsymbol{x}}_0) - \nabla \bar{\boldsymbol{G}}(\boldsymbol{x}_0)\boldsymbol{\lambda}_0 - \nabla \boldsymbol{H}(\boldsymbol{x}_0)\boldsymbol{\mu}_0 = \boldsymbol{0}, \\ \boldsymbol{\lambda}_0' \boldsymbol{G}(\boldsymbol{x}_0) = 0, \\ \boldsymbol{G}(\boldsymbol{x}_0) \geqslant \boldsymbol{0}, \\ \boldsymbol{H}(\boldsymbol{x}_0) = \boldsymbol{0}, \\ \boldsymbol{\lambda}_0 \geqslant \boldsymbol{0}, \\ \boldsymbol{\mu}_0 \text{ unrestricted}, \\ \boldsymbol{x}_0 \text{ unrestricted}, \end{array}\right\}$$

or

$$\left.\begin{array}{l} \nabla f(\boldsymbol{x}_0) - \sum_{j=1}^{m+n} \lambda_j^0 \nabla \hat{g}^j(\boldsymbol{x}_0) - \sum_{k=1}^{p} \mu_k^0 \nabla \hat{h}^k(\boldsymbol{x}_0) = \boldsymbol{0}, \\ \sum_{j=1}^{m+n} \lambda_j^0 \hat{g}^j(\boldsymbol{x}_0) = 0, \\ \left.\begin{array}{l} \hat{g}^j(\boldsymbol{x}_0) \geqslant 0, \\ \lambda_j^0 \geqslant 0, \end{array}\right\} \quad j = 1, \ldots, m+n, \\ \left.\begin{array}{l} \hat{h}^k(\boldsymbol{x}_0) = 0, \\ \mu_k^0 \text{ unrestricted}, \end{array}\right\} \quad k = 1, \ldots, p, \\ x_i^0 \text{ unrestricted}, \quad i = 1, \ldots, n, \end{array}\right\} \tag{13.3.1}$$

since $\min f = -\max\{-f\}$. Under this same transformation, eq. (13.4) becomes

$$\left.\begin{array}{l} \nabla f(\boldsymbol{x}_0) - \nabla \boldsymbol{G}(\boldsymbol{x}_0)\boldsymbol{\lambda}_0 - \nabla \boldsymbol{H}(\boldsymbol{x}_0)\boldsymbol{\mu}_0 \geqslant \boldsymbol{0}, \\ \boldsymbol{x}_0'(\nabla f(\boldsymbol{x}_0) - \nabla \boldsymbol{G}(\boldsymbol{x}_0)\boldsymbol{\lambda}_0 - \nabla \boldsymbol{H}(\boldsymbol{x}_0)\boldsymbol{\mu}_0) = 0, \\ \boldsymbol{\lambda}_0' \boldsymbol{G}(\boldsymbol{x}_0) = 0, \\ \boldsymbol{G}(\boldsymbol{x}_0) \geqslant \boldsymbol{0}, \\ \boldsymbol{H}(\boldsymbol{x}_0) = \boldsymbol{0}, \\ \boldsymbol{\lambda}_0 \geqslant \boldsymbol{0}, \\ \boldsymbol{\mu}_0 \text{ unrestricted}, \\ \boldsymbol{x}_0 \geqslant \boldsymbol{0}, \end{array}\right\}$$

or

$$\left.\begin{aligned}
&\nabla \mathrm{f}(\boldsymbol{x}_0) - \sum_{j=1}^{m} \lambda_j^0 \nabla \hat{g}^j(\boldsymbol{x}_0) - \sum_{k=1}^{p} \mu_k^0 \nabla \hat{h}^k(\boldsymbol{x}_0) \geqslant \mathbf{0}, \text{ or}\\
&\mathrm{f}_i^0 - \sum_{j=1}^{m} \lambda_j^0 \hat{g}_i^j(\boldsymbol{x}_0) - \sum_{k=1}^{p} \mu_k^0 \hat{h}_i^k(\boldsymbol{x}_0) \geqslant 0, \quad i = 1, \ldots, n,\\
&\sum_{i=1}^{n} x_i^0 \left(\mathrm{f}_i^0 - \sum_{j=1}^{m} \lambda_j^0 \hat{g}_i^j(\boldsymbol{x}_0) - \sum_{k=1}^{p} \mu_k^0 \hat{h}_i^k(\boldsymbol{x}_0)\right) = 0,\\
&\sum_{j=1}^{m} \lambda_j^0 \hat{g}^j(\boldsymbol{x}_0) = 0,\\
&\left.\begin{aligned}&\hat{g}^j(\boldsymbol{x}_0) \geqslant 0,\\ &\lambda_j^0 \geqslant 0,\end{aligned}\right\} \quad j = 1, \ldots, m,\\
&\left.\begin{aligned}&\hat{h}^k(\boldsymbol{x}_0) = 0,\\ &\mu_k^0 \text{ unrestricted,}\end{aligned}\right\} \quad k = 1, \ldots, p,\\
&x_i^0 \geqslant 0, \quad i = 1, \ldots, n.
\end{aligned}\right\} \tag{13.4.1}$$

Example 13.1. Maximize the real-valued function $y = \mathrm{f}(\boldsymbol{x}) = \frac{1}{8}(x_1-5)^2 + (x_2-4)^2$ subject to

$$\hat{h}^1(\boldsymbol{x}) = 6 - x_1 - x_2 = 0, \qquad \hat{g}^1(\boldsymbol{x}) = 3 - x_1^2 + x_2 \geqslant 0,$$
$$\hat{g}^2(\boldsymbol{x}) = x_1 \geqslant 0, \qquad \hat{g}^3(\boldsymbol{x}) = x_2 \geqslant 0.$$

Forming

$$\bar{\boldsymbol{G}}(\boldsymbol{x}) = \begin{bmatrix} \hat{g}^1(\boldsymbol{x}) \\ \hat{g}^2(\boldsymbol{x}) \\ \hat{g}^3(\boldsymbol{x}) \end{bmatrix} = \begin{bmatrix} 3 - x_1^2 + x_2 \\ x_1 \\ x_2 \end{bmatrix} \geqslant \mathbf{0},$$
$$\boldsymbol{H}(\boldsymbol{x}) = [\hat{h}^1(\boldsymbol{x})] = [6 - x_1 - x_2] = 0,$$

we obtain, from eq. (13.3),

$$\left.\begin{aligned}
&\nabla \mathrm{f}(\boldsymbol{x}) + \nabla \bar{\boldsymbol{G}}(\boldsymbol{x})\boldsymbol{\lambda} + \nabla \boldsymbol{H}(\boldsymbol{x})\boldsymbol{\mu} = \begin{bmatrix} \frac{1}{4}(x_1-5) - 2\lambda_1 x_1 + \lambda_2 - \mu_1 \\ 2(x_2-4) + \lambda_1 \qquad + \lambda_3 - \mu_1 \end{bmatrix}\\
&\qquad = \mathbf{0},\\
&\boldsymbol{\lambda}' \bar{\boldsymbol{G}}(\boldsymbol{x}) = \lambda_1(3 - x_1^2 + x_2) + \lambda_2 x_1 + \lambda_3 x_2 = 0,\\
&\bar{\boldsymbol{G}}(\boldsymbol{x}) = \begin{bmatrix} 3 - x_1^2 + x_2 \\ x_1 \\ x_2 \end{bmatrix} \geqslant \mathbf{0}, \qquad \boldsymbol{H}(\boldsymbol{x}) = [6 - x_1 - x_2] = 0,\\
&\boldsymbol{\lambda} = \begin{bmatrix} \lambda_1 \\ \lambda_2 \\ \lambda_3 \end{bmatrix} \geqslant \mathbf{0}, \qquad \boldsymbol{\mu} = [\mu_1] \text{ unrestricted.}
\end{aligned}\right\} \tag{13.4}$$

For $j = 1 \in \mathscr{J}$,

$$\left.\begin{array}{ll}\text{(a)} & \tfrac{1}{4}(x_1-5)-2\lambda_1 x_1-\mu_1 = 0;\\ \text{(b)} & 2(x_2-4)+\lambda_1-\mu_1 = 0;\\ & \lambda_1(0)+0(x_1)+0(x_2) = 0;\\ \text{(c)} & 3-x_1^2+x_2 = 0,\ \lambda_1 \geqslant 0;\\ \text{(d)} & 6-x_1-x_2 = 0,\ \mu_1 \text{ unrestricted};\\ & x_1>0,\ \lambda_2 = 0;\\ & x_2>0,\ \lambda_3 = 0.\end{array}\right\} \tag{13.4.1}$$

From eq. (13.4.1c, d) we obtain $\boldsymbol{x}_0' = (2.54,\ 3.46)$. A substitution of these values into eq. (13.4.1a, b) yields $\lambda_1^0 = 0.07$, $\mu_1^0 = 1.01$. Hence, f has a strong local constrained maximum at $\boldsymbol{x}_0$ with $\mathrm{f}(\boldsymbol{x}_0) = 1.04$.

For $j = 2 \in \mathscr{J}$, eq. (13.4) becomes

$$\left.\begin{array}{ll}\text{(a)} & \tfrac{1}{4}(x_1-5)+\lambda_2-\mu_1 = 0;\\ \text{(b)} & 2(x_2-4)\qquad -\mu_1 = 0;\\ & 0(3-x_1^2+x_2)+\lambda_2(0)+0(x_2) = 0;\\ \text{(c)} & x_1 = 0,\ \lambda_2 \geqslant 0;\\ \text{(d)} & 6-x_1-x_2 = 0,\ \mu_1 \text{ unrestricted};\\ & 3-x_1^2+x_2>0,\ \lambda_1 = 0;\\ & x_2>0,\ \lambda_3 = 0.\end{array}\right\} \tag{13.4.2}$$

In this instance $\boldsymbol{x}_1' = (0,\ 6)$ with $\lambda_2^1 = \frac{21}{4}$, $\mu_1^1 = 4$, and $\mathrm{f}(\boldsymbol{x}_1) = 7.12$. Thus the strong global constrained maximum of f occurs at $\boldsymbol{x}_1$.[5]

13.2. Lagrangian duality with mixed constraints

Let us take as the primal problem the general constrained maximization problem of the previous section, i.e.

PRIMAL PROBLEM. *Maximize the real-valued function* $y = \mathrm{f}(\boldsymbol{x})$ *subject to*

$$\boldsymbol{x} \in \mathscr{K} = \{\boldsymbol{x} \,|\, \overline{\boldsymbol{G}}(\boldsymbol{x}) \geqslant \boldsymbol{0},\ \boldsymbol{H}(\boldsymbol{x}) = \boldsymbol{0},\ \boldsymbol{x} \in \mathscr{E}^n\}$$

or simply $\max_{\boldsymbol{x} \in \mathscr{K}} \{\mathrm{f}(\boldsymbol{x})\}$.

Then the dual to this problem is

DUAL PROBLEM. *Minimize the real-valued function*

$$L(\boldsymbol{x}, \boldsymbol{\lambda}, \boldsymbol{\mu}) = \mathrm{f}(\boldsymbol{x}) + \boldsymbol{\lambda}'\overline{\boldsymbol{G}}(\boldsymbol{x}) + \boldsymbol{\mu}'\boldsymbol{H}(\boldsymbol{x})$$

[5] In more complicated problems a numerical technique which approximates the components of the optimal vector must be employed. See Appendix A to this chapter for an extension of the sequential unconstrained technique to the mixed constraint case.

subject to

$$(\boldsymbol{x}, \boldsymbol{\lambda}, \boldsymbol{\mu}) \in \mathscr{K}_{\mathrm{d}} = \{(\boldsymbol{x}, \boldsymbol{\lambda}, \boldsymbol{\mu}) \mid \nabla_{\boldsymbol{x}} L = \boldsymbol{0}, (\boldsymbol{x}, \boldsymbol{\lambda}, \boldsymbol{\mu}) \in \mathscr{E}^{m+2n+p}, \boldsymbol{\lambda} \geqslant \boldsymbol{0}\}$$

or

$$\min_{(\boldsymbol{x}, \boldsymbol{\lambda}, \boldsymbol{\mu}) \in \mathscr{K}_{\mathrm{d}}} \{L(\boldsymbol{x}, \boldsymbol{\lambda}, \boldsymbol{\mu})\}.$$

In this regard we state

DUALITY THEOREM 1. *Let the real-valued function* $y = \mathrm{f}(\boldsymbol{x})$ *and the vector-valued functions* $\bar{\boldsymbol{G}}(\boldsymbol{x})$, $\boldsymbol{H}(\boldsymbol{x})$ *be concave and differentiable for all*

$$\boldsymbol{x} \in \mathscr{K} = \{\boldsymbol{x} \mid \bar{\boldsymbol{G}}(\boldsymbol{x}) \geqslant \boldsymbol{0}, \boldsymbol{H}(\boldsymbol{x}) = \boldsymbol{0}, \boldsymbol{x} \in \mathscr{E}^n\}$$

with the property that for some $\boldsymbol{x}_* \in \mathscr{K}$, $\bar{\boldsymbol{G}}(\boldsymbol{x}_*) \geqslant \boldsymbol{0}$, $\boldsymbol{H}(\boldsymbol{x}_*) = \boldsymbol{0}$. *If* $\boldsymbol{x}_0$ *solves the primal problem, then there exist vectors* $\boldsymbol{\lambda}_0 \geqslant \boldsymbol{0}$, $\boldsymbol{\mu}_0 \geqslant \boldsymbol{0}$ *such that* $(\boldsymbol{x}_0, \boldsymbol{\lambda}_0, \boldsymbol{\mu}_0) \in \mathscr{E}^{m+2n+p}$ *solves the dual problem. Conversely, let* $\mathrm{f}(\boldsymbol{x})$, $\bar{\boldsymbol{G}}(\boldsymbol{x})$, and $\boldsymbol{H}(\boldsymbol{x})$ *be concave and differentiable with the associated Lagrangian* $L(\boldsymbol{x}, \boldsymbol{\lambda}, \boldsymbol{\mu})$ *twice differentiable for all* $\boldsymbol{x} \in \mathscr{E}^n$. *If*

$$(\boldsymbol{x}_0, \boldsymbol{\lambda}_0, \boldsymbol{\mu}_0) \in \mathscr{K}_{\mathrm{d}} = \{(\boldsymbol{x}, \boldsymbol{\lambda}, \boldsymbol{\mu}) \mid \nabla_{\boldsymbol{x}} L = \boldsymbol{0}, (\boldsymbol{x}, \boldsymbol{\lambda}, \boldsymbol{\mu}) \in \mathscr{E}^{m+2n+p}, \boldsymbol{\lambda} \geqslant \boldsymbol{0}\}$$

solves the dual problem and the nth-order Hessian matrix of $L(\boldsymbol{x}, \boldsymbol{\lambda}, \boldsymbol{\mu})$ *is non-singular at* $(\boldsymbol{x}_0, \boldsymbol{\lambda}_0, \boldsymbol{\mu}_0)$, *then, subject to the above constraint qualification,* $\boldsymbol{x}_0$ *solves the primal problem. In each instance* $\mathrm{f}(\boldsymbol{x}_0) = L(\boldsymbol{x}_0, \boldsymbol{\lambda}_0, \boldsymbol{\mu}_0)$.

Proof. If $\boldsymbol{x}_0$ solves the primal problem, then eq. (13.3) holds, i.e. $(\boldsymbol{x}_0, \boldsymbol{\lambda}_0, \boldsymbol{\mu}_0) \in \mathscr{K}_{\mathrm{d}}$. For $(\boldsymbol{x}, \boldsymbol{\lambda}, \boldsymbol{\mu}) \in \mathscr{K}_{\mathrm{d}}$,

$$L(\boldsymbol{x}_0, \boldsymbol{\lambda}_0, \boldsymbol{\mu}_0) - L(\boldsymbol{x}, \boldsymbol{\lambda}, \boldsymbol{\mu}) = \mathrm{f}(\boldsymbol{x}_0) - \mathrm{f}(\boldsymbol{x}) - \boldsymbol{\lambda}'\bar{\boldsymbol{G}}(\boldsymbol{x}) - \boldsymbol{\mu}'\boldsymbol{H}(\boldsymbol{x}).$$

With f, $\bar{\boldsymbol{G}}$, and $\boldsymbol{H}$ concave at each $\boldsymbol{x} \in \mathscr{E}^n$,

$$\begin{aligned}
\mathrm{f}(\boldsymbol{x}_0) &\leqslant \mathrm{f}(\boldsymbol{x}) + \nabla \mathrm{f}(\boldsymbol{x})'(\boldsymbol{x}_0 - \boldsymbol{x}),\\
\bar{\boldsymbol{G}}(\boldsymbol{x}_0) &\leqslant \bar{\boldsymbol{G}}(\boldsymbol{x}) + \nabla \bar{\boldsymbol{G}}(\boldsymbol{x})'(\boldsymbol{x}_0 - \boldsymbol{x}),\\
\boldsymbol{H}(\boldsymbol{x}_0) &\leqslant \boldsymbol{H}(\boldsymbol{x}) + \nabla \boldsymbol{H}(\boldsymbol{x})'(\boldsymbol{x}_0 - \boldsymbol{x}).
\end{aligned}$$

Then

$$\begin{aligned}
L(\boldsymbol{x}_0, \boldsymbol{\lambda}_0, \boldsymbol{\mu}_0) - L(\boldsymbol{x}, \boldsymbol{\lambda}, \boldsymbol{\mu}) &\leqslant \nabla \mathrm{f}(\boldsymbol{x})'(\boldsymbol{x}_0 - \boldsymbol{x}) - \boldsymbol{\lambda}'\bar{\boldsymbol{G}}(\boldsymbol{x}_0)\\
&\quad + \boldsymbol{\lambda}'\nabla \bar{\boldsymbol{G}}(\boldsymbol{x})'(\boldsymbol{x}_0 - \boldsymbol{x})\\
&\quad - \boldsymbol{\mu}'\boldsymbol{H}(\boldsymbol{x}_0) + \boldsymbol{\mu}'\nabla \boldsymbol{H}(\boldsymbol{x})'(\boldsymbol{x}_0 - \boldsymbol{x})\\
&= (\nabla \mathrm{f}(\boldsymbol{x}) + \nabla \bar{\boldsymbol{G}}(\boldsymbol{x})\boldsymbol{\lambda} + \nabla \boldsymbol{H}(\boldsymbol{x})\boldsymbol{\mu})'(\boldsymbol{x}_0 - \boldsymbol{x})\\
&\quad - \boldsymbol{\lambda}'\bar{\boldsymbol{G}}(\boldsymbol{x}_0) - \boldsymbol{\mu}'\boldsymbol{H}(\boldsymbol{x}_0).
\end{aligned}$$

With $\nabla \mathrm{f}(\boldsymbol{x}) + \nabla \bar{\boldsymbol{G}}(\boldsymbol{x})\boldsymbol{\lambda} + \nabla \boldsymbol{H}(\boldsymbol{x})\boldsymbol{\mu} = \boldsymbol{0}$, $\bar{\boldsymbol{G}}(\boldsymbol{x}_0) \geqslant \boldsymbol{0}$, $\boldsymbol{H}(\boldsymbol{x}_0) = \boldsymbol{0}$, and $\boldsymbol{\lambda} \geqslant \boldsymbol{0}$,

$$L(\boldsymbol{x}_0, \boldsymbol{\lambda}_0, \boldsymbol{\mu}_0) - L(\boldsymbol{x}, \boldsymbol{\lambda}, \boldsymbol{\mu}) \leqslant -\boldsymbol{\lambda}'\bar{\boldsymbol{G}}(\boldsymbol{x}_0) \leqslant 0$$

or

$$L(\boldsymbol{x}_0, \boldsymbol{\lambda}_0, \boldsymbol{\mu}_0) \leqslant L(\boldsymbol{x}, \boldsymbol{\lambda}, \boldsymbol{\mu}).$$

Thus $(\boldsymbol{x}_0, \boldsymbol{\lambda}_0, \boldsymbol{\mu}_0)$ minimizes $L(\boldsymbol{x}, \boldsymbol{\lambda}, \boldsymbol{\mu}) \in \mathscr{K}_{\mathrm{d}}$. Additionally,

$$L(\boldsymbol{x}_0, \boldsymbol{\lambda}_0, \boldsymbol{\mu}_0) = \mathrm{f}(\boldsymbol{x}_0) + \boldsymbol{\lambda}_0' \bar{\boldsymbol{G}}(\boldsymbol{x}_0) + \boldsymbol{\mu}_0' \boldsymbol{H}(\boldsymbol{x}_0) = \mathrm{f}(\boldsymbol{x}_0).$$

(Conversely.) The Lagrangian associated with the dual problem is

$$\begin{aligned} L_{\mathrm{d}}(\boldsymbol{x}, \boldsymbol{\lambda}, \boldsymbol{\mu}, \boldsymbol{v}) &= L(\boldsymbol{x}, \boldsymbol{\lambda}, \boldsymbol{\mu}) - \boldsymbol{v}' \nabla_{\boldsymbol{x}} L \\ &= -\mathrm{f}(\boldsymbol{x}) - \boldsymbol{\lambda}' \bar{\boldsymbol{G}}(\boldsymbol{x}) - \boldsymbol{\mu}' \boldsymbol{H}(\boldsymbol{x}) - \boldsymbol{v}'(\nabla \mathrm{f}(\boldsymbol{x}) \\ &\qquad + \nabla \bar{\boldsymbol{G}}(\boldsymbol{x}) \boldsymbol{\lambda} + \nabla \boldsymbol{H}(\boldsymbol{x}) \boldsymbol{\mu}). \end{aligned}$$

If $(\boldsymbol{x}_0, \boldsymbol{\lambda}_0, \boldsymbol{\mu}_0)$ represents a solution to the dual problem, it is necessary that there exists a $\boldsymbol{v}_0$ such that

$$\left.\begin{aligned} \nabla_{\boldsymbol{x}} L_{\mathrm{d}}^0 &= -\nabla \mathrm{f}(\boldsymbol{x}_0) - \nabla \bar{\boldsymbol{G}}(\boldsymbol{x}_0) \boldsymbol{\lambda}_0 - \nabla \boldsymbol{H}(\boldsymbol{x}_0) \boldsymbol{\mu}_0 - \nabla_{\boldsymbol{x}}^2 L^0 \, \boldsymbol{v}_0 = \mathbf{0}, \\ \text{or} \quad & \nabla \mathrm{f}(\boldsymbol{x}_0) + \nabla \bar{\boldsymbol{G}}(\boldsymbol{x}_0) \boldsymbol{\lambda}_0 + \nabla \boldsymbol{H}(\boldsymbol{x}_0) \boldsymbol{\mu}_0 + \nabla_{\boldsymbol{x}}^2 L^0 \, \boldsymbol{v}_0 = \mathbf{0}, \\ \nabla_{\boldsymbol{\lambda}} L_{\mathrm{d}}^0 &= -\bar{\boldsymbol{G}}(\boldsymbol{x}_0) - \nabla \bar{\boldsymbol{G}}(\boldsymbol{x}_0)' \boldsymbol{v}_0 \leqslant \mathbf{0}, \\ & \boldsymbol{\lambda}_0'(-\bar{\boldsymbol{G}}(\boldsymbol{x}_0) - \nabla \bar{\boldsymbol{G}}(\boldsymbol{x}_0)' \boldsymbol{v}_0) = 0, \\ \nabla_{\boldsymbol{\mu}} L_{\mathrm{d}}^0 &= -\boldsymbol{H}(\boldsymbol{x}_0) = \mathbf{0} \quad \text{or} \quad \boldsymbol{H}(\boldsymbol{x}_0) = \mathbf{0}, \\ \nabla_{\boldsymbol{v}} L_{\mathrm{d}}^0 &= -\nabla \mathrm{f}(\boldsymbol{x}_0) - \nabla \bar{\boldsymbol{G}}(\boldsymbol{x}_0) \boldsymbol{\lambda}_0 - \nabla \boldsymbol{H}(\boldsymbol{x}_0) \boldsymbol{\mu}_0 = \mathbf{0} \\ \text{or} \quad & \nabla \mathrm{f}(\boldsymbol{x}_0) + \nabla \bar{\boldsymbol{G}}(\boldsymbol{x}_0) \boldsymbol{\lambda}_0 + \nabla \boldsymbol{H}(\boldsymbol{x}_0) \boldsymbol{\mu}_0 = \mathbf{0}, \\ & \boldsymbol{x}_0 \text{ unrestricted}, \\ & \boldsymbol{\lambda}_0 \geqslant \mathbf{0}, \\ & \boldsymbol{\mu}_0 \text{ unrestricted}, \\ & \boldsymbol{v}_0 \text{ unrestricted}. \end{aligned}\right\} \qquad (13.5)$$

Substituting $\nabla_{\boldsymbol{v}} L_{\mathrm{d}}^0$ into $\nabla_{\boldsymbol{x}} L_{\mathrm{d}}^0$ yields $\nabla_{\boldsymbol{x}}^2 L^0 \boldsymbol{v}_0 = \mathbf{0}$. If $|\nabla_{\boldsymbol{x}}^2 L^0| \neq 0$,

$$\boldsymbol{v}_0 = [\nabla_{\boldsymbol{x}}^0 L^0]^{-1} \mathbf{0} = \mathbf{0}$$

and thus eq. (13.4) becomes

$$\left.\begin{aligned} & \nabla \mathrm{f}(\boldsymbol{x}_0) + \nabla \bar{\boldsymbol{G}}(\boldsymbol{x}_0) \boldsymbol{\lambda}_0 + \nabla \boldsymbol{H}(\boldsymbol{x}_0) \boldsymbol{\mu}_0 = \mathbf{0}, \\ & \left.\begin{aligned} & \bar{\boldsymbol{G}}(\boldsymbol{x}_0) \geqslant \mathbf{0}, \\ & \boldsymbol{H}(\boldsymbol{x}_0) = \mathbf{0}, \end{aligned}\right\} \text{(i.e. } \boldsymbol{x} \in \mathscr{K}\text{)}, \\ & \boldsymbol{\lambda}_0' \bar{\boldsymbol{G}}(\boldsymbol{x}_0) = 0, \\ & \boldsymbol{\lambda}_0 \geqslant \mathbf{0}. \end{aligned}\right\} \quad \text{or eq. (13.3).}$$

Hence we are provided with a necessary and sufficient condition for a saddle point of $L(\boldsymbol{x}, \boldsymbol{\lambda}, \boldsymbol{\mu})$ at $(\boldsymbol{x}_0, \boldsymbol{\lambda}_0, \boldsymbol{\mu}_0)$, as well as a necessary and sufficient condition for a solution to the primal problem. With $\boldsymbol{\lambda}_0' \bar{\boldsymbol{G}}(\boldsymbol{x}_0) = 0$, $\boldsymbol{H}(\boldsymbol{x}_0) = \mathbf{0}$, it is also true that $\mathrm{f}(\boldsymbol{x}_0) = L(\boldsymbol{x}_0, \boldsymbol{\lambda}_0, \boldsymbol{\mu}_0)$. Q.E.D.

Since f, $\bar{\boldsymbol{G}}$, and $\boldsymbol{H}$ are all concave, the solutions to the primal and dual problems are global in character.

If the primal–dual pair of problems is rewritten as

Primal

$$\max\{f(\boldsymbol{x})\}, \quad \text{where } \boldsymbol{x}\in\mathscr{K}$$
$$\mathscr{K} = \{\boldsymbol{x}\,|\,\boldsymbol{G}(\boldsymbol{x})\geqslant\boldsymbol{0},\ \boldsymbol{H}(\boldsymbol{x}) = \boldsymbol{0},\ \boldsymbol{x}\geqslant\boldsymbol{0},\ \boldsymbol{x}\in\mathscr{E}^n\}$$

Dual

$$\min\{L(\boldsymbol{x}, \boldsymbol{\lambda}, \boldsymbol{\mu})-\boldsymbol{x}'\nabla_{\boldsymbol{x}}L\}, \quad \text{where } (\boldsymbol{x}, \boldsymbol{\lambda}, \boldsymbol{\mu})\in\mathscr{K}_{\mathrm{d}}$$
$$\mathscr{K}_{\mathrm{d}} = \{(\boldsymbol{x}, \boldsymbol{\lambda}, \boldsymbol{\mu})\,|\,\nabla_{\boldsymbol{x}}L\leqslant\boldsymbol{0},\ (\boldsymbol{x}, \boldsymbol{\lambda}, \boldsymbol{\mu})\in\mathscr{E}^{m+n+p},\ \boldsymbol{\lambda}\geqslant\boldsymbol{0}\}$$

with f, $\boldsymbol{G}$, and $\boldsymbol{H}$ concave and differentiable, and $L(\boldsymbol{x}, \boldsymbol{\lambda}, \boldsymbol{\mu})$ twice differentiable for all $\boldsymbol{x}\in\mathscr{E}^n$, the dual Lagrangian appears as

$$\begin{aligned} L_{\mathrm{d}}(\boldsymbol{x}, \boldsymbol{\lambda}, \boldsymbol{\mu}, \boldsymbol{v}, \boldsymbol{t}) = {} & -f(\boldsymbol{x})-\boldsymbol{\lambda}'\boldsymbol{G}(\boldsymbol{x})-\boldsymbol{\mu}'\boldsymbol{H}(\boldsymbol{x})+\boldsymbol{x}'(\nabla f(\boldsymbol{x}) \\ & +\nabla\boldsymbol{G}(\boldsymbol{x})\boldsymbol{\lambda}+\nabla\boldsymbol{H}(\boldsymbol{x})\boldsymbol{\mu})-\boldsymbol{v}'(\nabla f(\boldsymbol{x}) \\ & +\nabla\boldsymbol{G}(\boldsymbol{x})\boldsymbol{\lambda}+\nabla\boldsymbol{H}(\boldsymbol{x})\boldsymbol{\mu}+\boldsymbol{t}), \end{aligned} \tag{13.6}$$

where $\boldsymbol{v}$ and $\boldsymbol{t}$ are, respectively, vectors of Lagrange multipliers and non-negative slack variables. Here eq. (13.6) may be used to demonstrate that if $(\boldsymbol{x}_0, \boldsymbol{\lambda}_0, \boldsymbol{\mu}_0)$ solves the dual problem, then, given that $\nabla^2_{\boldsymbol{x}}L^0$ is non-singular and the constraint qualification is in effect, eq. (13.4) also holds, i.e. the primal problem is solved. In addition, the complementary slackness conditions may also be derived by utilizing eq. (13.6) and the primal Lagrangian

$$L(\boldsymbol{x}, \boldsymbol{\lambda}, \boldsymbol{\mu}, \boldsymbol{s}) = f(\boldsymbol{x})+\boldsymbol{\lambda}'(\boldsymbol{G}(\boldsymbol{x})-\boldsymbol{s})+\boldsymbol{\mu}'\boldsymbol{H}(\boldsymbol{x}),$$

where $\boldsymbol{s}$ represents a vector of non-negative slack variables.

13.3. Appendix A: A sequential unconstrained technique for mixed constraints[6]

In this section we shall extend the sequential unconstrained technique developed in the previous chapter to cover the case where equality constraints are admitted to the constraint set. Hence our problem appears as: maximize the real-valued function $y = f(\boldsymbol{x})$ subject to

$$\boldsymbol{x}\in\mathscr{K} = \{\boldsymbol{x}\,|\,\bar{\boldsymbol{G}}(\boldsymbol{x})\geqslant\boldsymbol{0},\ \boldsymbol{H}(\boldsymbol{x}) = \boldsymbol{0},\ \boldsymbol{x}\in\mathscr{E}^n\}.$$

In chapter 12 we noted that, for a set of inequality constraints, the constrained maximum of f is approached from the interior of the constraint set

$$\mathscr{K}_{\bar{\boldsymbol{G}}} = \{\boldsymbol{x}\,|\,\bar{\boldsymbol{G}}(\boldsymbol{x})\geqslant\boldsymbol{0},\ \boldsymbol{x}\in\mathscr{E}^n\}.$$

[6] See Fiacco and McCormick (1966), pp. 816–828; Fiacco and McCormick (1968), pp. 53–65.

Such a method may thus be termed an 'interior method'. However, for problems involving equality constraints, interior methods do not apply since the interior of the feasible region is empty. In this regard, given the presence of equality constraints, we shall utilize a technique which maintains strict satisfaction of the inequality constraints $\hat{g}^j \geqslant 0, j = 1, \ldots, m$, as the calculations proceed, while requiring the equality constraints $\hat{h}^k = 0, k = 1, \ldots, p$, to be satisfied only as the constrained maximum of f is approached. Let us assume that the said maximum occurs at $\boldsymbol{x}_* \in \mathscr{K}$.

To construct an appropriate penalty function with which to handle the mixed constraint case, let us, for the moment, ignore the inequality constraints $\hat{g}^j \geqslant 0, j = 1, \ldots, m$, and write the kth equality constraint $\hat{h}^k = 0$ as the two inequality constraints $\hat{h}^k \geqslant 0$, $-\hat{h}^k \geqslant 0$, $k = 1, \ldots, p$. If we next apply the *quadratic loss function*

$$\theta\{\min[0, \phi(\boldsymbol{x})]\}^2 = \theta\{(\phi(\boldsymbol{x}) - |\phi(\boldsymbol{x})|)/2\}^2$$

to the preceding inequalities, we obtain

$$\theta\{(\hat{h}^k - |\hat{h}^k|)/2\}^2 + \theta\{(-\hat{h}^k - |-\hat{h}^k|)/2\}^2 = \theta(\hat{h}^k)^2, \quad k = 1, \ldots, p.$$

If this procedure is applied to each of the p equality constraints $\hat{h}^k = 0$ in turn, we ultimately form the penalty term

$$\theta \sum_{k=1}^{p} \hat{h}^k(\boldsymbol{x})^2 = r^{-1} \sum_{k=1} \hat{h}^k(\boldsymbol{x})^2.$$

Note that this penalty term is constructed in a fashion such that if any constraint $\hat{h}^k = 0, k = 1, \ldots, p$, is violated, the magnitude of the penalty incurred is proportional to the square of the divergence of $\boldsymbol{x}$ from $\mathscr{K}_{\boldsymbol{H}} = \{\boldsymbol{x} \,|\, \boldsymbol{H}(\boldsymbol{x}) = \boldsymbol{0}, \boldsymbol{x} \in \mathscr{E}^n\}$. So if $\boldsymbol{x}(r_i)$ deviates away from $\mathscr{K}_{\boldsymbol{H}}$ when r_i decreases, the size of the penalty term increases. Thus, as $r_i \to 0$, $r_i < r_{i-1}$, the sequence of points $\boldsymbol{x}(r_i)$ is drawn toward $\mathscr{K}_{\boldsymbol{H}}$ in order to minimize the effect of the penalty term. Accordingly, for the subset of contraints $\hat{h}^k = 0$, $k = 1, \ldots, p$, the path taken to the constrained maximum of f necessarily lies outside $\mathscr{K}_{\boldsymbol{H}}$. Hence, this method will be termed an 'exterior method' with associated penalty function

$$T(\boldsymbol{x}, r) = \mathrm{f}(\boldsymbol{x}) - r^{-1} \sum_{k=1}^{p} \hat{h}^k(\boldsymbol{x})^2. \tag{A.1}$$

Let us now combine the interior and exterior methods to determine a 'mixed interior–exterior method' by forming the *mixed penalty function*

$$V(\boldsymbol{x}, r) = \mathrm{f}(\boldsymbol{x}) - r \sum_{j=1}^{m+n} \frac{1}{\hat{g}^j(\boldsymbol{x})} - r^{-1} \sum_{k=1}^{p} \hat{h}^k(\boldsymbol{x})^2. \tag{A.2}$$

Thus, if we can determine an

$$\boldsymbol{x}(r_i) \in \mathscr{K}^0_{\bar{\boldsymbol{G}}} = \{\boldsymbol{x} \,|\, \bar{\boldsymbol{G}}(\boldsymbol{x}) > \boldsymbol{0},\ \boldsymbol{x} \in \mathscr{E}^n\}$$

which maximizes $V(\boldsymbol{x}, r_i)$ for each $r_i < r_{i-1}$, we obtain a sequence of $\boldsymbol{x}(r_i)$ values such that $\boldsymbol{x}(r_i) \rightarrow \boldsymbol{x}_* \in \mathscr{K}_{\bar{\boldsymbol{G}}} \cap \mathscr{K}_{\boldsymbol{H}}$, with $\mathrm{f}(\boldsymbol{x}(r_i)) \rightarrow \mathrm{f}(\boldsymbol{x}_*)$, as $r_i \rightarrow 0$, $i = 1, 2, \ldots$ A summary of the conditions which insure convergence of the sequence $\{V(\boldsymbol{x}, r_i)\}_{i=1}^{\infty}$ to $\mathrm{f}(\boldsymbol{x}_*)$ is provided by

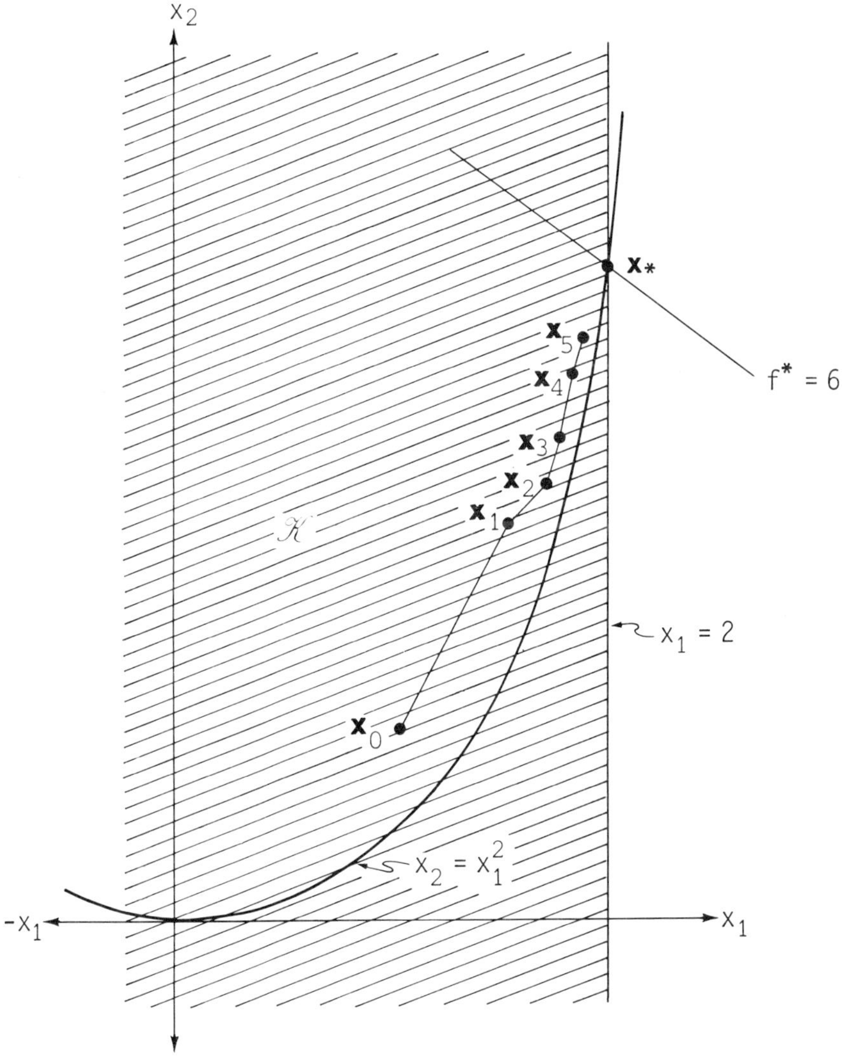

Fig. A.1.

THEOREM A.1.[7] *Let the real-valued function* $y = \mathrm{f}(\boldsymbol{x})$ *and the vector-valued functions* $\bar{\boldsymbol{G}}(\boldsymbol{x}) \geqslant \boldsymbol{0}$, $\boldsymbol{H}(\boldsymbol{x}) = \boldsymbol{0}$, $\boldsymbol{x} \in \mathscr{E}^n$, *be twice differentiable over*

$$\mathscr{K} = \{\boldsymbol{x} \mid \bar{\boldsymbol{G}}(\boldsymbol{x}) \geqslant \boldsymbol{0},\ \boldsymbol{H}(\boldsymbol{x}) = \boldsymbol{0},\ \boldsymbol{x} \in \mathscr{E}^n\}.$$

In addition, let f, $\bar{\boldsymbol{G}}$ *be concave (with at least one of the functions* f, $\hat{\mathrm{g}}^j$, $j = 1, \ldots, m+n$, *strictly concave) over* $\mathscr{K}_{\bar{G}} \cap \mathscr{K}_{H}$ *with* $\boldsymbol{H}(\boldsymbol{x})'\boldsymbol{H}(\boldsymbol{x}) = \Sigma_{k=1}^{p} \hat{h}^k(\boldsymbol{x})^2$ *convex in* $\mathscr{K}_{\bar{G}}$. *Then*

$$V(\boldsymbol{x}, r_i) = \mathrm{f}(\boldsymbol{x}) - r_i \sum_{j=1}^{m+n} \frac{1}{\hat{\mathrm{g}}^j(\boldsymbol{x})} - r_i^{-1} \sum_{k=1}^{p} \hat{h}^k(\boldsymbol{x})^2, \quad i = 1, 2, \ldots, \quad r_i > 0,$$

is twice differentiable and strictly concave over $\mathscr{K}^{0}_{\bar{G}}$. *If* $\lim_{i\to\infty} r_i = 0$, *then the strong global constrained maximum of* f *is determined as*

$$\lim_{r_i \to 0} \{\max_{\boldsymbol{x} \in \mathscr{K}^{0}_{\bar{G}}} V(\boldsymbol{x}, r_i)\} = \mathrm{gl} \max_{\boldsymbol{x} \in \mathscr{K}_{\bar{G}} \cap \mathscr{K}_{H}} \mathrm{f}(\boldsymbol{x}) = \mathrm{f}(\boldsymbol{x}_*).$$

Example A.1. Maximize the real-valued function $y = \mathrm{f}(\boldsymbol{x}) = x_1 + x_2$ subject to $\hat{\mathrm{g}}^1 = 2 - x_1 \geqslant 0$, $\hat{h}^1 = x_2 - x_1^2 = 0$. If we arbitrarily choose $r_1 = 1$, the mixed penalty function appears as

$$V(\boldsymbol{x}, r_1) = x_1 + x_2 - 1/(2 - x_1) - (x_2 - x_1^2)^2.$$

Setting $\nabla V(\boldsymbol{x}, r_1) = \boldsymbol{0}$ yields

$$1 - (2 - x_1)^{-2} + 4x_1(x_2 - x_1^2) = 0, \qquad 1 - 2(x_2 - x_1^2) = 0.$$

On combining these latter two expressions and employing the Newton–Raphson method to approximate x_1 for $\boldsymbol{x}_0' = (1, 1.5)$ (note that $\boldsymbol{x}_0 \in \mathscr{K}^{0}_{\bar{G}}$, $\boldsymbol{x}_0 \notin \mathscr{K}_{H}$), we obtain $x_1 = 1.5$. Hence, $\boldsymbol{x}_1' = (1.5, 2.75)$. To generate the next approximation to $\boldsymbol{x}_*$, $\boldsymbol{x}_2$, let us choose $r_2 = 0.5 < r_1$ and maximize $V(\boldsymbol{x}, r_2)$. Here $\boldsymbol{x}_2' = (1.64, 2.94)$ is determined as the solution of $\nabla V(\boldsymbol{x}, r_2) = \boldsymbol{0}$.

Table A.1.

r	$x_1(r)$	$x_2(r)$	$\mathrm{f}(\boldsymbol{x}(r))$
r_1 1	1.5	2.75	4.25
r_2 0.5	1.64	2.94	4.58
r_3 0.25	1.75	3.19	4.94
r_4 0.125	1.83	3.41	5.24
r_5 0.06	1.88	3.56	5.44
⋮ ⋮	⋮	⋮	⋮

By repeating this process for a monotonic decreasing sequences of r values, the components of $\boldsymbol{x}_*$ are ultimately obtained. Table A.1 provides a summary of how the process converges to $\boldsymbol{x}_*' = (2, 4)$ with $\mathrm{f}(\boldsymbol{x}_*) = 6$.

[7] See Fiacco and McCormick (1966), pp. 817–819.

BIBLIOGRAPHY

Books

Abadie, J. (Ed.) (1967). *Nonlinear Programming.* Amsterdam: North-Holland Publishing Co.

Apostol, T. (1964). *Mathematical Analysis.* Massachusetts: Addison-Wesley Publishing Co., Inc.

Arrow, K., Hurwicz, L., and Uzawa, H. (Eds.) (1958). *Studies in Linear and Nonlinear Programming.* California: Stanford University Press.

Berge, C. (1963). *Topological Spaces.* New York: The Macmillan Co.

Birkhoff, G. and MacLane, S. (1960). *A Survey of Modern Algebra.* Rev. ed. New York: The Macmillan Co.

Brand, L. (1955). *Advanced Calculus.* Rev. ed. New York: John Wiley and Sons, Inc.

Bushaw, D. and Clower, R. (1957). *Introduction to Mathematical Economics.* Illinois: Richard D. Irwin, Inc.

Fiacco, A. and McCormick, G. (1968). *Nonlinear Programming: Sequential Unconstricted Minimization Techniques.* New York: John Wiley & Sons, Inc.

Frisch, R. (1966). *Maxima and Minima: Theory and Economic Applications.* The Netherlands: D. Reidel Publishing Co.

Gale, D. (1960). *The Theory of Linear Economic Models.* New York: McGraw-Hill Book Co.

Geoffrion, A. (Ed.) (1972). *Perspectives on Optimization.* Reading, Mass.: Addison-Wesley Publishing Co.

Graves, R. and Wolfe, P. (Eds.) (1963). *Recent Advances in Mathematical Programming.* New York: McGraw-Hill Book Co.

Gue, R. and Thomas, M. (1970). *Mathematical Methods in Operations Research.* New York: The Macmillan Co.

Hadley, G. (1964). *Linear Algebra.* Reading, Mass.: Addison-Wesley Publishing Co., Inc.

Hadley, G. (1964). *Nonlinear and Dynamic Programming.* Reading, Mass.: Addison-Wesley Publishing Co.

Halmos, P. (1958). *Finite-Dimensional Vector Spaces.* 2nd ed. New Jersey: D. van Nostrand Co., Inc.

Hirschman, I. (1962). *Infinite Series.* New York: Holt, Rinehart, and Winston.

Hoffman, K. and Kunze, R. (1961). *Linear Algebra.* New Jersey: Prentice-Hall, Inc.

Karlin, S. (1959). *Mathematical Methods and Theory in Games, Programming, and Economics,* vol. 1. Massachusetts: Addison-Wesley Publishing Co., Inc.

Kemeny, J., Mirkil, H., Snell, J., and Thompson, G. (1959). *Finite Mathematical Structures.* New Jersey: Prentice-Hall, Inc.

Künzi, H., Krelle, W., and Oettli, W. (1966). *Nonlinear Programming,* F. Levin (Tr.). Massachusetts: Blaisdell Publishing Co.

Mangasarian, O. (1969). *Nonlinear Programming.* New York: McGraw-Hill Book Co.

Neyman, J. (Ed.) (1951). *Proceedings of the Second Berkeley Symposium on Mathematical Statistics and Probability.* California: University of California Press.

Noble, B. (1969). *Applied Linear Algebra.* New Jersey: Prentice-Hall, Inc.

Olmsted, J. (1961). *Advanced Calculus.* New York: Appleton-Century-Crofts, Inc.

Ralton, A., Wilf, H. (Eds.) (1964). *Mathematical Methods for Digital Computers.* New York: John Wiley & Sons, Inc.

Rockafellar, R. (1970). *Convex Analysis.* New Jersey: Princeton University Press.

Royden, H. L. (1963). *Real Analysis.* New York: The Macmillan Co.

Saaty, T. and Bram, J. (1964). *Nonlinear Mathematics.* New York: McGraw-Hill Book Co.

Simmons, G. (1953). *Topology and Modern Analysis.* New York: McGraw-Hill Book Co., Inc.

Taylor, A. E. (1955). *Advanced Calculus.* New York: Ginn and Co.

Thomas, G. B. (1960). *Calculus and Analytic Geometry.* 3rd ed. Massachusetts: Addison-Wesley Publishing Co., Inc.

Whitesitt, J. (1961). *Boolean Algebra and its Applications.* Massachusetts: Addison-Wesley Publishing Co., Inc.

Zangwill, W. (1969). *Nonlinear Programming: A Unified Approach.* New Jersey: Prentice-Hall, Inc., pp. 139–144.

Periodicals

Arrow, K. and Hurwicz, L. (1957). Gradient methods for constrained maxima. *Journal of the Operations Research Society of America*, **5**, 258–265.

Box, M. (1966). A Comparison of several current optimization methods. *British Computer Journal*, **9**, 67–77.

Debreu, G. (1952). Definite and semi-definite quadratic forms. *Econometrica*, **20**, 597–607.

Dorn, W. (1963). Nonlinear programming—a survey. *Management Science*, **9**, 171–208.

Fiacco, A. and McCormick, G. (1964a). The sequential unconstrained minimization technique for nonlinear programming, a primal–dual method. *Management Science*, **10**, 2, 360–368.

Fiacco, A. and McCormick, G. (1964b). Computational algorithm for the sequential unconstrained minimization technique for nonlinear programming. *Management Science*, **10**, 4, 601–617.

Fiacco, A. and McCormick, G. (1966). Extensions of SUMT for nonlinear programming: equality constraints and extrapolation. *Management Science*, **12**, 11, 816–828.

Fletcher, R. and Powell, M. (1963) A rapidly convergent descent method for minimization. *British Computer Journal*, **6**, 163–168.

Fletcher, R. and Reeves, C. (1964). Function minimization by conjugate gradients. *British Computer Journal*, **8**, 149–154.

Mangasarian, O. (1962). Duality in nonlinear programming. *Quarterly Journal of Applied Mathematics*, **20**, 3, 300–302.

Pearson, J. (1969). Variable metric methods of minimization. *British Computer Journal*, **12**, 171–178.

Powell, M. (1964). An efficient method for finding the minimum of a function of several variables without calculating derivatives. *British Computer Journal*, **7**, 155–162.

Wolfe, P. (1961). A duality theorem for nonlinear programming. *Quarterly Journal of Applied Mathematics*, **19**, 3, 239–244.

SUBJECT INDEX